HIGH POLYMERS

Vol. I: **Collected Papers of W. H. Carothers on High Polymeric Substances**
Edited by H. Mark and G. S. Whitby

Vol. II: **Physical Chemistry of High Polymeric Systems**
Second Edition. By H. Mark and A. V. Tobolsky

Vol. III: **Mechanism of Polymer Reactions**
By G. M. Burnett

Vol. V: **Cellulose and Cellulose Derivatives** (in three parts)
Second Edition. Edited by Emil Ott, H. M. Spurlin, and M. W. Grafflin

Vol. VI: **Mechanical Behavior of High Polymers**
By Turner Alfrey, Jr.

Vol. VII: **Phenoplasts: Their Structure, Properties, and Chemical Technology**
By T. S. Carswell

Vol. IX: **Emulsion Polymerization**
By F. A. Bovey, I. M. Kolthoff, A. I. Medalia, and E. J. Meehan

Vol. X: **Polymer Processes**
Edited by Calvin E. Schildknecht

Vol. XII: **Analytical Chemistry of Polymers** (in three parts)
Edited by Gordon M. Kline

Vol. XIII: **Polyethers** (in three parts)
Edited by Norman G. Gaylord

Vol. XIV: **Polyesters** (in two parts)
Edited by Norman G. Gaylord

Vol. XV: **Radiation Chemistry of Polymeric Systems**
By Adolphe Chapiro

Vol. XVI: **Polyurethanes: Chemistry and Technology** (in two parts)
By J. H. Saunders and K. C. Frisch

Vol. XVII: **Configurational Statistics of Polymeric Chains**
By M. V. Volkenstein. Translated by Serge N. Timasheff and Marina J. Timasheff

Vol. XVIII: **Copolymerization**
Edited by George E. Ham

Vol. XIX: **Chemical Reactions of Polymers**
Edited by E. M. Fettes

Vol. XX: **Crystalline Olefin Polymers** (in two parts)
Edited by R. A. V. Raff and K. W. Doak

Vol. XXI: **Macromolecules in Solution**
By Herbert Morawetz

Vol. XXII: **Conformations of Macromolecules**
By T. M. Birshtein and O. B. Ptitsyn. Translated by Serge N. Timasheff and Marina J. Timasheff

Vol. XXIII: **Polymer Chemistry of Synthetic Elastomers** (in two parts)
Edited by Joseph P. Kennedy and Erik G. M. Törnqvist

HIGH POLYMERS

A SERIES OF MONOGRAPHS ON THE CHEMISTRY, PHYSICS, AND TECHNOLOGY OF HIGH POLYMERIC SUBSTANCES

VOLUME XXIII

POLYMER CHEMISTRY OF SYNTHETIC ELASTOMERS

Part II

EDITED BY

JOSEPH P. KENNEDY

Esso Research and Engineering Company
Linden, New Jersey

AND

ERIK G. M. TÖRNQVIST

Esso Research and Engineering Company
Linden, New Jersey

INTERSCIENCE PUBLISHERS

A DIVISION OF JOHN WILEY & SONS, NEW YORK · LONDON · SYDNEY · TORONTO

LIBRARY OF CONGRESS CATALOG CARD NUMBER 67-13948

SBN 470 39237 1

PRINTED IN THE UNITED STATES OF AMERICA

To Robert McKay Thomas
Inspirer, Inquirer, Inventor

——THE EDITORS

PREFACE

This book, as its title indicates, is a collection of treatises of various aspects of the chemistry of synthetic elastomers. It emphasizes polymer chemistry, and in particular the chemistry involved in polymer formation, as contrasted to polymer physics. The reasons for limiting the book to chemical aspects are manifold but are largely the same as those which prompted the publication of this book in the first place.

To begin with, the discovery of the complex organometallic catalysts by Karl Ziegler and coworkers in 1953 and the subsequent development of numerous stereospecific catalysts of this type has led to the practical synthesis of several novel and highly useful elastomers, including *cis*-1,4 polyisoprene or "synthetic natural rubber"—the original and ultimate goal of chemists interested in synthetic rubber.

These developments alone could very well have justified the publication of this book, especially since they have taken place after the last preceding comprehensive treatise of the same general subject, namely, *Synthetic Rubber*, edited by G. S. Whitby, was published in 1954. However, this book could have been justified equally well on the basis of developments in other areas of elastomer chemistry. The tremendous progress made in the area of alkyllithium initiated polymerization leading among others to another method of making *cis*-1,4 polyisoprene may be mentioned as a typical example, but many developments involving more conventional polymerization methods (cationic, free radical, condensation, etc.) could also be used to illustrate the rapid progress made in elastomer synthesis during the past 10–15 years.

Since even before the very rapid and in many respects revolutionary progress in elastomer synthesis began some 15 years ago, it had barely been possible to treat all important aspects of synthetic elastomers in one volume, it was obvious that a satisfactory presentation of the chemical aspects in one volume would require the deletion of many if not most other aspects of synthetic elastomers. Inasmuch as many of the latter and notably the relationship between structure and physical properties in elastomers had been treated recently in great depth and considerable detail in other books and numerous review articles, it was decided to limit the scope of this book to the chemistry of synthetic elastomers and to treat other related subjects only to the extent necessary for a clear presentation of the chemical aspects. This general approach led to the inclusion of an introductory chapter on "Structure–Property Relationships for Elastomeric Materials" and two immediately following chapters dealing primarily with the history and the status and future of synthetic elastomers.

Even with these limitations, the subject matter of the book remained so diverse and extensive that it could hardly be treated in a satisfactory manner by one author or even by a few closely cooperating authors, at least not within a reasonable period of time. In view of the rapid progress still being made in this field, it was obvious, therefore, that a truly satisfactory and up to date book could be written only by a large number of specialists. At first, this seemed to pose some problems, since many of the foremost experts on elastomer synthesis were associated with industrial firms having considerable economic interests in this area. However, it turned out that not only did most of the scientists invited to contribute to our book respond enthusiastically but the various firms with which many of the prospective authors were associated also readily gave them permission to contribute.

While offering the only satisfactory solution, the publication of a book written by numerous authors also poses certain problems. For instance, every author has his personal style and preferences. This leads automatically to a considerable variation in the method of presentation of the various subjects. It will also lead to some repetition that could be avoided in a book written by a single author. It is one of the duties of the editors to minimize these negative aspects of multiple authorship; however, there is a limit to what can and should be done in this respect. It has been the policy of the editors to give the individual authors as much freedom as possible not only in selecting their methods of presentation but also in deciding what should be included for a proper presentation of their subject matter within the guidelines offered by the editors.

Some alert readers will undoubtedly notice that certain elastomeric materials, e.g., elastomeric polyesters, polycarbonates, polyalkylene sulfides, nitroso rubbers, and certain recently developed A-B-A type block copolymers and related graft copolymers, etc., have not been treated or could not be treated in detail. The decision not to discuss these materials is somewhat arbitrary, but is based primarily on the fact that they are presently of limited importance. Even with these omissions, it turned out, ironically, that our hope of publishing this book in one volume was unrealistic. This, of course, is a further indication of the great expansion of our knowledge of elastomer synthesis that has occurred in recent years.

The publication of this book would not have been possible had it not been for the positive and encouraging attitude of a large number of industrial firms and scientific institutions which gave the various authors permission and opportunity to contribute. We, the editors, should like in particular to express our gratitude to the Esso Research and Engineering Company and its management for the encouraging attitude which was shown during the preparation of this book. We should also like to express our gratitude for many valuable suggestions and much good advice offered by Drs. John Rehner, Jr. and F. P. Baldwin as well as by many other colleagues.

J. P. Kennedy
E. G. M. Törnqvist
March, 1968

CONTRIBUTORS TO VOLUME XXIII

GLEN ALLIGER, *The Firestone Tire and Rubber Company, Akron, Ohio*

M. B. BERENBAUM, *Thiokol Chemical Corporation, Trenton, New Jersey*

J. R. COOPER, *E. I. du Pont de Nemours and Company, Wilmington, Delaware*

GINO DALL'ASTA, *Montecatini S.p.A., Milano, Italy*

J. V. DAWKINS, *Duke University, Durham, North Carolina*

C. FITZSIMMONDS, *University of Liverpool, Liverpool, England*

L. E. FORMAN, *The Firestone Tire and Rubber Company, Akron, Ohio*

J. FURUKAWA, *Kyoto University, Sakyo, Kyoto, Japan*

R. H. GOBRAN, *Thiokol Chemical Corporation, Trenton, New Jersey*

M. A. GOLUB, *Stanford Research Institute, Menlo Park, California*

CHESTER HARGREAVES, II, *E. I. du Pont de Nemours and Company, Wilmington, Delaware*

W. HOFMANN, *Farbenfabriken Bayer A.G., Leverkusen-Bayerwerk, Germany*

S. IDO, *Japan Synthetic Rubber Company, Limited, Tokyo, Japan*

A. H. JORGENSEN, *The B. F. Goodrich Chemical Company, Avon Lake, Ohio*

J. P. KENNEDY, *Esso Research and Engineering Company, Linden, New Jersey*

W. R. KRIGBAUM, *Duke University, Durham, North Carolina*

JOGINDER, LAL, *The Goodyear Tire and Rubber Company, Akron, Ohio*

A. LEDWITH, *University of Liverpool, Liverpool, England*

F. M. LEWIS, *General Electric Company, Waterford, New York*

H. S. MAKOWSKI, *Esso Research and Engineering Company, Linden, New Jersey*

GIULIO NATTA, *Istituto di Chimica Industriale del Politecnico, Milano, Italy*

LIDO PORRI, *Istituto di Chimica Industriale del Politecnico, Milano, Italy*

R. E. RINEHART, *Uniroyal-U.S. Rubber Company, Wayne, New Jersey*

GUIDO SARTORI, *Esso Research S.A., Brussels, Belgium*

J. H. SAUNDERS, *Mobay Chemical Company, Pittsburgh, Pennsylvania*

W. H. SHARKEY, *E. I. du Pont de Nemours and Company, Wilmington, Delaware*

ERIK G. M. TÖRNQVIST, *Esso Research and Engineering Company, Linden, New Jersey*

H. A. TUCKER, *The B. F. Goodrich Company Research Center, Brecksville, Ohio*

CARL A. URANECK, *Phillips Petroleum Company, Bartlesville, Oklahoma*

ALBERTO VALVASSORI, *Montecatini, S.p.A., Milano, Italy*

OTTO VOGL, *E. I. du Pont de Nemours and Company, Wilmington, Delaware*

F. C. WEISSERT, *The Firestone Tire and Rubber Company, Akron, Ohio*

S. YAMASHITA, *Kyoto University, Kyoto, Japan*

CONTENTS FOR PART II

6. ELASTOMERS FROM CATALYSTS OF THE ALKALI METALS. *By L. E. Forman* 491

7. ELASTOMERS BY COORDINATED ANIONIC MECHANISM
   A. DIENE ELASTOMERS. *By G. Natta and L. Porri* 597
   B. ETHYLENE-PROPYLENE RUBBERS. *By G. Natta, A. Valvassori, and G. Sartori* 679
   C. ELASTOMERS FROM CYCLIC OLEFINS. *By G. Natta and G. Dall'Asta* 703

8. ELASTOMERS BY CONDENSATION POLYMERIZATION
   A. POLYURETHANE ELASTOMERS. *By J. H. Saunders* . . . 727
   B. THE CHEMISTRY OF SILICONE ELASTOMERS. *By F. M. Lewis* 767
   C. POLYSULFIDE AND MONOSULFIDE ELASTOMERS. *By R. H. Gobran and M. B. Berenbaum* 805

9. ELASTOMERS BY MISCELLANEOUS OR UNKNOWN MECHANISMS
   A. LIQUID RUBBERS. *By J. Furukawa, S. Yamashita, and S. Ido* 843
   B. CATALYSIS BY TRANSITION METALS SALTS IN WATER AND OTHER POLAR SOLVENTS. *By R. E. Rinehart* 867
   C. POLY(THIOCARBONYL FLUORIDE) AND RELATED ELASTOMERS. *By W. H. Sharkey* 893

10. ELASTOMERS BY POSTPOLYMERIZATION TECHNIQUES
   A. HALOGENATION. *By H. S. Makowski* 905
   B. CYCLIZED AND ISOMERIZED RUBBER. *By M. A. Golub* . . 939

AUTHOR INDEX FOR PART II 991

CUMULATIVE SUBJECT INDEX FOR PARTS I AND II 1019

CONTENTS FOR PART I

1. STRUCTURE-PROPERTY RELATIONSHIPS FOR ELASTOMERIC MATERIALS. *By W. R. Krigbaum and J. V. Dawkins* 1

2. THE HISTORICAL BACKGROUND OF SYNTHETIC ELASTOMERS WITH PARTICULAR EMPHASIS ON THE EARLY PERIOD. *By Erik G. M. Törnqvist* 21

3. THE STATUS AND FUTURE OF ELASTOMER TECHNOLOGY, 1966. *By G. Alliger and F. C. Weissert*. 95

4. ELASTOMERS BY RADICAL AND REDOX MECHANISMS
   A. BUTADIENE-STYRENE RUBBERS (SBR) AND RUBBERS FROM SUBSTITUTED BUTADIENES AND STYRENES. *By C. A. Uraneck*. 127
   B. NITRILE RUBBER AND OTHER NITROGEN-CONTAINING RUBBERS EXCEPT POLYURETHANES. *By W. Hofmann* . . . 185
   C. NEOPRENE. *By C. Hargreaves* 227
   D. ACRYLIC ELASTOMERS. *By H. A. Tucker and A. H. Jorgensen* 253
   E. FLUORINE-CONTAINING ELASTOMERS. *By J. R. Cooper* . . 273

5. ELASTOMERS BY CATIONIC MECHANISMS
   A. POLYISOBUTENE AND BUTYL RUBBER. *By J. P. Kennedy* . 291
   B. POLY(VINYL ETHERS). *By J. Lal* 331
   C. ELASTOMERS FROM CYCLIC ETHERS. *By A. Ledwith and C. Fitzsimmonds* 377
   D. ELASTOMERIC POLYACETALS. *By O. Vogl* 419

AUTHOR INDEX 455

SUBJECT INDEX 477

CHAPTER 6

ELASTOMERS FROM CATALYSTS OF THE ALKALI METALS

L. E. Forman

The Firestone Tire & Rubber Company, Akron, Ohio

Contents

A. Lithium and Organolithium Catalysts 492
I. Homopolymers of Butadiene and Isoprene 492
A. Introduction 492
B. Polymerization by Lithium Metal 493
C. Polymerization by Organolithium Compounds 497
1. Unique Nature of Organolithium Compounds 497
2. Polymer Growth Reactions 499
3. Polymerization Effects 516
4. Mechanism of Polymerization 530
5. Chemical Reactions 534
II. Homopolymers of Piperylene 535
III. Copolymers of Butadiene, Isoprene, and Piperylene 540
A. Irregular and Alternating Copolymers 544
B. Piperylene Copolymers 552
C. Block Copolymers 553
1. Type $(A—B)_n$ 554
2. Type A—B—A or B—A—B 554
D. Physical Properties 555
B. Sodium, Potassium, Rubidium, and Cesium and Their Organometal Compounds 559
IV. Homopolymers of Butadiene, Isoprene, and Piperylene 559
A. Introduction 559
B. Polymerization 561
C. Microstructure 565
D. Macrostructure 571
V. Copolymers 572
VI. Physical Properties 574
VII. The Alfin Catalyst 575
References 582

A. Lithium and Organolithium Catalysts

I. HOMOPOLYMERS OF BUTADIENE AND ISOPRENE

A. Introduction

Charles F. Kettering once said that "research . . . is nothing but a state of mind—a friendly welcoming attitude toward change."

The chemists of the rubber industry have that state of mind. They participated creatively in the development of synthetic rubber during World War II and brought about the startling growth of a new synthetic rubber industry including many ancillary goods and services. This was of tremendous importance to the military effort during the national emergency, and has been of even greater public benefit since the conclusion of the war.

The science of emulsion polymerization of hydrocarbon monomers having been extensively explored and developed, scientists of the industry were challenged to seek new elastomers having physical properties of even greater suitability for tires and other rubber products. It was appropriate to return to the quest of the early seekers of a synthesis for natural rubber and to extend their search. Happily, success has crowned these efforts. Not only one but two principal methods of synthesis have been discovered. One of these based on transition metal chemistry is discussed elsewhere in this book (Chapter 7A by G. Natta and L. Porri). Syntheses based on lithium and organolithium compounds, and their application to several monomers and derived polymers, are discussed in this chapter.

The first mention of the use of alkali metals as catalysts for the polymerization of isoprene appears to be that of Matthews and Strange in 1910 (1) and Harries in 1911 (2,3). It has been suggested that they used lithium for the preparation of polymers of isoprene according to the disclosure in their patents. However, there seems to be nothing in their patents nor in Harries' extensive description of his work with isoprene (2) that indicates any use of lithium. It seems more likely that these patents referred to the alkali metals on the basis of experiments with only sodium and potassium.

The first definite study of lithium in reactions with diolefins appears to be that reported two decades later by Ziegler and co-workers (4) in a series of papers beginning in 1934. They conducted an extensive investigation of the nature of the addition reaction of lithium and alkyllithium compounds with butadiene, isoprene, piperylene, and 2,3-dimethylbutadiene. Ziegler reported that they had obtained resinous and rubberlike substances from butadiene using butyllithium in ether solution (5). In the light of later research (18), however, it appears that such pdybutadienes resembled polymers prepared with sodium.

Research chemists of Firestone* made high polymers primarily formed of 1,4 units from lithium metal and diolefin monomers (6,7) no later than early 1953. In 1952, Firestone's director of research, Dr. F. W. Stavely, instituted research programs for the purpose of exploring synthetic routes hopefully leading to the synthesis of *cis*-1,4 polyisoprene. During those investigations, a polymer exhibiting the important structural features of the natural rubber hydrocarbon was obtained from the reaction of lithium metal with isoprene.

The process for the synthesis of an elastomer closely resembling natural rubber and methods for the technological use of that elastomer in tire compounds were disclosed by Firestone to the United States Department of Defense and to the Office of Synthetic Rubber of the Federal Facilities Corporation in 1955 (8). Later that year extensive details were presented to the scientific world at a meeting of the American Chemical Society (9), and then published (10). At a subsequent meeting of the Society, Foster and Binder (11) delineated some relationships between microstructure and important physical properties of both polyisoprenes and polybutadienes prepared by way of all of the alkali metals except francium.

It was abundantly clear that, of the alkali metals, only lithium and organolithium compounds were able to cause the formation of predominantly 1,4 polymers from diolefins, most dramatically shown in the case of polyisoprene. Realization of this unique capability of lithium catalysts touched off a continuing series of investigations, worldwide, among industrial and academic chemists alike, that led, in turn, to a greater knowledge of the molecular structures of the principal diolefin elastomers and to an improved and more detailed understanding of their polymerization mechanisms. As a further consequence of that discovery, numerous manufacturing facilities have been constructed around the world for the commercial production of rubbery polymers and copolymers based on polymerization catalysis by lithium compounds.

B. Polymerization by Lithium Metal

The impetus for the study of polymerization catalysis by lithium metal and organolithium compounds stemmed from the observation that

* The Firestone Tire & Rubber Company.

isoprene could be transformed to a high polymer having much of the chemical structure and physical properties of natural rubber (*Hevea brasiliensis*) (9,10). This exciting observation of Firestone chemists was the first indication that the long cherished hope of synthesizing the commercially important natural product might be realizable. They found that isoprene monomer in contact with lithium metal at a moderate temperature of about 40°C was transformed into a high molecular weight polymer comprising 94% *cis*-1,4 structure. Isoprene of high purity was necessary as were also conditions excluding oxygen, water, and polar organic substances. The polymerization process involved an induction period during which initiation takes place and is followed by a more rapid propagation phase. The initiation can be accelerated by higher temperatures, but without careful control of temperature, which is difficult in polymerizations of undiluted monomer ("bulk" polymerizations), the reaction can proceed with explosive velocity. The length of the induction period is relatively unreproducible, but, in general, is an inverse function of the lithium concentration (12,13,18,19). The situation is improved by abrading the metal particles (10,12) to eliminate possible oxide, nitride, or carbide coatings. Thus the dull gray particles of the original dispersion are transformed into shiny silvery platelets of seemingly uniform dimensions. It may be of interest in this connection that cold working of lithium metal is reported to transform the crystal structure partially from a body centered cubic form to one featuring hexagonal closest packing with some packing faults (14). Whether this change has any significant effect on the reaction of a diolefin with the metal surface is unknown and appears not to have been investigated, although there has been speculation that the stereoregularity of polymer structure could be attributed to the metal surface (25,27–29).

Polymers made in bulk have variable amounts of gel except when the propagation temperature is reduced to about 5°C or lower after the initiation. Inasmuch as the reaction of the monomer with lithium metal yields a soluble organolithium compound, two sequences are possible. If the newly formed organometallic compound dissolves in the monomer and becomes separated from particulate metal, polymerization continues but no insoluble polymer is formed (15). On the contrary, if the polymerlithium compound remains on the surface of the metal, polymerization proceeds but other reactions leading to isomerization, branching and crosslinking may occur also (12,15–17).

The molecular weight of the polymer increases with conversion, in the absence of adventitious impurities (5,12,13,19–22). The conversion of monomer to polymer increases linearly as a function of the formation of alkenyllithium from lithium (19,20,22). Thus the number average molecular weight is equal to the amount of monomer converted to polymer divided by the total number of moles of alkenyllithium originally present or later formed.

$$\bar{M}_n = \frac{M_0 \times C}{L} \tag{1a}$$

where

$\bar{M}_n$ = number average molecular weight
M_0 = initial weight of monomer
C = fraction of M_0 converted to polymer
L = number of moles of alkenyllithium

When the metal is used and totally consumed in the generation of the dilithium adduct (see below) the equation is properly

$$\bar{M}_n = \frac{M_0 \times C}{\frac{1}{2}L} \tag{1b}$$

as was shown by Szwarc and coworkers (23).

The rate of polymerization of undiluted isoprene (13,22) increases rapidly with increasing concentrations of lithium (Table I). In the case of butadiene, Ortlieb (12*a*) reported that the rate was constant when the catalyst concentration exceeded 4.1×10^{-3} mole/liter. For isoprene in solution, the rate after 9% conversion was nearly constant over a wide range of lithium concentration (13). The energy of activation of the initiation process was found to be 10.6 kcal/mole and that of the propagation process 15.6 kcal/mole (24). The latter value compares with the value of 15 kcal/mole found with butyllithium as the initiator.

Although the formation of a high *cis*-1,4 polyisoprene was first recognized by the similarity between its physical properties and those of

TABLE I
Bulk Polymerization of Isoprene by Lithium (13)

Isoprene, mole/liter	Li, mole/liter	Induction period, hr	Polymerization temp., °C	$-dM/dt$, mole/liter-min $\times 10^{-4}$
9.83	0.006	20	30	2.5
9.83	0.014	0.67	30	7.4
9.83	0.028	3	30	32

natural rubber, the use of spectrometric methods of analysis have subsequently become indispensable for the determination of microstructure of polymers prepared by means of organometallic initiators. In earlier studies only the standard methods of classical organic chemistry were available. By these means Ziegler (5) showed that monomer units could be joined by 1,2 and 1,4 types of addition. In the case of 2,3-dimethylbutadiene-1,3, a 1,4 adduct was formed exclusively (4,5).

$$\begin{array}{l} CH_3C{=}CH_2 \\ \quad | \\ CH_3C{=}CH_2 \end{array} + 2Li \rightarrow \begin{array}{l} CH_3C{-}CH_2Li \\ \quad \| \\ CH_3C{-}CH_2Li \end{array} \qquad (2)$$

On the addition of more monomer a growth reaction occurred and the product corresponded to the general formula

$$Li(CH_2C(CH_3){=}C(CH_3)CH_2)_nLi \qquad (3)$$

where n varied from 1 to 6. Clear-cut cases such as this did not occur in the investigations of butadiene and isoprene (5,25,26). A discussion of the various types of arrangements will be presented in a later section.

The apparent relationships noted between the physical properties of polyisoprenes and their microstructures as determined by infrared analysis promoted a great interest in structure-property relationships. It was first suspected that the metallic surface controlled the microstructure (27–29). Lithium in an amalgam (11), molten (17), supported on sodium fluoborate (30), on carbon (31), or reacted with aluminum chloride (32), as well as soluble organolithium compounds, all can lead to polymers having the same microstructure as those formed by the metal alone. However, the addition of sodium to lithium leads to less 1,4 and proportionately more vinyl type addition (33).

It had been observed in early studies (10,11,12b,18) that polar materials had a marked effect on microstructure. Hsieh, Kelley, and Tobolsky (29) found that in the presence of tetrahydrofuran no *cis*- or *trans*-1,4 structures were formed but only 3,4 and 1,2 addition structures, and the latter in the ratio of about 3 to 1.

Aside from the work of Ziegler, the polymerization of butadiene by lithium metal appears to have been less extensively studied than that of isoprene. With lithium metal, butadiene like isoprene yields polymers having a distinctively higher proportion of total 1,4 addition than those obtained with the other alkali metals (11,34,35). In the case of butadiene, however, the amount of *cis*-1,4 does not necessarily predominate over *trans*-1,4. Polar solvents such as aliphatic ethers generally bring about a change to high 1,2 addition structure and a corresponding decrease in 1,4 structure. This change in microstructure has an important effect on the low temperature and dynamic properties of raw and compounded polymers. The unmodified lithium polymer of largely 1,4 addition structure has a much lower glass transition temperature and has dynamic properties superior to those found in sodium polymers, emulsion polymers, or ether modified lithium polymers.

The early work with lithium metal as a polymerization initiator revealed several important facts. These were (1) that butadiene polymer and isoprene polymer predominating in 1,4 structures and having advantageous physical properties were easily attainable in contrast to what had been observed with the other alkali metals; (2) that a polyisoprene closely resembling the hydrocarbon structure of natural rubber could be synthesized; (3) that polymerization in hydrocarbons favored polymer formation by 1,4 addition in contrast to polymerization in polar solvents such as ethers and amines which favored 1,2 addition, and (4) that the reaction of lithium with a monomer resulted in a hydrocarbon soluble organolithium compound. The latter fact led to the practical possibilities of using soluble organolithium initiators and made the study of homogeneous systems feasible. Such studies have abounded; they, in large part, are the subject of the remainder of this review.

C. Polymerization by Organolithium Compounds

Before proceeding to discuss the polymerization activity of organolithiums compounds it is desirable to consider some of the important characteristics of this interesting and valuable class of compounds. Such consideration will be helpful in ascertaining the role of the organolithium initiator and that of the subsequently formed polymerlithium species.

1. Unique Nature of Organolithium Compounds

The alkyl derivatives of the metals of Group I are well known and their preparation, properties and reactions have been reviewed by others (36–40,47–51,71,127–129). The relative reactivity of these highly active compounds appears to be in accord with the percent ionic character of the carbon–metal bond (see Table II) (41). The C bond with alkali metal is increasingly ionic and saltlike as the Group is traversed. All alkyl compounds of sodium, potassium, rubidium, and cesium are saltlike as noted from their nonvolatility, insolubility in hydrocarbon solvents, and the electrolyte-like character of their solutions in diethylzinc (42,43).

The alkyllithium compounds are unique among the metals of Group I in their solubility in hydrocarbons, in their volatility in some cases, and in

TABLE II
Characteristics of Alkali Metals Bonds (41)

	Li	Na	K	Rb	Cs
M–C % ionic	43	47	52	52	57
Ionic radius, Å	0.60	0.95	1.33	1.48	1.69
Bond energy for M–H, kcal/mole	58.5	48.2	43.6	40.	41.9
Bond energy for M–M, kcal/mole	26.5	18.0	13.2	12.4	10.7
First ionization energy, kcal/mole	124.3	118.4	100.0	96.3	89.7

their association to form electron-deficient bonds. They form complexes with many Lewis bases. Alkyl compounds of the other alkali metals are also associated but rather like insoluble ionic compounds in a polymeric or saltlike lattice structure.

Only methyllithium, the first member of the alkyllithium series, is insoluble in hydrocarbons, and it melts at a high temperature with decomposition (44). Ethyllithium and *n*-butyllithium are distillable at high vacuum (80–90°C at 10^{-4} mm Hg) although *n*-butyllithium decomposes when heated at atmospheric pressure (40,45). Secondary-butyllithium has been found to decompose at an appreciable rate at room temperature according to a first-order process to yield lithium hydride and the olefin (46). The higher members of the series are also soluble in hydrocarbons but probably cannot be distilled even at reduced pressures without decomposition because of their high boiling points.

Alkyllithium compounds are soluble in hydrocarbon solvents in accord with their diminished ionic character and self-association. The self-association has been reported in a number of investigations involving the techniques of cryoscopy (52) ebulliometry (53), vapor pressure measurements (54), infrared spectroscopy (55,56), ultraviolet spectroscopy (57–61), NMR spectrometry (52,53,56,62–65), mass spectrometry (66), x-ray diffractometry (55,67,68), dielectric measurements (69), and measurement of dipole moment (70). Brown (71) has reviewed these critically. Ethyllithium and *n*-butyllithium are found as hexamers in alkanes and in benzene. Branched and longer chain compounds appear to be tetramers (67,71). Morton and coworkers (72–74) found a dimeric association of polybutadienyllithium and polyisoprenyllithium compounds; Worsfold and Bywater (103), Spirin, Gantmakher, and Medvedev (91), and Crammond, Lawry, and Urwin (106), on the basis of kinetic results, reported even higher states of association. Cross association occurs readily as shown by NMR, spectroscopic and viscosity measurements (60,71,74,75,132). Unassociated species have not been identified among the known alkyllithium compounds, although Rodionov and his associates reported that measurements of dipole moments of ethyllithium in hexane at low concentrations indicated a monomeric R—Li bond, and that progressive association was observed with increasing concentration (70). The rapid equilibration of mixed RLi species was demonstrated by Brown and his students by NMR and mass spectrometry (62).

Although alkyllithium is a powerful base, it has the Lewis acid property of forming complexes with Lewis bases (71). Complex formation was observed early by Wittig in the case of phenyllithium (77), and has been studied quantitatively in the last several years for alkyllithium compounds with ethers (53,62,69,76,78–85), and amines (52,86). Compound formation ranging from $(RLi)_4 \cdot THF$ to $RLi \cdot 4THF$ has been reported (60,130).

The possibilities for cross-association and for complex formation with polar substances were not recognized in the early studies of lithium catalyzed polymerizations. Now it is realized that proper consideration of such phenomena is necessary for understanding the seemingly disparate observations reported by many workers, particularly in kinetics.

2. Polymer Growth Reactions

a. Initiation. A wide variety of alkyllithium and aryllithium compounds can initiate the polymerization of butadiene and isoprene. Methyllithium and its higher homologs to dodecyllithium at least, have been used as initiators (19,87). Methyllithium (87) and ethyllithium have been studied by various workers (88–92,132). Butyllithium has been most frequently used (17,22,33,72,93–114). The references do not represent a complete listing and are intended only to be illustrative. The higher monoalkyllithium compounds have been used infrequently. Aliphatic polylithium compounds also have been reported for the polymerization of isoprene and other diolefins (114–117). Aryllithium compounds such as phenyl-, benzyl-, naphthyl-, trityl-, and triphenylmethylsilyllithium (118–125) have been reported as well as the addition products of lithium metal to naphthalene and to biphenyl (126). The aliphatic organolithium (monolithium) compounds are soluble in hydrocarbon solvents and provide homogeneous systems. The lower members of the alkylene polylithium series and aryllithium compounds are only sparingly soluble in hydrocarbons.

The variety of organolithium catalysts and their varying degrees of association do not seem to affect the nature of the polymers resulting from their use. There appears to be no evidence that the nature of the R group in RLi has any effect on the mechanism of initiation (19,33,88, 97,101,104,105) although the rate may be altered, particularly in the case of less soluble initiators where the effective concentration may be very low. The rate is dependent on the initiator concentration. This is supported by studies of Waack and Doran (60,61,64,130) who studied the addition of RLi compounds to 1,1-diphenylethylene, also investigated by Casling, Evans, and Rees (164). In this prototype system it was shown from relative reaction rates that the activity of the RLi compounds is concentration dependent.

The initiation reaction has been the subject of considerably fewer detailed studies than the propagation reaction. Some authors, in fact, have chosen to bypass the initiation step by using a so-called seeded polymerization whereby the initiation can be discounted. Elimination of the initiator is important for establishing absolute rates of propagation since substantial amounts of the initiator molecules are present throughout a portion of the reaction period. Their presence was observed by Sinn (102,131) who followed the disappearance of the alkyllithium initiator chromatographically, and by Hsieh (104) who also used gas chromatography to study the disappearance of the many different butyllithium initiators. He noted that *n*-butyllithium persisted in a polymerizing system up to 50% conversion. The R group did become a factor in this instance since the rate of disappearance followed the order *n*-BuLi < *i*-BuLi < *tert*-BuLi < *sec*-BuLi. Additionally, *tert*-BuLi was reported to be a relatively slow initiator for styrene although the polymerization of butadiene and isoprene started rapidly. *sec*-Butyllithium was the most active initiator of this group and had disappeared by about the time 10% conversion of monomer had occurred.

The initiation reaction is first order with respect to monomer and initiator (104,131,132).

$$R_i = k_i [\mathrm{M}][\mathrm{BuLi}] \tag{4}$$

Rates and rate constants conforming to this equation are listed in Table III. Energies of activation for the first step in the reaction of isoprene with alkyllithium (Table IV) appear to vary as a function of solvent and of initiator R group. Reasons for the disparities are not clear.

TABLE III
Rate of Initiation of Butadiene and Isoprene (109)[a]

RLi	Solvent	Butadiene (1.7 *M*) k_i	Butadiene (1.7 *M*) R_i	Isoprene (1.3 *M*) k_i	Isoprene (1.3 *M*) R_i
n-BuLi	Hexane	0.024	0.12	0.018	0.07
	Cyclohexane	0.015	0.08	0.012	0.05
	Toluene	0.51	2.4	0.43	1.6
sec-BuLi	Cyclohexane	0.90	4.0	0.44	1.5
tert-BuLi	Cyclohexane	0.16	0.7	0.27	0.9

[a] [BuLi] = 0.0026 mole/liter; k_i = liter/mole-min; R_i = mole/liter-min × 10^3.

TABLE IV
Energy of Activation for Initiation of Isoprene by RLi

Initiator	Solvent	t°,C	E_{A_i}, kcal/mole	A, liter/mole-sec	Ref.
EtLi	Benzene	15	22		132
EtLi	Cyclohexane	15	27		132
n-BuLi	Heptane	20	15	$10^{8.7}$	102

For a given initiator, the solvent type also showed an effect on rate according to the order cyclohexane < *n*-hexane < toluene. It may be noted that this is the same order as that of the kinetic acidity of these hydrocarbons (133) and thus suggests a more sophisticated role for the solvent than merely that of a diluent. The possibility of a solvent cage effect in alkyllithium exchange reactions was suggested by Williams and Brown (81). Screttas and Eastham recently discussed the role of solvent in alkyllithium reactions in terms of a charge transfer process (85). Such an explanation could be advanced to account for the difference in initiation rate for the reaction of *n*-butyllithium with either butadiene or isoprene in benzene versus *n*- or *cyclo*-hexane. Although there is a short induction period (98,134) the rate is more rapid in benzene which certainly should be able to provide considerably greater support for an electron transfer process than either of the hexanes. The concepts of solvent cage effect and charge transfer favor the association complex of the alkyllithium instead of the monomeric form as the kinetically active initiating species. A number of investigators (95,102,131,132,134–136) deduced from their kinetic studies that the monomeric species, especially at low concentrations, is the active initiator. To the contrary, Brown (137) has provided evidence from thermodynamic considerations and from observations of mass spectra that monomeric alkyllithium is not the active species either in hydrocarbon solution or in ether.

One further consideration of importance in the initiation reaction is the possibility of cross association of initiator and first formed oligomer-lithium. Morton and Pett (74) found a cross association equilibrium between ethyllithium and polyisoprenyllithium in hexane resulting in the species (polyisoprenyllithium·3EtLi). François, Sinn, and Parrod (132) who studied the system ethyllithium–polyisoprenyllithium also expressed the view that the association equilibrium is of great importance in the initiation process. It is clear that a greater knowledge of these equilibria and the factors influencing them would contribute much to a better understanding of the initiation process.

The addition of polar substances, e.g., ether, tetrahydrofuran, triethylamine, to hydrocarbon solvents increases the rate of initiation and of propagation (91,127,135,138–140). A number of workers have expressed the view that the addition of a polar substance to an alkyllithium results in the formation of a complex having greater ionicity than the alkyllithium alone. To the increased ionic character of the complex was ascribed the increase in overall polymerization rate as well as the changes observed in microstructure. Indeed it has been observed that there is a sharp increase in electrical conductivity (140) on the addition of tetrahydrofuran (THF) to ethyllithium. Apparently, however, the addition of THF in small amounts does not bring about a dissociation of the alkyllithium but the formation of a complex with the tetramer. From their determinations of molecular weight, Waack, West, and Doran (130) reported that *n*-BuLi exists in ether and in THF as the tetramer over a concentration range up to one molar. Seitz and Brown (62) observed an ionized species in the mass spectra of alkyllithiums involving the dissociation

$$R_4Li_4 \rightarrow R_3Li_4^{\oplus} + R^{\ominus} \tag{5}$$

They cited support for the idea that ionization proceeds readily in ether. The presence of alkoxide also may contribute to an ionization process since the alkoxide ion is the more stable anion.

$$R_3Li_4^{\oplus} + OR^{\ominus}$$

Conceivably, a very limited ionization is possible in a tetrameric alkyllithium coordinated to alkoxide even in hydrocarbon solution. At this point it is appropriate to recall that Worsfold and Bywater (103) found the addition of oxygen (air) to eliminate the slow initiation reaction of butyllithium with isoprene in cyclohexane. It is known that oxygen reacts with RLi compounds to form the corresponding lithium alkoxide, and that alkoxides coordinate to alkyllithiums as indicated above. One might infer that the alkoxide resulting from the introduction of air was the primary cause of the rate enhancement. On the other hand, it is germane to recall also that complexes of alkyllithium with LiX, where X = alkoxide or halide, generally react more sluggishly than the alkyllithium itself (127,141,142). Hence the enhancement of the initiation rate by air remains yet to be explained. Further, it is clear that more information is needed concerning the effects of various types of lithium salts associated with alkyl- and alkenyllithium compounds.

b. Propagation. The overall polymerization reaction can be divided into three primary phases, i.e., initiation, propagation, and termination. In a good deal of the work reported in the literature, the first two phases have shown some overlap in that the initiator is not converted completely in the first step to the alkenyllithium that represents the growing species. This is due to the association characteristics of the alkyllithium compounds and to substantial differences in the rates of initiation and propagation. As was seen above, *n*-butyllithium persists during the conversion of monomer to polymer up to 50% or more (131,143). Even *sec*-butyllithium, the most rapidly consumed of the alkyllithiums, persists up to 10% conversion of monomer. These and other difficulties that have an important bearing on the propagation reaction will be discussed.

The salient features of the propagation reaction have been thoroughly reviewed (127,128,144–146). Under ideal conditions of no adventitious impurities and moderate temperatures of polymerization, the conversion of monomer to polymer as a function of time is characterized by an S-shaped curve (72,103,104,131,132,147,148). There is an induction period of variable length, increasing with increasing catalyst concentration (103,106,134), that is properly a part of the initiation phase. There is no termination in uncontaminated systems. The available evidence indicates that each molecule of alkyllithium, regardless of its state of association, initiates one chain. The molecular weight of a resulting polymer therefore can be estimated (72,138,143) by the following relation: (cf. Eq. 1a)

$$\bar{M}_k = \frac{M_0 \times C}{[\mathrm{RLi}]} = \frac{P}{[\mathrm{RLi}]} \qquad (6)$$

where

$\bar{M}_k$ = kinetic molecular weight
M_0 = weight of initial monomer
C = conversion fraction
P = weight of polymer formed
[RLi] = net moles of alkyllithium used

The kinetic molecular weight, $\bar{M}_k$, and number average molecular weight, $\bar{M}_n$, approach equality under conditions of preinitiated or "seeded" polymerization, since only a propagation reaction is operative.

$$\bar{M}_k = \bar{M}_n \tag{7}$$

Morton (139) showed that it is possible to achieve good concordance of molecular weights estimated by these methods. This relationship also demonstrates the absence of a transfer reaction as part of the polymerization mechanism. If a transfer reaction were to occur, the observed values of $\bar{M}_n$ would be less than $\bar{M}_k$. On the contrary, $\bar{M}_n > \bar{M}_k$ values are usually observed due to the practical difficulties of eliminating impurities in the system. The molecular weight as measured by any of the usual means, but most commonly by viscometry, is linear with conversion (19,20,23,33,149).

A propagation reaction uncomplicated by slow initiation or by association of growing polymerlithium species with unconverted alkyllithium initiator is expected to produce a polymer having a very narrow distribution of molecular weights. In such a case, all of the growing chains compete more or less equally for monomer and therefore grow to approximately equal size (Poisson distribution). Consequently, under the best conditions, the ratio of weight average to number average molecular weight may be expected to approach unity. It is very difficult however to get away from the effect of the initiation step even in seeded polymerizations, particularly if *n*-butyllithium is used. Hsieh (150) compared the ratios of the rate constants of initiation and propagation (k_i/k_p) with the ratios of weight average and number average molecular weights ($\bar{M}_w/\bar{M}_n$) for systems initiated by *n*-BuLi, *sec*-BuLi, and *tert*-BuLi and showed that considerable differences resulted from variation in the initiator (Table V). This is in keeping with the observation of the persistence of unreacted *n*-BuLi up to 50–70% conversion of monomer to polymer (131,143) mentioned earlier. Hsieh's data indicated that, where a very narrow molecular weight distribution is desired, the use of *sec*-BuLi having a high ratio of k_i/k_p may even be preferred over a seeded system preinitiated with *n*-BuLi.

TABLE V
Effect of Catalyst on Molecular Weight Distribution (150)

	n-BuLi	*sec*-BuLi	*tert*-BuLi
	Polybutadiene		
k_i/k_p	0.18	11.0	2.0
$\bar{M}_w/\bar{M}_n$	1.20	1.10	1.12
$\bar{M}_k \times 10^{-4}$	3.3	3.6	3.3
$\bar{M}_n \times 10^{-4}$			3.13
	Polyisoprene		
k_i/k_p	0.03	1.2	0.7
$\bar{M}_w/\bar{M}_n$	1.35	1.13	1.18
$\bar{M}_k \times 10^{-4}$	3.6	4.1	3.3
$\bar{M}_n \times 10^{-4}$			3.12

A discussion of molecular weight distribution and other features of macrostructure will be presented in a subsequent section.

The kinetics of the polymer growth reaction of conjugated diolefins leading to elastomer-like polymers have been more extensively studied than almost any other feature of polymerization (17,88,95,102,106,128, 132,134,145,146). In spite of ingenious and seemingly very careful work there has been some lack of agreement among the various workers both as to the values of the rate constants obtained and as to the interpretation of the data. Their experiments, with or without preinitiation, have differed in the type and concentration of initiator used. In some cases of preinitiation, it was assumed that the initiator was completely consumed without evidence to that effect being provided. Independent verification of the complete conversion of *n*-BuLi to oligomerlithium or low molecular weight polymerlithium would need to be established. Complications by chain transfer and termination reactions were assumed absent without this being demonstrated. A question of temperature control could be raised in cases where the monomer concentration was high and heat transfer from the exothermic reaction may have been inadequate.

Impurities in the catalyst undoubtedly exert some influence on both the initiation and the propagation reactions. Many investigators used *n*-BuLi or EtLi prepared from lithium metal and the appropriate alkyl halide in their studies. Where an alkyl bromide has been the precursor of the alkyllithium, association with lithium bromide is a factor to be considered in the kinetic analysis of the polymerization. Waack and Doran showed, for instance, that association of lithium bromide with phenyllithium slowed the rate of polymerization of styrene and diminished the ratio k_i/k_p (151). Lithium chloride undoubtedly has a lesser effect but it may still be significant. Alkyl chloride remaining as a result of incomplete reaction during the formation of alkyllithium may also exert an influence on the activity of a catalyst through complex formation. Lithium alkoxide, which also coordinates with alkyllithium, has an effect on polymerization kinetics (145). Halide and alkoxide contaminants of a catalyst are not differentiated in the assay for alkyllithium by the Gilman-Haubein (152) or Gilman-Cartledge (153) methods, only the net RLi. The difference between net and titratable base is usually attributed to alkoxide only. Quantitative information on the polymerization effects of separate addition of these adjuncts to a catalyst is lacking. Alkyllithium prepared from the corresponding mercury compound is reported to be more reactive than salt-containing preparations (142).

Impurities in the monomer also may be expected to introduce complications in the kinetic analysis of a polymerization reaction. Most investigators dry their monomers and solvents thoroughly and some have reported distilling butadiene or isoprene from butyllithium before beginning a polymerization study. However, in view of the report of Eberly and Adams (154) and Adams et al. (155) that 1,2-butadiene, a frequent contaminant of 1,3-butadiene, reacts only slowly with butyllithium, it is doubtful that this contaminant is totally eliminated by distillation of the monomer from either butyllithium or ethyllithium. A decrease in the rate of butyllithium catalyzed polymerization of butadiene monomer to which 1,2-butadiene had been added at the start has been observed (156). Acetylenes such as ethyl acetylene, when present, react quickly with alkyllithium. The lithium acetylide that is formed reacts in turn with additional alkyllithium to form a soluble complex which slowly undergoes further metallation (154,157). All such reactions affect the estimate of the equilibrium constant for the associated lithium species and complicate the kinetic analysis of the polymerization reaction.

The rate of polymerization is affected by a number of factors, physical and chemical. As is to be expected, the rate of propagation increases with temperature (22,72,95,102,104,106,132,138,143,148), the increase being nearly fourfold per 10°C rise according to Hsieh (104) for butadiene and isoprene catalyzed by *n*-BuLi. On the other hand, François, Sinn, and Parrod (132) found that the rate was little more than doubled for isoprene with EtLi in the same temperature range. Pressure significantly increases the rate of polymerization as can be judged by the time to reach 100% conversion in a system comprised of isoprene in heptane catalyzed by *n*-BuLi: 40 min at 4,000 kg/cm^2, 30 min at 8,000 kg/cm^2, and 20 min at 12,000 kg/cm^2 (158).

There is a noticeable effect of solvent type on rate of polymerization, i.e., hexane < cyclohexane < toluene (104,105). In general, polymerization rates are faster in aromatic than in aliphatic solvents (*vide supra*). In comparing *n*-hexane and cyclohexane, it should be noted that the relative initiation and propagation rates are reversed in the two solvents (104). Polar solvents will be discussed later in this section.

Studies of the relative reactivities of different monomers showed that under comparable conditions the polymerization rates for isoprene were higher than for butadiene. The reaction was found to be of second order by Korotkov (95) and Hsieh (104) where concentrations of catalyst were relatively high (10^{-3} to 10^{-2} mole/liter) and where initiation was at a slower rate than propagation. Below a certain critical catalyst concentration designated by Minoux, François and Sadron (17) as 4×10^{-3} mole/liter, the polymerization rate is proportional to the monomer concentration. Most authors confirm that the rate of monomer disappearance obeys first order kinetics even though the reaction is bimolecular. This is not an unfamiliar situation in reaction kinetics (159). Therefore the rate of the propagation may be expressed by the equation

$$R_p = -\frac{dM}{dt} = k_p[\mathrm{M}][\mathrm{RLi}] \tag{8}$$

where R_p = propagation rate
k_p = propagation rate constant
[M] = monomer concentration
[RLi] = alkyllithium concentration at start

Complete agreement about the coefficient of the last term, [RLi], has not been achieved.

Studies of the mode of action of the alkyllithium catalyst have been extensive but have not produced general agreement concerning mechanistic details or kinetic and thermodynamic constants involved (Tables VI and VII). Reaction orders with respect to the active lithium species of ½, ⅓, ⅕, ⅙ have been suggested (72,91,95,102,103,106,128,132,138, 143). Variations in kinetic order were found to occur over a range of concentrations of lithium (102,143,146). Attempts to minimize these complications by resorting to "seeded" systems were made (102,106,132, 145,146). However, in view of the well-established cross association, some doubt concerning the completeness of preinitiation must be entertained.

Association phenomena have been an important cause of difficulty in the interpretation of the kinetic data. It has been noted in several studies (21,72,103,132) that excess EtLi or n-BuLi tends to depress the rate of propagation. This fact serves to explain the crossover in the early stages of the conversion-time curves for low and high concentrations of catalyst (104,134,147). It is known also that even a small amount of

TABLE VI
Rate of Propagation

		RLi					
Monomer	Solvent	Type	Concn.[a]	t, °C	$R_p \times 10^{4b}$	E_A	Ref.
Butadiene	Toluene	EtLi	0.005–0.02	20–45	1.2	20.5	88
	Toluene	EtLi	1×10^{-5}	20–45	0 4	16.9	88
Isoprene	Toluene	EtLi	75×10^{-3}	27–40	2.1	19.5	88
	Toluene	EtLi	5×10^{-4}	27–40	1.6	17.9	88
	Toluene	EtLi	2.3×10^{-5}	27–40	0.54	14.7	88
Isoprene	Toluene	EtLi	0.23×10^{-4}	30	0.54	16.5	91
	Toluene	EtLi	13×10^{-4}	30	1.9	18.8	91
	Heptane	EtLi	0.20×10^{-4}	30	0.36	16.5	91
	Cyclohexane	EtLi	13.5×10^{-4}	30	8.07		132
Isoprene	Benzene	BuLi	1×10^{-3}	30	1.39	15.	22
	Heptane	BuLi	6×10^{-2}	30	4.8		131
Butadiene	Hexane/ Et_3N	EtLi	4×10^{-3}	−3–+20	4.8	13.9	88
	Hexane	EtLi	1.1×10^{-2}	−3–+20	5.7	14.4	88
	THF (80%)	EtLi	0.25×10^{-3}	−60–−25	0.25	7.3	88
Isoprene	Et_3N	EtLi	4.3×10^{-3}	11–30	6.2	10.6	88

[a] mole/liter.
[b] mole/liter-sec.

TABLE VII
Propagation Rate Constants

RLi	Solvent	t, °C	k_p, liter/mole-sec	A, liter/mole-sec	E_A, kcal/mole	Ref.
			Isoprene			
EtLi	Toluene	30	0.5	10^{10}	14.3	92
	Toluene	30	—	—	19.2	92
	$\phi CH_3/Et_3N$	30	0.03	1.4×10^5	9.2	92
	Cyclohexane	15	1.93		19.0	132
	Cyclohexane	15	1.72			132
n-BuLi	Heptane	20	0.67			162
	Ether	20	0.03			162
	Cyclohexane	50	3.1×10^{-4}			104
	Hexane	50	2.5×10^{-4}			104
	Toluene	50	1.93×10^{-3}			104
sec-BuLi	Cyclohexane	30	2.58×10^{-3}			143
PLi	Heptane	20	6.5×10^{-1}	10^{14}	19.2	102
	Benzene	30	1.28×10^{-3}	10^9	13.3	106
	Hexane	30	4.7	3.4×10^3	22	160
	THF	30	1.4×10^{-1}	1.5×10^4		160
	Hexane	30	5.2			160
		40	15.7		22.6	160
		50	50.8			160
			Butadiene			
n-BuLi	Cyclohexane	50	1.8×10^{-4}			104
	Hexane	50	1.3×10^{-4}			104
	Toluene	50	7.4×10^{-4}			104
sec-BuLi	Cyclohexane	30	2.58×10^{-3}			143

an alkyllithium initiator can depress the solution viscosity of an unterminated polymer (72,75,132). It is interesting that a noninitiating organolithium compound such as fluorenyllithium also can reduce the solution viscosity of an unterminated polymer. Morton (75) found a small increase in the rate of polymerization as a result of adding fluorenyllithium (Table VIII) although there was no change in the stoichiometry of the reaction. Lithium acetylides, unless undergoing further metallation, probably form complexes like fluorenyllithium and act similarly in a polymerization system.

Independent measurements of the degree of association of the active polymerizing species by viscometry (72,87,102,132,136,148) and light

TABLE VIII
Effect of Fluorenyllithium Complex (75) on Polymerization Rate of Isoprene
[M] = 2.5, t = 25°C

EtLi (mole/liter)	FlLi (mole/liter)	Total RLi (mole/liter)	k_1 (10^3/min)
4.12	—	4.12	9.0
4.12	1.92	6.04	10.1
0.92	—	0.92	5.6
0.92	3.73	4.65	7.8

scattering (103) have been cited in support of the apparent kinetic order. Thus Morton found an association number of two from viscometric measurements on unterminated and terminated polymer solutions (72, 148,160). This finding indicated that the active chains are associated as dimers in agreement with an observed kinetic order of one-half. Worsfold and Bywater, by a light-scattering method, found polyisoprenyllithium associated to about four even at concentrations as low as 10^{-5} mole/liter (103). Their finding was consonant with an observed kinetic order of one-fourth. Spirin (91) also reported association states of four for polyisprenyllithium and six for polybutadienyllithium species on the basis of kinetic and viscometric results. Bywater (127) suggested that the lower association states reflect the presence of small amounts of impurities.

Virtually all of the workers who studied the kinetics of initiation and propagation postulated that the kinetically active species is a monomeric lithium compound. Sinn and Patat (136) concluded from their data, however, that associated lithium species are rate determining. Moreover, Brown (71,137) on the basis of probable heats of dissociation of polymeric forms of alkyllithium concluded that the monomeric form is not present and therefore not a kinetically likely species. His estimate of the heat of dissociation compared well with that calculated by Morton and Fetters (160) from viscosity data (37 kcal/mole) obtained for dimeric polyisoprenyllithium. Brown has suggested that since there is no physical evidence for a monomeric form of alkyllithium as an active species, fractional reaction orders corresponding to the inverse of the association number (91,134) are not justified.

On the basis of present understanding, Morton (160) and Fetters (163) give the following expression for the rate of polymerization in hydrocarbons:

$$R_p = -\frac{d[M]}{dt} = k_p K_e^{1/2} [(RM_j Li)_2]^{1/2}[M] \tag{9}$$

where
R_p = rate of propagation
$-\frac{d[M]}{dt}$ = disappearance of monomer per unit time
k_p = propagation rate constant
K_e = equilibrium constant for associated and unassociated states
$[M]$ = monomer concentration
$[(RM_jLi)_2]$ = concentration of growing polymer species

It was assumed that the equilibrium constant K_e pertained to a dissociation of an active dimeric species to monomeric, i.e.

$$(RM_jLi)_2 \rightleftarrows 2(RM_jLi) \tag{10}$$

although a dissociation of tetrameric to dimeric species

$$(RM_jLi)_4 \rightleftarrows 2(RM_jLi)_2 \tag{11}$$

appears more likely. For isoprene in hexane (seeded system), the rate constant was given as

$$\begin{aligned} k_p &= 3.4 \times 10^3 \exp(-4100/RT) \\ &= 8.9 \text{ liter/mole-sec at } 60°C \end{aligned} \tag{12}$$

In a more recent study also made under stringent conditions, Cramond, Lawry, and Urwin (106) determined the rate constant of propagation for isoprene in benzene (a system with lower molecular weight seed than that of Morton) as

$$\begin{aligned} k_p &= 10^9 \exp(-13{,}300/RT) \\ &= 1.3 \times 10^{-3} \text{ liter/mole-sec at } 30°C \end{aligned} \tag{13}$$

Cramond and associates also observed by spectroscopic means that the average association of the unterminated polymerlithium species varied as a function of concentration from 2 in dilute solutions to higher association states in more concentrated solutions.

Attempts to determine the absolute rate constants of propagation have been made by several authors (102,103,132,160). Morton determined the equilibrium constant from viscosity data and estimated that the energy of activation for propagation included half the heat of dissociation of the associated polymerlithium species. On this basis Morton (160) arrived at kinetic values for the polymerization of isoprene in hexane:

$$k_p \text{ (liter/mole-sec)} = 4.7 \text{ at } 30°\text{C (8.9 at } 60°\text{C)}, \quad E_p \text{ (kcal/mole)} = 4.1, \text{ and } A \text{(liter/mole-sec)} = 3.4 \times 10^3$$

The addition of polar materials such as ethers, tertiary amines, and Lewis bases in general, is accompanied by a sharp increase in the apparent rate of polymerization (72,87,91,103,127,138,161). According to Polyakov and coworkers (160), triethylamine causes a greater rate increase than THF. Due to its greater steric hindrance, triethylamine has less capability for solvation and complexing. Among the ethers, the greatest rate effect is observed with THF (138). Sinn and Bandermann (162) found $k_p = 0.03$ liter/mole-sec for the polymerization of isoprene in ethyl ether by butyllithium at 20°C vs. 0.67 liter/mole-sec in heptane. Morton and Fetters (145,160) found $k_p = 0.14$ liter/mole-sec for the polymerization of isoprene in THF by ethyllithium at 30°C vs. 5.1 liter/mole-sec in hexane. They observed also that the rate of polymerization increased as a function of added THF to a ratio of about 800 THF/RLi and thereafter decreased as more THF was added (Table IX). At a THF to RLi ratio of about 100, the association number N had declined from 2 to about 1.3, indicating that most of the polymerizing species had been complexed by THF.

The kinetics of polymerization in ethers indicated that the reaction is first order in both monomer and catalyst (145):

$$R_p = k_p \, [\text{M}][\text{RLi}] \tag{14}$$

In this equation, k_p probably includes one or more equilibria since it is likely that associated polymerlithium species can react with ethers to form several etherates (60,71,127,130). In addition, the coordinated ether promotes an ionization process of the complex (71) although associated organolithium species may still be present. Morton (160) noted that at small ratios of THF/RLi the rate of polymerization rose slowly and linearly but that there was an abrupt drop in the *cis*-1,4 content in the range of the mono- or dietherate followed thereafter by a gradual decrease as a function of higher ratios. The abrupt change in microstructure is likely indicative of a change in reaction mechanism to an ionic process.

At the conclusion of the propagation step in a polymerization of the type under discussion, the monomer has become consumed but the system remains catalytically active. The polymer should then be in equilibrium with its monomer according to Szwarc (165,166) and the rate of propa-

TABLE IX
Polymerization of Isoprene in Hexane at 30°C (160)
Effect of Tetrahydrofuran

THF/RLi[a]	k_1	N
1.2	5.8	1.95
4.7	6.7	1.87
8.2	7.4	1.79
12.2	8.2	1.69
35.0	13.7	—
50.0	17.0	1.36
55.0	18.0	1.35
102	23.9	1.28
214	33.0	—
450	40.0	—
810	40.0	—
1380	36.0	—
1800	27.8	—
2000	27.6	—
2560	14.7	—

[a] [RLi] = 1.4×10^{-3} mole/liter.

gation R_p should be equal to the rate of depropagation R_d

$$R_p = R_d \tag{15}$$

Because of this equilibrium, a redistribution of lengths of chains may become possible, depending on the temperature–time requirements of a particular system. Flory (167) predicted that such a system would eventually reach a Poisson distribution of chain lengths. Kinetics of the forward and backward reactions have been worked out by Szwarc (166) and Miyake and Stockmayer (168). In polybutadienyllithium and polyisoprenyllithium systems, little change is observed at moderate temperatures. At high temperatures, other reactions such as branching and eventual crosslinking may occur.

c. Termination. Cessation of the propagation reaction may occur as a result of the depletion of monomer without the chain-end complex having lost its ability to continue the growth reaction in the presence of monomer. It is also possible for an active chain-end complex to be imbedded within a polymer system, especially in a crosslinked polymer, so that growth may continue only at such a rate as corresponds to the monomer diffusion to the active site. These situations do not constitute true termination.

True termination of the ability for further propagation by the chain-end complex can be brought about by the addition of protonic agents such as water, alcohols, primary or secondary amines

$$\mathrm{PLi^{*} + ROH \rightarrow PH + RO^{\ominus}Li^{\oplus}} \tag{16}$$

$$\mathrm{PLi + R_2NH \rightarrow PH + R_2N^{\ominus}Li^{\oplus}} \tag{17}$$

by acidic hydrocarbons (154,155) such as α-acetylenes, cyclopentadiene, or other hydrocarbons of similar $\mathrm{p}K_a$,

$$\mathrm{PLi + RC{\equiv}CH \rightarrow PH + RC{\equiv}C^{\ominus}Li^{\oplus}} \tag{18}$$

by loss of lithium hydride (40)

$$\mathrm{PCH_2CH_2Li \rightarrow LiH + PCH{=}CH_2} \tag{19}$$

by loss of lithium to form an inorganic salt (37,38),

$$\mathrm{PLi + RX \rightarrow PR + LiX} \tag{20}$$

by complexing with an organometallic reagent to form a noninitiating species (40),

$$\mathrm{PLi + Bu_3Al \rightarrow PAlBu_3Li} \tag{21}$$

by cleavage of an ether or an olefin oxide (169–171),

$$\mathrm{PLi + ROR \rightarrow PR + RO^{\ominus}Li^{\oplus}} \tag{22}$$

or

$$\mathrm{PLi} + \begin{array}{l}\mathrm{H_2C}\\ \;|\;\;\;\diagdown\\ \;|\;\;\;\;\;\;\mathrm{O}\\ \;|\;\;\;\diagup\\ \mathrm{H_2C}\end{array} \rightarrow \mathrm{PCH_2CH_2O^{\ominus}Li^{\oplus}} \tag{23}$$

by initiation of polymerization of an ester such as methyl methacrylate,

$$\mathrm{PLi + MMA \rightarrow P{-}CH_2{-}}\begin{array}{c}\mathrm{CH_3}\\ |\\ \mathrm{CH^{\ominus}Li^{\oplus}}\\ |\\ \mathrm{COOMe}\end{array} \tag{24}$$

and by reaction with CO_2 or CS_2 (169,171),

$$\mathrm{PLi + CO_2 \rightarrow PC}\begin{array}{l}\mathrm{{\diagup\!\!\diagup}O}\\ \\ \mathrm{\diagdown O^{\ominus}Li^{\oplus}}\end{array} \tag{25}$$

to form the salt of a carboxy acid.

* PLi is used as a shortened notation for polymerlithium species without regard to state of association or molecular weight.

Molecular oxygen and peroxides can terminate an active chain by forming first the lithium salt of a hydroperoxide which then reacts with a second molecule of polymerlithium (169).

$$2PLi + O_2 \rightarrow 2PO^{\ominus}Li^{\oplus} \quad (26)$$

Sulfur can react in an analogous manner. Ketones and aldehydes have been used to introduce hydroxyl groups (172,173).

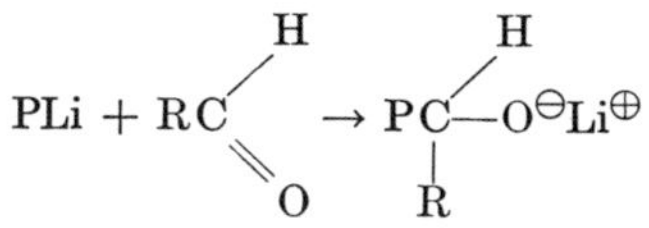

(27)

The above simplified equations constitute the principal processes in use for terminating carbanionic polymerization reactions where alkali metals constitute the counterion. The references supplied are intended only to be illustrative.

Processes in which chain transfer either to monomer or to solvent occurs constitute systems in which a part of the growing chains are terminated but the system itself remains viable. Such processes are not usually observed but may become important in polymerization at high temperatures. The occurrence of such chain transfers may be recognized by the fact that $\bar{M}_n < \bar{M}_k$ since the catalyst concentration is not necessarily diminished. In addition, the molecular weight distribution is broadened (174). In the presence of acidic hydrocarbon impurities the catalyst concentration is diminished (reaction 18 above). In that case $\bar{M}_n > \bar{M}_k$ and a Poisson distribution of molecular weights can be expected to be maintained (175,176). This did not appear to be the case in the presence of slow-acting hydrocarbon impurities such as 1,2-butadiene and 1-butyne where broadened distributions shifted toward lower molecular weights (155) were found. Complex formation between butynyllithium and butyllithium, and between butynyllithium and polymerlithium also, undoubtedly complicate the situation. Conversion of lithium ethylacetylide to the 1,3-dilithio derivative which has the capability of acting as an initiator possibly accounts for the bimodal distribution (155) that has been observed. Similarly, a bimodal distribution was observed in polymers initiated by poly(α-methylstyrene)$^{2\ominus}$ with Na as the counter ions where one end of the growing chain was presumed to have been destroyed. This was cited by Szwarc (166) in his thorough review of the many varieties and facets of termination processes and their consequences.

It will have been noticed above that reactions 23 and 24 show two possibilities where diene hydrocarbon polymerization can be ended by the addition of polar monomers. In such cases the addition of more diene monomer will not be followed by further chain extension of the hydrocarbon moiety. Instead, the addition of ethylene oxide (reaction 23) or methyl methacrylate (reaction 24) is followed by chain extension with the polar monomer. Thus, hetero-block copolymers can be generated (166). These are beyond the scope of this review. Hydrocarbon block copolymers will be discussed in the section on copolymers.

3. Polymerization Effects

The formation of a polymer, an aggregation of macromolecules resulting from the processes of initiation, propagation, and termination, has been discussed from the standpoint of polymerization. It is appropriate now to consider the characteristics of the products and some ways in which polymerization details have an influence on the properties of the polymers. It is recognized that the molecular structure of an elastomer strongly influences its physical properties and significantly affects its performance under different conditions of use. This subject has been reviewed recently (177–181) (cf. Part I, Chapters 1 and 3).

Most polymers that may be classified as elastomers are essentially linear macromolecules of high molecular weight, e.g., >50,000, exhibit a high degree of extensibility with corresponding rapid retraction, and are resilient. In other words, elastomers are substances that deform under stress and quickly retract when the stress is released. Such polymers also display a temperature–time dependence in some of their properties. Elastomers generally have a glass transition temperature, T_g, below about $-30°C$. The prototype elastomer, natural rubber, has a T_g of $-72°C$, and linear polybutadiene derived from alkyllithium catalysis displays an unusually low T_g of $-95°C$.

The molecular characterization of polymer structure is frequently considered according to:

1. Microstructure which deals with the manner in which the monomer units are assembled in a polymer chain and the geometric forms of that assembly, and

2. Macrostructure which deals with molecular weight and the distribution of molecular weights of the individual chains in a group, with short and long chain branching, and with the overall characteristics of the macromolecule. These two principal subdivisions will be considered separately.

a. Microstructure. The polymerization of a diolefin by a lithium based catalyst involves the transformation of the monomer to a polymer consisting of repeating units. More than one route of assembly of the monomer units is possible. If the monomer units are joined by carbon atoms 1 and 4,

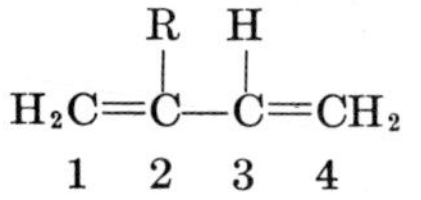

R = H, butadiene
R = CH_3, isoprene

two double bonds are eliminated and a new one appears between the second and third carbon atoms. Chain growth is 1,4 and can be on the same side of the double bond, i.e., *cis*-1,4, or it can be on opposite sides of the double bond, i.e., *trans*-1,4.

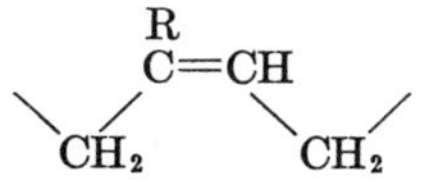

cis-1,4

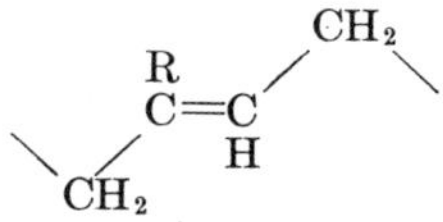

trans-1,4

These two structures are typified by the well-known elastomer, natural rubber, and by the hard, nonresilient plastics, balata and gutta-percha (R = CH_3), respectively.

Alternatively, if the monomer units are joined by carbon atoms 1 and 2 or 3 and 4 (vinyl type polymerization), only one of the original double bonds is eliminated and a pendant vinyl group is obtained.

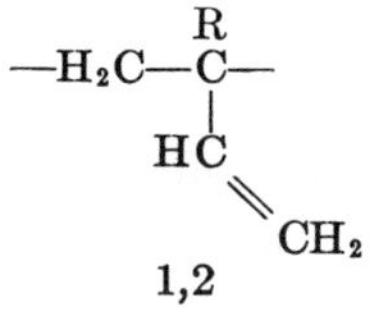

1,2

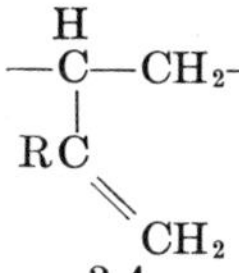

3,4

Polymers having a preponderance of *cis*-1,4 or mixed *cis*-1,4 and *trans*-1,4 units are generally elastomers while those having a preponderance of structures resulting from vinyl type polymerization more closely resemble plastics. Hard and fast lines of demarcation cannot be given because of time–temperature effects on chain flexibility.

The importance of microstructure can be seen from a comparison of the results of infrared spectrometric analysis with physical properties for some synthetic polyisoprenes derived from alkyllithium catalysis (Table X). It is apparent that the tensile strengths of the gum and reinforced vulcanizates diminish with increasing irregularity of the polymer structures. Natural rubber, a *cis*-1,4 polyisoprene having little or no *trans*-1,4

TABLE X
Average Microstructure vs. Tensile Strength of Polyisoprene Vulcanizates (213)

No. of tests	Microstructure *cis*-1,4	*trans*-1,4	3,4	Total found	Viscosity, ML/4/212	Gum[a] tensile, psi	Black[b] tensile, psi
18	89.4	3.4	7.1	91.3	61	3270	3660
25	91.5	1.7	6.8	90.4	65	3280	3770
8	92.4	1.0	6.6	91.8	74	3410	3940

[a] ACS #1 gum stock formula.
[b] 30 parts HAF carbon black.

or vinyl type structures, displays tensile strengths of about 4000 lb/in.^{2} in comparable recipes. It is clear from various discussions of the structure of elastomers vs. their physical properties (177–181) that geometric regularity of the structures in the polymer chain is highly important. Irregularities interfere with the crystallization that may occur in segments of the polymer chain. Highly oriented or partially crystalline segments in a polymer chain have an important influence on stress–strain properties.

The formation of a high *cis*-1,4 polyisoprene was first recognized by its physical properties. Because of the apparent correlation between some desirable physical properties and microstructure, the use of infrared methods of analysis has been of great value in the study of polydienes prepared by means of organometallic initiators. This method of analysis has reduced the need for extensive physical tests on polymers obtained in laboratory studies. Binder (182) has reviewed the application of infrared spectroscopy to elastic polymers from 1,3-diolefins. Variations in methods of analysis have been reported by a number of workers in the field (183–191). Isaac (190) proposed the use of a near infrared method of analysis. Binder (182) included in his analyses a total found value determined separately and not identical with the sum of the *cis*-1,4, *trans*-1,4, 1,2, and 3,4 components of structure to show that these components may or may not account for all of the polymer. Some authors have chosen to neglect the total found value and to normalize the percentage composition thus obtaining misleadingly high values. Stearns and Forman (33) pointed out also that some idea of the number of *cis*-1,4 sequences in a polyisoprene can be obtained by multiplying the total found value with the *cis*-1,4 content to obtain a net *cis*-1,4 value which correlates with possible maximum sequences.

Nuclear magnetic resonance has been applied in the last few years to the analysis of polybutadienes and polyisoprenes (192–197) and also to polymers of piperylene and 2,3-dimethylbutadiene-1,3. Bywater (127), Golub (193), and Schué (194) have noted their preference for NMR analysis over infrared spectrometry because of greater accuracy and speed in analysis. The NMR method, however, is not satisfactory for distinguishing between *cis*- and *trans*-1,4 polybutadienes. A number of workers have applied NMR methods to the study of segment mobility in elastomers (198–200).

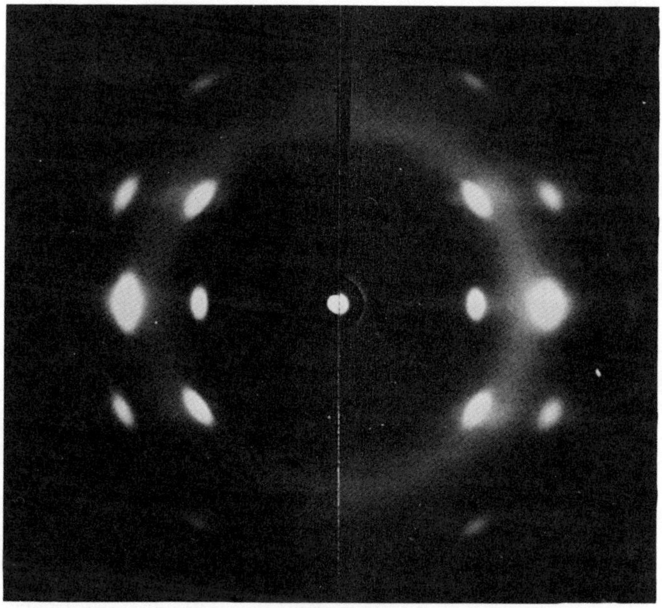

Fig. 1. X-Ray diffraction patterns of *cis*-1,4 polyisoprenes. Left: Natural Rubber. Right: Alkyllithium polyisoprene.

Other methods of characterization of elastomers have been used. Hanson and Halverson (201) described the use of X-ray diffractometry for distinguishing elastomer structures. This method provided a striking demonstration of the identity of a lithium based *cis*-1,4 polyisoprene (10) with the natural rubber hydrocarbon (Fig. 1). Ozonolysis of elastomers has been used to indicate structural features. From the determination of the products obtained from the ozonized polymer, deductions can be made as to the original composition. In this way structures derived from 1,4–1,2–1,4 and 1,4–$(1,2)_2$–1,4 addition of monomer have been identified (202). These structures indicate head-tail and head-head features not shown by infrared spectrometry or NMR. It is to be hoped that high frequency NMR methods will be developed for the quantitative estimation of head-head and tail-tail features of chain structure. Methods are needed also for identifying quantitatively sequence lengths and distributions of vinyl, *trans*-1,4, and *cis*-1,4 units in elastomers.

The ability to prepare polybutadienes and polyisoprenes possessing desired structural features is practically important. It is appropriate therefore to consider the effect of polymerization variables on polymer microstructure.

The principal factor on which microstructure appears to depend is the ratio between the concentrations of monomer and organolithium. It has been noted that the *cis*-1,4 content of a polyisoprene is an inverse function of the catalyst concentration (33,102,105), but some authors (97,145) report that no such change occurs with butadiene. The difficulty may stem from the fact that different catalyst levels are involved for the two monomers. Polyisoprenes of high molecular weight and high *cis*-1,4 contents are preferred in industrial use whereas polybutadienes of a much lower molecular weight are preferred for reasons of processibility. Considerable variation in molecular weight within the commercial range (150,000–300,000) does not produce large variations in the microstructure for polybutadienes. However, when they are made in a high molecular weight range comparable to the polyisoprenes, the *cis*-1,4 content is elevated. Alliger, Johnson, and Forman (149) and Hsieh (105) showed that the *cis*-1,4 content rose at least to 60% as the catalyst concentration was reduced. Values as high as 87% *cis*-1,4 have been observed in polybutadienes and as high as 95% in polyisoprenes (204,205). The final *cis* levels attained may be affected by electronic factors operating in the respective monomers. Rates of polymerization have been correlated with such factors (206,207). Morton (160) showed that the *cis*-1,4 level decreased sharply as a function of the ratio of THF/RLi in an isoprene system. It is interesting to note also Morton's observation (75) that cross association of the initiator with a noninitiating organolithium compound, viz., fluorenyllithium, was accompanied by a decrease in *cis*-1,4 thus reflecting the effect of the total concentration of organolithium species. Several workers (19,33) reported that microstructure varied in polyisoprenes as a function of percent polymer formed. However,

Kuntz and Gerber (97) and Hsieh (105) found microstructure to be invariant with conversion. To the contrary, Makowski and Lynn (203) found at very low degrees of polymerization high levels of 1,2 addition which decreased rapidly as the $\overline{DP}$ increased. This is another case of observations made at widely different catalyst concentrations.

The *cis*-1,4 content of the polyisoprenes is also an inverse function of the polymerization temperature (19,33,105). The vinyl component of both polymers increases with increasing temperature (17,33,99,105). High polymerization temperatures undoubtedly also influence the introduction of other structures than those usually measured. Korotkov (100) noted some variance in the energy of activation for the propagation reaction as a function of temperature. He attributed this effect to the occurrence of a cyclization reaction.

No effect of the R group—whether it be alkyl, alkenyl, aryl, or aryl radical ion—of the organolithium initiator on the microstructure of polybutadienes or polyisoprenes has been reported for polymerizations in hydrocarbon systems.

Solvents, as long as they are hydrocarbons, affect microstructure only slightly under normal polymerization conditions. Polymers prepared in aliphatic solvents consistently contain higher amounts of 1,4 units than when prepared in monomer alone, or in aromatic solvents (19,105). These variations are small and can be compensated to some extent by adjustment of the polymerization conditions or the catalyst concentration.

Polar solvents substituted for the hydrocarbon solvent in whole or in part have a considerable effect not only on the polymerization kinetics, as discussed earlier, but also on the microstructure. The role of ethers has been most frequently examined (18,33,97,105,145,208,209). Amines (105,211,208,212), sulfides (26,105,128,208,209,210,212), and tertiary phosphines, arsines, and stibines (212), like the ethers, coordinate with the catalyst and bring about a change in the microstructure in the direction of increased vinyl component. The extent of the change is dependent on the basicity of the polar adjuvant and on its concentration with respect to the catalyst. Small differences among the electron donor compounds can be observed by changing their *R* groups. The addition of molecular oxygen materially increases the vinyl component in polybutadiene (96,128). The addition of more basic substances such as THF or triethylamine is accompanied by extensive changes in the microstructure in proportion to the amount added (Table XI). It is noteworthy that important differences are apparent in the polyisoprene

TABLE XI
Effect of Polar Substances on Microstructure

Solvent	RLi	*cis*-1,4	*trans*-1,4	1,2	3,4
		Polyisoprenes (103)			
Cyclohexane	BuLi	80	15	—	5
	BuLi + LiOH	68	27	—	5
	BuLi + BuOLi	69	26	—	5
	BuLi + 2 THF	68	19	—	13
	BuLi + 15 THF	69	—	—	31
Cyclohexane/THF (90/10)	BuLi	—	26	9	66
		Polybutadienes (210)			
Hexane	EtLi	43	50	7	
Toluene	EtLi	44	47	9	
Benzene-Et_3N	EtLi	23	40	37	
Benzene-THF	EtLi	13	13	74	
Heptane-THF	EtLi	4	4	92	
THF	EtLi	0	9	91	

microstructures depending on whether THF is coordinated to the catalyst in low relative concentration or is present in appreciable volume.

Numerous reports relating microstructure to the physical properties of polybutadienes (215,217,221) and of polyisoprenes (214,216,218–220) have appeared. Short and coworkers (217) depicted on three dimensional models the three components of microstructure (*cis*-1,4, *trans*-1,4, and 1,2) in respect to the glass transition temperature, stress–strain behavior, and resilience of polybutadienes. Relatively little change is observed except in the vicinity of single structures. High *trans*-1,4 polybutadiene was reported by Railsback, Haws, and Wilder (222) to resemble balata and gutta-percha. Thermodynamic functions of *cis*-1,4 and *trans*-1,4 polybutadienes and of natural *cis*-1,4 polyisoprene are available (223,224).

The isomerization of *cis* and *trans* polybutadienes and polyisoprenes is known to occur under conditions of vulcanization (117,182,225–227, 233–236) and has stimulated an interest in the isomerization of the polymers themselves. Isomerization studies carried out by heating the polymer with sulfur or selenium, or induced by ultraviolet radiation in the presence of a sensitizer show that the products are an equilibrium mixture of *cis*-1,4 and *trans*-1,4. In polybutadienes the equilibrium approaches 75% *trans*-1,4 (182,225,228–231), and 50/50 to 40/60 *cis/trans* in polyisoprenes (232). The isomerization of polybutadiene double bonds in a vulcanizate by sulfur (218) may account for the relatively small differences in physical properties observed between vulcanizates of alkyllithium derived polybutadienes and the high *cis*-1,4 polybutadienes obtained by way of other catalyst systems.

b. Macrostructure. Because of its profound influence on the physical properties of the polymer both in the unvulcanized and vulcanized state, the macrostructure (*vide supra*) is of great practical importance and has become the subject of much scientific interest.

The solution properties of polybutadienes and polyisoprenes are important because they reveal various kinds of information about the physical chemistry of these macromolecules. Molecular weight and molecular weight distribution, branching, coil size and distance between ends of chains, and some thermodynamic properties can be obtained by studying solutions of these polymers, using solvents appropriate to the determination to be made. Discussions of these general topics are available in standard texts (e.g., 167).

It is of practical interest that linear polybutadienes of about 200,000 molecular weight are soluble in *n*-pentane and higher homologues but insoluble in isopentane (237). Linear polyisoprenes of high molecular weight are soluble in *n*-butane and higher homologues but insoluble in isobutane. It had been expected that better solubility relationships would be observed in the isoalkanes since branched compounds are frequently better solvents than the straight chain counterparts. Sheehan and Bisio (238) have shown that the solubility trends can be predicted correctly from the solubility parameters of solvent and polymer.

(*1*) *Molecular Weight.* The characterization of the broad features of the structure of polymers includes a determination of the average molecular weight of the aggregation of chains that constitute the polymer and the distribution of molecular weights among these chains. Molecular weight values are determined according to

(1) $\bar{M}_v$ viscosity average molecular weight based on viscosity
(2) $\bar{M}_n$ number average molecular weight based on osmometry
(3) $\bar{M}_w$ weight average molecular weight based on light scattering
(4) $\bar{M}_k$ kinetic molecular weight based on polymer yield divided by effective moles of initiator

$\bar{M}_k$ and its relationship to $\bar{M}_n$ was discussed earlier. Methods of measuring $\bar{M}_v$, $\bar{M}_n$, and $\bar{M}_w$ are described in various textbooks of polymer chemistry. The viscosity average molecular weight is in general use for routinely indicating molecular weights and is calculated from the relative flow rates of a polymer solution vs. the pure solvent by means of the well known Mark-Houwink equation.

$$[\eta] = KM^{\alpha} \tag{28}$$

where $[\eta]$ = intrinsic viscosity
K = constant
M = molecular weight
α = constant

It is common practice in the rubber industry to use toluene as the solvent and to make flow rate measurements at 25°C. The values of K and α vary somewhat with the polymer system and the conditions of polymerization. The value for the exponent α is high for linear polymers and decreases with branching. Several values of K and α recorded in the literature for polybutadienes and polyisoprenes are shown in Table XII. In the polybutadiene group it can be seen that a value of α as high as 0.80 has been obtained for an alkyllithium derived polybutadiene (239). Therefore the molecular weights of these linear polybutadienes can be calculated according to the relation:

$$[\eta] = 1.42 \times 10^{-4} M^{0.80} \tag{29}$$

TABLE XII
Viscosity Molecular Weight

$K \times 10^4$	α	Ref.
	Polybutadienes	
1.3	0.77	240
1.54	0.57	240
1.42	0.80	239
2.17	0.75	244
1.56	0.78	245
	Polyisoprenes	
5.02	0.67	246
6.84	0.58	247
2.0	0.73	248

Four of the polybutadienes compare closely and are indicated to be largely linear polymers. The polymer having a low value for α is branched (240).

(2) Molecular Weight Distribution. In the polymerization systems under discussion, all chains are not initiated simultaneously, and therefore, a distribution of chain lengths is found at any time. The usual determinations of the molecular weight of a polymer provide an average value. Investigations of the molecular weight distribution (MWD) have been made experimentally by ultracentrifugation (249), precipitation chromatography (250), and the classical method of fractional precipitation from solution by the controlled addition of a non-solvent. By the latter means it was observed that polymers such as BuLi derived polybutadiene made in a homogenous system had a narrow MWD (239). Polyisoprene made with metallic lithium had a broad MWD (10). Bresler (242,243) has used MWD determinations as an aid in studying polymerization mechanisms. He observed that MWD plots are sensitive to and indicative of side reactions.

Gel permeation chromatography (GPC), a rapid and efficient method for determining molecular weight distributions, is a relatively recent development (251–253). Adams, Farhat, and Johnson (239) applied the method to the study of the molecular weight distributions of various polybutadienes made by alkyllithium catalysis and showed that a better estimate of the MWD was obtained by this means than by solvent non-solvent precipitation methods. A comparison of $\bar{M}_v$, $\bar{M}_n$, and $\bar{M}_w$ is shown on a graph of MWD obtained by the GPC method which illustrates the difference in these values (Fig. 2). From the data of a GPC curve, values of $\bar{M}_n$ and $\bar{M}_w$ can be calculated. The ratio $\bar{M}_w/\bar{M}_n$ is often used to indicate the breadth of distribution. Bahary (254) proposed that the $\bar{M}_w/\bar{M}_n$ ratio can be obtained from the ratio of the intrinsic viscosity to the viscosity of a 10% solution of a polymer. Bahary's method is claimed to be useful where GPC equipment is not available.

Besides yielding theoretically interesting information, the study of macrostructure may lead to information of considerable practical importance in polymer technology. Linear polybutadienes within the molecular weight range in industrial use and having a narrow MWD have a property known as "cold flow." Such polymers are essentially high viscosity liquids. Polymers made to molecular weights conveniently processible suffer from dimensional instability, require extra packaging, and are difficult to handle. Commercial polymers have broadened MWD and branching which leads to less cold flow and easy processing in factory equipment. Numerous examples of methods of controlling cold flow

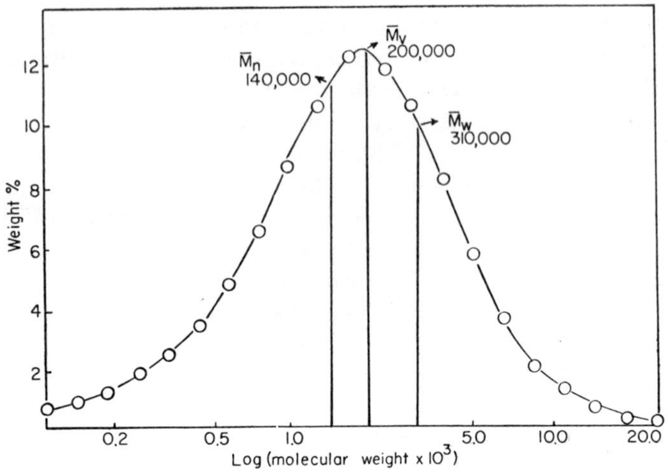

Fig. 2. Molecular weight distribution of commercial polybutadiene.

have been reported in the patent literature by altering MWD and branching, in various ways. These have included the incorporation of small quantities of a difunctional compound such as divinylbenzene to introduce branching, treatment of the polymer with oxygen or a peroxide, heating, inducing a small amount of cyclization, and the incorporation of special additives (255–266).

(*3*) *Branching.* Linear polymers from diolefins and alkyllithium compounds are ordinarily obtained under moderate polymerization conditions. Polymerization at high temperatures may lead to branching, presumably by the addition of an active polymerlithium species to the double bond of a nearby chain. Such behavior is not unexpected since Oliver has shown that —CH_2Li can perturb a nearby double bond (267) and Lansbury (268) has shown that lithium can add to the internal double bond of a bicyclic compound under mild conditions. It is not unreasonable therefore to suspect that, during polymerization at high temperature, after the monomer has been largely consumed, such addition of polymeric alkenyllithium could take place within the polymer system. One could envision a mechanism of chain extension or branching based on a possible reaction sequence as shown in Figure 3. Such a reaction would inevitably lead to long chain branching and could extend to crosslinked species. Flory (167) has discussed the consequences of this kind of branching in polymers and the ease with which branching reactions can lead to crosslinking and gel formation. Indeed, branching in polybutadienes (240) and gel formation in polyisoprenes (17) have been reported as an effect of high polymerization temperatures.

From kinetic studies, Zimm and Kilb (269) found that branching in polybutadienes is promoted by high reaction temperatures. They observed that α in the Mark-Houwink equation decreased as a function of increasing polymerization temperature. They suggested that the decrease in the value of the exponent is a measure of the extent of branching (cf. Table XII) in line with an earlier proposal of Johnson and Wolfangel (270) for emulsion polymers. Kilb (271) suggested that branching could be determined by comparing the intrinsic viscosities of branched vs. linear polymers of the same weight average molecular weight. In their investigation of branching, Poddubnyi and Ehrenburg (272) estimated the presence of one branch point per 4000 units in lithium initiated polyisoprenes over a wide range of molecular weights.

Due to the versatility of lithium based polymerization systems, methods are available for precise studies of the effects of long chain branching. Szwarc (273), some time ago, proposed methods for the

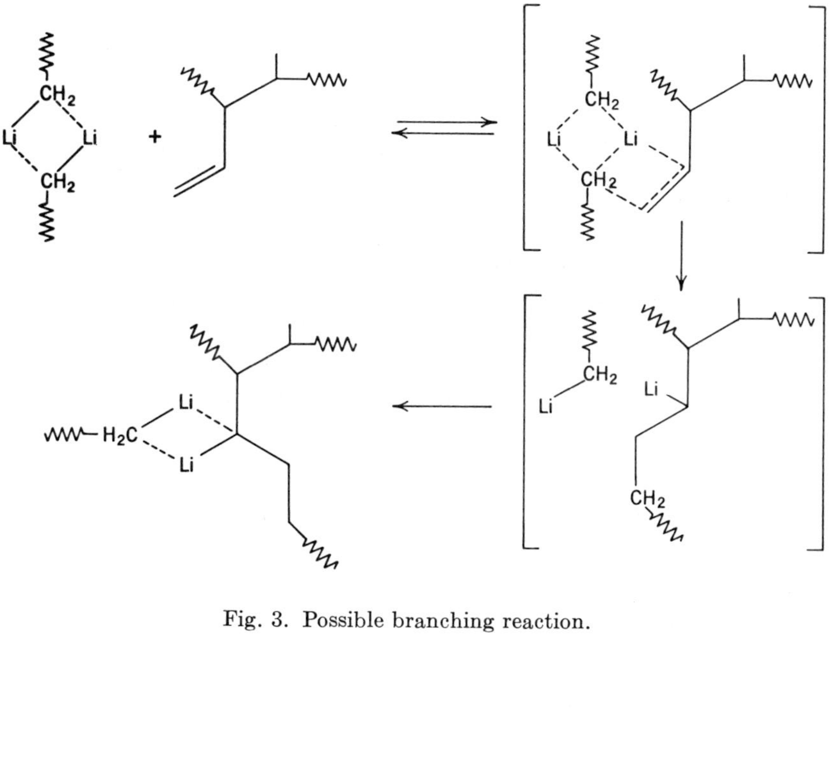

Fig. 3. Possible branching reaction.

preparation of star shaped macromolecules (tetra-branched) by a tetra functional organolithium initiator, viz., $C(CH_2C_6H_4Li)_4$. Zelinski and Wofford (274) have synthesized trichain and tetrachain polybutadienes. The unterminated linear polybutadienes obtained by initiation with BuLi were branched by treatment with a multifunctional agent such as methyltrichlorosilane or with silicon tetrachloride (275). They found that the viscous flow of these branched polymers is profoundly influenced by the long chain branching.

In order to calculate the molecular weights of branched polymers from viscosity measurements, the Mark-Houwink equation needs to be modified by a branching term g (269), so that

$$[\eta] = KgM^{\alpha} \tag{30}$$

as applied by others (72,274). More elaborate discussions of flow behavior of linear and branched polymers are available (244,245,274, 276–281).

(*4*) *Rheology*. The flow properties of various polybutadienes were investigated by van der Hoff, Henderson, and Small (240). These workers found that the Mooney viscosity of bulk polybutadienes increases as the value of α, determined on solutions of the corresponding polymers, decreases. Their data also indicate that for a given intrinsic viscosity, the Mooney viscosity increases as a function of the degree of branching. Thus, a comparison of the bulk viscosity of a polymer with its solution viscosity can be used as a measure of branching.

Gruver and Kraus investigated the rheological properties of linear polybutadienes (245) and multichain polybutadienes (244). Newtonian flow was exhibited by BuLi initiated linear polybutadienes of molecular weights up to several hundred thousand. They concluded that Newtonian flow was favored by chain linearity and a narrow MWD. On the other hand, in branched or multichain polybutadienes, Newtonian flow was characteristic of only the lower molecular weight polymers. Non-Newtonian flow characterized the branched polymers of over 50,000–100,000 molecular weight. At low molecular weights, the viscosity of a branched polybutadiene is lower than that of the corresponding linear polymer of the same molecular weight. At higher molecular weights, the reverse becomes true. These investigators suggest that this latter behavior is a result of an increasing number of chain entanglements at higher molecular weights and that the branch points severely limit the slippage of the chains.

It is clear from the above considerations that a knowledge of the flow behavior of polydienes can be useful in the technological applications of these polymers.

(*5*) *Physical Properties.* Throughout the preceding discussion relationships of various structures to physical properties have been pointed out. One of the important parameters that underlies many physical properties of elastomers is the glass transition temperature, T_g. This important property is related to the segmental motion in polymers and thus is a function of the "rubberiness" of a polymer. The glass transition temperature has been related to molecular properties and polymer behavior by a number of workers (282–287). Boyer (283) has written a comprehensive review concerning this important parameter and its relationship to some aspects of polymer structure. Alliger and Weissert (181) (cf. Part I, Chapter 3, p. 101) recently discussed the relationship of the T_g of polybutadienes to a number of their vulcanizate properties and the practical consequences thereof in tire performance. Low values of T_g appear to be necessary not only for satisfactory service at low temperatures but also for high speed performance under normal conditions.

Dynamic properties of linear polybutadienes appear to be a function of molecular weight up to about 350,000 after which a steady state is reached (149) (Fig. 4). This was shown by measuring resilience (288) using the steel ball rebound test. Smith and Willis (289) compared the resilience of vulcanizates of several commonly encountered elastomers

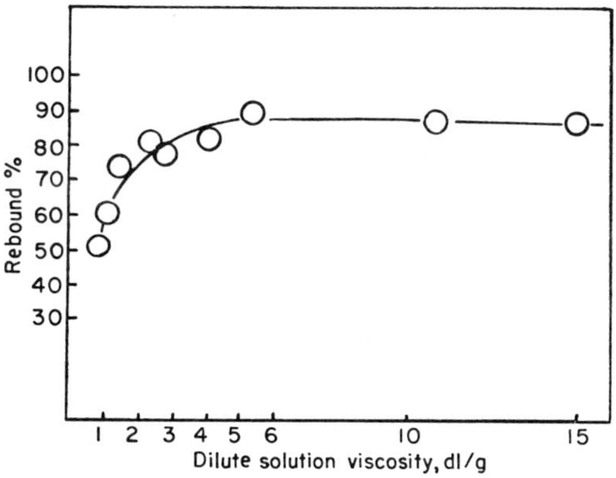

Fig. 4. Effect of molecular weight on resilience of polybutadienes.

containing reinforcing carbon black as a function of temperature. They reported that the lithium derived polybutadiene showed greater resilience than other elastomers. Curves showing % rebound as a function of temperature display a minimum which occurs at a significantly lower temperature for lithium polybutadiene than for natural rubber, emulsion polybutadiene, or SBR.

Many other relationships of polymer structure to physical properties of polymers and corresponding vulcanizates have been reported (177–181, 221) but they are beyond the scope of this presentation.

4. *Mechanism of Polymerization*

The reaction of lithium or an organolithium compound with butadiene or isoprene to form a high polymer initially seemed to be a relatively simple process. That the reaction is far from simple should have become apparent from the foregoing discussion. Despite the application of a wide range of experimental techniques and theoretical analyses, no clear-cut and unified explanation of the detailed process of initiation and propagation has yet been advanced.

In an early discussion of a possible mechanism for the polymerization of isoprene, Stearns and Forman (33) pointed out that isoprene monomer was reported to exist in an equilibrium state having 85% *cisoid* conformation which was considered to bear on the formation of *cis*-1,4 polymer. Evidence was cited also with respect to the hydrocarbon soluble RLi catalyst, that the bonding of the metal with carbon is largely covalent, that lithium has a tendency to become hybridized and engage in multiple bonding, and that organolithium compounds in hydrocarbon solution exhibit a high degree of stereoretention in some of their reactions. They visualized that the reaction begins with an orbital overlap of the Li atom of the RLi compound and a terminal carbon of the *cisoid* monomer. The coordination complex thus established reacts with a new monomer unit forming a six-membered ring which serves as a pathway for electron transfer. Sigma bonds then arise between the terminal carbon atom of one monomer unit and a terminal carbon of an incoming unit. The process is repetitive. The reaction sequence is relatively slow relative to ionic processes and allows adequate time for the maintenance of an equilibrium in favor of the *cisoid* monomer. In this way a high *cis*-1,4 polymer can be obtained. The small percentage of 3,4 structure found in the polymer was accounted for by the presence of a vinyl type resonance structure of the monomer.

Kuntz and Gerber (97) discussed a similar arrangement for the formation of *cis*- and *trans*-1,4 polybutadienes and further suggested the possibility of a *trans* coordination complex in which a dual site is necessary for steric control. They proposed that chain growth occurred in an aggregate of monomer molecules surrounding the soluble organolithium chain end. Complexes of an ill-defined nature were suggested also by Korotkov (95), Sinn (102), and Morton (145) to account for the slowness of reaction, high entropy of activation and stereoregularity of products.

Bawn (290) and Bawn and Ledwith (144) proposed a reaction scheme similar to that of Stearns and Forman involving an overlap of the π electrons of the monomer with vacant *s* or *p* orbitals of the organolithium. This leads to a pseudo six-membered ring which is followed by migration of the alkyl carbanion to the more electropositive carbon of the unsaturated moiety. Chain extension from the newly formed alkenyllithium end proceeds by repetitive steps. They proposed that ethers in the system promoted a dissociation of the C—Li bond to the extent of forming an intimate ion pair and even a solvent separated ion pair of the type previously proposed by Winstein. This proposal was made to account for the departure from the high stereospecificity observed with isoprene in hydrocarbon solution. Tate (291) suggested that the mixed *cis* and *trans* species were the result of a rapid allylic exchange that permits rotation of the central bond. The NMR studies of allylic systems by Roberts (310) and Seyferth (311) support the concept.

Uelzmann (292) and Roha (20,293) regarded the initiation as due to a cationic attack by organolithium on the diolefin monomer. These authors viewed the catalyst as acting through an ionic species such as a contact ion pair or solvent separated ion pair. In the case of isoprene, the polymerization was "stereopreserving" rather than "stereospecific" since the equilibrium state of the monomer was strongly in favor of the *cisoid* form. Roha noted that an increase in extent of dissociation of the C—Li was reflected by an increase in the amount of *trans*-1,4 product. However, Medvedev (294) reports that ultraviolet spectral data show a polarized C—Li bond in unterminated polydienes (hydrocarbon solvents) rather than an ion pair. This observation is consonant with Brown's studies (71) of alkyllithium compounds.

Kennedy and Langer (295) also considered a cationic attack by the organolithium on the monomer as the first step leading to anionic addition. They proposed that the vacant orbitals of the lithium were directed tetrahedrally so that both double bonds of a *cisoid* diolefin could be complexed. A six-membered transition state is formed and followed by the establishment of a sigma bond between the R group and a monomer-end. They noted that in organolithium dimers only two orbitals were vacant and available for coordination. They noted further that after a base such as tetrahydrofuran had been added, only one orbital would be available for coordinating monomer. This, along with the increased ionic character of the C—Li bond, would favor vinyl type addition. Roha (20) and Kennedy and Langer (295) favored the term "coordinated anionic" polymerization because of the postulated first step complex.

O'Driscoll, Yonezawa and Higashimura (296) also used the concept of the tetrahedral sp^3 hybridized configuration of lithium following Kennedy and Langer. O'Driscoll illustrated diagramatically the ways in which the bidentate allylic anion could react in the transition state with monomer. Support for the various possibilities was obtained from molecular orbital calculations. The results of these calculations were in agreement with experimental data.

Roha (20) regarded the alkyl group as an important part of the initiator and pointed out that it would have an influence on the rate of polymerization and could influence the molecular weight distribution of the product. Indeed, Kuntz and Gerber (97) and Hsieh (104) found an effect of the R group of the initiator on the rate of polymerization. It should be pointed out, however, that no essential change in microstructure was observed nor has the microstructure been found to vary as a result of even greater changes in the R group such as in going from alkyl to alkenyl or aryl. Therefore it is unlikely that the nature of the initiator R group has much influence on the mechanism of propagation.

Szwarc (297) has considered a mechanistic scheme for the stereo-addition of monomer to a growing chain. He proposed that a two center process was operative as in a Diels-Alder reaction. The approach of a butadiene molecule to a C—Li bond and their interaction is followed by a 1,4 addition and the formation of a double bond between the center carbons. This fixes the configuration of the newly attached unit in the *cis* form. Where the C—Li bond is dissociated or consists of a solvent separated ion pair, the resulting allylic structure reacts preferably with monomer having a *transoid* conformation. Recent studies (298) have shown that *s-cis* conformations of the first excited state of butadiene are stabilized with respect to *s-trans* even though *transoid* butadiene is more stable than the *cisoid* monomer in the ground state by about 2–3 kcal/mole. In the isoprene anion, a U shaped geometry is favored and the *cis*-methyl anion is stabilized over the *trans* isomer. This finding suggests that the monomer transition states have energetic constraints that favor the final structures appearing in the polymer.

Surprisingly, no mechanistic scheme based on an electron transfer process from an organolithium catalyst has been advanced. Such a scheme would seem to parallel naturally the process starting with lithium metal. Alkyllithium such as butyllithium can act as an electron donor (85) as has been demonstrated by ultraviolet spectra and electron spin resonance measurements (299,300). Such a mechanism also would reconcile initiation by means of alkyllithium, hexamer or tetramer, phenyllithium dimer, aryl radical anions, and monomeric ionized species such as tritylithium. All furnish the same product microstructure at equivalent catalyst concentrations.

Brown (71) suggested four reaction schemes that could serve as kinetic models, and he provided a critique of each. His *first* scheme involved a dissociation of hexameric alkyllithium to the corresponding monomer followed by a slow reaction with the diolefin. This scheme was subsequently ruled out on the basis that there is no evidence that hexameric alkyllithium dissociates to the monomeric form. Energetic considerations make such a dissociation also highly unlikely since it would involve an enthalpy change of about 100 kcal/mole. His *second* reaction scheme starts with a dissociation of a hexamer to tetramer and dimer. Dimeric alkyllithium then reacts with the diolefin monomer. The final kinetic expression for this sequence culminates in a rate equation closely similar to that obtained by Morton (145) and conforms to the $\frac{1}{2}$ order he obtained. A *third* reaction scheme begins with the formation of a complex of hexameric alkyllithium with the diolefin monomer. Such a concept had been proposed earlier by Korotkov (95), Kuntz and Gerber (97), Sinn (102), and Morton (145). According to this scheme the rate would be seen as a function of the first power of the catalyst concentration and of the diolefin monomer. In his *fourth* reaction scheme Brown postulated an ionization of the hexamer followed by reaction of an anion with the diolefin. Such an ionization in hydrocarbon solvent was ruled out because of its high activation energy but it could conceivably be a route in the presence of polar solvents. Makowski and Lynn (203) have made a similar proposal.

Sinn (102) proposed that the initial step was the formation of an adduct for which he computed an activation energy of 15 kcal/mole and a rate constant of 0.003 l./mole-sec. Morton (145) also suggested the presence of some specific complex which could account for the very high entropy of activation indicated by the low frequency factors. On the other hand,

Bywater (146) rejected the postulate of a highly specific transition state on the grounds of a lack of homogeneity of microstructure as revealed by NMR analyses.

The mechanistic schemes that have been proposed by various workers in the field are deficient in several respects particularly for polymerizations in hydrocarbon solvents. The principal deficiencies are:

1. The active alkyllithium catalysts have been assumed to be monomeric, whereas the physical evidence points only to associated states.

2. Alkyllithium is said to be dissociated at least partly to ionic species, whereas the evidence points only to associated states even at high dilution and there is no direct evidence of ionization in hydrocarbon solutions.

3. The effect of catalyst concentration on microstructure has not been elucidated. The structural pictures presented so far have led one to believe that high *cis*-1,4 polyisoprenes would be produced by a given catalyst. Actually a range of microstructures can be obtained with a given catalyst depending on its concentration relative to the monomer.

4. It has been assumed from kinetics that the catalyst is monomeric in polar solvents. Recent evidence indicates that there may be association states even in such solvents. The data of Morton and Fetters (160) display a range of association states in THF.

5. *Chemical Reactions*

The termination reactions listed above (p. 514) do not only illustrate some means by which the propagation in polymerization systems initiated by lithium can be interrupted, but also illustrate a number of methods by which functional groups can be introduced into polymeric compounds to yield new products having a great variety of uses. Many of these have been discussed or described by Szwarc (166), Schoenberg (301), Hayashi and Marvel (302), Samoletova and Motovilova (303), and Verdol et al. (304), and have also been the subject of many disclosures in the patent literature. New names to describe certain features have appeared. Thus the term "pleionomers" has been used to denote homologous polymers in a range of molecular weights varying from over 1000 to about 50,000 (303,305). The term "telechelic" was coined (306) to designate polymers (generally of low molecular weight) having reactive endgroups,

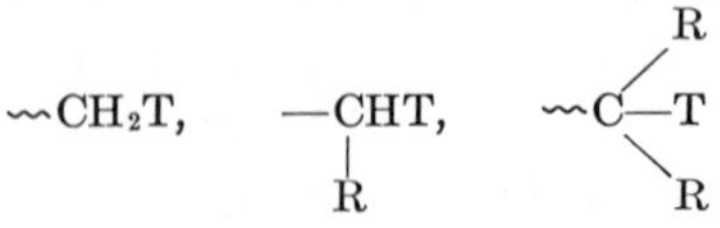

where T may represent either an alkali metal or a group such as —OH, —NHR, —S—, —SH, —COOH, —COOR, $-O-\underset{H}{\overset{H}{C}}-\underset{H}{\overset{H}{C}}-O-$, etc. Such endgroups may be reacted to extend the chain with such agents as ethylene oxide or imine, diisocyanates, metal oxides, complex nitrogen compounds, viz., an aziridinyl phosphine oxide. Crosslinking by way of functional groups at chain-ends is thought to introduce crosslinks at more regular intervals than can be obtained by the usual methods of vulcanization with sulfur. The use of special crosslinking methods has provided products having tensiles up to 1400 lb/in.^{2} (306) from liquid polybutadienes of molecular weights of only about 20,000. Vulcanizates of this kind have a disadvantage in that the elongation at break is not greater than about 200% and are limited to specialty applications therefore. Hydroxy terminated polymers can be reacted with polyfunctional isocyanates (307,308) and thus the diene hydrocarbon polymers can be adapted to polyurethane technology. Similarly, some of the diene hydrocarbon technology such as sulfur vulcanization conceivably can be adapted to the polyurethanes.

II. HOMOPOLYMERS OF PIPERYLENE

The polymerizations of the two principal diolefins, butadiene and isoprene, have been discussed above. Another diolefin, 1-methylbutadiene-1,3 (pentadiene-1,3) needs likewise to be considered. This diolefin more commonly known as *piperylene*, is a byproduct in the synthesis of isoprene from C_5 petroleum sources. As such it has an effect on the economics of the synthesis of isoprene by a dehydrogenation process.

TABLE XIII
Physical Properties of 1,3-Pentadiene Isomers (309)

Isomer	*cis*	*trans*
Formula weight, g/mole	68.12	68.12
Bp, °C (760 mm)	44.068	42.032
Fp, °C	−140.82	−87.47
Density, g/ml, 20°C	0.69102	0.67603
Refractive index, 20°/D	1.43634	1.43008

In spite of many efforts to convert piperylene into a commercially valuable polymer, little success has been reported.

Piperylene is a water white mobile hydrocarbon liquid consisting of a mixture of the *cis* and the *trans* isomers in varying proportions. Properties (309) of the isomers are shown in Table XIII.

The *cis* and *trans* isomers each may have two conformations (**1a–d**) (312).

cisoid *transoid*

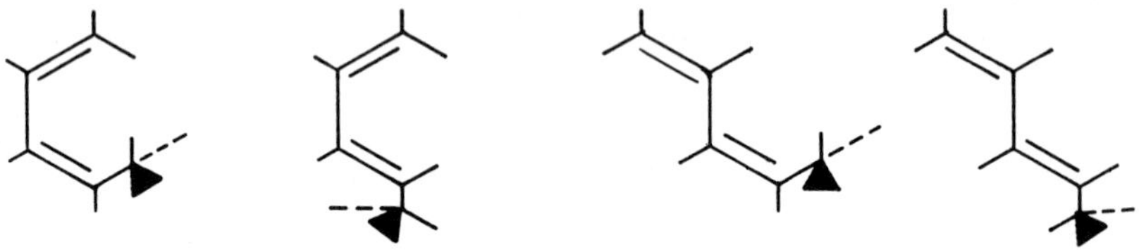

cis (**1a**) *trans* (**1b**) *cis* (**1c**) *trans* (**1d**)

Models show that in the *cisoid* conformations either the methyl group or the hydrogens are in a position to interfere with the close approach of a bulky associated organometallic agent such as butyllithium. Both *transoid* forms are more open and available for interaction. This is particularly true if polymerization proceeds by way of a resonating allylic anion (297,311), and is in agreement with the fact that piperylene polymers derived by lithium catalysis are largely *trans*-1,4 polymers. Models show also that conformers **1***a* and **1***c*, as well as **1***b* and **1***d* are interconvertible by rotation around the central single bond. This bond has some partial double bond character in butadiene and isoprene. This double bond character is probably enhanced in pentadiene-1,3 by the electron donating contribution of the methyl group. Thus the interconversion of the *cisoid* and *transoid* forms may be less likely in this case than in butadiene and isoprene due to a higher energy barrier to rotation. Craig (312) has shown that although the *trans* isomer reacts quickly with maleic anhydride to form 1,2,3,6-tetrahydrophthalic anhydride, the *cis* isomer reacts only slowly to form a polymeric product containing no tetrahydrophthalic anhydride. However, sulfur dioxide reacts with both *cis*- and *trans*-piperylene to provide 2,5-dihydro-2-methylthiophene-1-dioxide which decomposes to the *trans*-diolefin only. Isomerization reportedly can be accomplished by irradiation with ultraviolet light (313). An equilibrium mixture containing 73% *cis* isomer was obtained. A detailed study of *cis-trans* isomerization of piperylene in the presence of various photosensitizers was reported more recently by Hammond et al.

(314). These workers, however, found a stationary state varying from 53 to 77% *trans* isomer depending on the photosensitizer used.

The polymerization of piperylene has been reported by a number of investigators and by a variety of methods. Details of the polymerization by radicals and the characteristics of the resulting polymers have been reviewed (315,316). Polymers and processes involving piperylene and transition metal containing catalysts are reviewed elsewhere in this book (Part II, Chapter 7A by G. Natta and L. Porri, p. 643).

Polymers that can be synthesized from piperylene and lithium metal or an organolithium compound may have the basic structural units (**2**–**5**)

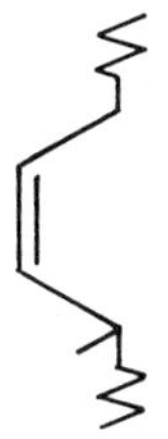

cis-1,4
(**2**)

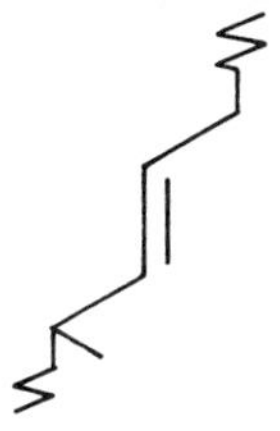

trans-1,4
(**3**)

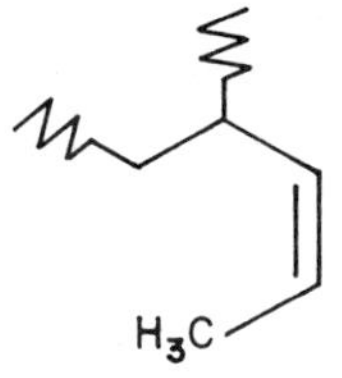

1,2-*cis*
(**4**)

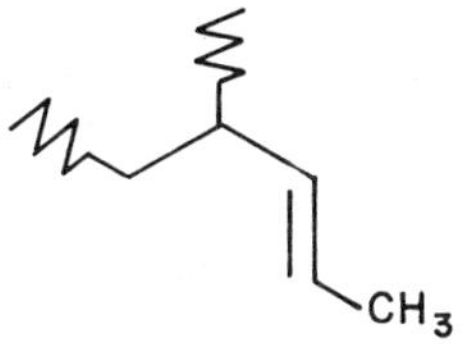

1,2-*trans*
(**5**)

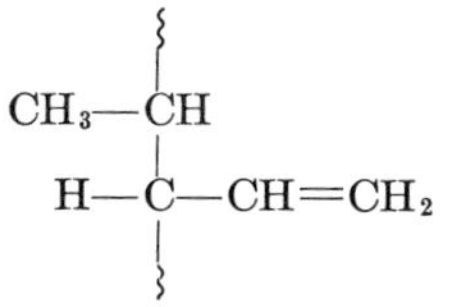

(**6**)

and one isomer by 3,4 addition (**6**). Thus, there are at least four possibilities of having a double bond in either *cis* or *trans* configuration, and only one possibility for unsubstituted vinyl. Isotactic, syndiotactic and atactic placements of all of the polymers derived by 1,2 or 3,4 addition are possible. Aside from a disclosure by Porri et al. (319) that a small amount of crystalline *trans*-1,4 polypentadiene was formed in a polymerization with *n*-butyllithium at −10°C, crystalline polymers resulting from lithium catalysis have not been reported. Elastomeric polymers have been realized by way of emulsion–radical processes and by lithium catalysis. These polymers have very little structure attributable to polymerization involving only one double bond (1,2 or 3,4).

The *cis* isomer of piperylene was reported by Marvel (315) to polymerize in an emulsion system (radical process) more rapidly than the *trans* monomer. Where lithium or organolithium compounds were used as catalysts, the *trans* monomer was found to polymierze more rapidly than the *cis* monomer (317). Polymerization of either of the pure isomers furnishes polymers having both *cis* and *trans* addition structures. Investigation of the ozonization products of a lithium piperylene rubber revealed that, in addition to 1,2 units, three possible 1,4 structures, 1,4–1,4 (24%), 1,4–4,1 (6%), and 4,1–1,4 (8%) were present in the chain (318). Polymerization of a piperylene monomer mixture (39 *cis*/61 *trans*) by 1,4-tetramethylene dilithium catalyst provided, after 57.5% conversion, a polymer having 27.6% *cis*-1,4, 71.9% *trans*-1,4, and 0.5% 1,2 addition structure as determined by infrared spectrometry (317). The unreacted monomers were found to consist of 76.5% *cis* and 23.5% *trans* isomers. A group of scientists at Strasbourg (197,320–325) also found a preponderant tendency to form 1,4 polymer and no 3,4 addition in piperylene polymers obtained from a monomer of mixed isomers used either undiluted or in hydrocarbon solvent and catalyzed either by lithium metal or by butyllithium (Table XIV). Monomer or catalyst concentration changes appeared to affect the polymer microstructure

TABLE XIV
Polymerization of Pentadiene-1,3

Catalyst	Solvent	Monomer *cis/trans*	Microstructure by NMR % 1,4	% 1,2	% 3,4	Ref.
		Autogenous Pressure				
Li	Pentane	—	77	23	20	194
BuLi	Pentane	—	85	15	0	197
Li	THF	—	60	30	5	197
Li	Pentane	—	73–82	18–23	0	197
Li or BuLi	Pentane	10/90	78	22	0	323
	Pentane	33/67	85	15	0	323
	Pentane	53/47	85	15	0	323
	Pentane	99/0	73	27	0	323
	THF		61	39	0	323
		At 10,000 kg/cm^2				
BuLi	Heptane	26/74	79	14	7	324
BuLi	Heptane	100/0	78	16	6	324
BuLi	Heptane	0/100	70	20	10	324
Radical	Aq. emulsion	34/66	80	17	3	325

TABLE XV
Polymerization of 4-Methylpentadiene-1,3 by Butyllithium (326)

Solvent	Microstructure, % 1,2
$(i\text{-Pr})_2O$	34
Et_2O	25
Et_3N	21
$CH_2(OMe)_2$	17.4
THF	12.7
Hexane	13.5

but little. Jenner (324) found polymers of higher 1,2 content from polymerization at 10,000 kg/cm^2, the pressure reportedly having the same effect as increasing the ionic character of the catalyst. A more pronounced effect was obtained at normal pressures by changing from hydrocarbon to polar solvents. In THF the *cis*- + *trans*-1,2 addition structures approximately doubled, changing from about 20 to 40%, but remained at less than half the vinyl content found in polybutadiene or polyisoprene. Sodium, in pentane, also catalyzed the formation of piperylene polymer having 40% 1,2 addition structure.

4-Methylpentadiene-1,3, an analog of piperylene, was found to furnish polymers of similar microstructure where comparable methods of polymerization were used (326). As with piperylene, no 3,4 addition was found with this monomer. The variation in 1,2 addition as a function of solvent basicity was relatively small (Table XV). Most surprising is the reversal in the effect of THF and ethyl ether on the microstructure as compared to polybutadiene and polyisoprene. Full understanding of these processes is not yet at hand.

The physical properties of emulsion polymers of piperylene have been reviewed (315). In view of the close similarity of the microstructure of the emulsion polymers and those obtained by lithium catalysis it is unlikely that they differ greatly in their physical properties. The known resistance of 1,4-polypiperylene to attack by ozone has led to consideration of this polymer as a desirable material for sidewall stocks of tires. Polypiperylenes have the advantage over other rubbers resistant to oxygen in being completely compatible with existing polymers in commercial use. However, there appears to be no large scale usage of polypiperylenes at the present time.

III. COPOLYMERS OF BUTADIENE, ISOPRENE, AND PIPERYLENE

Up to this point only homopolymers of butadiene, isoprene, and piperylene have been considered. The discussion of the polymerization of these monomers by lithium and organolithium catalysts would not be complete without considering the copolymers derivable from these monomers.

Copolymers may be defined as macromolecules consisting of two or more kinds of repeating monomer-derived units. Strictly speaking, even the homopolymers that have been discussed *in extenso* in the first section of this chapter could be considered as copolymers since they consist of mixed groups of repeating units formed by different types of addition (1,2, *cis*-1,4, *trans*-1,4, etc.) In the case of commercial polybutadienes made by way of an organolithium catalyst (149), all of the above structures are revealed by infrared spectrometry. Such polymers, in a sense, are terpolymers. That they are generally considered only as homopolymers is arbitrary but based on the fact that they stem from a single monomer, as well as on the fact that no method has been developed for determining the distribution of sequences of the three structures.

In this discussion only elastomers derived from a pair of the four monomers, butadiene, isoprene, piperylene, and styrene will be considered. Styrene is a vinyl type monomer and, as such, is outside the group of diolefin monomers being discussed in this chapter. However, copolymers derived from butadiene and styrene are of great commercial importance and have been widely investigated on a theoretical as well as a technological basis. Thus their inclusion is justified.

When two monomers react under the influence of a lithium based catalyst, three kinds of situations are possible. The monomer units can join in an irregular manner, i.e.,

—AAAABAABBBAAB—

or in a regular manner which may take two forms, i.e. (*1*) in groups or blocks

—AAAAABBBBB—

or (*2*) in an alternating fashion

—ABABABAB—

The arrangement of A and B units in irregular copolymers may vary from an almost block to an almost alternating copolymer depending on the polymerization system. In the case of diolefin copolymers there is also the possibility of having the different structural units (*cis*-1,4; *trans*-1,4; 1,2; etc.) normally found in the homopolymers. Pendant vinyl groups derived, e.g., from 1,2 addition of butadiene interfere with chain regularity in the copolymers, just as in the homopolymers, and have an influence on the physical properties of the polymer.

The general theories of copolymerization developed over several decades were brought to a satisfactory state of development during the World War II period of intensive development of GR-S (now SBR, cf. Part I, Chapter 4A by C. Uraneck), a copolymer of butadiene and styrene. Additions to and improvements in the general theories of copolymerization are appearing almost continuously. These have been the subject of recent reviews (327–329). As it was developed and is evolving, copolymerization theory rests on the basic principles of reaction rate theory. In recent years the theory has been applied with some success to anionic and coordinate–anionic polymerization systems (127,128,145,146,329,330).

It is generally accepted that there are four possible reactions involved in a binary copolymerization. In an anionic system, they may be represented as*

$$\sim M_1\ominus + M_1 \xrightarrow{k_{11}} M_1M_1\ominus \quad (31)$$

$$\sim M_1\ominus + M_2 \xrightarrow{k_{12}} M_1M_2\ominus \quad (32)$$

$$\sim M_2\ominus + M_1 \xrightarrow{k_{21}} M_2M_1\ominus \quad (33)$$

$$\sim M_2\ominus + M_2 \xrightarrow{k_{22}} M_2M_2\ominus \quad (34)$$

where M_1 and M_2 are the monomers, and the k's are the propagation rate constants. These equations lead to the conventional copolymerization equation

$$\frac{d[M_1]}{d[M_2]} = \frac{[M_1]}{[M_2]} \times \frac{r_1[M_1] + [M_2]}{r_2[M_2] + [M_1]} \quad (35)$$

where r_1 and r_2 represent the reactivity ratios defined as

$$r_1 = \frac{k_{11}}{k_{12}} \quad \text{and} \quad r_2 = \frac{k_{22}}{k_{21}} \quad (36)$$

The usual restrictions regarding the comparison of rate constants apply to this equation. Important factors are constant temperature, mainte-

* For the derivation of these and subsequent equations as applicable to free radical initiated polymerizations, see Part I, Chapter 4B by W. Hofmann.

nance of favorable solution characteristics, and constancy of active sites. The latter are fairly well assured in the absence of terminating impurities and when so-called "seeded" polymerization systems are used. Indeed, it may be recalled that the constancy of active sites was demonstrated for the homopolymerization of isoprene catalyzed by ethyllithium (132). Bresler (329), who has discussed the importance of constant active sites, noted that they are not assured when the initiation process extends over a period of time. Similarly, in the presence of slow termination, unequal disappearance of the different anion species may occur. How these factors affect the cross-propagation rate constants has not been established experimentally.

For most copolymer systems the reactivity ratios are usually calculated directly from the charge ratio of the monomers and the initial copolymer composition. The data are frequently analyzed according to the integral equation of Mayo and Lewis (331) or according to the linear method of Fineman and Ross (332) applicable to an intermediate conversion range. The integral equation can be used over a wider range of conversion but is more cumbersome to handle unless computer service is available. Reactivity ratios may be determined graphically by either method. Various authors have proposed simplifications and refinements (333–340). Behnken (334) and Mortimer and Tidwell (335) recommended the use of statistical methods to maximize the information obtainable and to avoid subjective weighting of the data. Durgaryan (336) derived a copolymer composition equation assuming reversibility of the propagation reactions and pointed to the desirability of determining reactivities in two solvents where anionic systems are involved. Solvent effects are relatively unimportant in radical systems but are known to cause profound changes in anionic systems.

Igarashi (337) used a triangular coordinate system for representing the copolymer composition and illustrating the tendency toward formation of blocks. The curves relating composition to the product of the reactivity ratios showed a tendency toward formation of blocks at high values of r_1r_2. The tendency toward alternation increases as r_1r_2 becomes very small. Tada, Fueno, and Furukawa (338) devised an index for alternation by which the most favorable monomer composition for maximum alternation can be calculated:

$$(r_2/r_1)^{1/2} = \frac{[M_1]}{[M_2]} \qquad (37)$$

Data for a comonomer system of butadiene and styrene in hydrocarbon solvents to which the alternation index is applied can be seen in Table XVI. Very high concentrations of styrene are shown to be required for maximum alternation in the copolymer, a factor that could be of great importance in anionic copolymerization practice. Harwood and Ritchey (339) devised a method for determining reactivity ratios from analysis of the sequence distribution in a copolymer. Where such analyses can be made, it is possible to obtain reactivity ratios *post facto* without determining them from polymerization data. In addition, the determination of sequence distribution may reveal subtle kinetic effects that might otherwise have gone unnoticed.

TABLE XVI
Copolymerization of Butadiene with Styrene by Butyllithium
Effect of Solvent

Solvent	Benzene		Hexane	Cyclohexane		THF
(r_1)	20.0	18.0	12.2	12.0	26.0	1.030
(r_2)	0.05	0.10	0.1	0.4	0.04	0.744
r_1r_2[a]	1.0	1.8	1.22	4.8	1.04	0.765
$(r_2/r_1)^{1/2}$[a]	0.050	0.0745	0.0905	0.1826	0.0392	0.8499
$[M_1]$[b]	0.0476	0.0694	0.0830	0.1544	0.0378	0.4594
$[M_2]$[b]	0.9524	0.9306	0.9170	0.8456	0.962	0.5406
Reference	345	357	357	357	349	361

[a] Calculated values.
[b] Calculated from equation 37.

A general method for predicting reactivity ratios was proposed by Alfrey and Price (340) and was reviewed recently by Alfrey and Young (341). The Alfrey-Price relationship uses two fundamental parameters. These are comprised of a resonance stabilization factor, Q, and a polar factor, e. The equations derived are

$$r_1 = \frac{k_{11}}{k_{12}} = \left(\frac{Q_1}{Q_2}\right) \exp\{-e_1(e_1 - e_2)\} \tag{38}$$

and

$$r_2 = \frac{k_{22}}{k_{21}} = \left(\frac{Q_2}{Q_1}\right) \exp\{-e_2(e_2 - e_1)\} \tag{39}$$

TABLE XVII
Q–e Values for Monomers (341)

	Q	e
Styrene	1.00	−0.80
Butadiene	2.39	−1.05
Isoprene	3.33	−1.22

Values for Q and e were developed for radical systems and have been tabulated for a large variety of monomers. Values for the two principal diolefin monomers, butadiene and isoprene, and for styrene are tabulated in Table XVII. Reactivity ratios calculated from the equations are compared with ratios determined by experiment (Table XVIII). In view of the considerable lack of agreement, the conclusion is inescapable that the Q–e relationship is not directly applicable to coordinate–anionic and anionic systems.

A molecular orbital method has been used with some success to overcome the deficiencies of the Q–e scheme (342). However, the LCAO-MO method has not been applied to the copolymerization systems under discussion and its value therefore cannot be assessed at this time.

A. Irregular and Alternating Copolymers

In homopolymerization the general rate relationship among the monomers of interest in this discussion is

styrene > isoprene > butadiene > piperylene

In copolymerization, a different order is observed:

butadiene > isoprene > piperylene > styrene

TABLE XVIII
Reactivity Ratios from Q–e Values

	r_1	r_2	r_1r_2	Ref.
Calculated				
Butadiene-styrene	1.85	0.343	0.635	—
Butadiene-isoprene	0.858	1.132	0.972	—
Experimental				
Butadiene-styrene in benzene	20	0.05	1.00	345
Butadiene-styrene in tetrahydrofuran	1.03	0.744	0.77	361
Butadiene-isoprene in benzene	3.38	0.47	1.59	344

In early studies of anionic copolymerization, Kelley and Tobolsky (343) found that the copolymer obtained from lithium acting on an equimolar mixture of isoprene and styrene in a polar solvent contained high proportions of styrene in keeping with its relative position in homopolymerization. On the other hand, in a hydrocarbon solvent such as benzene, only a small proportion of styrene was found in the copolymer. In a series of papers Korotkov and his collaborators (18,344–346) drew attention to the reversal of activity of butadiene with respect to both isoprene and styrene. In both pairs the rate of incorporation of butadiene into the resulting copolymer is considerably greater than that of either of the other monomers. A plot of percent isoprene in a butadiene-isoprene copolymer, or of percent styrene in a butadiene-styrene copolymer, shows only a slight rise in the second monomer as a function of percent conversion until the butadiene is consumed. After that there is a sharp rise representing virtually only homopolymerization of the remaining monomer.

Rakova and Korotkov (344) suggested that the active site of polymerization is a dipole that affects its surrounding medium so that the dipole would be surrounded by an envelope of polarized monomer molecules. In a system containing butadiene the envelope would consist principally of butadiene molecules. In a later paper (346) Korotkov and Rakova explained that the solvation of the active polymerization centers by butadiene was to be viewed as having to do with the formation of fairly stable complexes. Such a concept would seem to be in accord with Morton's observation of a high entropy requirement (145). Szwarc (347) expressed the opinion that Korotkov's concept is probably correct and that eventually systems may be found that will provide a convincing demonstration. O'Driscoll and Kuntz (350), following Landler (351) who had earlier recognized reactivity differences in the chain-end carbanions of another system, pointed out that Korotkov's observation could be explained in terms of classical copolymerization theory by assuming that $k_{SB} \gg k_{SS}$ and $k_{BB} \gg k_{BS}$, the symbols S and B referring to styrene and butadiene, respectively. They suggested that, because of differences in the absolute entropies of the respective transitions states, the different chain-ends did not necessarily have to have the same reactivity with respect to a given monomer. Indeed, striking differences in the relative reactivities of these monomers with their chain-end carbanions have been shown by Korotkov (18,330) (Table XIX), and have been confirmed by Morton and Ells (348) and by Johnson and Worsfold (349).

The reactivity ratios for the pairs butadiene-isoprene, butadiene-

TABLE XIX
Copolymerization of Butadiene and Styrene by BuLi (18,330)

	Relative reactivity
$S^{\ominus} + S \rightarrow SS^{\ominus}$	13.7
$S^{\ominus} + B \rightarrow SB^{\ominus}$	424.
$B^{\ominus} + S \rightarrow BS^{\ominus}$	0.2
$B^{\ominus} + B \rightarrow BB^{\ominus}$	2.

styrene, and isoprene-styrene are tabulated in Table XX for polymerization in hydrocarbon solution, and in Table XXI for polymerization in the presence of polar solvents. The broad spread in the reactivity ratios for the monomers of a pair in a hydrocarbon solvent speaks clearly of the divergence in their rate of incorporation into the copolymer chain. The situation can be shown graphically (Figs. 5 and 6) with even greater clarity. It can be seen that copolymers having maximum alternation are not obtainable on the basis of equimolar initial charge.

Copolymer azeotropes are known but not abundant. These are copolymers for which the molar composition is equal to the molar charge ratio (cf. Chapter 4B by W. Hofmann, p. 194). Seiner (352) recently

TABLE XX
Copolymerization in Hydrocarbon Solvents

M_1	M_2	RLi	Solvent	t,°C	r_1	r_2	r_1r_2	Ref.
Bd	I	BuLi	Hexane	50	3.38 ± 0.14	0.47 ± 0.03	1.58	344
Bd	I	BuLi	Benzene	40	3.6 ± 0.3	0.5 ± 0.1	1.80	355
Bd	St	BuLi	Benzene	30–50	20	0.05	1.0	345
Bd	St	BuLi	Benzene	50	18	0.1	1.80	357
Bd	St	BuLi	Hexane	50	12.2	0.1	1.22	357
Bd	St	BuLi	Cyclohexane	40	26	0.04	1.04	349
Bd	St	EtLi	Toluene	25	12.5	0.1	1.25	88
Bd	St	BuLi	Heptane	30	7	0.1	0.70	362
I	St	BuLi	Benzene	30	7.0 ± 0.6	0.14 ± 0.12	1.0	346
I	St	EtLi	Toluene	27	9.5	0.25	1.38	88, 360
I	Pip	BuLi	Hexane	60	17 ± 5	0.06 ± 0.02	1.0	367

TABLE XXI
Copolymerization in Polar Solvents

M_1	M_2	RLi	Solvent	t,°C	r_1	r_2	r_1r_2	Ref.
Bd	I	BuLi	TEA	20	3.6	0.11	0.396	356
Bd	I	BuLi	THF	20	4.5	0.13	0.585	356
Bd	St	EtLi	40% TEA in ΦCH_3	25	5.5	0.3	1.65	88
Bd	St	EtLi	THF	−35	0.2 ± 0.1	8 ± 1	1.6	88
Bd	St	BuLi	Et_2O	30	1.78	0.11	0.20	358
Bd	St	BuLi	THF	30	1.03	0.744	0.765	361
I	St	EtLi	TEA	27	1.0	0.8	0.8	88, 360
I	St	EtLi	THF	27	0.1	9.	0.9	88
I	St	EtLi	THF	−35	0	40		88

presented a simple test for the possibility of forming a polymer azeotrope with a monomer pair for which the reactivity ratios are known, and provided a means for estimating the azeotrope composition.

One practical consequence of the wide spread in reactivities is the difficulty of preparing copolymers having a minimum of blocks. Theo-

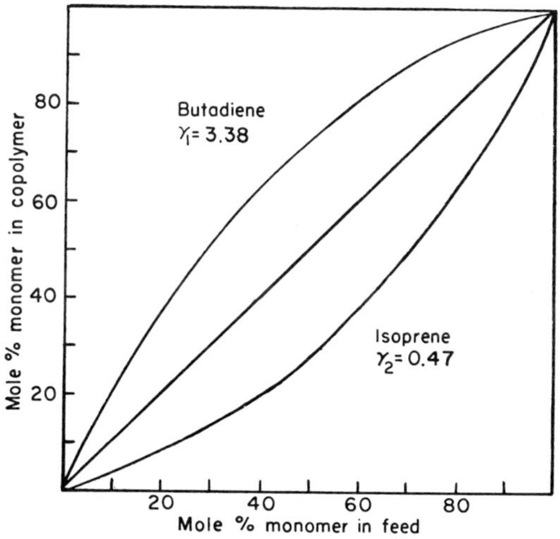

Fig. 5. Copolymerization of butadiene and isoprene in hexane with butyllithium (344).

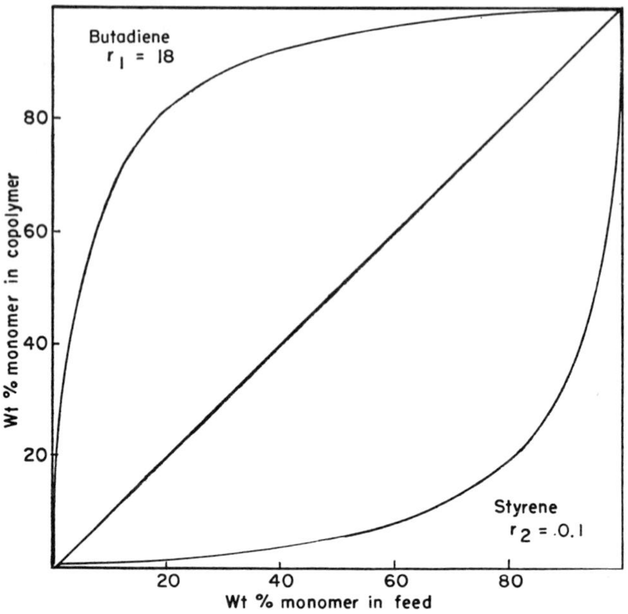

Fig. 6. Copolymerization of butadiene and styrene in benzene with butyllithium (357).

retically, such polymers could be made from monomer mixtures according to equation 37. It can be seen from Table XVI, however, that the rapidly propagating monomer would disappear very quickly. Therefore, in such a situation, it would be necessary to replenish the supply of M_1 so as to maintain the ratio. Some commercial processes for butadiene-styrene copolymers make use of this approach (353,354) with the rapidly disappearing monomer being added either in increments or continuously.

Butadiene-isoprene copolymers have not enjoyed the prominence of the butadiene-styrene copolymers. Butadiene and isoprene, while not having as widely divergent reactivity ratios as butadiene and styrene, display the same general behavior in copolymerization. Data for butadiene-isoprene copolymers have been provided by Rakova and Korotkov (344). Analysis of such copolymers would be difficult by the usual infrared spectrometric method but could be accomplished by means of nuclear magnetic resonance spectroscopy (192). NMR was not available at the time of Rakova and Korotkov's experiments, therefore they labeled the isoprene with carbon 14. In this way the isoprene content could be measured quantitatively (Table XXII) and the copolymer composition established. The data clearly show the greater reactivity of the butadiene, particularly at lower levels of conversion. The Russian workers calculated the reactivity ratios by means of the integral equation of Mayo and Lewis and found the reactivity ratio for butadiene, $r_1 = 3.38 \pm 0.14$, and for isoprene $r_2 = 0.47 \pm 0.03$. Similar values were obtained by Furukawa, Saegusa, and Irako — $r_1 = 3.6 \pm 0.3$ and $r_2 = 0.5 \pm 0.1$ — although these authors may have made their determinations based on analysis by infrared spectrometry (355). It would be interesting to compare data for both sets of polymers analyzed by the NMR method.

The influence of polar substances has been of interest to many workers (18,88,145,146,329,343,358–362). When various ethers or triethylamine are present in the polymerization system, there is a decline in the energy of activation and an increase in the rate of polymerization. In copolymerization, the reactivity ratios are brought closer together and the relative amount of styrene in the copolymer approaches more closely the ratio in the monomer mixture. Mitzengendler et al. (18,361) found that ethyl ether, dioxane, and methylal had about the same activity. Tetra-

TABLE XXII
Copolymerization of Butadiene and Isoprene in Hexane with Butyllithium[a]

Initial mixture, mole %		Conversion,	Copolymer composition, mole %	
Butadiene	Isoprene	%	Butadiene	Isoprene
21.1	78.9	42.3	42.5	57.5
22.0	78.0	50.8	37.0	63.0
30.3	69.7	16.8	45.6	54.4
47.8	52.2	13.4	71.3	28.7
48.8	51.2	35.4	68.1	31.9
48.9	51.1	84.6	56.3	43.7
51.0	49.0	14.5	73.0	27.0
51.0	49.0	65.5	65.5	34.5
51.3	48.7	25.2	71.7	28.3
79.1	20.9	11.9	92.0	8.0
79.3	20.7	40.2	93.4	6.6
80.2	19.8	64.5	90.5	9.5

[a] Data of Rakova and Korotkov (344); r_1 (butadiene) = 3.38 ± 0.14; r_2 (isoprene) = 0.47 ± 0.03.

hydrofuran and dimethoxyethane also were similar in their effect and five to six times more active than ethyl ether. The use of electron donor substances in the polymerization system to promote a more efficient incorporation and special distribution of styrene in elastomeric copolymers has been disclosed in the patent literature (363). Reich and Stivala (364) have developed a mathematical treatment for describing copolymerization in polar solvents assuming the formation of mono- or diether complexes. They found no necessity for the concept of solvation of active sites by a monomer.

Copolymers that more nearly approach maximum alternation can be prepared by introducing polar substances into the system. Table XXI presents data for systems to which ethers or triethylamine have been

TABLE XXIII
Sequence Distribution in Butadiene-Isoprene Copolymers[a]

Analysis			Calculated from run number					
A	B	Random, %	AA, %	BB, %	AB + BA, %	f_{AAA}	f_{BAA} and f_{AAB}	f_{BAB}
42.5	57.5	48.9	21.1	36.3	42.9	0.245	0.500	0.255
37.0	63.0	46.6	15.3	41.3	43.4	0.171	0.485	0.344
45.6	54.4	49.6	23.6	32.4	44.0	0.268	0.500	0.232
71.3	28.7	40.9	53.5	10.9	35.7	0.562	0.375	0.063
68.1	31.9	43.5	50.6	14.4	35.0	0.552	0.382	0.066
56.3	43.7	49.2	38.9	26.3	34.9	0.476	0.428	0.096
73.0	27.0	39.4	55.8	9.8	34.5	0.583	0.361	0.056
65.5	34.5	45.2	48.8	17.8	33.5	0.554	0.381	0.065
71.7	28.3	40.6	55.1	11.7	33.3	0.589	0.357	0.054
92.0	8.0	14.7	85.3	1.3	13.4	0.860	0.135	0.005
93.4	6.6	12.3	86.8	0.0	13.3	0.863	0.132	0.005
90.5	9.5	17.2	84.2	3.2	12.7	0.865	0.131	0.005

[a] A = % butadiene species in copolymer by analysis; B = % isoprene species in copolymer by analysis; AA and BB are respective percentage probabilities of diads; AB + BA = run number calculated by method of Harwood (339) and is the percentage probability that an A unit is either preceded or followed by a B unit; f_{BAA} (or f_{AAB}) = fraction of A units centered in triad. Copolymer analysis from data of Rakova and Korotkov (344). A and B are units derived from butadiene and isoprene, respectively.

TABLE XXIV

Copolymerization of Butadiene and Styrene in Tetrahydrofuran with Butyllithium[a]

Mole % in feed		Conv.,	Mole % in copolymer		
Bd	St	%	Bd	St	Run no.
80	20	6	82.4	17.6	31.72
80	20	34	81.3	18.7	31.72
50	50	76	51.6	48.4	52.99
50	50	79.2	51.7	48.3	52.99
30	70	61.9	32.6	67.4	47.90
30	70	67.8	33.6	66.4	47.90

Calculated Sequence Distribution

AB + BA, %	AA, %	BB, %	Random, %	f_{AAA}	f_{BAA}	f_{BAB}
31.7	66.6	1.8	29.0	0.65	0.31	0.04
31.7	65.5	2.9	30.4	0.65	0.31	0.04
53.0	25.1	21.9	49.9	0.24	0.50	0.26
53.0	25.2	21.8	49.9	0.24	0.50	0.26
47.9	8.7	43.5	43.9	0.07	0.39	0.54
47.9	9.7	42.5	44.6	0.08	0.41	0.51

[a] Polymerization data of Korotkov et al. (361) $r_{Bd} = 1.030$, $r_{St} = 0.744$. System: Butadiene-styrene/THF/BuLi. Sequences calculated according to Harwood and Ritchey (339).

added. The previously widely differing reactivity ratios are brought closer together. The copolymers have compositions more nearly approaching those of the comonomers. It should be emphasized, however, that these copolymers are not of the same nature as those made in hydrocarbon solution because of the thorough revision of the microstructure brought about by the ether or amine. Differences in physical properties such as elevated glass transition temperatures, diminished flexibility of chain segments, and less favorable hysteretic characteristics are to be expected. In brief, these copolymers have less elastomeric character than the copolymers made in hydrocarbon solvents.

No analyses of sequence distribution in elastomeric copolymers have appeared. It was of interest therefore to subject the data of Rakova and Korotkov (344) for the polymerization of butadiene and isoprene in hexane by butyllithium to an analysis of sequence distribution according to the method of Harwood and Ritchey (339). The sequence analysis is shown in Table XXIII. The data are listed in the same order as shown for the monomer mixture and percent conversion in Table XXII. The distribution of diads and triads follows the expected course.

Application of sequence distribution analysis to the butadiene-styrene copolymers obtained by Korotkov et al. (361) in polar solvent also furnished interesting data as shown in Table XXIV. These data demonstrate the possibilities for changing the composition of the copolymer as a function of the mole ratio of butadiene and styrene in the monomer mixture.

B. Piperylene Copolymers

The piperylene commercially available is usually a mixture of about one-third *cis*-pentadiene-1,3 and two-thirds *trans*-pentadiene-1,3. Polymerization of such a mixture has been treated as a copolymerization system (365), and piperylene appears to be the only monomer so treated. The reactivity ratios were determined as $r_{cis} = 1.15$ and $r_{trans} = 0.44$ in a radical polymerization system at a pressure of 12,000 kg/cm^2 (325). Reactivity ratios for the coordinate–anionic system have not been reported although the *cis* and *trans* isomers have been polymerized either

TABLE XXV
Copolymerization of Isoprene and Piperylene in Hexane (367)[a]

M_1 (initial)	Et_2O in solvent, %	t°C	% Conv.	M_1 in polymer	r_1	r_2
19.8	—	50	19.4	67.7	13.6	0.074
20.2	—	60	20.6	65.7	12.0	0.083
20.0	—	70	21.2	62.8	10.5	0.095
20.0	—	70	24.2	64.4	13.3	0.075
20.0	—	80	28.0	62.8	15.0	0.067
20.6	—	80	28.6	56.6	9.1	0.110
20.0	5	60	26.4	54.5	7.8	0.128
20.0	10	60	27.9	44.7	5.0	0.200
20.0	20	60	34.9	43.4	4.9	0.204

[a] Catalyst: butyllithium; r_1 calculated by Wall's equation; $r_2 = 1/r_1$.

alone or mixed by butyllithium in alkane solvents under conventional conditions (317,322) and at 10,000 kg/cm^2 (324) but only polymer microstructures were determined. A copolymer of piperylene with styrene was reported by Schué and coworkers (321) but properties and reactivity ratios were not divulged.

Rakova, Korotkov, and Tszuan-Chan Li (367) prepared a series of isoprene-piperylene copolymers in both hydrocarbon and ether solvents (Table XXV). The temperature of polymerization had no important effect. From this fact the authors deduced that the energies of activation for isoprene and for piperylene were approximately equal. An observed rate difference by about a factor of 20 was ascribed to a steric factor in piperylene. The reactivity ratios calculated by the equation of Wall was given as $r_1 = 17 \pm 5$, and $r_2 = 1/r_1$. Polymerization in the presence of ether lowers the value of r_1 to about 5 and is accompanied by an increased proportion of piperylene in the copolymer.

C. Block Copolymers

One of the important ways in which the versatility of the lithium catalyst system is put to practical use is in the preparation of block copolymers. Such polymers are characterized by a chain consisting of two or more sequences of polymer segments. Each of the long segments has its own individual attributes which are much the same as those of a homopolymer prepared under corresponding conditions. Block copolymers can vary widely in their composition. The simplest case would comprise a polymer from two monomers polymerized successively (AAAA · · · BBBB · · ·). A great number of combinations are possible wherein segment length and number of sequences of A and B segments may be varied widely. The study of the properties of block copolymers of varied block lengths and monomer composition is of current interest and practical importance.

Although block copolymers were previously known, the first significant report of a convenient method for their preparation was that of Szwarc, Levy, and Milkovich (368,369), who in 1956, pointed to the possibilities inherent in the anionic polymerization where there was no termination and little or no chain transfer. In such a system, after one monomer had been entirely consumed, another monomer could be introduced causing the polymerization to be resumed. In this way, a copolymer of two or more sequences, each consisting of like units, could be made. Although Szwarc's early publications did not mention lithium initiators (he used sodium), it was quickly realized that they were ideal catalysts for this type of polymerization. These initiators offered the advantage of being soluble in hydrocarbon systems and of producing the customary microstructure, the narrow molecular weight distribution, and the linearity of chain that were characteristic of the homopolymers obtained under equivalent conditions. In this system, more than in any other, it was possible to tailormake a polymer according to specification and to study the physical consequences of structural features.

Block copolymer systems have been reviewed by Szwarc (370), Champetier (371), Kolesnikov and Yaralov (372), and Fetters (373). These authors pointed out many of the principal features and the practical and theoretical advantages of block copolymerization. Champetier drew attention to a possible correlation between the electron affinity of monomers and the basic strength of their anions. He proposed that for polymerization to occur, a monomer must have a higher reduction potential than the polyanion. Closeness of the electron affinity of two monomers was judged to be necessary for the formation of multiblock sequences (371).

Several methods are reported for the preparation of block sequences. All of them require the highest possible degree of purity to avoid adventitious termination. Only in this way can the sequence length of individual blocks be adequately controlled and correlated with various properties.

1. Type $(A—B)_n$

Addition of a second monomer to an unterminated homopolymer system (one active site per initiator molecule). As long as the system remains operative, the first and second monomers can be added alternately. It is only necessary that there be no termination and that one monomer be consumed before the second is added. In this way, Korotkov et al. (374) prepared polymers with up to nine block sequences from isoprene and styrene using butyllithium initiator in benzene or hexane. Comparison of one of the copolymers with a mechanical mixture of the corresponding homopolymers by means of turbidimetric precipitations and by ultraviolet spectroscopy verified the block copolymerization.

2. Type A—B—A *or* B—A—B

Polymerization with two active sites per initiator molecule. In this case the initiator may be lithium metal or a difunctional organolithium initiator. Minoux and Leng (375) prepared block polymers of isoprene and styrene in benzene starting with lithium metal and either monomer. Thus both types of block copolymers (trisequence) were made.

$$2Li + n\,\text{isoprene} \rightarrow Li^{\oplus\ominus}(CH_2{-}\overset{\displaystyle CH_3}{\overset{|}{C}}{=}CH{-}CH_2)_n{}^{\ominus}Li^{\oplus} \qquad (40)$$

$$Li^{\oplus\ominus}(CH_2{-}\overset{\displaystyle CH_3}{\overset{|}{C}}{=}CH{-}CH_2)_n{}^{\ominus}Li^{\oplus} + 2m\ St \rightarrow Li^{\oplus\ominus}(St)_mI_n(St)_m{}^{\ominus\oplus}Li \qquad (41)$$

and

$$2Li + 2\phi CH{=}CH_2 \rightarrow 2(\phi\dot{C}H{-}CH_2)^{\ominus}Li^{\oplus} \qquad (42)$$

$$2(\phi\dot{C}H{-}CH_2)^{\ominus}Li^{\oplus} \rightarrow Li^{\oplus\ominus}CH_2\underset{\underset{\displaystyle \phi}{|}}{CH}{-}\underset{\underset{\displaystyle \phi}{|}}{CH}{-}CH_2{}^{\ominus}Li^{\oplus} \qquad (43)$$

$$Li^{\oplus\ominus}CH_2\underset{\underset{\displaystyle \phi}{|}}{CH}{-}\underset{\underset{\displaystyle \phi}{|}}{CH}{-}CH_2{}^{\ominus}Li^{\oplus} + n - 2St \rightarrow Li^{\oplus\ominus}(St)_n{}^{\ominus}Li^{\oplus} \qquad (44)$$

$$Li^{\oplus\ominus}(St)_n{}^{\ominus}Li^{\oplus} + 2m\ \text{isoprene} \rightarrow Li^{\oplus\ominus}(I)_m(St)_n(I)_m{}^{\ominus}Li^{\oplus} \qquad (45)$$

and

$$Li^{\oplus\ominus}CH_2(CH_2)_xCH_2{}^{\ominus}Li^{\oplus} + n\ \text{butadiene} \rightarrow \begin{array}{l} Li^{\oplus\ominus}(CH_2CH{=}CHCH_2)_{n/2}{-}CH_2 \\ \qquad\qquad\qquad\qquad\qquad\qquad | \\ \qquad\qquad\qquad\qquad\qquad\quad (CH_2)_x \\ \qquad\qquad\qquad\qquad\qquad\qquad | \\ \qquad\qquad\qquad\qquad\qquad\quad CH_2 \\ \qquad\qquad\qquad\qquad\qquad\ / \\ Li^{\oplus\ominus}(CH_2CH{=}CHCH_2)_{n/2} \end{array} \qquad (46)$$

$$Li^{\oplus\ominus}(Bd)_{n/2}CH_2(CH_2)_xCH_2(Bd)_{n/2}{}^{\ominus}Li^{\oplus} + 2m\ St \rightarrow$$
$$Li^{\oplus\ominus}(St)_m(Bd)_{n/2}CH_2(CH_2)_xCH_2(Bd)_{n/2}(St)_m{}^{\ominus}Li^{\oplus} \qquad (47)$$

Examples of the types cited can be found in the patent literature from which a few representative references are given (376–385).

D. Physical Properties

Interesting observations have been reported about the physical behavior of various block copolymers. Bresler (386) prepared a block copolymer having four blocks of polystyrene and five blocks of polyisoprene. The polymer was made in benzene with butyllithium as initiator and had a molecular weight of 77,000 as determined in 2-butanone. Films were made by evaporation of polymer solutions in benzene, heptane, and 2-butanone and strips were cut from the films for tests of stress-strain properties. The tensile values of polymer films obtained from heptane solution were low, while those of films from 2-butanone were relatively high. The latter behaved like plasticized polystyrene, whereas films obtained from the aliphatic hydrocarbons, in which polystyrene is insoluble, were rubber-like. On evaporation, the alkane insoluble blocks adopt a minimum coil size and thus tend, in effect, to precipitate from solution while the polyisoprene blocks tend to hold the polystyrene blocks in solution. The polystyrene moieties therefore form globules and may be said to be like beads strung on a flexible polyisoprene thread. Conversely, when the 2-butanone solvent is evaporated, the polystrene blocks act like the thread and the polyisoprene blocks as the beads. Bresler et al. (386) suggested that the rubbery film could be viewed as a polyisoprene having a chemically bound glassy filler whereas the tougher film was like a polystyrene with a chemically bound plasticizer.

A similar study of block polymers in preferential solvents was reported recently by Gallot, Mayer, and Sadron (387). They examined bisequence and trisequence block polymers of isoprene and styrene prepared in toluene via butyllithium initiation. Acetone (for polystyrene) and acrylic acid (for polyisoprene) were chosen as preferential solvents. They found that, at appropriate concentrations, cylindrical filaments were formed which contained the less soluble blocks in a hexagonal network. The interstitial medium consisted of a solution of the more soluble blocks in their preferred solvent. The roles of each type of block were reversible. The dimensions of the cylindrical structures were found to depend on the molecular weight of the whole polymer and the ratio of the molecular weights of the blocks, and on the solvent. A new stable cubic structure was observed in isoprene solution. When examined under a polarizing microscope the trisequence polymer showed a diffuse birefringence. They prepared a series of iridescent samples extending from indigo to turquoise blue to green, and they reported that the iridescence was like that of a butterfly wing.

Iridescent colors were also observed by Vanzo (388) in block copolymers of butadiene and styrene polymerized by butyllithium catalyst. He suggested that the colors were due to the interference of reflected light waves just as in liquid crystals. He observed that solutions of the copolymer in ethylbenzene changed reflectance with concentration and that, under careful conditions of drying, the color would be retained. This behavior suggested that these optically ordered structures should be accompanied by a distinct film structure. Indeed, electron photomicrographs showed distinct patterns, and it seemed reasonable to suggest that the molecules might be arranged not unlike soap molecules in an aqueous solution.

The photomicrographs shown by Vanzo (388), it is interesting to note, resembled those displayed by Kargin (178) for striped and incipient fibrillate structures of various polymers including synthetic rubbers. These are the organized forms which he declares responsible for the strength of polymeric materials. Globular structures in elastic polymers are low in strength and generally have unfavorable mechanical properties. It can be seen that various structures are possible and profoundly affect the mechanical properties of polymers and even their vulcanizates. Kargin drew attention also to the fact that macromolecular organization begins early in the polymerization and this phenomenon can affect polymerization kinetics. It is important in studies of elastomer polymerization and copolymerization to be mindful of the range of structural possibilities and to select polymerization conditions favorable to those structures which tend to yield optimum mechanical properties. The development of this kind of forecasting could lead to exciting advances in the use of elastomers as materials of construction.

Organolithium initiated butadiene-styrene block copolymers of the A-B-A type (see p. 554) having the compositional arrangement $(St)_l$—$(Bd)_m$—$(St)_n$ constitute an interesting and important recent development (389,390). The center and end blocks can be varied in size with consequent variations in morphology and in some physical properties. For elastomers, the center block of polybutadiene must be of a higher molecular weight than the polystyrene segments. The polybutadiene segment imparts elastomeric flexibility, extensibility and retractibility, resilience, resistance to abrasion, and a low glass transition temperature. The polystyrene segments have a high glass transition temperature, act somewhat like reinforcing agents, and have an effect similar to chemical crosslinking. The effect disappears when the polymers are heated above the melting point of the polystyrene segments but returns on cooling. This thermoplastic character permits the polymers to be molded and extruded in a temperature range of 65–250°C. The particular processing range varies for different copolymers depending on their segment sizes. With increasing polystyrene segment size, hardness, modulus, and molding temperatures rise, and resilience decreases. Since vulcanizing agents are not necessary in many applications of these polymers, scrap pieces can be recycled with consequent economic advantages. It should be noted, however, that unvulcanized polymers do not withstand hydrocarbon solvents and are limited thereby in their applications. Polymers of the type described above have been called elastoplastics (180), and have been given the trade name Thermolastics by the Shell Chemical Company (389).

Another block copolymer of butadiene-styrene made in solution by way of organolithium catalysis is the A-B type such as Solprene 1205 of the Phillips Petroleum Company (180,391,392). Polymers of this type are also thermoplastic and have been reported as having applications in molded and extruded goods. This polymer has a weight percent composition not much different from that of SBR, the most abundantly produced synthetic elastomer. The polymer is reported to have excellent low temperature properties, flexibility, and resistance to abrasion, presumably due to the predominant polybutadiene chain. Vulcanizates of this polymer are used in shoe soles and heels, wire coatings, and floor coverings (391).

A solution copolymer of butadiene and styrene called Solprene 1204 that appears to have an irregular placement of monomer units is also available (392,393). This copolymer also has about the same percentage composition on a weight basis as SBR but is otherwise different in its microstructure and in its narrower molecular weight distribution. The reported values for *cis*-1,4, *trans*-1,4 and 1,2 content of the polybutadiene segments are 32/41/27 as compared with 8/74/18 for SBR. The high vinyl content of the solution polymer suggests that a polar substance was included in the polymerization process. The high vinyl content is probably accompanied by a slightly higher glass transition temperature. However, both polymers are reported to have adequate low-temperature properties for general use (392).

Duradene,* Firestone's copolymer having a mixed distribution of units of butadiene and styrene polymerized in a solution process by an organolithium catalyst has a low vinyl content of about 9%. The polymer is used principally for tire stocks where its low glass transition temperature, high resilience and resistance to abrasion can be of most advantage. Alliger and Weissert reported better wet traction than for comparable SBR tread compounds (180). These authors related glass transition temperatures to the coefficient of friction, skid resistance, and abrasion wear in tires from SBR and Duradene polymers (181), and pointed out the advantages of a high degree of chain flexibility reflected by the low T_g. The SBR polymers have a lower degree of chain flexibility as seen in diminished resilience and higher brittle point (394).

Phase effects in elastomeric copolymers appear not to have been studied in detail. In butadiene-styrene copolymers, it might be expected that increasing heterogeneity would accompany an increasing size of poly-

* Trademark, The Firestone Tire & Rubber Company.

styrene segments in both irregular and block copolymers. Differences in the mutual solubility of segments might well be expected in the presence of larger blocks of polystyrene. No information is available concerning the distribution of the three possible microstructural sequences in the polybutadiene segments but it is conceivable that any large blocks of either 1,2 or *trans*-1,4 units would also contribute to heterogeneity. Kargin (178) has drawn attention to the fact that the presence of these diverse structures also implies the existence of structural boundaries, density differences, and unequal mechanical strains. In polymers where such conditions exist it is possible for relatively small quantities of substances of suitable molecular weight and physical characteristics to become distributed along such structural boundaries and to act as a lubricant or interstructural plasticizer, sometimes to great effect. This kind of phenomenon has been observed in an unrelated polymer system wherein the T_g was decreased by 80° upon the addition of only a tenth of a percent of an insoluble plasticizer. It appears therefore that it should be advantageous to study the heterogeneity and the boundary relationships of the supramolecular structures of copolymers in addition to the usual examinations of microstructural and macrostructural features. A better understanding of the relationships of morphological structure to mechanical properties would surely be the fruit of such studies.

B. Sodium, Potassium, Rubidium, and Cesium and Their Organometallic Compounds

IV. HOMOPOLYMERS OF BUTADIENE, ISOPRENE, AND PIPERYLENE

A. Introduction

The development of emulsion processes for synthesizing elastomers from conjugated diolefins prior to and during World War II greatly reduced interest in the alkali metals and their compounds as catalysts for the synthesis of elastomers. However, a limited amount of work was continued under the Rubber Reserve Program in the United States. Following the war, further investigations of the alkali metals at Firestone (395) led to the discovery of the unique benefits conferred by lithium and organolithium compounds in the polymerization of isoprene (10). As interest in this first member of Group I grew, still less attention was given to the remaining members of the group. Nevertheless some work on the other alkali metal systems has continued and has begun to yield information regarding the nature and role of active species in the polymerization of diolefins initiated by the alkali metals (other than lithium) and their compounds.

It is not surprising that sodium should have been the first alkali metal observed to act as a catalytic agent for the polymerization of a diolefin in view of the not uncommon practice of using this metal as a drying agent for organic liquids (396). Matthews and Strange (1), in their search for a synthetic substitute for natural rubber, discovered and patented a method for polymerizing isoprene and other diolefins by metallic sodium. Harries (2,3) reported that he, also, had found butadiene and isoprene to form rubbery products at moderate temperatures under the influence of bright sodium metal. He observed that the polymer was formed on the surface of the metal, and that very little of the metal was consumed. The polymers were soluble in hydrocarbons and thus differed from the products obtained by autopolymerization.

Methods for the preparation of butadiene, isoprene, and dimethylbutadiene homopolymers and butadiene-styrene copolymers by sodium or potassium metal catalysis were developed thereafter on a large scale in Russia and Germany, particularly during the period between the world wars (397). Numerous variations were made to improve the polymerization conditions in order to obtain polymers having satisfactory physical properties for use as elastomers, especially in tires. Polymerizations were conducted both without solvent and in hydrocarbon or ether solvents. Various additives were employed to increase the rate of polymerization and to eliminate the formation of insoluble polymer. Several reviews covering the early work are available (398–401) (see also Part I, Chapter 2).

Ziegler and his collaborators made extensive studies of the reactions of the first three metals of Group I and some of their organometal compounds with butadiene and other diolefins. They established that with butadiene, for instance, the alkali metal formed both 1,4 and 1,2 adducts, the latter occurring generally to a greater degree than the former. The organometallic compound formed was catalytically active and allowed further addition of monomer. Thus polymeric materials comprising a range of numbers of butadiene units (5,24) could be formed. Ziegler demonstrated that a free radical reaction was not involved. It is now generally agreed that the process is ionic and, at least in the early stages, is heterogeneous. The significant chemistry of this work has been reviewed by the principal author (5,25,26) as well as by others (37,38,402).

B. Polymerization

The polymerization of diolefins by alkali metals (other than lithium) is a heterogeneous reaction both in bulk and in hydrocarbon solvents although it may become homogeneous in highly polar solvents. Control of the reaction velocities was an important consideration in the early development of commercial polymerization processes. Indeed, both very slow and very fast reactions were a concern of pioneer workers, and they used various additives to regulate the rate of polymer formation (398). Later studies of polymerization kinetics appear to have been made largely for the purpose of establishing and understanding the mechanism of the polymerization reactions. However, the reaction velocities reported in the literature are composite rate values, since detailed studies to separate the rate of initiation from the rate of propagation in the manner done for the lithium systems appear not to have been undertaken.

A significant early study of the kinetics of the polymerization of butadiene by sodium was reported by Abkin and Medvedev (403) who confirmed Ziegler's observation that the primary reaction of sodium and butadiene was slow and was followed by a rapid further addition of monomer. They found the time–conversion curve to be sigmoidal. Abkin and Medvedev found that the rate of polymerization during the steady state was approximately proportional to the square of the pressure of the butadiene vapor in the system. Bolland (404), who investigated the polymerization of isoprene by sodium, also observed a sigmoidal time–conversion relationship, and he concluded that diffusion of the monomer to the surface of the catalyst was the rate controlling factor. He found that toluene lowered the molecular weight of the polymer through a chain transfer reaction.

Recently, the kinetics of the sodium initiated polymerization of butadiene in a mixture of toluene and THF at 40°C were investigated by Kume and coworkers (405). In their experiments the growing chains were terminated at a very early stage by a transfer reaction with toluene. The ratio of the rate constants for propagation and transfer reached a critical level at a toluene concentration of 2.5 moles per liter. The authors concluded that, above this level, the toluene drastically reduced the solvation of the sodium counterions by THF.

The anionic polymerization of butadiene and isoprene initiated by the naphthalene–sodium complex in THF was examined by Szwarc and his coworkers (23) but the kinetic behavior was not reported at that time.

Alkali metal catalyzed polymerizations of butadiene, isoprene, and styrene in hydrocarbon media, in hydrocarbons to which minor proportions of polar substances were added, and in polar media have been studied by Russian investigators (18,294,359,406–411). These workers determined both polymerization rates and polymer microstructures for various systems. Their results showed that the monomer activity increased in the series

$$\text{isoprene} < \text{butadiene} < \text{styrene}$$

both in straight hydrocarbon media and in media with added polar substances (408,409). The rate of polymerization increases sharply on the addition of small amounts of polar (electron donating) substances such as THF (408). Basova et al (407) noted that the greatest dependence on the nature of the alkali metal existed in hydrocarbon media. Polymerization rates in hydrocarbons increased in the series

$$\text{Li} < \text{Na} < \text{K}$$

The addition of a polar solvent has less effect on potassium than on sodium initiated polymerization.

The kinetics of the polymerization of butadiene in THF were investigated by Arest-Yakubovich and Medvedev (410,411) using the sodium-biphenyl radical ion complex as the initiator. The reaction rate was found to be first order with respect to monomer, and to be proportional to the initiator concentration in the range of 10^{-3} to 10^{-2} molar. There was a strong effect of temperature on the rate of propagation (Table XXVI). The Arrhenius plot showed that the energy of activation was lower for 1,2 addition than for 1,4 addition.

The application of ion concepts to alkali metal catalyzed polymerization systems has been discussed by a number of authors (20,144,165, 292–295,407–411). The hydrocarbyl compounds of the alkali metals from sodium to cesium are considered to be ionized salts (38,412). They are insoluble in hydrocarbon solvents but may have varying degrees of solubility in highly polar substances such as tetrahydrofuran and other ethers. Thus, the ionic species have been widely discussed both as contact ion pairs, as in hydrocarbon solvents, and as solvent separated ion pairs or even free ions in strongly dissociating solvents. Szwarc and Smid have considered the possibility of triple ions and more complex aggregates (413,414). Kinetic and conductivity measurements have been used principally as the means for studying these ionic states. The use of ultraviolet spectroscopy has not always been entirely satisfactory as a diagnostic tool, since the spectra do not necessarily reflect the nature of the species active in the polymerization (59,408).

TABLE XXVI
Polymerization Rate Constants

Initiator	Solvent	Temp., °C	R_P,[a] liter/mole-sec	E_A,[b] kcal/mole	A,[c] liter/mole-sec	Ref.
			Butadiene			
Na	—	25	—	7.3	4.7×10^3	403
Na	THF	+10	5.4			410
		−30	1.05			410
		−56	0.60			410
		−96	0.29			410
				4.4	1.6×10^4	410
K	THF	+10	70			410
		−30	17			410
		−56	3.1			410
		−96	0.16			410
				5.9	3.1×10^6	410
RK	Ether			7.5		462
RK	Benzene/heptane	0	0.09			294
RK	Cumene	−25	0.003			294
Cs	THF	+10	~50			410
		−30	7.3			410
		−56	1.6			410
		−96	0.05			410
				6.5	5×10^6	410
			Isoprene			
Na	—	25	—	11.0	—	404
Na	Hexane	50	—	8.5	—	463
K	Hexane	50	—	8.0	—	463

[a] R_P = polymerization rate constant.
[b] E_A = energy of activation.
[c] A = frequency factor.

Among the Group I counterions, polymerization rates appear to be a function of the basicity of the metal, the degree of solvation of the ion pair, and the polymerization temperature. Low rates have been attributed to association of ionic species, which may occur especially in media having a low dielectric constant, to formation of complexes between the solvent and the propagating ion pair, and to low polymerization temperatures.

In hydrocarbon media, the polymer carbanion and its alkali metal counterion probably exist as a contact ion pair. Proceeding from sodium to cesium, the extent of dissociation of such ion pairs increases with increasing ionic radius of the counterion. Reaction rates increase similarly.

In polar, dissociating solvents such as ethers, more complex equilibria exist (415). The propagation in anionic polymerization necessarily reflects the relative concentrations and reactivities of the various ion forms (414). Bhattacharya, Lee, Smid, and Szwarc (416) have discussed the ionic equilibria and their effect on polymerization rate for the polystyryl anion–alkali metal counterion systems. They showed that the dissociation constant for $\sim\!\!\sim S^{\ominus},M^{\oplus}$ ion pairs in THF solution decreases as the counterion radius increases, i.e. the dissociation constant follows the order

$$Li^{\oplus} > Na^{\oplus} > K^{\oplus} > Rb^{\oplus} > Cs^{\oplus}$$

The larger $Na^{\oplus}$ ion is less solvated than the $Li^{\oplus}$, and the $Cs^{\oplus}$ ion is solvated little if at all. The propagation rate constants in this series decrease as the dissociation diminishes, i.e.

$$Li^{\oplus} > Na^{\oplus} > K^{\oplus} > Rb^{\oplus} > Cs^{\oplus}$$

On the other hand, in dioxane (417), a less effective dissociating solvent than THF, the propagation rate constants were found to be in reverse order, i.e.,

$$Li^{\oplus} < Na^{\oplus} < K^{\oplus} < Rb^{\oplus} < Cs^{\oplus}$$

The slight tendency of the cesium ion toward solvation is shown by the fact that the rate constants are essentially the same in both solvents. The sodium ion, on the other hand, is highly solvated and is more reactive in THF than in dioxane by a factor of over twenty. The larger potassium ion is only about three times more reactive in THF than in dioxane.

Polymerization rates are enhanced by dilution if this increases the dissociation of the ion pair. Temperature variations, according to Szwarc, have a complicating effect. Opposing effects appear as the temperature is lowered since the dielectric constant increases and with it the dissociation of the ion pairs. The accompanying increase in viscosity reduces the mobility of the ions, however. These and related effects have been reviewed (414,418).

It has been proposed (413,414,419) that in highly dissociating systems, so-called *free* ions are formed from contact ion pairs

$$P^{\ominus}M^{\oplus} \underset{}{\overset{\text{Polar solvent}}{\rightleftarrows}} P^{\ominus} + M^{\oplus} \qquad (48)$$

(where $P^{\ominus}$ represents a growing polymer carbanion) and are responsible for the high rates of propagation. This concept devolved from conductivity measurements and from observations of an increase in rate on addition of monomer and a retardation of rate on addition of a salt such as $NaBPh_4$ which could exert a common ion effect. Korotkov and Podolsky (420) pointed out that the retardation might also be explained by a direct association effect. Since sodium tetraphenyl borate is essentially an undissociated salt, it could react with a chain-end to form a new associated complex of the polymer,

$$P^{\ominus}Na^{\oplus} + \phi_4BNa \rightleftarrows [PB\phi_3]Na + \phi^{\ominus}Na^{\oplus} \qquad (49)$$

amounting in effect to a termination reaction.

Unfortunately, it is not known to what extent the information about ion pairs available for styrene polymerization can be applied to reactions involving butadiene and isoprene. The ion states of the alkali metals with butadiene and isoprene are likely somewhat different from those with styrene and are not well understood at the present time. However, there appears to be general agreement about the main effects in these systems.

In agreement with Szwarc (413) and the principles set forth above, Yakubovich and Medvedev (410) observed that reaction velocities for the polymerization of butadiene in 1,2-dimethoxyethane (DME) are greater than in THF for both sodium and lithium systems. Ion pairs would be expected to dissociate to a greater extent in the diether, a more efficient solvent. Their kinetic data did not indicate to them that *free* ions played a significant part where sodium was the counterion. These authors considered that the presence of *free* ions was of lesser importance in butadiene polymerization because the negative charge on the butadiene carbanion is delocalized less than on the styryl carbanion. It would be of interest to establish the specific ion combinations that can occur in the diene systems in view of the occasional explosive polymerizations that happen when potassium is the counterion (421,422). The presence of either *free* ions or the triple ions suggested by Szwarc (414) could lead to enhanced rates.

C. Microstructure

The development of infrared spectrometric analyses contributed significantly to the resurgence of interest in polymers catalyzed by the alkali metals. In emulsion polymers the microstructure was observed to change but little with variation in the polymerization conditions. By contrast, wide differences were possible when alkali metal catalysts were used (395), as illustrated for polybutadiene (Table XXVII), for polyisoprene (Table XXVIII), and for polypiperylene (Table XXIX) with data collected from the literature. The following generalizations can be made about these data:

1. None of the alkali metals from sodium to cesium or their organometal compounds catalyze the formation of high *cis*-1,4 structures in hydrocarbon solution, as does lithium.

2. The alkali metals, other than lithium, and their compounds generally catalyze the formation of butadiene and isoprene polymers having a high 1,2 or 3,4 addition structure (vinyl type). The tendency toward increasing amounts of vinyl structure increases with the basicity and concentration of the metal counterion. The addition of alkoxides, in certain cases, drastically diminishes the amount of vinyl structure. In the case of piperylene polymers, 1,4 structures generally predominate.

3. The use of a dissociating solvent such as THF contributes to a rise in the vinyl component of the microstructure. Likewise, a decrease in the temperature of polymerization results in a higher proportion of vinyl component.

4. Polymers obtained from mixtures of alkali metals have the microstructure corresponding to that produced by the more basic metal (11). Polymers of similar microstructure are obtained with a given counterion regardless of whether it was introduced as the metal, its radical ion complex, or its alkyl derivative.

The concept that the structure of isoprene polymers depends on the ionic character of the growing ion pair (118,423) appears to have been accepted by most workers. Tobolsky and Rogers (423) pointed out some years ago that the degree of charge separation of the ion pair is of great importance and increases with the polarity of the suspending or solvent medium:

$$\text{hydrocarbon} < \text{ether} < \text{dioxane} < \text{THF} < \text{DME}$$

They noted that isoprene polymers initiated by sodium or potassium in the presence of phenyl ether or phenyl sulfide did not quite fit in the series since higher proportions of 1,4 microstructure were observed than even in hydrocarbons. They attributed this effect to the low basicity of phenyl ether and phenyl sulfide resulting from extensive electron delocalization due to the phenyl groups. Moreover, these bulky groups were thought to contribute to steric inhibition of cation coordination. Yakubovich and Medvedev (411) observed that there was a small

TABLE XXVII
Microstructure of Polybutadienes from Alkali Metal Catalysts

Initiator	Solvent[a]	Temp., °C	*cis*-1,4, %	*trans*-1,4, %	1,2, %	Ref.
		Sodium				
Na	Vapor	5	5	15	80	460
	Vapor	60	20	15	65	460
	Aliph. HC	5	6.7	17.3	76.0	430
		30	11.4	22.1	66.5	430
		45	14.3	25.6	60.1	430
	Benzene	25	23	45	32	407
	Toluene	25	24	45	32	407
	Bulk	50	10	25	65	11
Na–Hg	Bulk	50	13	20	67	11
Na	Bulk	60	20	15	65	460
	ϕH/TEA	25	17	40	43	407
	ϕH/THF	25	13	43	44	407
	THF	10	5	15	80	410
	THF	−30	1.5	15.5	83	410
	THF	−56	0	12	88	410
	THF	−96	0	7	93	410
$\phi 3C^-Na^+$(1:10) Bd)	Et_2O	25	0	11	89	422
$\phi 3C^-Na^+$(1:100) Bd)	Et_2O	25	6	15	79	422
$Na^+/C_{10}H_8^{\dot{-}}$	THF	0	—	9	91	424
	Cumene/THF	−50	—	12	88	407
	THF	−50	—	12	88	407
	THF	−90	—	7	93	407
Alfin	Pentane	25	11	71	18	11
	Hexane	25	10	66	24	443
		Potassium				
K	Vapor	var.	10	30	60	460
	Bulk	50	15	40	45	11
	Aliph. HC	5	10.4	35.6	54.0	430
		30	14.9	37.5	47.6	430
		45	16.5	37.5	46.0	430
	Benzene	25	16.5	48.5	35	407
	Toluene	0	13	49	38	407
	ϕH/TEA	25	17	46	37	407
$K^+/C_{10}H_8^{\dot{-}}$	THF	0		17.5	82.5	424
K			0	56	46	464
C_8K			0	49	51	464
$C_{24}K$			0	35	65	464
K^+/Biphenyl$^{\dot{-}}$	THF	40	7	37	56	410
	THF	10	6	30	64	410

(continued)

TABLE XXVII (*concluded*)

Initiator	Solvent[a]	Temp., °C	*cis*-1,4, %	*trans*-1,4, %	1,2, %	Ref.
		Potassium (continued)				
K^+/Biphenyl$^{\dot{-}}$	THF	−30	3	21	76	410
	THF	−56	2	15	83	410
	THF	−96	0	12	88	410
	DME	40	7	26	67	411
	DME	10	5	26	69	411
	DME	−30	2	19	79	411
	DME	−56	0	13	87	411
ϕCH_2K	Benzene	0	12	43	45	404
$K^+/C_{10}H_8^{\dot{-}}$	Heptane/THF	−50	5	33	62	407
	Cumene/THF	−50	6	35	59	407
	THF	−50	0	15	85	407
Allyl K[b]	Hexane	25	0	42	58	422
	Hexane			93	7	422
		Rubidium				
Rb	THF	0	0	25	75	424
	Bulk	−5	0	51	49	465
	Bulk	60	0	58	42	465
	Bulk		7	31	62	11
		Cesium				
Cs	Bulk		6	35	59	11
	Hexane	25	6	40	54	422
BuCs[c]	Hexane	25	6	43	52	422
BdCs[d]	Hexane	0	0	39.6	60.4	424
	Benzene	0	0	46.4	53.6	424
	THF	0	0	42.4	57.6	424
	THF	−25	0	44.6	55.4	424
	THF	−78	0	44.2	55.8	424
$Cs^+/C_{10}H_8^{\dot{-}}$	THF	0	0	25.5	74.5	424
	THF	−46	0	16.7	83.3	424
	THF	−78	0	13.9	86.1	424
	THF	+10	8	31.4	60.6	410
Cs^+ diphenyl$^{\dot{-}}$	THF	−30	0	27.3	72.7	410
	THF	−56	0	17.1	82.9	410
	THF	−96	0	10.9	89.0	410

[a] THF, tetrahydrofuran; TEA, triethylamine; DME, 1,2-dimethoxyethane.
[b] Allylpotassium prepared from allyl ether and potassium metal.
[c] Butylcesium prepared from dibutylmercury and cesium metal.
[d] Butadienylcesium prepared from butadiene and cesium metal.

TABLE XXVIII
Microstructure of Polyisoprenes from Alkali Metal Catalysts

Initiator	Solvent	Temp., °C	*cis*-1,4, %	*trans*-1,4, %	1,2, %	3,4, %	Ref.
Na	Hexane		0	48	10	42	463
K	Hexane		0	58	7	35	463
Rb	Bulk		5	47	8	39	463
Cs	Bulk		4	51	8	37	463
Na	Cyclohexane		29	29	—	42	103
Na	THF				18	82	103
			0	43	6	51	11
K			0	52	8	40	11
Rb			5	47	8	39	11
Cs			4	51	8	37	11
Na	Bulk or HC	25	0	46	9	45	423
	Xylene	25	0	55	9	36	423
	ϕ_2O, ϕ_2S	25	0	62	7	31	423
	Aliph. ethers	25	0	33	12	55	423
	THF	25	0	33	13	54	423
K	Bulk or HC	25	0	55	9	36	423
	ϕ_2O, ϕ_2S	25	0	65	7	28	423
	Aliph. ethers	25	0	51	10	39	423
	THF	25	0	48	16	36	423
Na	Pentane		0	43	6	51	33
EtNa	Pentane		6.3	42	7.1	44.6	33
BuNa	Pentane		4.1	34.9	6.7	54.4	33
K	Pentane		0	52	8	40	33
EtK	Pentane		23.7	39.2	5.7	31.4	33
BuK	Pentane		19.6	40.8	6.2	33.5	33
EtNa	Ether		0	14.3	10.2	75.6	33
Alfin	Pentane		27	52	5	16	11
	Hexane		11	59	5	25	443
Cs	Pentane	25	15	49	7	29	
Isoprenyl Cs	Heptane	−78	0	32	13	55	424
	Toluene	−78	0	31	17	52	424
$Cs^+/C_{10}H_8^{\cdot-}$	THF	−78	0	28	29	43	424
BuCs	Pentane	+25	12	46	7	35	422

decrease in the amount of 1,4 structure when DME was used as solvent in place of THF. There was also an increase in the rate of propagation. It may be recalled that M. Morton (160) showed an inverse relationship between *cis*-1,4 content and k_p for polyisoprene in a lithium initiated system involving varying concentration of THF.

There is relatively little change in the microstructure of any of the

TABLE XXIX
Microstructure of Polypiperylenes from Alkali Metal Catalysts

Initiator	Solvent[a]	Temp., °C	Yield, %	1,4, % *cis* + *trans*	1,2, % *cis* + *trans*	3,4, %	Ref.
Na	Pentane	30		63	40	0	320
K	Pentane	30		81	15	<5	320
Na	HMPA	25	39	58	32	5	427
K	HMPA	25	28	57	31		427
Rb	HMPA	25	10	31	42	0	427
Cs	HMPA	25	12	37	37	0	427

[a] HMPA, Hexamethylphosphoramide.

polydiolefins in going from potassium to cesium initiators. Presumably the basicity and size of these ions are little influenced by solvation by the monomer inasmuch as they are not well solvated even by polar solvents. It is observed however that polymers from potassium have generally higher *trans* structures than those from sodium. An explanation was advanced by Szwarc (297) on the basis that the large potassium ion is most advantageously approached by butadiene in its *trans* conformation.

Relatively little has been reported about the effect of varying the catalyst concentration. Where the initiator concentration has been considered, it has been varied over a narrow range. Wider variation should be investigated. For example, in Table XXVII, it can be seen that tritylsodium reacts with butadiene in ether at mole ratios of 1:10 and 1:100 to form polybutadienes differing by 10% in their content of 1,2 units. Another seemingly neglected aspect is the effect of associated salts such as alkali metal halides, alkoxides, etc., on the structure of the resulting polymers. The effects of adding such salts are being studied in the polymerization chemistry of lithium and have already been documented for the Alfin catalyst.

Almost nothing has been reported in recent years about piperylene homopolymers initiated by Group I catalysts. The little that has appeared involved free radical or lithium catalysis except for two reports by French workers. Schué (320) reported that predominately 1,4 addition polymers resulted from initiation by sodium or potassium in a hydrocarbon solvent. Friedman and Brini (427) investigated the polymerization of piperylene (*trans* isomer) by the alkali metals in the presence of hexamethylphosphoramide. Low molecular weight polymers were obtained. The microstructure of these polymers varied progressively to higher proportions of vinyl structures as the alkali metal initiator varied in order from lithium to cesium (Table XXIX). The yield decreased similarly. Simultaneously there appeared increasing amounts of a cyclic structure which was identified by NMR and infrared spectroscopy. The cyclic structure was postulated as arising from a Diels-Alder type addition of monomer to the di-metal adduct.

D. Macrostructure

The molecular weight of polymers catalyzed by the alkali metals is an inverse function of the metal concentration (23,359,402,408) as shown in Eq. 1b. Foster and Binder (11) reported that polymer molecular weight decreases as the electropositivity of the metal increases. In bulk polymerizations, low molecular weight polymers have been obtained generally with the more basic metal catalysts, but it should be possible to obtain polymers of high molecular weight by providing adequate dilution and suitable temperature control. The tendency toward gel formation (three dimensional structures) increases with the temperature. This tendency is greater with the more basic metals. Insoluble polymer has been observed to form on cesium metal in a stirred mixture of butadiene and hexane at 25°C (422). Extraction of this polymer with toluene provided a major soluble portion having a DSV of 5.2, demonstrating that a soluble high molecular weight polymer can be obtained. Rembaum, Ells, Morrow, and Tobolsky (424) found that cesium and organocesium catalysts yield soluble polybutadiene and polyisoprene polymers over a range of molecular weights and in high yields.

In the early industrial production of elastomers, gel was a continuing problem and a variety of modifiers were used (398) with variable degree of success. Eberly and Johnson (425) made a study of modifiers in the vapor phase polymerization of butadiene with sodium metal because of the sizeable amounts of gel occurring in unmodified polymers. They found that ethyl chloride served as an effective modifier. With its use they observed the elimination of insoluble polymer, a lower viscosity of the whole polymer, and a narrower distribution of molecular weights. Their study may be the earliest to have employed molecular weight distribution as a measure of modifier activity in anionic polymerization and for evaluating the resulting polymers and their vulcanizates. It was apparent that the ethyl chloride had acted as a chain transfer agent and also that the resulting polymer had more satisfactory physical properties.

Toluene also was found to be an effective transfer agent in sodium

TABLE XXX
Molecular Weight vs. Intrinsic Viscosity[a] for Polybutadienes and Polyisoprene from Sodium Catalysts

	$K \times 10^4$	α	Ref.
Polybutadiene (Na)	11.0	0.62	466
Polybutadiene (Na)	1.0	0.77	368
Polybutadiene (Alfin)	0.125	0.77	467
Polyisoprene (Na)	1.5	0.74	368

[a] $[\eta] = KM^{\alpha}$.

(403–405,426) and potassium (406–409) catalyzed polymerizations of butadiene and isoprene. Basova and Gantmakher (406) observed that isoprene polymers initiated by potassium in toluene had lower molecular weights than those polymerized in benzene by factors ranging from ten to twenty-five. The molecular weight of butadiene polymers under like conditions decreased by a factor of about nine. Isobutylene was indicated to be an active transfer agent although less effective than toluene (404,406). The activity of several hydrocarbon solvents as transfer agents (406) follows the order:

$$\text{toluene} > \text{isobutylene} > \text{cumene} > \text{benzene}$$

The occurrence of branching in polymers catalyzed by the alkali metals is related to the basicity of the latter, i.e.,

$$\text{Li} < \text{Na} \ll \text{K} < \text{Cs}$$

Poddubnyi and Ehrenburg (272) found that considerable branching occurred during the polymerization of butadiene by potassium, whereas relatively little branching was obtained with sodium in the temperature range from 10 to 70°C, the percent of 1,2 units decreasing significantly, however. In the potassium catalyzed polymers, the extent of branching was notably less for polymerization at 0°C than at 60°C.

Constants of the Mark-Houwink equation for estimation of the molecular weight of sodium polymers are given in Table XXX.

V. COPOLYMERS

Early work on sodium and potassium initiated copolymerizations of butadiene and styrene has been reviewed by Taft and Tiger (399). Renewed interest in alkali metal catalyzed copolymerization was stimulated by the discovery that polymer microstructure and composition could be varied more widely with these initiator systems than in emulsion copolymerizations (395). Still further stimulus was provided by the discovery of the interesting catalytic properties of lithium discussed in the first part of this chapter.

The work of Marvel, Bailey, and Innskeep (428) and of Korotkov (18) indicated that butadiene has a slightly higher reactivity than styrene in copolymerizations catalyzed by sodium or butylsodium in hydrocarbon media.

The copolymerization of a butadiene–isoprene equimolar mixture to low conversion by tritylsodium resulted in a higher rate of incorporation of isoprene than butadiene (359).

Copolymerization of an equimolar isoprene–styrene mixture by sodium, undiluted or in benzene, provided a copolymer having 66% styrene (343). The styrene content of the copolymer made in ether increased to about 75% and in THF to about 80%. The use of a potassium or organopotassium initiator in hydrocarbon media furnished copolymers containing 70–75% styrene (406,408). Kelley and Tobolsky (343) postulated that the styrene content of a copolymer resulting from anionic polymerization was a function of the ionic character of the propagating ion pair. This idea appears to be confirmed by data of Basova, Gantmakher, and Medvedev (406,408) and by that of Rembaum et al. (424)(Table XXXI).

TABLE XXXI
Styrene Content in Copolymers Catalyzed by Alkali Metals[a]

Monomers	Initiator	Solvent	% St in copolymer	Ref.
Bd-ST	BuNa	Hydrocarbon	48	18
	Na	Hydrocarbon	50	406
	RK	Toluene	67.5	406
	Cs–$C_{10}H_8$		67–83	424
I-ST	Na	Toluene	56	424
	K	Toluene	70	424
	RK	Toluene	75	424
	Na	Hydrocarbon	66	343
	Na	Et_2O	75	343
	Na	THF	80	343
	Cs–$C_{10}H_8$		98	424

[a] Monomer mixtures were equimolar for experiments with Na and K, and ~50 wt % in experiments with Cs.

The styrene content does indeed increase as a function of the tendency of the alkali metal to ionize, i.e.,

$$\text{Na} < \text{K} < \text{Cs}$$

and, in the case of sodium, according to the basicity of the solvent, i.e.,

$$\text{hydrocarbon} < \text{ether} < \text{THF}$$

The tendency of the monomers to be incorporated into a copolymer in the experiments cited is

$$\text{isoprene} < \text{butadiene} < \text{styrene}$$

Shima, Smid, and Szwarc (207) reported that the rate of addition of butadiene to a styryl anion ($Na^{\oplus}$ counterion) in THF is twice that of isoprene. A block copolymer results from the polymerization of isoprene and styrene with a cesium initiator even at −78°C (424), indicating a very high preference for styrene.

It is of interest that Schlick and Levy (429) employing the technique advanced earlier by Szwarc, Levy, and Milkovich (368) succeeded in preparing a series of isoprene-styrene block copolymers which differed from each other in the size of the homopolymer blocks. Precipitation studies on these polymers revealed that both the solubility in toluene and the intrinsic viscosity of the solution thus obtained increased with decreasing block size.

VI. PHYSICAL PROPERTIES

Based on chemical methods of analysis it was recognized rather early in the development of sodium and potassium catalyzed polybutadienes and polyisoprenes that these polymers contained large proportions of units derived from vinyl type addition (1,2 or 3,4) (5,25,398,399). It was also recognized that polymer stiffness was related to this structural feature. In 1952, Meyer, Hampton, and Davison (430) correlated the glass transition temperature with the microstructure of polybutadienes catalyzed by both sodium and potassium. They showed a direct relationship between the percent 1,2 addition and the T_g. This correlation has been amply confirmed. It is apparent that as the amount of 1,2 addition increases in a polymer, the polymer chain more nearly resembles a substituted polyethylene with a stiffer, less extensible, skeletal structure having a lower entropy of elasticity and a higher T_g.

It is of interest that partial hydrogenation of a sodium catalyzed polybutadiene lowers the T_g. In a series of such polymers, the T_g was decreased by 11°C as the unsaturation was decreased from 87% to 20%. In this series, a maximum for the polymer plasticity was observed at about 40% unsaturation. The tensile strength of the corresponding vulcanizates corresponded to a minimum (431).

High *cis*-1,4 and *trans*-1,4 polybutadienes and polyisoprenes have low values of T_g (283), and are "rubbery" at temperatures above their T_m. Polymers of mixed 1,4 and 1,2 (or 3,4) addition structures are usually amorphous at room temperature and develop less tensile strength on stretching due to the inability of the chains to form regions of reinforcing crystallites (177,432,433). Indeed, sodium initiated polyisoprene which has a low proportion of 1,4 structure is leathery and non-resilient at room temperature but becomes flexible and rubbery on warming to 50°C or above. Vulcanizates of this and similar amorphous polymers of irregular structure are low in tensile strength (399,434).

Tensile properties of vulcanizates of the potassium polymers were observed to decrease markedly with increased branching (272,435).

There appears to be no current technological use of elastomers derived from butadiene, isoprene, or piperylene catalyzed by the alkali metals except for lithium. However, there are numerous patents indicating technological interest in low molecular weight polymeric oils obtained from butadiene, and mixtures of butadiene and styrene, catalyzed by sodium. These oils are used in protective coatings applications (436,437) and as adhesives and plasticizers (438) as shown by samples from the patent literature.

VII. THE ALFIN CATALYST

A discussion of sodium and its compounds as initiators of diolefin polymerization would not be complete without considering the special case known as the Alfin catalyst. This catalyst is peculiarly successful in polymerizing butadiene to a very high molecular weight elastomer which, unfortunately, in spite of a great deal of effort, has not found any important commercial application.

The Alfin catalyst is a complex involving $R^{\ominus}$ $Na^{\oplus}$, $R'O^{\ominus}$ $Na^{\oplus}$ and $Cl^{\ominus}$ $Na^{\oplus}$. The name was coined by Professor A. A. Morton (439) because an *al*cohol and an ole*fin* are involved in the preparation. As first discovered, the combination was derived from the cleavage of isopropyl ether by amylsodium. Morton observed that when butadiene dissolved in isopropyl ether was added dropwise to a rapidly stirred suspension of amylsodium in pentane, a band of rubbery polymer was formed which fouled the stirring propeller. Subsequent investigation of the process showed that a series of reactions had occurred.

$$C_5H_{11}^{\ominus}Na^{\oplus} + (CH_3)_2CH{-}O{-}CH(CH_3)_2 \rightarrow (CH_3)_2CHO^{\ominus}Na^{\oplus} + CH_2{=}CHCH_3 \quad (50)$$

$$C_5H_{11}^{\ominus}Na^{\oplus} + CH_2{=}CHCH_3 \rightarrow CH_2{=}CHCH_2^{\ominus}Na^{\oplus} + C_5H_{12} \quad (51)$$

$$CH_2{=}CHCH_2^{\ominus}Na^{\oplus} + (CH_3)_2CHO^{\ominus}Na^{\oplus} + \text{butadiene} \rightarrow \text{poly(butadiene)} \quad (52)$$

He reported that separate polymerization tests of each component were negative, but that the combination was highly active.

Later, a less expensive method of preparing the catalyst was developed based on the following reaction sequence:

$$2Na + n\text{-}C_5H_{11}Cl \rightarrow NaCl + n\text{-}C_5H_{11}^{\ominus}Na^{\oplus} \quad (53)$$

$$C_5H_{11}^{\ominus}Na^{\oplus} + (CH_3)_2CHOH \rightarrow (CH_3)_2CHO^{\ominus}Na^{\oplus} + C_5H_{12} \quad (54)$$

$$C_5H_{11}^{\ominus}Na^{\oplus} + (CH_3)_2CHO^{\ominus}Na^{\oplus} + CH_2{=}CHCH_3 \rightarrow CH_2{=}CHCH_2^{\ominus}Na^{\oplus} + (CH_3)_2CHO^{\ominus}Na^{\oplus} + C_5H_{12} \quad (55)$$

A further improvement, particularly with respect to cost reduction and manufacturing efficiency, was reported by Hansley and Greenberg (440).

$$Na + (CH_3)_2CHOH \rightarrow (CH_3)_2CHO^{\ominus}Na^{\oplus} + \tfrac{1}{2}H_2 \quad (56)$$

$$(CH_3)_2CHO^{\ominus}Na^{\oplus} + 2Na + n\text{-}C_4H_9Cl \rightarrow C_4H_9^{\ominus}Na^{\oplus} + (CH_3)_2CHO^{\ominus}Na^{\oplus} + Na^{\oplus}Cl^{\ominus} \quad (57)$$

$$\text{Suspension} + CH_3{-}CH{=}CH_2 \rightarrow \text{Alfin catalyst} \quad (58)$$

By this reaction sequence all of the *n*-butyl chloride is utilized for making *n*-butylsodium which is stabilized by the sodium isopropoxide already present. Losses due to a Wurtz-type reaction are also minimized in this procedure.

A study of the effect of varying the ratio of allysodium to sodium isopropoxide revealed that maximum activity was reached when the alkoxide constituted about a third of the catalyst components. Hence it was suggested by Morton (439) that the allylsodium coordinated with the sodium isopropoxide to form, at least in part, a structure such as

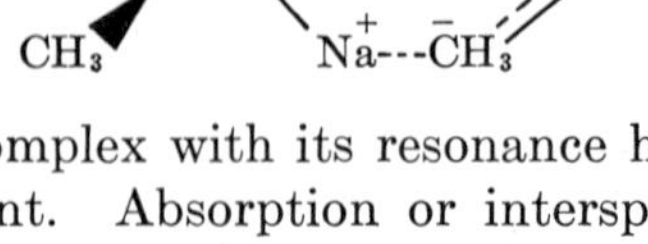

and that this cyclic complex with its resonance hybrids constituted the effective catalytic agent. Absorption or interspersion of the complex with sodium chloride was believed to provide a further stabilizing influence. Morton suggested the Alfin reagent to be an insoluble aggregate of ions arranged in a lattice like form. A variety of forms may be possible. It was reported by Morton that the greatest catalyst activity occurs just after the reagent has been prepared. The activity then gradually diminishes with time. Unfortunately, no analytical data on the organosodium concentration as a function of time was supplied. The possibility of internal rearrangement to less active ionic combinations, along the lines suggested by Szwarc (414) for other systems, has not been investigated. Uelzmann (292) has suggested that the activity of the Alfin catalyst results from the stabilization of the carbon-metal bond in a resonance complex comprising the allylsodium, sodium isopropoxide and sodium chloride. This stabilized complex acts on butadiene monomer to promote 1,4 addition preferentially. The steric requirements of the bulky complex may favor the approach of only the transoid configuration of the butadiene monomer as was suggested by Szwarc (297) for sodium or potassium metal.

Of the many RNa compounds investigated by Morton, very few gave evidence of forming an Alfin catalyst. Of these, allylsodium is probably the best. Morton did find that both 1-methylcyclohexene-1 and 1-methylcyclopentene-1 were capable of forming Alfin catalysts, whereas cyclohexene and cyclopentene were unable to do so (441). Morton attributed the activity of the methyl substituted cyclic olefins to an ability to form a planar cyclic transition state similar to the complex proposed for allylsodium (**7**,**8**).

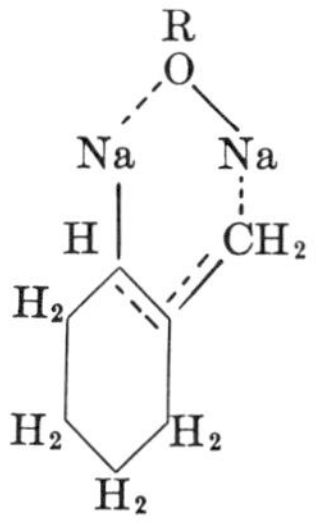

(**7**)

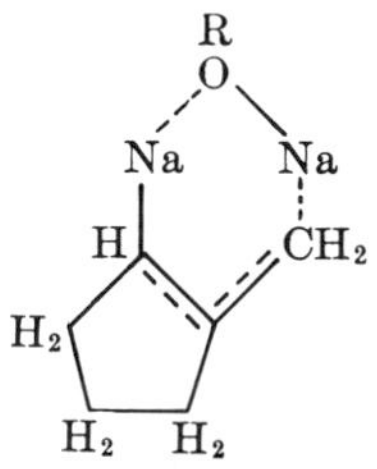

(**8**)

With these catalysts, optimum activity was reached with a ratio of RONa to RNa of 2.2, whereas with allylsodium a ratio of 1:1 appeared most suitable. β-Naphthylmethylsodium, inactive by itself, was reported to have an enhancing effect on the standard Alfin catalyst in terms of polymer yield which was doubled or tripled although polymer microstructure and dilute solution viscosity were unaffected (442).

A potassium analogue of the Alfin catalyst has also been used to polymerize butadiene. A little more than half the polymer that was obtained in one case consisted of 93% *trans*-1,4 polybutadiene, and the remainder had a microstructure typical of normal potassium initiated polybutadienes (443).

The role of the alkoxide in Alfin polymerization has been investigated. Allylsodium, by itself or in the presence of sodium chloride, furnishes a polybutadiene very much like sodium does, in that the polymerization rate is slow, the viscosity is dependent largely on the initiator concentration, and the microstructure is similar, comprising about 70% 1,2 addition structure. Upon addition of sodium isopropoxide, however, a dramatic change takes place as evidenced by a very rapid polymerization to a high molecular weight polymer having about 70% *trans*-1,4 structure (11,444, 445). With isoprene, lower molecular weights are obtained and the *trans*-1,4 content is decreased by about 15%.

A "*trans*" effect was observed by Morton and Ward (446) for a system of sodium hydroxide and amylsodium in triethylamine acting on butadiene. Ratios of *trans*-1,4/1,2 up to 1.75 were obtained. This combination, however, was rated only a weak 'Alfin' catalyst. It was pointed out by Roha (20) that the wide variation in the amount of *trans*-1,4 is an effect of the nucleophilic agent, i.e., isopropoxide, which promotes a greater separation of charges of the carbanion and its positive counterion.

Partial substitution of sodium isopropoxide by the *n*-propoxide brought a proportionate decrease in the yield of polymer. There was little or no change in microstructure (444) up to three-fourths replacement after which the *trans*-1,4/1,2 ratio declined. More than the nucleophilic character appears to be involved. Substitution of sodium isopropoxide by potassium isopropoxide brought about a gradual decrease in the ratio of *trans*-1,4 to 1,2 units until a rapid drop of the *trans*-1,4/1,2 ratio from about 2.8 to 1.2 occurred in the range of 75–85% potassium alkoxide. An explanation for this abrupt change was not presented and could be an interesting problem for future work. The presence of sodium *iso*propoxide enhances the polymerization reaction. A stabilizing and moderating role is indicated since smaller proportions of crosslinked polymer (gel) are found as the alkoxide ratio is increased.

Studies of the importance of the salt component in Alfin catalysts have also been made (439,444,447). Sodium chloride generated *in situ* was found necessary for best activity. Crystalline sodium chloride, even though finely divided, was ineffective when added to allylsodium/sodium isopropoxide. Substitution of sodium chloride by other alkali metal halides was found feasible but restricted to compounds having lattice bond distances within the narrow range of 2.81–3.29 Å. The most effective replacement salts were NaBr, KCl, and KBr (444). These investigations established the alkali metal halide as a functional part of the Alfin catalyst and reinforced a concept of surface activity in orienting the monomer.

Reaction rates appear not to have been thoroughly studied for the Alfin catalyst with butadiene. Morton's papers usually specified a reaction time of 30 min after which the reaction was terminated. In general Morton regarded the most rapid reaction as the most suitable and least likely to produce gel. D'Ianni (448) likewise reported 30 min reaction times in laboratory work with butadiene and 60 min periods for isoprene. Stewart and Williams (449) provided data for a slower reaction showing a smooth polymerization to 100% conversion in 90 min. It was noted that the reaction is first order with respect to monomer (449,450) and dependent on the catalyst concentration. The addition of water, methanol, acetone, or acetic acid reduced the efficiency of the catalyst. Water at a concentration of 2% of the monomer destroyed the catalyst and inhibited polymerization against further additions of catalyst. Contrariwise, sodium hydroxide as a 50% aqueous solution could be added without damage. Apparently the normal contaminants present in butadiene-olefin mixtures, components of the so-called "lean streams" were without harmful effect (449).

The kinetics of the polymerization of isoprene and of styrene were investigated by Cleland, Letsinger, Magat, and Stockmayer (451) using the conventional catalyst allylsodium/sodium isopropoxide/sodium chloride. They too found that the reaction was first order with respect to monomer and that the rate was proportional to the amount of initiator present. They determined that the overall energy of activation for the polymerization of isoprene was 10 kcal per mole.

An interesting recent development is the finding of Greenberg and Hansley (440,452) that the molecular weight of polybutadienes produced by the Alfin catalyst can be lowered by the addition of 1,4-dihydrobenzene or 1,4-dihydronaphthalene to the polymerization system. Only these two compounds out of more than thirty tested were effective. They were effective in regulating the molecular weight of polymers of isoprene, piperylene, and styrene, as well. Polybutadienes in a molecular weight range from a million to a hundred thousand were made by the addition of varying concentrations of 1,4-dihydronaphthalene (451,452), whereas the unmodified systems produced polymers in a molecular weight range up to seven million. No change in the microstructure was observed. Experiments with 1,4-dihydrobenzene containing C^{14} indicated that one six-carbon ring was incorporated per polymer chain. 1,4-Dihydronaphthalene was shown to be more efficient than 1,4-dihydrobenzene.

Mechanism. The mechanism of polymerization of dienes by the Alfin catalyst has not been settled to the satisfaction of all.

Professor Morton, the discoverer of the Alfin catalyst, favored a mechanism based on a free radical process (442).

Uelzmann (292) considered the Alfin polymerization to be an ionic process wherein sodium isopropoxide in combination with sodium chloride provided extensive resonance stabilization of the allylsodium and of the growing chain. He proposed a reaction sequence to account for the predominant 1,4 addition but he did not account for the appreciable 1,2 proportion of the microstructure. Nonetheless, the view is widely held that only ionic processes are involved.

Bykhovskii and Minsker (453) have suggested that lattice defects of the color center type play an important part in the polymerization process. Presumably centers of this type can take part in the activation of a monomer molecule oriented on the catalyst surface. However, such a concept would not appear to require the participation of allylsodium, and it implies that it should be possible to obtain an "Alfin" polybutadiene by means of a proper dispersion of sodium metal in a Wurtz-type sodium chloride where color centers are produced. No such observation has been reported.

It is possible, in all these models, that an electron transfer process is involved. Because of the rapidity of formation of a very high molecular weight polymer, which obviously involves an extremely fast process of zipping monomer units together, it is reasonable to assume that an electron transfer process is operative. Russell, Janzen, and Strom (468) have suggested that one-electron transfer is important in reactions of carbanions with unsaturates. In this case, the allylsodium initiates the reaction by donating an electron to the butadiene acceptor. Studies with radioactive C^{14} have established (429) that an allyl radical has been incorporated into each chain,

$$Na^{\oplus}R^{\ominus} + CH_2{=}CH{-}CH{=}CH_2 \rightarrow RCH_2CH{=}CH{-}CH_2^{\ominus}Na^{\oplus} \quad (59)$$

$$RCH_2CH{=}CH{-}CH_2^{\ominus}Na^{\oplus} + CH_2{=}CH{-}CH{=}CH_2 \rightarrow RCH_2CH{=}CHCH_2CH_2CH{=}CHCH_2^{\ominus}Na^{\oplus} \quad (60)$$

$$(R = \text{allyl})$$

The reacting butadiene is in close contact with other butadiene molecules so that electron transfer to them in turn should be easily accomplished. The function of the insoluble substrate may be that of providing a field effect to facilitate the polarization of nearby butadiene monomer molecules and ready acceptance of the electron transfer. Orientation on the catalyst surface may not be essential. The heterogenous substrate may, in effect, act as a constant-potential regulator of the electron supply. The formation of a substantial proportion of 1,2 structure which has a lower activation energy suggests that some additional process is operative.

Alfin Copolymers. The activity of Alfin catalysts in copolymerization has been investigated by a number of workers (440,448,449). Most of this work understandably involved butadiene with minor proportions of styrene as comonomer since comparisons with commercial SBR was of great technological interest. According to Morton (439) styrene polymerizes more rapidly than butadiene under the influence of an organosodium reagent such as amylsodium. With an Alfin catalyst, however, butadiene polymerizes about five times more rapidly than styrene (439,449,469). In copolymerization, the rates are more nearly the same, although the styrene tends to enter the copolymer a little more rapidly than butadiene. This was confirmed by D'Ianni (448) and Stewart and Williams (449), contrary to the data by Korotkov (18). Viscosities of the copolymers were somewhat lower and gel contents were considerably lower than those observed for the butadiene homopolymer. It was suggested by Hansley and Greenberg (440) that as little as 2–3% styrene was sufficient to prevent gel formation. The intrinsic viscosity increases gradually during copolymerization until maximum conversion is attained, contrary to the situation with butadiene, which gives very high viscosities almost immediately (449).

Copolymerization of butadiene with α-methylstyrene was notable in that no more than about 25% α-methylstyrene could be introduced into the copolymer. The intrinsic viscosity of the copolymer was found to vary inversely with the proportion of α-methylstyrene in the monomer mixture (449).

Copolymerization of butadiene with isobutylene by Alfin catalysis was also attempted by Stewart and Williams (449). No isobutylene was detected in the resulting polymer, and it was their opinion that the reduction of intrinsic viscosity proportional to the isobutylene content of the monomer mixture was due to a chain-terminating effect. Copolymers of butadiene with propylene (454), with butene-2 (455–458), and with butene-1 or isobutylene (459) have been patented. In view of the report of Stewart and Williams above, analytical evidence showing the extent of butadiene-olefin copolymerization would be welcomed.

The copolymerization of divinylbenzene and of vinyl crotonate with butadiene by the Alfin catalyst was also investigated by Stewart and Williams (449). The soft gel formed in varying degree in Alfin catalyzed butadiene polymerizations could frequently be eliminated by increasing the solvent fraction in the polymerization, or by milling the polymer. They attempted to form a more tightly crosslinked gel by this copolymerization. The swelling index of the resulting copolymers was erratic and did not vary sufficiently from that of the homopolymers for a conclusion to be made that a tight gel structure had been formed. The addition of larger proportions of divinylbenzene increased the percent of gel in the resulting polymer, but the intrinsic viscosity of the remaining soluble polymer decreased. Some broadening of the MWD occurred. Conversion was not affected by the addition of varying amounts of divinylbenzene, but was decreased by increasing amounts of vinyl crotonate. They concluded that vinyl crotonate was not a crosslinking agent in this system. The polymerization of butadiene and of butadiene-styrene in the presence of a processing oil as a plasticizer for the high molecular weight polymers raised the catalyst consumption but did not alter the polymer structure (399,449,460).

Alfin catalyzed copolymers of butadiene and styrene were found to have an irregularly oriented crystalline component varying with the composition of the copolymer. Studies by x-ray diffraction and by dilatometry disclosed less crystallinity for the copolymers than for the polybutadiene (448). The tendency for crystallization is presumed to be a consequence of the predominating *trans*-1,4 sequences, their regularity of occurrence being interrupted by the introduction of another monomer.

The physical properties of Alfin polymers have been discussed extensively (399,448,449,461). High molecular weight Alfin catalyzed polybutadienes have not been commercialized primarily because of the difficulties in processing them. A thorough treatment of the physical properties of lower molecular weight modifications (440) and their vulcanizates has not appeared.

References

1. F. E. Matthews and E. H. Strange, Brit. Pat. 24,790 (1910).
2. C. H. Harries, *Ann.*, **383,** 157 (1911).
3. C. H. Harries, U.S. Pat. 1,058,056 (April 8, 1913)(to Bayer).
4. K. Ziegler, F. Dersch, and H. Wollthan, *Ann.*, **511,** 13 (1934); K. Ziegler and

L. Jakob, *Ann.*, **511,** 45 (1934); K. Ziegler, L. Jakob, H. Wollthan, and A. Wenz, *Ann.*, **511,** 64 (1934).
5. K. Ziegler, *Angew. Chem.*, **49,** 499 (1936).
6. J. D. D'Ianni, in Kirk-Othmer *Encyclopedia of Chemical Technology,* First Supplement Volume, p. 746.
7. R. H. Mayor, W. M. Saltman, and R. M. Pierson, paper presented before the Div. of Petrol. Chem., Am. Chem. Soc., San Francisco, Calif., April 1958.
8. Private communication to the Office of Synthetic Rubber of the Federal Facilities Corporation; *Chem. Eng. News,* **33,** 3553 (Aug. 29, 1955).
9. Anon., *Chem. Eng. News,* **33,** 3716 (Sept. 5, 1955); *ibid.*, **33,** 5026, (Nov. 21, 1955).
10. F. W. Stavely and coworkers, *Ind. Eng. Chem.*, **48,** 778 (1956), Presented before the Div. Rubber Chem., Am. Chem. Soc., Philadelphia, Pa., November 1955.
11. F. C. Foster and J. L. Binder, Advances in Chemistry Series No. 19, *Am. Chem. Soc.*, 1957, p. 26.
12. (*a*) C. Ortlieb, *Rev. Gén. Caoutchouc,* **36,** 1708 (1959); C. Ortlieb, Th. Wolff, J. Marchal, and A. Hinschberger, *ibid.*, **36,** 1863 (1959); (*b*) *ibid.*, **37,** 825 (1960).
13. F. Schué, A. Hinschberger, and J. Marchal, *Rev. Gén. Caoutchouc,* **39,** 572 (1962).
14. L. Pauling, *The Nature of the Chemical Bond,* 3rd ed., Cornell Univ. Press, Ithaca, N.Y., 1960, p. 412.
15. L. E. Forman, unpublished results; see also U.S. Pat. 3,285,901, (Nov. 15, 1966) (to The Firestone Tire & Rubber Company).
16. C. G. Overberger and N. Yamamoto, *Polymer Preprints,* **7** (1), 115 (1966).
17. J. Minoux, B. François, and Ch. Sadron, *Makromol. Chem.*, **44–46,** 519 (1961).
18. A. A. Korotkov, Paper No. 66, International Symposium on Macromolecular Chemistry, Prague, Sept. 1957.
19. H. E. Diem, H. Tucker, and C. F. Gibbs, *Rubber Chem. Technol.*, **34,** 191 (1961).
20. M. Roha, *Advan. Polymer Sci.*, **1,** 512 (1960).
21. V. Sinn and J. Minoux, *Comptes Rend.*, **250,** 2020 (1960).
22. J. Minoux, *Rev. Gén. Caoutchouc,* **39,** 779 (1962).
23. R. Waack, A. Rembaum, J. D. Coombes, and M. Szwarc, *J. Am. Chem. Soc.*, **79,** 2026 (1957); H. Brody, M. Ladacki, R. Milkovich, and M. Szwarc, *J. Polymer Sci.*, **25,** 221 (1957).
24. J. Minoux and J. Parrod, *Comptes Rend.*, **252,** 2887 (1961).
25. K. Ziegler, *Collection Czechoslov. Chem. Commun.*, **22,** 295 (1957).
26. K. Ziegler, *Rubber Chem. Technol.*, **38,** xxiii, 1965.
27. H. Mark and F. Eirich, *J. Colloid Sci.*, **11,** 748 (1956).
28. A. V. Tobolsky, *Am. Scientist,* **45,** 34 (1957).
29. H. Hsieh, D. J. Kelley, and A. V. Tobolsky, *J. Polymer Sci.*, **26,** 240 (1957).
30. L. E. Forman, U.S. Pat. 3,280,094 (Oct. 18, 1966)(to The Firestone Tire & Rubber Company).
31. R. W. Kibler and T. B. Talcott, U.S. Pat. 3,205,211 (Sept. 7, 1965)(to The Firestone Tire & Rubber Company); G. Pampus and H. Groene, U.S. Pat. 3,072,621 (Jan. 8, 1963)(Bayer).
32. Brit. Pat. 826,990 (Jan. 27, 1960)(to The Firestone Tire & Rubber Company).
33. R. S. Stearns and L. E. Forman, *J. Polymer Sci.*, **41,** 381 (1959).
34. Brit. Pat. 817,693 (Aug. 6, 1959)(to The Firestone Tire & Rubber Company).
35. H. E. Diem, U.S. Pat. 3,049,528 (Aug. 14, 1962).
36. E. Krause and A. V. Grosse, *Die Chemie der metall-organischen Verbindungen,*

Borntraeger, Berlin, 1937, chap. 2, Edwards Brothers Inc., Ann Arbor Mich., 1943.

37. F. Runge, *Organo-metallverbindungen*, Stuttgart, 1944, Edwards Brothers, Ann Arbor, Mich., 1944.
38. H. Gilman, "Organometallic Compounds," in H. Gilman, Ed., *Organic Chemistry —An Advanced Treatise*, Vol. I, Wiley, New York, 1943, chap. 5.
39. E. G. Rochow, D. T. Hurd, and R. N. Lewis, *The Chemistry of Organometallic Compounds*, Wiley, New York, 1957, chap. 4.
40. G. E. Coates, *Organometallic Compounds*, 2nd ed., Methuen, London, 1960, chap. 1.
41. L. Pauling, *Nature of the Chemical Bond*, 3rd ed., Cornell Press, Ithaca, N.Y., 1960.
42. S. V. Anantakrishnan, *Proc. Indian Acad. Sci.*, **34A**, 299–303 (1951); through *Chem. Abstr.*, **46**, 6446 (1952).
43. J. Eisch and H. Gilman, "Organometallic Compounds," in *Progress in Inorganic Chemistry and Radiochemistry*, Vol. II, Academic Press, New York, 1960, pp. 61–99.
44. E. Weiss and E. A. Lucken, *J. Organomet. Chem.*, **2**, 197 (1964).
45. K. Ziegler and H. G. Gellert, *Ann.*, **567**, 179 (1950); *Chem. Abstr.* **44**, 7757 (1950).
46. W. H. Glaze and G. M. Adams, *J. Am. Chem. Soc.*, **88**, 4653 (1966).
47. R. G. Jones and H. Gilman, "The Halogen-Metal Interconversion Reaction with Organolithium Compounds," in R. Adams, Ed., *Organic Reactions*, Vol. VI, Wiley, New York, 1951, chap. 7, p. 339.
48. H. Gilman and J. W. Morton, "The Metalation Reaction With Organolithium Compounds," in R. Adams, Ed., *Organic Reactions*, Vol. VIII, Wiley, New York, 1954, chap. 6, p. 258.
49. E. A. Braude, "Organic Compounds of Lithium," in J. W. Cook, Ed., *Progress in Organic Chemistry*, Vol. III, Academic Press, New York, chap. 4.
50. Georg Wittig, "Syntheses With Organolithium Compounds," transl. and rev. by John R. Thirtle, in *Newer Preparations in Organic Chemistry*, Interscience, New York, 1948, pp. 571–591.
51. R. L. Letsinger, *Angew. Chem.*, **70**, 151 (1958).
52. T. L. Brown, R. L. Gerteis, D. A. Bafus, and J. A. Ladd, *J. Am. Chem. Soc.*, **86**, 2134 (1964).
53. T. L. Brown, J. A. Ladd, and G. N. Newman, *J. Organomet. Chem.*, **3**, 1 (1965).
54. D. Margerison and J. P. Newport, *Trans. Faraday Soc.*, **59**, 2058 (1963).
55. T. L. Brown and M. T. Rogers, *J. Am. Chem. Soc.*, **79**, 1859 (1957).
56. T. L. Brown, D. W. Dickerhoof and D. A. Bafus, *J. Am. Chem. Soc.*, **85**, 1371 (1962).
57. R. Waack and M. A. Doran, *J. Am. Chem. Soc.*, **85**, 1651 (1963).
58. D. K. Polyakov, A. R. Gantmakher, and S. S. Medvedev, *Polymer Sci.* (*USSR*). **7**, 198 (1965).
59. S. Bywater, A. F. Johnson, and D. J. Worsfold, *Can. J. Chem.*, **42**, 1255 (1964).
60. R. Waack, M. A. Doran, and P. E. Stevenson, *J. Am. Chem. Soc.*, **88**, 2109 (1966).
61. R. Waack and M. A. Doran, *J. Am. Chem. Soc.*, **85**, 2861 (1963).
62. L. M. Seitz and T. L. Brown, *J. Am. Chem. Soc.*, **88**, 2174 (1966).
63. G. Fraenkel, D. G. Adams, and J. Williams, *Tetrahedron Letters*, **12**, 767 (1963).
64. R. Waack and M. A. Doran, *J. Am. Chem. Soc.*, **85**, 4042 (1963).
65. M. A. Weiner and R. West, *J. Am. Chem. Soc.*, **85**, 485 (1963).

66. J. Berkowitz, D. A. Bafus, and T. L. Brown, *J. Phys. Chem.*, **65**, 1380 (1961).
67. M. Weiner, G. Vogel, and R. West, *Inorg. Chem.*, **1**, 655 (1962).
68. H. Dietrich, *Acta Cryst.*, **16**, 681 (1963).
69. R. A. Settle, M. Haggerty, and J. F. Eastham, *J. Am. Chem. Soc.*, **86**, 2076 (1964).
70. A. N. Rodionov, V. N. Vasil'eva, T. V. Talalaeva, D. N. Shigorin, E. N. Gur'yanova and K. A. Kocheshkov, *Dokl. Akad. Nauk, SSSR*, **125**, 562–5 (1959); through Chem. Abstr., **53**, 16693 (1959).
71. T. L. Brown, "The Structure of Organolithium Compounds," in F. G. A. Stone and R. West, Eds., *Advances In Organometallic Chemistry*, Vol. III, Academic Press, New York, 1965, p. 365 et seq.
72. M. Morton, E. E. Bostick, and R. Livigni, *Rubber Plastics Age*, **42**, 397 (1961).
73. M. Morton and L. J. Fetters, *J. Polymer Sci.*, **A2**, 3311 (1964).
74. M. Morton and R. A. Pett, *Polymer Preprints* **7** (1), 151 (1966).
75. M. Morton, N. Calderon, L. J. Fetters, and J. F. Meier, *ACS Polymer Preprints*, **2** (2), 310 (1961).
76. J. A. Dixon, P. A. Gwinner, and D. C. Lini, *J. Am. Chem. Soc.*, **87**, 1379 (1965).
77. G. Wittig, F. J. Meyer, and G. Lange, *Ann.*, **571**, 167 (1951).
78. A. N. Rodionov, D. N. Shigorin, T. V. Talalaeva, and K. A. Kocheshkov, *Dokl. Akad. Nauk, (SSSR)*, **143**, 137 (1962); through *Chem. Abstr.*, **57**, 5935 (1962).
79. Z. K. Cheema, G. W. Gibson, and J. F. Eastham, *J. Am. Chem. Soc.*, **85**, 3517 (1963).
80. J. F. Eastham and G. W. Gibson, *J. Am. Chem. Soc.*, **85**, 2171 (1963).
81. K. C. Williams and T. L. Brown, *J. Am. Chem. Soc.*, **88**, 4134 (1966); *ibid.*, **88**, 5460 (1966).
82. L. M. Seitz and T. L. Brown, *J. Am. Chem. Soc.*, **88**, 4140 (1966).
83. R. Waack and P. West, *J. Organometal. Chem.*, **5**, 188 (1966).
84. C. G. Screttas and J. F. Eastham, *J. Am. Chem. Soc.*, **87**, 3276 (1965).
85. C. G. Screttas and J. F. Eastham, *J. Am. Chem. Soc.*, **88**, 5668 (1966).
86. A. W. Langer, Jr., *ACS Polymer Preprints* **7** (1), 132 (1966).
87. N. I. Nikolayev, N. M. Geller, B. A. Dolgoplosk, V. N. Zgonnik, and V. A. Kropachev, *Polymer Sci. (USSR)*, **4**, 1528 (1963).
88. Yu. L. Spirin, D. K. Polyakov, A. R. Gantmakher, and S. S. Medvedev, *Dokl. Akad. Nauk, (USSR)*, **139**, 899 (1961); *Proc. Acad. Sci. (USSR)*, **139**, 778 (1961).
89. G. C. East, P. F. Lynch, and D. Margerison, *Polymer*, **4**, 139 (1963).
90. M. Morton, L. J. Fetters, and E. E. Bostick, *J. Polymer Sci.*, **C1**, 311 (1963).
91. Yu. L. Spirin, A. R. Gantmakher, and S. S. Medvedev, *Dokl. Akad. Nauk, (USSR)*, **146**, 368 (1962); through *Proc. Acad. Sci. (USSR)*, **146**, 815 (1962).
92. Yu. L. Spirin, D. K. Polyakov, A. R. Gantmakher, and S. S. Medvedev, *Polymer Sci. (USSR)*, **3**, 233 (1963).
93. H. Hsieh and A. V. Tobolsky, *J. Polymer Sci.*, **25**, 245 (1957).
94. H. Morita and A. V. Tobolsky, *J. Am. Chem. Soc.*, **79**, 5853 (1957).
95. A. A. Korotkov, N. N. Chesnokova, and L. B. Truckmanova, *Vysokomol. Soedin.*, **1** (1), 46 (1959); through *Rubber Chem. Technol.*, **33**, (3), 610 (1960).
96. V. A. Kropachev, B. A. Dolgoplosk, and N. I. Nikolaev, *Proc. Acad. Sci (USSR)*, **115**, 516 (1957); *Rubber Chem. Technol.*, **33**, 636 (1960).
97. I. Kuntz and A. Gerber, *J. Polymer Sci.*, **42**, 299 (1960).
98. J. Minoux and J. Marchal, *Compt. Rend.*, **250**, 3650 (1960).

99. C. E. Rogers, *ACS Polymer Preprints*, **2** (2), 75 (1961).
100. A. A. Korotkov and E. W. Marandzheva, *Vysokomol. Soedin.*, **4**, 793 (1962); through *Chem. Abstr.*, **58**, 8049 (1963).
101. I. Kuntz, *J. Polymer Sci.*, **A2** (6), 2827 (1964).
102. H. Sinn, C. Lundborg, and O. T. Onslager, *Makromol. Chem.*, **70**, 222 (1964).
103. D. J. Worsfold and S. Bywater, *Can. J. Chem.*, **42**, 2884 (1964); *Rubber Chem. Technol.*, **38**, 627 (1965).
104. H. L. Hsieh, *J. Polymer Sci.*, **A3**, 153 (1965) and subsequent papers in series.
105. H. L. Hsieh, *Rubber Plastics Age*, **46**, 394 (1965); *Rubber Chem. Technol.*, **39** (3), 491 (1966).
106. D. N. Cramond, P. S. Lawry, and J. R. Urwin, *European Polymer J.*, **2**, 107 (1966).
107. Brit. Pat. 847,824 (Sept. 14, 1960)(to B. F. Goodrich Company).
108. Brit. Pat. 876,587 (Sept. 6, 1961)(to Esso Research & Engineering Company).
109. H. L. Hsieh, *J. Polymer Sci.*, **A3**, 163 (1965).
110. R. J. Ehrig and H. L. Vincent, Belg. Pat. 612, 647 (Jan. 15, 1961)(to Shell Internatl. Research).
111. Belg. Pat. 639,116 (Feb. 2, 1962)(to Phillips Petroleum Company).
112. L. M. Porter, U.S. Pat. 3,105,828 (Oct. 1, 1963)(to Shell Oil Company).
113. J. F. Van der Castle, U.S. Pat. 3,207,742 (Sept. 21, 1965)(Esso Research & Engineering Company).
114. L. E. Forman and C. H. Hammond, U.S. Pat. 3,284,430 (Nov. 8, 1966)(to The Firestone Tire & Rubber Company).
115. L. E. Forman, R. W. Kibler, and F. A. Bozzacco, U.S. Pat. 3,208,988 (Sept. 28, 1965)(to The Firestone Tire & Rubber Company).
116. L. E. Forman, U.S. Pat. 3,254,062 (May 31, 1966)(to The Firestone Tire & Rubber Company).
117. L. E. Forman, R. S. Stearns, R. W. Kibler, and F. A. Bozzacco, U.S. Pat. 3,265,680 (Aug. 9, 1966)(to The Firestone Tire & Rubber Company).
118. A. V. Tobolsky and C. E. Rogers, *J. Polymer Sci.*, **38**, 205 (1959).
119. Belg. Pat. 639,265 (Dec. 22, 1961)(to Phillips Petroleum Company).
120. Brit. Pat. 962,518 (Dec. 22, 1961)(to Phillips Petroleum Company).
121. Brit. Pat. 910,227 (Nov. 14, 1962)(to The Firestone Tire & Rubber Company).
122. C. A. Uraneck and G. R. Kahle, U. S. Pat. 3,159,587 (Dec. 1, 1964)(to Phillips Petroleum Company).
123. Brit. Pat. 946,016 (Jan. 8, 1964)(to Phillips Petroleum Company).
124. W. J. Trepka, *J. Polymer Sci.*, **B1**, 683 (1963).
125. E. W. Duck and M. N. Thornber, *Chem. Ind. (London)*, (48), 1904 (1963).
126. R. S. Stearns, U.S. Pat. 3,170,903 (Feb. 23, 1965)(to The Firestone Tire & Rubber Company).
127. S. Bywater, *Advan. Polymer Sci.*, **4**, 66 (1965).
128. R. C. P. Cubbon and D. Margerison, in G. Porter, Ed., *Progress in Reaction Kinetics*, Vol. III, Pergamon Press, New York, 1965, p. 420.
129. R. Dessy and W. Kitching, "Organometallic Reaction Mechanisms," in F. G. A. Stone and R. West, Ed., *Advances in Organometallic Chemistry*, Vol. IV, Academic Press, New York, 1966, p. 269.
130. R. Waack, P. West, and M. A. Doran, Paper No. 41, presented before the Div. Petr. Chem., Am. Chem. Soc., New York, September 1966.
131. H. Sinn and W. Hofmann, *Makromol. Chem.*, **56**, 234 (1962).

132. B. François, V. Sinn, and J. Parrod, *J. Polymer Sci.*, **C4**, 375 (1963).
133. D. J. Cram, *Fundamentals of Carbanion Chemistry*, Academic Press, New York, 1965, pp. 19, 21.
134. C. Lundborg and H. Sinn, *Makromol. Chem.*, **41**, 242 (1960).
135. H. Sinn and O. T. Onsager, *Makromol. Chem.*, **55**, 167 (1962).
136. H. Sinn and F. Patat, *Angew. Chem. Intern. Ed.*, **3**, 93 (1964).
137. T. L. Brown, *J. Organometal. Chem.*, **5**, 191 (1966).
138. Yu. L. Spirin, A. A. Arest-Yakubovich, D. K. Polyakov, A. R. Gantmakher, and S. S. Medvedev, *J. Polymer Sci.*, **58**, 1181 (1962).
139. M. Morton, E. E. Bostick, and R. G. Clarke, *J. Polymer Sci.*, **A1**, 475 (1963).
140. A. Kh. Bagdasar'yan, V. M. Frolov, E. I. Tinyahova, and B. A. Dolgoplosk, *Proc. Acad. Sci., USSR*, **162**, 582 (1965).
141. G. Wittig, *Quart. Rev.*, **1966**, 191.
142. H. J. S. Winkler and H. Winkler, *J. Am. Chem. Soc.*, **88**, 969 (1966).
143. H. L. Hsieh, *J. Polymer Sci.*, **A3**, 173 (1965).
144. C. E. H. Bawn and A. Ledwith, *Quart. Rev.*, **16**, 361 (1962).
145. M. Morton, "The Nature of Organometallic Polymerization," in B. L. Johnson and M. Goodman, Ed., *Elastomer Stereospecific Polymerization*, (Advances in Chemistry Series 52), American Chemical Society, Washington, D.C., 1966, p. 1.
146. S. Bywater and D. J. Worsfold, "Polymerization Mechanism of Nonpolar Monomers by Lithium Alkyls," in B. L. Johnson and M. Goodman, Ed., *Elastomer Stereospecific Polymerization*, (Advances in Chemistry Series 52), American Chemical Society, Washington, D.C., 1966, p. 36.
147. H. Sinn and C. Lundborg, *Makromol. Chem.*, **47**, 86 (1961).
148. M. Morton, E. E. Bostick, R. A. Livigni, and L. J. Fetters, *J. Polymer Sci.*, **A1**, 1735 (1963).
149. G. Alliger, B. L. Johnson, and L. E. Forman, *Kautschuk Gummi*, **14**, WT 248 (1961).
150. H. L. Hsieh and O. F. McKinney, *J. Polymer Sci. B.*, **4**, 843 (1966).
151. R. Waack and M. A. Doran, *Chem. Ind.*, **1964**, 496.
152. H. Gilman and A. H. Haubein, *J. Am. Chem. Soc.*, **66**, 1515 (1944).
153. H. Gilman, F. K. Cartledge, and S. Y. Sim, *J. Organometal. Chem.*, **1**, 8 (1963).
154. K. C. Eberly and H. E. Adams, *J. Organometal. Chem.*, **3**, 165 (1965).
155. H. E. Adams, R. L. Bebb, K. C. Eberly, B. L. Johnson, and E. L. Kay, *Kautschuk Gummi*, **18** (ii), 709 (1965).
156. L. E. Forman, unpublished results, The Firestone Tire & Rubber Company.
157. R. West, P. A. Carney, and I. C. Mineo, *J. Am. Chem. Soc.*, **87**, 3788 (1965).
158. G. Jenner, *Bull. Soc. Chim. France*, **1966**, 3133.
159. J. L. Latham, *Elementary Reaction Mechamisms*, Butterworths, London, 1964, p. 67.
160. M. Morton and L. J. Fetters, *J. Polymer Sci.*, **A2**, 3311 (1964).
161. D. K. Polyakov, Yu. L. Spirin, A. R. Gantmakher, and S. S. Medvedev., *Proc. Acad. Sci.*, (*USSR*), **150**, 490 (1963), Eng. transl.
162. H. Sinn and F. Bandermann, *Makromol. Chem.*, **62**, 134 (1963).
163. L. J. Fetters, *J. Res. Natl. Bur. Std.*, **69A**, 159 (1965).
164. R. A. H. Casling, A. G. Evans, and N. H. Rees, *J. Chem. Soc.*, **1966**, (6)B, 519.
165. M. Szwarc, *Makromol. Chem.*, **35**, 132 (1960).
166. M. Szwarc, *Advan. Polymer Sci.*, **2**, 275 (1960).
167. P. J. Flory, *Polymer Chemistry*, Cornell Univ. Press, Ithaca, N.Y., 1953.

168. A. Miyake and W. M. Stockmayer, *ACS Polymer Preprints*, **6** (1), 273 (1965).
169. (*a*) Brit. Pat. 921,803 (Aug. 18, 1960)(to Phillips Petroleum Company); (*b*) C. A. Uraneck, J. N. Short, R. P. Zelinski, and H. Hsieh, Ger. Pat. 1,169,674 (May 6, 1964)(to Phillips Petroleum Company); (*c*) Brit. Pat. 946,092 (Jan. 8, 1964); (*d*) Ger. Pat. 1,185,369 (July 29, 1957)(to B. F. Goodrich Company); (*e*) W. B. Reynolds, U.S. Pat. 3,074,917 (Jan. 22, 1963)(to Phillips Petroleum Company).
170. (*a*) French Pat. 1,426,952 (Dec. 27, 1965)(to National Distillers Corp.); (*b*) E. J. Goldberg, U.S. Pat. 3,055,952 (Sept. 25, 1962)(to DuPont), through *Chem. Abstr.*, **58**, 645 (1963); (*c*) Brit. Pat. 946,092 (Jan. 8, 1964)(to National Distillers Corp.), through *Chem. Abstr.*, **60**, 10820 (1964); (*d*) Brit. Pat. 945,851 (Jan. 8, 1964)(to Phillips Petroleum Company), through *Chem. Abstr.*, **60**, 10905 (1964).
171. (*a*) K. Hayashi and C. S. Marvel, *J. Polymer Sci.*, **A2** (6), 2571 (1964); (*b*) J. N. Short and R. P. Zelinski, U.S. Pat. 3,269,978 (Aug. 30, 1966)(to Phillips Petroleum Co.).
172. Brit. Pat. 1,001,352 (July 17, 1962)(to DuPont).
173. R. P. Zelinski, H. L. Hsieh, and C. W. Strobel, U.S. Pat. 3,109,871 (Nov. 5, 1963) (to Phillips Petroleum Co.); Brit. Pat. 945,851 (Jan. 8, 1964)(to Phillips Petroleum Co.).
174. M. Litt and M. Szwarc, *J. Polymer Sci.*, **42**, 159 (1960).
175. M. Szwarc and M. Litt, *J. Phys. Chem.*, **62**, 568 (1958).
176. B. D. Coleman, F. Gornick, and G. Weiss, *ACS Polymer Preprints*, **4** (2), 307 (1963).
177. W. Cooper and N. S. Grace, *J. Polymer Sci.*, **C13**, 133 (1966).
178. V. A. Kargin, *Pure Appl. Chem.*, **12** (1–4), 35 (1966).
179. A. J. Staverman, *Pure Appl. Chem.*, **12** (1–4), 473 (1966).
180. G. Alliger and F. C. Weissert, *Ind. Eng. Chem.*, **58**, 36 (1966).
181. G. Alliger and F. C. Weissert, Presented before the International Rubber Conference, Paris, France, May 25, 1966.
182. J. L. Binder, *Rubber Chem. Technol.*, **35**, 57 (1962).
183. J. L. Binder and H. C. Ransaw, *Anal. Chem.*, **29**, 605 (1957); J. L. Binder, *Anal. Chem.*, **31**, 529 (1959); J. L. Binder, *J. Polymer Sci.*, **A1**, 37 (1963).
184. W. S. Richardson and A. Sacher, *J. Polymer Sci.*, **10**, 353 (1953).
185. R. S. Silas, J. Yates, and V. Thornton, *Anal. Chem.*, **31**, 529 (1959).
186. I. Koessler and J. Vodehnal, *J. Polymer Sci. B*, **1**, 415 (1963).
187. F. Ciampelli and I. Manoviciu, *Gazz. Chim. Ital.*, **91**, 1045 (1961); through *Chem. Abstr.*, **57**, 998 (1962).
188. E. O. Schmalz and G. Geiseler, *Z. Anal. Chem.*, **190**, 293 (1962); *ibid.*, **191**, 1 (1963).
189. D. Morero, A. Santambrogio, L. Porri, and F. Ciampelli, *Chim. Ind.*, **41**, 758 (1959); through *Chem. Abstr.*, **54**, 4269g (1960).
190. R. Isaac, Third National Meeting, Society for Applied Spectroscopy, September, 1964, Cleveland, Ohio, Paper No. 139, p. 255.
191. P. J. Corrish, *Rubber Chem. Technol.*, **33**, 975 (1960).
192. H. Y. Chen, *Anal. Chem.*, **34**, 1134, 1793 (1962).
193. M. A. Golub, S. A. Fuqua, and N. S. Bhacca, *J. Am. Chem. Soc.*, **84**, 4981 (1962).
194. F. Schué and J. P. Dole-Robbe, *Bull. Soc., Chim., France,* **1963,** (5), 975.
195. M. A. Golub, *J. Polymer Sci. B*, **4**, 227 (1966).
196. H. Y. Chen, *J. Polymer Sci. B*, **4**, 891 (1966).

197. F. Schué, *Bull. Soc. Chim., France,* **1965,** 980.
198. W. P. Slichter, *Rubber Chem. Technol.,* **34,** 1574 (1961).
199. W. P. Slichter and D. D. Davis, *J. Appl. Phys.,* **35,** 3103 (1964); *Rubber Chem. Technol.,* **38,** 517 (1965).
200. Ya. Slonim, *Russ. Chem. Rev.,* **35** (5), 308 (1962), and references therein.
201. E. E. Hanson and G. Halverson, *J. Am. Chem. Soc.,* **70,** 779 (1948).
202. A. I. Yakubchik and V. D. Nikitina, *Zh. Prikl. Khim.,* **35,** 2749 (1962); through *Chem. Abstr.,* **58,** 11551 (1963).
203. H. S. Makowski and M. Lynn, *J. Macromol. Chem.,* **1** (3), 443 (1966).
204. L. E. Forman, unpublished results, The Firestone Tire & Rubber Company.
205. T. B. Talcott, unpublished results, The Firestone Tire & Rubber Company.
206. K. F. O'Driscoll, *J. Polymer Sci.,* **A3,** 2223 (1965).
207. M. Shima, J. Smid, and M. Szwarc, *J. Polymer Sci. B,* **2,** 735 (1964).
208. A. V. Tobolsky and C. E. Rogers, *J. Polymer Sci.,* **40,** 73 (1959).
209. B. A. Dolgoplosk and E. I. Tinyakova, *Dokl. Akad. Nauk, SSSR,* **146,** 362 (1962).
210. R. V. Basova, A. A. Arest-Yakubovich, D. A. Solovykh, N. V. Desyatova, A. R. Gantmakher, and S. S. Medvedev, *Dokl. Akad. Nauk, SSSR,* **149,** 1067 (1963); through *Chem. Abstr.,* **59,** 5343 (1963).
211. N. I. Nikolayev, N. M. Geller, B. A. Dolgoplosk, V. N. Zgonnik, and V. A. Kropachev, *Polymer Sci. (USSR),* **4,** 1528 (1963); *Chem. Abstr.,* **59,** 10323 (1963).
212. H. Groene and G. Pampus, Ger. Pat. 1,120,695 (Dec. 21, 1961); through *Chem. Abstr.* **56,** 11771 (1962).
213. L. E. Forman and C. H. Hammond, unpublished results, The Firestone Tire & Rubber Company.
214. A. A. Korotkov, K. B. Piotrovskii, and D. P. Feringer, *Proc. Acad. Sci. (USSR), Sect. Chem.,* **110,** 537–9 (1956); through *Chem. Abstr.,* **51,** 5015 (1957); cf. *ibid.,* **51,** 4037.
215. G. Kraus, J. N. Short, and V. Thornton, *Rubber Plastics Age,* **38,** 880 (1957).
216. M. Bruzzone, G. Corradini, and F. Amato, *Rubber Plastics Age,* **46,** 278 (1965); *Rubber Chem. Technol.,* **39,** 1593 (1966).
217. J. N. Short, G. Kraus, R. P. Zelinski, and F. E. Naylor, *Rubber Chem. Technol.,* **32,** 614 (1959).
218. K. W. Scott, G. S. Trick, R. H. Mayor, W. M. Saltman, and R. M. Pierson, *Rubber Plastics Age,* **42,** 175 (1961).
219. E. Butta and V. Frosini, *Chim. Ind. (Milan),* **45,** 703 (1963); through *Chem. Abstr.* **60,** 10898 (1964).
220. E. G. Kent and F. B. Swinney, *Ind. Eng. Chem. Prod. Res. Dev.,* **5,** (2), 134 (1966).
221. H. Bluemel, *Kautschuk Gummi,* **16,** 571 (1963); through *Rubber Chem. Technol.,* **37** (2), 408 (1964), in English.
222. H. E. Railsback, J. R. Haws, and C. R. Wilder, *Rubber World,* **142,** 67 (1960).
223. F. S. Dainton, D. M. Evans, F. E. Hoare, and T. P. Melia, *Polymer,* **3,** 297 (1962).
224. R. W. Warfield and M. C. Petree, *Rubber Chem. Technol.,* **39,** 143 (1966).
225. J. J. Shipman and M. A. Golub, *J. Polymer Sci.,* **58,** 1063 (1962).
226. C. A. Ceselli, T. Garlanda, M. Camia, and G. Manza, *Chim. Ind. (Milan),* **44,** 1203 (1962); through *Chem. Abstr.,* **58,** 9307 (1963).
227. D. J. Elliott, *Trans. Inst. Rubber Ind.,* **41,** T180 (1965).
228. I. I. Ermakova, B. A. Dolgoplosk, and E. N. Kropacheva, *Dokl. Akad. Nauk, SSSR,* **141,** 1363 (1961); through *Chem. Abstr.,* **56,** 12717 (1962).
229. M. A. Golub, *J. Am. Chem. Soc.,* **81,** 54 (1959).

230. W. A. Bishop, *J. Polymer Sci.*, **55,** 827 (1961).
231. D. J. Buckley, *J. Polymer Sci.*, **A1,** 2945 (1963).
232. M. A. Golub, *J. Polymer Sci.*, **36,** 523 (1959).
233. J. I. Cunneen, G. M. C. Higgins, and R. A. Wilkes, *J. Polymer Sci.*, **A3,** 3503 (1965).
234. D. Reichenbach, *Kautschuk Gummi, Kuntstoffe,* **18** (4), 213 (1965).
235. J. J. Cunneen, W. R. Fletcher, F. W. Shipley, and R. I. Wood, *Trans. Inst. Rubber Ind.*, **34,** 260 (1958).
236. N. A. Klauzen and B. A. Dogadkin, *Zavodsk Lab.*, **28,** 438 (1962); through *Chem. Abstr.*, **58,** 1613 (1963).
237. L. E. Forman, unpublished results, The Firestone Tire & Rubber Company.
238. C. J. Sheehan and A. L. Bisio, *Rubber Chem. Technol.*, **39** (1), 149 (1966).
239. H. E. Adams, K. Farhat, and B. L. Johnson, *Ind. Eng. Chem., Prod. Res. Dev.*, **5** (2), 127 (1966), and references therein.
240. B. M. E. van der Hoff, J. F. Henderson, and R. M. B. Small, *Rubber Plastics Age,* **July 1965,** 821.
241. F. Patat and G. Spott, *Makromol. Chem.*, **87,** 8 (1965); *Rubber Chem. Technol.*, **39,** 1411 (1966).
242. S. E. Bresler, *J. Polymer Sci.*, **30,** 285 (1958).
243. S. E. Bresler, A. A. Korotkov, M. I. Mosevitskii, and I. Ya. Poddubnyi, *Zh. Tekh. Fiz.*, **28,** 114 (1958); *Rubber Chem. Technol.*, **33,** 669 (1960).
244. G. Kraus and J. T. Gruver, *J. Polymer Sci.*, **A3,** 105 (1965).
245. J. T. Gruver and G. Kraus, *J. Polymer Sci.*, **A2,** 797 (1964).
246. W. C. Carter, R. L. Scott, and M. Magat, *J. Am. Chem. Soc.*, **68,** 1480 (1946).
247. I. Ya. Poddubnyi, V. A. Grechanovskii, and A. V. Podalinskii, *Vysokomolekul. Soedin.*, **5** (10), 1588 (1963).
248. W. H. Beattie and C. Booth, *J. Appl. Polymer Sci.*, **7,** 507 (1963).
249. J. F. Henderson, J. M. Hulme, R. M. B. Small, and H. L. Williams, *Rubber Chem. Technol.*, **38,** 817 (1965).
250. C. A. Uraneck, M. G. Barker, and W. D. Johnson, *Rubber Chem. Technol.*, **38,** 802 (1965).
251. J. E. Moore, *J. Polymer Sci.*, **A2,** 835 (1964).
252. L. W. Gamble, L. Westerman, and E. A. Knipp, *Rubber Chem. Technol.*, **38**(4), 823 (1965).
253. J. Cazes, *J. Chem. Educ.*, **43** (7), A567 (1966); *ibid.*, **43** (8), A625 (1966).
254. W. S. Bahary, *J. Appl. Polymer Sci.*, **10,** 473 (1966).
255. N. F. Keckler and B. L. Johnson, Belg. Pat. 621,659 (Feb. 25, 1963)(to The Firestone Tire & Rubber Company).
256. Ger. Pat. 951,831 (Dec. 3, 1960).
257. Belg. Pat. 638,995 (Oct. 22, 1963).
258. G. Kraus and J. J. Brennan, U.S. Pat. 3,238,187 (March 1, 1966).
259. Brit. Pat. 1,018,364 (Jan. 26, 1966)(to Phillips Petroleum Company).
260. French Pat. 1,336,414 (July 22, 1963).
261. Ger. Pat. 1,202,000 (July 31, 1963)(to Bayer).
262. Ger. Pat. 1,402,504 (July 28, 1964).
263. Ger. Pat. 1,219,228 (Aug. 1, 1963)(to Bayer).
264. Brit. Pat. 1,006,816 (Mar. 1, 1963).
265. Brit. Pat. 1,013,557 (Apr. 26, 1963).

266. Brit. Pat. 952,021 (Mar. 11, 1964).
267. J. P. Oliver, *J. Am. Chem. Soc.*, **88,** 4101 (1966).
268. P. T. Lansbury, Presented at American Chemical Society Meeting, New York, September 1966.
269. B. H. Zimm and R. W. Kilb, *J. Polymer Sci.*, **37,** 19 (1959).
270. B. L. Johnson and R. E. Wolfangel, *Ind. Eng. Chem.*, **41,** 1580 (1949); *ibid.*, **44,** 752 (1952).
271. R. W. Kilb, *J. Polymer Sci.*, **38,** 403 (1958).
272. I. Ya. Poddubnyi and E. G. Ehrenburg, *J. Polymer Sci.*, **29,** 605 (1958); *Polymer Sci., USSR,* **3,** 427 (1963).
273. M. Szwarc, *Proc. Royal Soc. (London)*, **A279,** 260 (1964).
274. R. P. Zelinski and C. F. Wofford, *J. Polymer Sci.*, **A3,** 93 (1965).
275. Brit. Pat. 985,614 (March 10, 1965).
276. F. Bueche, *J. Chem. Phys.*, **40,** 484 (1964).
277. J. S. Ham, *J. Chem. Phys.*, **26,** 625 (1957).
278. W. W. Graessley, *J. Chem. Phys.*, **43,** 2696 (1965); *Rubber Chem. Technol.*, **39** (5), 1460 (1966).
279. G. R. Dobson and M. Gordon, *J. Chem. Phys.*, **43,** 705 (1965); *Rubber Chem. Technol.*, **39,** 1472 (1966).
280. L. C. Case and R. V. Wargin, *Makromol. Chem.*, **77,** 172 (1964); *Rubber Chem. Technol.*, **39,** 1389 (1966).
281. T. G. Fox, S. Gratch, and S. Loshaek, "Viscosity Relationships for Polymers in Bulk and in Concentrated Solution," in F. R. Eirich, Ed., *Rheology,* Academic Press, New York, 1965, chap. 12.
282. J. R. Stevens and D. G. Ivey, *J. Appl. Physics,* **29,** 1390 (1958); *Rubber Chem. Technol.*, **32,** 434 (1959).
283. R. F. Boyer, *Rubber Chem. Technol.*, **36** (5), 1303 (1963).
284. R. F. Boyer, *ACS Polymer Preprints,* **6** (2), 503 (1965).
285. J. Lal and K. W. Scott, *J. Polymer Sci.*, **C9,** 113 (1965); *Rubber Chem. Technol.*, **39,** 881 (1966).
286. K. E. Polmanteer, J. A. Thorne, and J. D. Helmer, *Rubber Chem. Technol.*, **39,** 1403 (1966).
287. R. A. Hayes, *J. Appl. Polymer Sci.*, **5,** 318 (1961); *Rubber Chem. Technol.*, **35,** 558 (1962).
288. O. D. Cole, *Trans. Am. Soc. Mech. Engr.*, **65,** 15 (1943).
289. W. A. Smith and J. M. Willis, *Rubber Age,* **87,** 815 (1960); *Rubber Chem. Technol.* **34** (1), 176 (1961).
290. C. E. H. Bawn, *Rubber Plastics Age,* 267 (1961).
291. D. P. Tate, private communication.
292. H. Uelzmann, *J. Polymer Sci.*, **32,** 457 (1958); *Rubber Chem. Technol.*, **32,** 597 (1959).
293. R. Roha, *Advan. Polymer Sci.*, **4,** 353 (1965).
294. S. S. Medvedev., *Pure Appl. Chem.*, **12** (1–4), 403 (1966).
295. J. P. Kennedy and A. W. Langer, Jr., *Advan. Polymer Sci.*, **3,** 508 (1964).
296. K. F. O'Driscoll, T. Yonezawa, and T. Higashimura, *ACS Polymer Preprints,* **6** (2), 876 (1965).
297. M. Szwarc, *J. Polymer Sci.*, **40,** 583 (1959).
298. R. Hoffmann and R. A. Olofson, *J. Am. Chem. Soc.*, **88,** 943 (1966).

299. R. Waack and M. A. Doran, *J. Organometal. Chem.*, **3**, 92, 94 (1965).
300. H. W. Brown and R. C. Jones, *J. Chem. Phys.*, **37**, 1571 (1962).
301. E. Schoenberg, *J. Polymer Sci.*, **49**, 59 (1961).
302. K. Hayaski and C. S. Marvel, *J. Polymer Sci.*, **A2**, 2571 (1964).
303. V. V. Samoletova and N. N. Motovilova, *Kauchuk Rezina*, **24** (7), 31 (1965), Eng. transl. by P. G. Williams in *Soviet Rubber Technol.*, **24**, (7), 31 (1966).
304. J. A. Verdol, D. J. Carrow, P. W. Ryan, and K. L. Kuncl, *Rubber Age*, **98** (7), 57 (1966).
305. H. Zahn and G. B. Gleitsmann, *Angew. Chem. Intern. Ed.*, **2**, 410 (1963).
306. C. A. Uraneck, H. L. Hsieh, and O. G. Buck, *J. Polymer Sci.*, **46**, 535 (1960).
307. H. Hsieh, U.S. Pat. 3,203,944 (Aug. 31, 1965) (to Phillips Petroleum Company).
308. U.S. Pat. 3,109,871 (Nov. 5, 1963).
309. American Petroleum Institute, Table 11a, Research Project 44, Selected Values of Properties of Hydrocarbons.
310. J. E. Nordlander and J. D. Roberts, *J. Am. Chem. Soc.*, **81**, 1769 (1959); *ibid.*, **83**, 494 (1961); *ibid.*, **84**, 2010 (1962).
311. C. S. Johnson, Jr., M. A. Weiner, J. S. Waugh, and D. Seyferth, *J. Am. Chem. Soc.*, **83**, 1306 (1961); D. Seyferth and L. G. Vaughn, *J. Organometal. Chem.*, **1**, 201 (1963); *J. Am. Chem. Soc.*, **86**, 883 (1964).
312. D. Craig, *J. Am. Chem. Soc.*, **65**, 1006 (1943).
313. N. I. Shuikin and V. A. Tulupov, *Vest. Moscow Univ.*, **9**, (8), *Nauk*, **5**, 91 (1954); through *Chem. Abstr.*, **49**, 3776 (1955).
314. G. S. Hammond, J. Saltiel, A. A. Lamola, Nicholas J. Turro, J. S. Bradshaw, D. O. Cowan, R. C. Counsell, V. Vogt, and C. Dalton, *J. Am. Chem. Soc.*, **86**, 3197 (1964); through *Chem. Abstr.*, **61**, 8155 (1964).
315. W. K. Taft and G. J. Tiger, "Diene Polymers and Copolymers Other Than GR-S And The Specialty Rubbers," in G. S. Whitby, Ed., *Synthetic Elastomers*, Wiley, New York, 1954, p. 688.
316. J. D. D'Ianni, *Rubber Chem. Technol.*, **34**, 361 (1961).
317. R. S. Stearns, U.S. Pat. 3,147,242 (Sept. 1, 1964).
318. A. I. Yakubchik, V. K. Smirnova, and V. M. Zavalei, *Zh. Prikl., Khim.* **35**, 405 (1962); through *Chem. Abstr.*, **57**, 4808 (1962).
319. L. Porri, M. C. Gallazzi, and G. Natta, *Rend. Acad. Nazl. Lincei*, **36**, 752 (1964).
320. F. Schué, *Bull. Soc. Chim., France*, **1963** (5), 973.
321. F. Schué, C. Ortlieb, A. Maillard, and A. Deluzarche, *Bull. Soc. Chim., France*, **1965** (5), 982.
322. G. Friedman, F. Schué, M. Brini, A. Deluzarche, and A. Maillard, *Bull. Soc. Chim., France*, **1965**, 1343.
323. G. Friedman, F. Schué, M. Brini, A. Deluzarche and A. Maillard, *Bull. Soc. Chim., France*, **1965**, 1728, 3636.
324. G. Jenner, *Bull. Soc. Chim., France*, **1965**, 2851.
325. G. Jenner, *Bull. Soc. Chim., France*, **1966**, 1127.
326. I. A. Livshits and V. I. Stepanova, *Polymer Sci. (USSR)*, **1965**, 197.
327. G. E. Ham, "Theory of Copolymerization," in G. E. Ham, Ed., *Copolymerization*, in High Polymer Series, Vol. XVIII, Interscience, New York, 1964, p. 1.
328. G. E. Ham, "Copolymerization," in H. F. Mark, N. E. Gaylord, and N. M. Bikeles, Eds., *Encyclopedia of Polymer Science and Technology*, Vol. IV, Wiley, New York, 1966, p. 165.

329. L. S. Bresler, *Russian Chem. Rev.*, **34** (5), 366 (1965).
330. M. Morton, "Anionic Copolymerization," in G. E. Ham, Ed., *Copolymerization*, in High Polymer Series, Vol. XVIII, Interscience, New York, 1964, p. 421.
331. F. R. Mayo and F. M. Lewis, *J. Am. Chem. Soc.*, **66**, 1594 (1944).
332. M. Fineman and S. D. Ross, *J. Polymer Sci.*, **5**, 259 (1950).
333. I. Skeist, *J. Am. Chem. Soc.*, **68**, 1781 (1946).
334. D. W. Behnken, *J. Polymer Sci.*, **A2**, 645 (1964).
335. P. W. Tidwell and G. A. Mortimer, *J. Polymer Sci.*, **A3**, 369 (1965).
336. A. A. Durgaryan, *Polymer Sci.* (*USSR*), **8** (5), 867 (1966).
337. S. Igarashi, *J. Polymer Sci. B*, **1**, 359 (1963).
338. K. Tada, T. Fueno, and J. Furukawa, *J. Polymer Sci.*, **A1**, 2981 (1966).
339. H. J. Harwood and W. M. Ritchey, *J. Polymer Sci. B*, **2**, 601 (1964).
340. T. Alfrey, Jr. and C. C. Price, *J. Polymer Sci.*, **2**, 101 (1947).
341. T. Alfrey, Jr. and L. J. Young, "The *Q-e* Scheme," in G. E. Ham, Ed., *Copolymerization*, in High Polymer Series, Vol. XVIII, Interscience, New York, 1964, chap. 2, p. 67.
342. K. Higasi, H. Baba, and A. Rembaum, *Quantum Organic Chemistry*, Interscience, New York, 1965, p. 323 et seq.
343. D. J. Kelley and A. V. Tobolsky, *J. Am. Chem. Soc.*, **81**, 1597 (1959).
344. G. V. Rakova and A. A. Korotkov, *Rubber Chem. Technol.*, **33**, 623 (1960).
345. A. A. Korotkov and N. N. Chesnokova, *Polymer Sci.* (*USSR*), **2**, 284 (1961).
346. A. A. Korotkov and G. V. Rakova, *Polymer Sci.* (*USSR*), **3**, 990 (1962).
347. M. Szwarc and J. Smid, "The Kinetics of Propagation of Anionic Polymerization and Copolymerization," in G. Porter, Ed., *Progress in Reaction Kinetics*, Vol. 2, Macmillan, New York, 1964, p. 267.
348. M. Morton and F. R. Ells, *J. Polymer Sci.*, **61**, 25 (1962).
349. A. F. Johnson and D. J. Worsfold, *Makromol. Chem.*, **85**, 273 (1965).
350. K. F. O'Driscoll and I. Kuntz, *J. Polymer Sci.*, **61**, 19 (1962).
351. Y. Landler, *J. Polymer Sci.*, **8**, 63 (1952).
352. J. A. Seiner, *Ind. Eng. Chem. Fundamentals*, **4** (4), 477 (1965).
353. Brit. Pat. 994,726 (June 10, 1965)(to The Firestone Tire & Rubber Company).
354. Brit. Pat. 903,331 (Aug. 15, 1962)(to Phillips Petroleum Company).
355. J. Furukawa, T. Saegusa, and K. Irako, *Kogo Kagaku Zasshi*, **65**, 2079 (1962); through *Chem. Abstr.*, **58**, 11553 (1963).
356. L. S. Bresler, B. A. Dolgoplosk, M. F. Kolechkova, and E. N. Kropacheva, *Proc. Acad. Sci.*, (*USSR*), **144**, 420 (1963); *ibid.*, **149**, 248 (1963).
357. W. G. Mayes, private communication.
358. A. A. Korotkov, S. P. Mitzengendler, and K. M. Aleyev, *Polymer Sci.* (*USSR*), **2**, 487 (1961).
359. Yu. L. Spirin, A. R. Gantmakher, and S. S. Medvedev, *Polymer Sci.* (*USSR*), **1**, 497 (1960).
360. Yu. L. Spirin, D. K. Polyakov, A. R. Gantmakher, and S. S. Medvedev, *Polymer Sci.*, (*USSR*), **3**, 233 (1962); cf. *J. Polymer Sci.*, **53**, 233 (1961).
361. S. P. Mitzengendler, K. M. Aleyev, L. L. Dantzig, and A. A. Korotkov, *Polymer Sci.* (*USSR*), **4**, 831 (1963).
362. I. Kuntz, *J. Polymer Sci.*, **54**, 569 (1961).
363. U.S. Pat. 2,975,160 (Mar. 14, 1961); Brit. Pat. 884,490 (Dec. 13, 1961); French Pat. 1,450,847 (July 20, 1965).
364. L. Reich and S. Stivala, *J. Polymer Sci.*, **A2**, 2685 (1964).

365. G. Friedmann, M. Brini, A. Deluzarche, and A. Maillard, *Bull. Soc. Chim. France,* **1965,** 3636.
366. F. Schué and C. Ortlieb, *Bull. Soc. Chim. France,* **1965,** 982.
367. G. V. Rakova, A. A. Korotkov, and Tszuan-Chan Li, *Proc. Acad. Sci. (USSR),* **126,** 377 (1959).
368. M. Szwarc, M. Levy, and R. Milkovich, *J. Am. Chem. Soc.,* **78,** 2656 (1956).
369. M. Szwarc, *Nature,* **178,** 1168 (1956).
370. M. Szwarc, *Proc. Royal Soc. (London),* **A279,** 260 (1964).
371. G. Champetier, *Rev. Gén. Caoutchouc,* **39,** 565 (1962).
372. G. S. Kolesnikov and L. K. Yaralov, *Russ. Chem. Rev.,* **34** (3), 202 (1965).
373. L. J. Fetters, *J. Res. Bur. Std.,* **70A** (5), 421 (1966).
374. A. A. Korotkov, L. A. Shibayev, L. M. Pyrkov, V. G. Aldoshin, and S. Ia. Frenkel, *Polymer Sci. (USSR),* **1,** 157 (1960).
375. J. Minoux and M. Leng, *Compt. Rend.,* **252,** 277 (1961).
376. R. L. Huxtable and R. E. Dollinger, U.S. Pat. 3,198,774 (Aug. 3, 1965).
377. G. Holden and R. Milkovich, U.S. Pat. 3,231,635 (Jan. 25, 1966).
378. L. M. Porter, U.S. Pat. 3,149,182 (Sept. 15, 1964).
379. R. E. Dollinger, U.S. Pat. 3,297,793 (Jan. 10, 1967).
380. Brit. Pat. 1,000,090 (Aug. 4, 1965); Brit. Pat. 1,035,873 (July 13, 1966).
381. Brit. Pat. 888,624 (Jan. 31, 1962).
382. I. Kuntz, U.S. Pat. 3,140,278 (July 7, 1964).
383. R. P. Zelinski, U.S. Pat. 3,251,905 (May 17, 1966).
384. Brit. Pat. 1,044,862 (Oct. 5, 1966).
385. L. E. Forman, Can. Pat. 582,946 (Sept. 8, 1959).
386. S. Ye. Bresler L. M. Pyrkov S. Ya. Frenkel, L. A. Laius, and S. I. Klenin, *Polymer Sci. (USSR),* **4,** 89 (1963).
387. B. Gallot, R. Mayer, and Ch. Sadron, *Compt. Rend.,* **42,** 263 (1966).
388. E. Vanzo, *J. Polymer Sci. A-1,* **4,** 1727 (1966).
389. Anon., *Rubber Plastics Age,* **46,** 690 iv (1965); cf. *Rev. Gén. Caoutchouc,* **42** (11), 1471 (1965).
390. Anon., *Modern Plastics,* **43** (10), 77 (1966).
391. H. E. Railsback, C. C. Baird, J. R. Haws, and R. C. Wheat, *Rubber Age,* **94** (4), 583 (1964).
392. R. S. Hanmer and H. E. Railsback, *Rubber Age,* **Oct. 1964,** p. 73.
393. J. R. Haws, *Rubber Plastics Age,* **46,** 1144 (1965).
394. G. Bertrand, *Rev. Gén. Caoutchouc,* **43** (10), 1291 (1966).
395. R. F. Dunbrook, B. L. Johnson, J. L. Binder, J. M. Willis, and E. L. Carr, "Recent Studies of the Structure of Synthetic Rubber," in *Proceedings of the Third Rubber, Technology Conference,* Institution of the Rubber Industry, T. H. Messenger, Ed., W. Heffer & Sons, Ltd., Cambridge, 1954, p. 139.
396. G. S. Whitby, *Rubber Chem. Technol.,* **34** (4), xxv, 1961.
397. R. F. Dunbrook, "Historical Review" in *Synthetic Rubber,* G. S. Whitby, Ed., Wiley, New York, 1954, chap. 2.
398. A. Talalay and M. Magat, *Synthetic Rubber from Alcohol,* Interscience, New York, 1945, p. 144 et seq.
399. Ref. 315, p. 734 et seq.
400. R. L. Bebb and L. B. Wakefield, "German Synthetic Rubber Developments" in *Synthetic Rubber,* G. S. Whitby Ed., Wiley, New York, 1954, chap. 26, p. 959.

401. R. F. Dunbrook, *India Rubber World*, **117**, 747 (1948).
402. J. E. Mulvaney, C. G. Overberger, and A. M. Schiller, *Advan. Polymer Sci.*, **3**, 106 (1961).
403. A. Abkin and S. Medvedev, *Trans. Faraday Soc.*, **32**, 286 (1936).
404. J. L. Bolland, *Proc. Royal Soc. (London)*, **A178**, 24 (1941).
405. S. Kume, A. Takahashi, G. Nishikawa, M. Hatano, and S. Kambara, *Makromol. Chem.*, **84**, 137, 147 (1965).
406. R.V. Basova and A. R. Gantmakher, *Polymer Sci., USSR*, **4**, 118 (1963).
407. R. V. Basova, A. A. Arest-Yakubovich, D. A. Solovykh, N. V. Desyatova, A. R. Gantmakher, and S. S. Medvedev, *Proc. Acad. Sci., USSR*, **149**, 312 (1963).
408. S. S. Medvedev and A. R. Gantmakher, *J. Polymer Sci.*, **C4**, 173 (1963).
409. R. V. Basova, A. R. Gantmakher, and S. S. Medvedev, *Proc. Acad. Sci., USSR*, **158**, 994 (1964).
410. A. A. Arest-Yakubovich and S. S. Medvedev, *Proc. Acad. Sci., USSR*, **159**, 1305 (1964).
411. A. A. Arest-Yakubovich and S. S. Medvedev, *Polymer Sci., USSR*, **8**, 748 (1966).
412. M. Schlosser, *Angew. Chem., Intern. Ed.*, **3**, 28, 362 (1964).
413. M. Szwarc and J. Smid, "The Kinetics of Propagation of Anionic Polymerization and Copolymerization," in *Progress in Reaction Kinetics*, G. Porter, Ed., MacMillan, New York, 1964, Vol. 2, chap. 5.
414. M. Szwarc, *Pure Appl. Chem.*, **12** (1–4), 127 (1966).
415. M. Szwarc, *Makromol. Chem.*, **89**, 44 (1965).
416. D. N. Bhattacharyya, C. L. Lee, J. Smid, and M. Szwarc, *J. Phys. Chem.* **69**, 612 (1965).
417. D. N. Bhattacharyya, J. Smid, and M. Szwarc, *J. Phys. Chem.*, **69**, 624 (1965).
418. A. I. Shatenshtein and E. S. Petrov, *Russ. Chem. Rev.*, **36** (2), 100 (1967).
419. R. Chang and C. S. Johnson, Jr., *J. Am. Chem. Soc.*, **88**, 2338 (1966).
420. A. A. Korotkov and A. F. Podolsky, *J. Polymer Sci. B*, **3**, 901 (1965).
421. R. J. Orr, *J. Polymer Sci.*, **58**, 843 (1962).
422. L. E. Forman, unpublished data, The Firestone Tire & Rubber Co.
423. A. V. Tobolsky and C. E. Rogers, *J. Polymer Sci.*, **40**, 73 (1959); *Rubber Chem. Technol.*, **33**, 655 (1960).
424. A. Rembaum, F. R. Ells, R. C. Morrow, and A. V. Tobolsky, *J. Polymer Sci.*, **61**, 155 (1962).
425. K. C. Eberly and B. L. Johnson, *J. Polymer Sci.*, **3**, 283 (1948).
426. R. E. Robertson and L. Marion, *Can. J. Res.*, **26B**, 657 (1948).
427. G. Friedmann and M. Brini, *Bull. soc. Chim., France*, **1967**, 1420.
428. C. S. Marvel, W. J. Bailey, and G. E. Inskeep, *J. Polymer Sci.*, **1**, 275 (1946).
429. S. Schlick and M. Levy, *J. Phys. Chem.*, **64**, 883 (1960).
430. A. W. Meyer, R. R. Hampton, and J. A. Davison, *J. Am. Chem. Soc.*, **74**, 2294 (1952); *Rubber Chem. Technol.*, **26**, 522 (1953).
431. A. I. Yakubchik, V. N. Reikh, B. I. Tikhomirov, and A. V. Pavlikova, *Rubber Chem. Technol.*, **35**, 1052 (1962).
432. C. Sadron, *Rev. Gén. Caoutchouc*, **39**, 1925 (1962).
433. C. E. H. Bawn, *Trans. J. Plastics Inst.*, **Feb. 1967**, 337.
434. Z. F. Zharikova, Ye. V. Reztsova, Z. Ya. Berestneva, and V. A. Kargin, *Polymer Sci., USSR*, **8**, 622 (1966).
435. I. Ya. Poddubnyi and E. G. Ehrenburg, *Polymer Sci., USSR*, **3**, 427 (1962).

436. A. H. Gleason, U.S. Pat. 2,762,851 (Sept. 11, 1956)(to Esso Research & Engineering Co.).
437. Brit. Pat. 802,348 (Oct. 1, 1958), and 975,871 (Nov. 18, 1964)(to Esso Research & Engineering Co.).
438. W. W. Crouch, U.S. Pat. 2,577,677 (Dec. 4, 1951).
439. A. A. Morton, *Ind. Eng. Chem.*, **42,** 1488 (1950); *ibid.*, **44,** 2876 (1952); reprinted in *Rubber Chem. Technol.*, **24,** 35 (1951); *ibid.*, **26,** 543 (1953).
440. V. L. Hansley and H. Greenberg, *Rubber Chem. Technol.*, **38,** 103 (1965).
441. A. A. Morton and R. A. Finnegan, *J. Polymer Sci.*, **38,** 19 (1959).
442. A. A. Morton, "The Alfin Reagent," in *Advances in Catalysis Series IX*, A. Farkas, Ed., Academic Press, New York, 1957, p. 751.
443. L. E. Forman, unpublished data, The Firestone Tire & Rubber Co.
444. A. A. Morton, I. Nelidow, and E. Schoenberg, *Rubber Chem. Technol.*, **30,** 326 (1957).
445. J. L. Binder, *Anal. Chem.*, **26,** 1879 (1954).
446. A. A. Morton and F. K. Ward, *J. Org. Chem.*, **24,** 929 (1959).
447. A. A. Morton, F. H. Bolton, F. W. Collins, and E. F. Cluff, *Ind. Eng. Chem.*, **44,** 2876 (1952).
448. J. D. D'Ianni, F. J. Naples, and J. E. Field, *Ind. Eng. Chem.*, **42,** 95 (1950).
449. R. A. Stewart and H. Leverne Williams, *Ind. Eng. Chem.*, **45,** 173 (1953).
450. A. A. Morton, E. E. Magat, and R. L. Letsinger, *J. Am. Chem. Soc.*, **69,** 950 (1947).
451. R. R. Cleland, R. L. Letsinger, E. E. Magat, and W. H. Stockmayer, *J. Polymer Sci.*, **39,** 249 (1959).
452. H. Greenberg and V. L. Hansley, U.S. Pat. 3,067,187 (Dec. 4, 1962); Brit. Pat. 1,003,508 (Sept. 2, 1965).
453. V. K. Bykhovskii and K. S. Minsker, *Vysokomol. Soedin.*, **2,** 259 (1960), quoted in *Polymer Reviews*, Vol. 12, *Polymerization by Organometallic Compounds*," L. Reich and A. Schindler, Wiley, New York, 1966, p. 420.
454. Brit. Pat. 924,654 (May 1, 1963); *Chem. Abstr.*, **59,** 5347 (1963).
455. Ger. Pat. 1,093,094 (Nov. 17, 1960); *Chem. Abstr.*, **55,** 26498 (1961).
456. Belg. Pat. 606,644 (July 27, 1961).
457. Brit. Pat. 872,163 (July 5, 1961); *Chem. Abstr.*, **57,** 14003 (1962).
458. Ger. Pat. 1,138,548 (Oct. 25, 1962); *Chem. Abstr.*, **58,** 1613 (1963).
459. Brit. Pat. 964,826 (May 22, 1964); *Chem. Abstr.*, **61,** 9652 (1964).
460. K. V. Nelson, I. Ya. Poddubny, M. A. Krupyshev, and Z. D. Stepanova, *Kauchuk i Rezina*, **17** (11), 3 (1958); through *Chem. Abstr.*, **54,** 21824 (1960).
461. R. P. Dinsmore, *Trans. Inst. Rubber Ind.*, **28** (4), 166 (1952).
462. O. Mamontova, A. Abkin, and S. Medvedev, *Acta Physicochim., USSR*, **12,** 269 (1940); through *Chem. Abstr.*, **34,** 7709 (1940).
463. J. Minoux, *Compt. Rend.*, **252,** 4163 (1961); *Rev. Gén. Caoutchouc*, **39,** 788 (1962).
464. J. Parrod and G. Beinert, *J. Polymer Sci.*, **53,** 99 (1961).
465. A. I. Yakubchik and V. D. Nikitina, *Zh. Prikl. Khim.*, **35,** 2491 (1962); through *Chem. Abstr.*, **58,** 8115 (1963).
466. L. A. Wood, "Physical Chemistry of Synthetic Rubbers," in *Synthetic Rubber*, G. S. Whitby, Ed., Wiley, New York, chap. 10, p. 331.
467. R. L. Cleland, *J. Polymer Sci.*, **27,** 349 (1958).
468. G. Russell, E. G. Janzen, and E. T. Strom, *J. Am. Chem. Soc.*, **86,** 1807 (1964).
469. A. A. Morton and L. D. Taylor, *J. Polymer Sci.*, **38,** 7 (1959).

CHAPTER 7

ELASTOMERS BY COORDINATED ANIONIC MECHANISM

A. Diene Elastomers

Giulio Natta

Istituto di Chimica Industriale, Politecnico, Milano

AND

Lido Porri

Istituto di Chimica Organica Industriale, Università di Pisa, Italy

Contents

I. Homopolymers of Butadiene, Isoprene, and Piperylene 598
A. Introduction 598
B. Isomerism of Diolefin Polymers 599
C. Polymerization Catalysts 602
1. General Considerations 602
2. Catalysts from $TiCl_4$ 603
3. Titanium Based Catalysts Containing Iodine 605
4. Catalysts from Cobalt Compounds 606
D. Synthesis of the Polymers 610
1. Butadiene Polymers 610
2. Isoprene Polymers 632
3. Piperylene Polymers 643
E. Properties of the Diolefin Polymers 649
F. Mechanism of Polymerization 652
1. Nature of the Polymerization 652
2. Factors Determining or Influencing the Type of Addition of the Monomeric Units 659
3. Forces of Stereoregulation 664
II. Copolymers of Butadiene, Isoprene, and Piperylene 666
A. Introduction 666
B. Copolymers of Butadiene and 2-Phenyl-Butadiene 667
C. Copolymers of Butadiene and Piperylene 668
1. Copolymers Obtained by the Heterogeneous $AlEt_3$–VCl_3 System 668
2. Copolymers Obtained by the Homogeneous $AlEt_2Cl$–$V(acac)_3$ System 669

D. Copolymers of Butadiene and Isoprene 670
1. Copolymers Obtained with the Heterogeneous AlR_3–$CiCl_4$ System... 670
2. Copolymers Obtained with the Homogeneous AlR_2–ClCo Compound System 670
References 672

I. HOMOPOLYMERS OF BUTADIENE, ISOPRENE, AND PIPERYLENE

A. Introduction

Diolefins have represented and still represent the most widely used raw materials for the production of synthetic rubber. Methods for the polymerization of diolefins have been known for a long time. However, no method of polymerization known before 1954 (when stereospecific polymerization was discovered) allowed one to obtain polymers with a high regularity of structure from the most common diolefins.

With Na or K catalysts it was possible to obtain polymers consisting predominantly of 1,2 units, in some cases above 95% (1–3). However, no crystallinity has been detected in these polymers by x-ray examination, evidently because of the lack of steric regularity, that is lack of order in the configurations of the tertiary carbon atoms of each chain.

It is now known that, among the alkali metals, lithium and its derivatives can yield diolefin polymers with a certain degree of regularity (cf. Chapter 6). Thus, polymers which are 90–92% *cis*-1,4 can be obtained from isoprene (4–6), and polymers having a *trans*-1,4 isotactic structure can be obtained from 1,3-pentadiene (7). Such stereospecific properties of the lithium catalysts were recognized, however, only after the discovery of the coordination catalysts. Thus, it may be said that no polymer with a regular structure was synthesized by alkali metal catalysts before 1954.

Structurally very irregular polymers were obtained by cationic initiators, due to the formation of crosslinks and to cyclization (8,9). These products are completely amorphous by x-rays.

Polymers having a certain structural regularity were obtained by radical initiators, but only from some diolefins. By these initiators, it is possible to obtain butadiene polymers containing up to 80% *trans*-1,4 units (10). The most regular of these polymers exhibit, at low temperatures and under stretching, low crystallinity due to the presence of *trans*-1,4 sequences in the chain (11).

Polymers containing up to 90% *trans*-1,4 units can be obtained from isoprene with the help of radical initiators. However, they appear completely amorphous by x-rays, probably because of lack of a regular head-to-tail arrangement (12).

Only from particular diolefins is it possible to obtain, by radical initiators, polymers having a certain regularity of structure. Thus, from chloroprene, polymers consisting of about 95% *trans*-1,4 units were obtained, which showed good crystallinity at room temperature (13). Polymers of this type can be obtained only by operating at about −40°, while far more irregular polymers are obtained at room temperature (14).

The Alfin catalysts (15,16) (cf. Chapter 6, p. 575) certainly represent progress with respect to the previous catalysts as to the ability to yield regular polymers of diolefins. In fact, unstretched polybutadienes obtained by these catalysts show a certain amount of crystallinity even at room temperature due to the presence of *trans*-1,4 sequences in the chain (17,18). However, the polymers of isoprene obtained by these catalysts are completely amorphous (17).

The discovery of stereospecific catalysts based on transition metals completely changed the situation in the field of diolefin polymers. With these catalysts polymers have been obtained with 98–100% units of the same type (1,2; *trans*-1,4 or *cis*-1,4) in a regular head-to-tail arrangement, representing a far higher structural regularity than the synthetic polymers previously known. Moreover macromolecules with a high degree of steric regularity have been obtained from monomers yielding units that contain asymmetric carbon atoms. The results obtained during twelve years of activity in this field are not only of great scientific interest, but also of great practical importance, especially in the field of synthetic elastomers.

This chapter deals with the homopolymerization, by anionic coordination catalysts, of the three simplest diolefins, i.e., butadiene, isoprene, and 1,3-pentadiene. These are the most important diolefins from the industrial point of view.

This chapter presents a general outline of the polymerization of these monomers and the topics of interest from the elastomeric point of view will be emphasized.

B. Isomerism in Diolefin Polymers

Before considering the results obtained in the stereospecific polymerization of butadiene, isoprene, and pentadiene, we think it useful to describe the phenomena of isomerism that can occur in the polymerization of diolefins. A comparison between the theoretically foreseeable possibilities and the results actually obtained will show the progress that stereospecific polymerization has made in the field of conjugated diolefins.

Isomerism in conjugated diolefin polymers is a considerably more complex phenomenon than that encountered in vinyl polymers. Butadiene can polymerize to yield 1,4 or 1,2 units. The 1,4 units, —CH_2—CH= CH—CH_2—, contain an internal double bond, which represents a site of geometric isomerism, since it can be of the *cis* or the *trans* type. It is therefore possible to foresee two types of regular polybutadienes with 1,4 arrangement, i.e., *trans*-1,4 and *cis*-1,4 polybutadienes.

The 1,2 units,

$$
\begin{array}{l}
\text{—CH—CH}_2\text{—} \\
\;\;\;| \\
\;\;\text{CH} \\
\;\;\;\| \\
\;\;\text{CH}_2
\end{array}
$$

on the other hand, contain a site of steric isomerism, i.e., the tertiary carbon atom, which can assume two opposite configurations. 1,2 Polybutadienes, therefore, show the same type of isomerism as vinyl polymers. Hence two types of regular 1,2 polybutadienes are possible, one of the isotactic, the other of the syndiotactic type. Also, atactic-1,2 polybutadiene can exist, in which there is a statistical distribution of the two configurations of the tertiary carbon atoms of each chain.*

In the case of isoprene, two types of regular *cis*-1,4 and *trans*-1,4 polymers can be foreseen. When only one unsaturated group is involved in the polymerization, different polymers are obtained depending on whether the polymerization involves the vinyl (3,4 units) or the vinylidenic group (1,2 units). Both 1,2 and 3,4 polyisoprenes exhibit vinyl type isomerism; therefore two types of regular 3,4 stereoisomers (iso and syndio), two types of regular 1,2 stereoisomers (iso and syndio), as well as atactic 1,2 and 3,4 polyisoprenes can be foreseen. To summarize, six types of regular simple isomers of polyisoprene are possible: i.e., two 1,4 polyisoprenes, two 3,4 polyisoprenes, and two 1,2 polyisoprenes.

Isomerism becomes more complex in the case of pentadiene polymers. Every unit derived from this monomer, whatever its structure, shows two

* More complex phenomena of isomerism, such as those deriving from a regular alternation of units of different type (e.g., *trans*-1,4 and *cis*-1,4 units) or, in the case of 1,2 polymers, from a regular head-to-head, tail-to-tail structure will be neglected here. Polymers of this type, although possible, do not seem easily obtainable by simple homopolymerization by the catalysts known so far.

sites of isomerism. The 1,4 units show a site of geometric isomerism at the double bond and a site of steric isomerism at the asymmetric carbon atom:

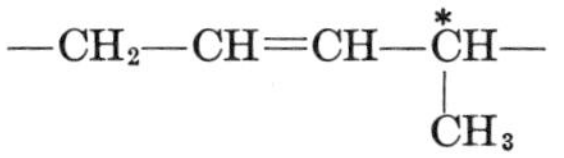

Consequently, while polybutadiene or polyisoprene can each have only one stereoisomer with *trans*-1,4 or *cis*-1,4 structure, in the case of pentadiene, due to the presence of an asymmetric carbon atom in each 1,4 unit, two different *trans*-1,4 or *cis*-1,4 stereoregular polymers are possible, namely the isotactic and syndiotactic isomers. Stereoregular polymers of this type, in which there are two sites of isomerism per monomer unit, have been called ditactic. Obviously, there can be 1,4 polypentadienes having regularity only with respect to one type of isomerism, e.g., all-*trans*-1,4 or all-*cis*-1,4 polymers, in which there is no order as to the configurations of the asymmetric carbon atoms of each chain.

Polymerization involving only the vinyl group gives rise to 1,2 units,

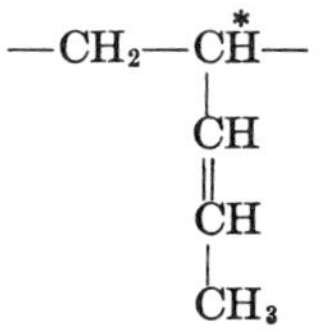

which contain a site of steric isomerism at the tertiary carbon atom and a site of geometric isomerism at the double bond of the side group. Four types of stereoregular 1,2 polypentadiene are therefore possible, two types of isotactic polymers, which differ in that they contain all-*cis* or all-*trans* double bonds in the side groups, and analogously, two types of syndiotactic polymers.

Polymerization involving only the internal double bond of pentadiene gives rise to 3,4 units,

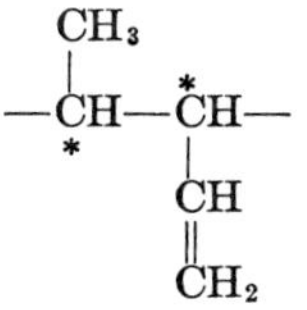

which contain two sites of steric isomerism. Three types of stereoregular 3,4 polypentadienes are possible: (*1*) disyndiotactic polymers, in every chain of which the configuration of each tertiary carbon atom of a monomer unit is opposite to that of the corresponding carbon atom of the preceding or following unit; (*2*) *erythro*-diisotactic polymers; (*3*) *threo*-diisotactic polymers. The latter (*2* and *3*) differ with regard to the relative configuration of the adjacent tertiary carbon atoms.

Isomerism becomes far more complex with polymers of 1,4 substituted butadienes. This case is beyond the scope of this chapter, and will not be discussed here. A more detailed discussion of the configurational possibilities shown by vinyl and diolefin polymers can be found in recent publications (19–22).

C. Polymerization Catalysts

1. General Considerations

The first coordination catalysts, based on transition metals, used for the polymerization of conjugated diolefins (principally butadiene and isoprene) were obtained by reacting $TiCl_4$ or $TiCl_3$ and an alkyl aluminum compound (trialkyl aluminum, dialkylaluminum halide, lithium aluminum tetraalkyls).

Subsequently, a vast number of compounds of transition metals from groups IV–VIII of the periodic table have been used in combination with alkylaluminum compounds for the preparation of catalysts for the polymerization of conjugated diolefins. These compounds include halides, alcoholates, acetylacetonates, complexes with CO, amines, isonitriles, nitriles, etc. A large number of catalysts can be prepared from the combination of one of the various aluminum alkyl derivatives with each of these transition metal compounds. This number increases if one considers that instead of aluminum alkyls, other organometallic compounds can be used, e.g., aluminum hydrides or alkyl derivatives of Be, Zn, Mg, Cd, etc.

Only a few catalysts, however, are of practical importance in the preparation of diolefin polymers, if one takes into account their activity and stereospecificity. These are the catalysts obtained from an aluminum trialkyl or an alkylaluminum halide and a compound of the following metals: Ti, V, Cr, Mo, Co, Ni. Catalysts from other transition metals are of less interest. The transition metal compounds mostly used are halides (particularly chlorides and iodides), complexes of the chlorides with a Lewis base, alcoholates, and acetylacetonates.

Some of the transition metal catalysts are heterogeneous, e.g., those obtained from AlR_3 or AlR_2Cl* and either $TiCl_4$, $TiCl_3$, VCl_3, $VOCl_3$, or VCl_4. Others are homogeneous, e.g., those from AlR_3 and either $Ti(OR)_4$, $VO(OR)_3$, $V(acac)_3$, $Cr(acac)_3$, or $Co(acac)_2$, and also those obtained from AlR_2Cl and a compound of Co (e.g., $CoCl_2{\cdot}2py$; $Co(acac)_2$) or V (e.g., $V(acac)_3$; $VCl_3{\cdot}3THF$).

The reactions between aluminum alkyls and transition metal compounds have been studied extensively but the nature of the reaction products has not been always clarified. These reactions proceed through several stages. One of these appears to be the alkylation of the transition metal compound, with formation of a transition metal–carbon bond. This bond is often (but not always) unstable under the reaction conditions and breaks homolytically with formation of a free alkyl radical. As a consequence, gas evolution is observed in most of the reactions between an aluminum alkyl and a transition metal compound. The cleavage of the transition metal–carbon bond also causes a decrease in the formal valence of the transition metal, which, in most of the cases, is stabilized in the lower valence state through complexation with the aluminum compound.

The following part of this section deals with a detailed examination of the catalyst systems most important for the polymerization of diolefins to elastomeric products. These are the catalysts based on either Ti halides or Co compounds.

2. Catalysts from $TiCl_4$

The use of catalysts from $TiCl_4$ for the polymerization of diolefins (23) dates back to shortly after Ziegler's discovery that the suspension obtained by treating $TiCl_4$ with $AlEt_3$ can polymerize ethylene. Several studies exist on the reaction between AlR_3 or AlR_2Cl and $TiCl_4$ (24–35). In hydrocarbon solvent, the reaction occurs with formation of a precipitate containing Ti in a reduced state, while gas is evolved simultaneously. The composition of the precipitate varies with the AlR_3/$TiCl_4$ ratio as well as with the reaction conditions. The preferred method of preparing the catalyst is gradual introduction of an AlR_3 solution into the $TiCl_4$ solution while stirring. Table I shows the composition of precipitates obtained at 15° from $AlEt_3$ and $TiCl_4$. The solid obtained at a molar ratio $AlR_3/TiCl_4 = 1$ is brown and contains Cl and Ti in a

* The following abbreviations will be used in this chapter: AlR_3 = aluminum trialkyl; AlR_2Cl = dialkylaluminum chloride; acac = acetylacetonate group; py = pyridine; $Me(OR)_n$ = metal alkoxide; THF = tetrahydrofuran.

TABLE I
Analyses of the Precipitates Obtained by Reacting $Al(C_2H_5)_3$ with $TiCl_4$ at 15°C (25,27)

$AlEt_3/TiCl_4$ molar ratio	Cl/Ti	Al/Ti	X-ray exam.	Average valence of Ti in the solids
0.5	3.4	0.24	Amorphous	—
1.2	3.08	0.07	Cryst. (β-$TiCl_3$)	3
2.0	2.36	0.33	Amorphous	2.31
2.5	2.15	0.30	Amorphous	—
3.0	2	0.32	Amorphous	•2.04
5	1.65	0.31	Amorphous	1.87

molar ratio very close to 3:1, while Al is present in small amounts. The product consists essentially of crystalline $TiCl_3$ which, by x-ray analysis, appears to be identical with that obtained by Böck and Moser by the action of dark discharges on a gaseous mixture of $TiCl_4$ and H_2 (36). The School of Milan designated this crystalline modification β-$TiCl_3$ to distinguish it from the violet modification (called α-$TiCl_3$) which is obtained by the action of H_2 on $TiCl_4$ at high temperatures (37). The differentiation between the two forms is important as they yield catalysts of different stereospecificity. See Sections I-D-1a, b and I-D-2a, b (38).

Upon increasing the $AlR_3/TiCl_4$ ratio, the Cl/Ti ratio in the precipitate decreases, due to alkylation of $TiCl_3$, while the color gradually turns black. The products obtained at a ratio ≥ 2 are amorphous by x-rays. The average valence of Ti in the precipitate is about 3 at an $AlR_3/TiCl_4$ ratio of 1, while it drops even below 2 at higher ratios.

On the other hand, AlR_2Cl does not reduce Ti to a valence below 3 at room temperature, and β-$TiCl_3$ is obtained even at high $AlR_2Cl/TiCl_4$ ratios.

Some data reported in the literature are slightly different from those of Table I; actually some authors report higher and others lower values for the Al content in the precipitates. Despite these disagreements, it is clear that the following reactions take place:

$$AlR_3 + TiCl_4 \rightarrow AlR_2Cl + TiCl_3 + R^{\cdot}$$
$$AlR_3 + TiCl_3 \rightarrow TiCl_2R + AlR_2Cl$$
$$TiCl_2R \rightarrow TiCl_2 + R^{\cdot}$$

Catalysts have recently been proposed for the polymerization of diolefins which, instead of AlR_3, use compounds containing Al—H bonds, such as $AlHCl_2 \cdot O(C_2H_5)_2$, $AlHCl_2 \cdot N(CH_3)_3$, $AlH_2Cl \cdot N(CH_3)_3$, $AlH_3 \cdot N(CH_3)$ (39,40). At low Al/Ti ratios the reaction between these compounds and $TiCl_4$ leads to the formation of β-$TiCl_3$ containing small amounts of Al, while H_2 is evolved. At higher Al/Ti ratios, the precipitate is amorphous by x-rays and the Cl/Ti ratio is lower than 3, while the percentage of Al present increases.

Therefore, the reaction between the above-mentioned Al hydrides and $TiCl_4$ is similar to that with aluminum trialkyls. It is, however, apparent that the former compounds have a higher reducing power than AlR_3; in fact, the reaction between $AlHCl_2 \cdot O(C_2H_5)_2$ and $TiCl_4$ occurs rapidly even at temperatures far below 0°C (39).

3. Titanium Based Catalysts Containing Iodine

It was realized early (41) that the AlR_3–TiI_4 system shows catalytic properties which differ somewhat from those of the AlR_3–$TiCl_4$ system. In fact, the AlR_3–TiI_4 system

1. gives polybutadienes having a higher *cis*-1,4 content than those obtained by the AlR_3–$TiCl_4$ system
2. is active and stereospecific over a wide range of Al/Ti ratios
3. does not polymerize isoprene

The reaction between AlR_3 and TiI_4 in benzene at room temperature, or slightly above, gives insoluble solids that contain reduced Ti (26,42). At sufficiently high Al/Ti ratios (≥ 2.5), practically all the Ti is in the solid phase. This phase also contains I and alkyl groups, while Al is present only in a small percentage. Some disagreement exists among the data published on the composition of the solids. It appears that the reaction of AlR_3 with TiI_4 is analogous to that with $TiCl_4$, except that it is slower. Thus, in the reaction between $Al(i\text{-}C_4H_9)_3$ and $TiCl_4$, at an Al/Ti ratio of 3, the Cl/Ti ratio in the precipitate is less than 2, while in the reaction between $Al(iC_4H_9)_3$ and TiI_4, at the same Al/Ti ratio, the I/Ti ratio in the solids is 2.3–2.4 even after 18 hr at room temperature. According to Saltman (42), also at $Al(i\text{-}C_4H_9)_3/TiI_4$ ratios of about 10, the I/Ti ratio in the solids is higher than 2, while the ratio of isobutyl groups to Ti is 0.5–0.6. This is the main difference between the $TiCl_4$ and TiI_4 systems. The fact that the chemical composition of the precipitate varies slowly with varying AlR_3/TiI_4 ratio, accounts for the fact that the system is active and stereospecific over a wide range of ratios (from 2–3 to about 8–9).

For the synthesis of *cis*-1,4 polybutadienes, the systems AlR_3–$TiCl_2I_2$

(equimolecular mixture of $TiCl_4$ and TiI_4) (26,43–45) and AlR_3–I_2–$TiCl_4$ (Al/Ti = 5–10; I_2/Ti = 1.5) (43,46,47) were found equivalent to the AlR_3–TiI_4 system. Both $TiCl_4$ and $TiCl_2I_2$ present the advantage of being far more soluble than TiI_4 in hydrocarbon solvents. In the system AlR_3–I_2–$TiCl_4$, iodine reacts readily with AlR_3 (while it does not with $TiCl_4$) to give AlR_2I (42); therefore the system behaves as though it consisted of AlR_3–AlR_2I–$TiCl_4$. The precipitates obtained from the systems based on $TiCl_2I_2$ or $TiCl_4 + I_2$ are practically the same as those from the TiI_4 system. Actually all the Cl passes into the filtrate as AlR_2Cl, while the precipitate contains the entire amount of iodine present in the system. This phenomenon is quite general in systems consisting of Al and Ti compounds and containing Cl and I. Thus, the reaction between $AlEt_2I$ and $TiCl_4$, as well as that between Al(*i*-C_4H_9)$_3$ and $TiCl_2I_2$ yield precipitates that practically consist of TiI_3 (26,48).

In a series of catalysts proposed for the *cis*-1,4 polymerization of butadiene, various metal hydrides are used instead of aluminum alkyls as reducing agents. The system $AlHCl_2 \cdot O(C_2H_5)_2$–$TiCl_4$–$AlI_3$ is particularly active and stereospecific (49). As the reducing compounds, $AlH_3 \cdot N(CH_3)_3$, $AlH_2Cl \cdot N(CH_3)_3$, or $AlH_2N(CH_3)_2$ can also be employed (49).

Other systems proposed (49,50) are: $AlHI_2 \cdot O(C_2H_5)_2$–$TiCl_4$;$AlHCl_2 \cdot O(C_2H_5)_2$–$TiI_4$; $LiAlH_4$–$TiCl_2I_2$; $LiAlH_4$–I_2–$TiCl_4$; CaH_2–$AlEt_2I$–$TiCl_4$. The similarity among all the above systems is shown by considering that:

1. they contain a strong reducing agent which is able to decrease the valence of Ti
2. iodine, regardless of the form in which it was initially present, always ends up bonded to Ti

To summarize, in all the iodine-containing systems mentioned above, practically the same solid is formed (TiI_3 and/or TiI_2R, where R = alkyl or H). The Al compounds present are different, but most likely they exert little influence on the stereospecificity.

4. Catalysts from Cobalt Compounds

a. Catalysts from Al Alkylhalides and Cobalt Compounds. These systems are the most stereospecific for the synthesis of *cis*-1,4 polybutadiene. They are used in homogeneous solution (usually in benzene or toluene) at a Co concentration of the order of 1–5 mg per liter of solvent-monomer mixture (51,52). AlR_2Cl, $AlRCl_2$, $Al_2Cl_3R_3$ or the corresponding phenyl derivatives can be used as the Al compound (53–58).

Co-based catalysts exhibit the following characteristics:

1. the Al/Co ratio can be varied within wide limits, from about 20 to more than 1,000 and even above, without varying stereospecificity
2. practically any soluble or insoluble cobalt compound can be used to obtain a stereospecific catalyst. The most commonly used Co compounds are the di- and triacetylacetonates, complexes of $CoCl_2$ with pyridine, ethers, or amines, complexes of Co with various chelates, and salts of organic and inorganic acids.

It can be demonstrated that even with an insoluble Co compound, e.g., a salt of an inorganic acid ($CoCl_2$, $CoSO_4$), a homogeneous catalytic complex is formed as a result of the reaction of the alkyl aluminum with the insoluble Co compound. In fact, if a suspension of insoluble Co compound (e.g., $CoCl_2$) in benzene containing $AlEt_2Cl$ is stirred at room temperature and subsequently filtered, the filtrate shows catalytic activity (51).

The fact that different Co compounds, as reported above, by reaction with $AlEt_2Cl$ (or $AlEtCl_2$, $Al_2Cl_3Et_3$), yield catalysts with equivalent activity and stereospecificity suggests that the catalytic complex is essentially the same in every case. It is actually possible to demonstrate that the first stage of the catalyst-forming reaction is the substitution of the groups bonded to Co by the —Cl of the Al compound (59,60).

The reaction probably occurs according to the scheme:*

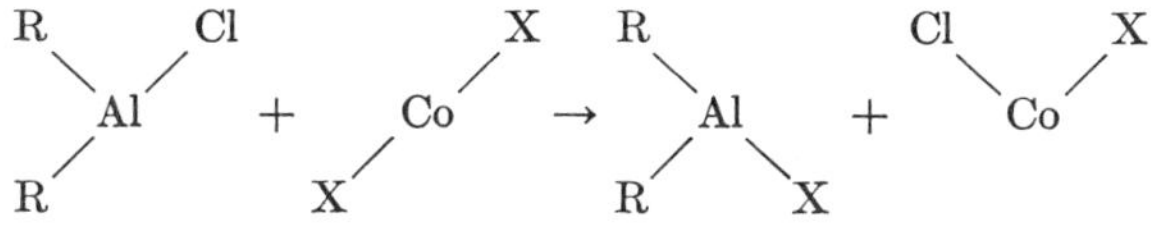

(1)

The formation of $CoCl_2$ can be easily demonstrated by performing the reaction in tetrahydrofuran (59). Crystals of $CoCl_2 \cdot THF$ are always isolated from this reaction when the tetrahydrofuran solution is concentrated, regardless of the starting Co compound ($CoSO_4$, Co 2-ethylhexanoate, Co di- or triacetylacetonate, etc.).

It is possible to show the occurrence of reaction 1 in aromatic solvent as well. This can be easily demonstrated by operating at a low Al/Co

* Reaction 1 is valid not only for Co compounds, but also for other transition metal compounds. Thus the reaction between AlR_2Cl and $Ti(OR)_4$ or $V(acac)_3$ gives β-$TiCl_3$ or VCl_2, respectively.

ratio and at a relatively high concentration of cobalt compound. Under these conditions at room temperature, a blue complex precipitate is formed containing Al, Co, Cl, and the groups initially bonded to the Co. The Co/Cl ratio is close to 1:2 in the precipitate. After separating the precipitate by filtration and treating it with THF, a blue solution is obtained which, after concentrating to a small volume, yields $CoCl_2$·THF crystals (59,61).

Under the conditions normally used for catalyst preparation (i.e., at 1–5 mg Co per liter of solution and at Al/Co ratios of about 30 or more), the $CoCl_2$ formed according to reaction 1 is rapidly alkylated by $AlEt_2Cl$ to give an unstable species Co(Et)Cl. The latter is transformed into Co^{I}–Cl by homolytic cleavage of the Co—C bond. The Co compound is stabilized in valency I by complexation with the Al compound.

Alkylation is indicated by gas evolution (mainly ethane*) observed in the reaction between $AlEt_2Cl$ and the cobalt compound.

The formation of a species containing Co(I) is indicated by the following facts:

1. if THF is added to the catalyst solution (preferably if the latter is prepared at a high Co concentration, about 10–20 mg Co/liter) the simultaneous formation of metallic Co and $CoCl_2$ is observed. Evidently the THF destroys the complexation between Co and Al and liberates the species containing Co(I), which disproportionates into metallic Co and $CoCl_2$

2. in the reaction between $AlEt_2Cl$ and $Co(acac)_2$ in benzene solution saturated with hexamethylbenzene† (HMB) it is possible to show the formation of the cation

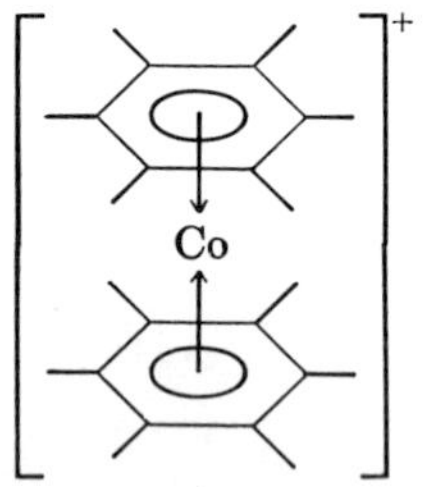

* The ethyl radicals formed by cleavage of the Co—C_2H_5 bond should give rise to butane or an equimolar mixture of ethylene and ethane. However, ethane is the major constituent of the gas evolved. The reason for this is not clear. Probably hydrogen is abstracted from the solvent by the ethyl radical, but this point is still to be clarified.

† Since HMB is a solid (mp 166°), it cannot be used alone as a solvent.

which can be precipitated by anions such as BPh_4^-, BF_4^-, etc. (62). An analogous complex containing benzene coordinated to Co could not be isolated owing to its low stability. It should be pointed out that HMB is a much stronger electron donor than benzene; therefore it coordinates to a metal more strongly than benzene.

The facts described above concerning the reaction between aluminum alkyl halides and Co compounds were confirmed by obtaining a Co (I)-containing crystalline complex that can polymerize butadiene by itself, i.e., without the addition of an aluminum alkyl (59). If equimolecular amounts of $AlPh_2Cl$, $AlPhCl_2$, and $CoCl_2$ are refluxed in benzene for 10–20 min and then filtered while hot, a light yellow solution is obtained. This solution exhibits catalytic activity for the polymerization of butadiene to *cis*-1,4 polymer. Upon cooling this solution, yellow brown crystals of the composition $(AlCl_2Ph)_2{\cdot}Co^ICl{\cdot}0{\cdot}5C_6H_6$ precipitate. These crystals, when dissolved in benzene, polymerize butadiene.

In conclusion: when an aluminum alkyl (or aryl) chloride and a cobalt compound are reacted in a hydrocarbon solvent, a catalytic complex is formed which contains the species Co^ICl complexed with the Al compound.

b. Catalysts from Al Trihalides and Co Compounds. Co catalysts which are obtained not from Al alkyl chlorides, but from Al trihalides are also known. These catalysts can be prepared, according to some authors, from $AlCl_3$, metallic Al and $CoCl_2$, in benzene (63). By heating the suspension, an oil is formed which appears to be slightly soluble in benzene. The solution of this oil, particularly in the presence of thiophene, exhibits catalytic activity for the *cis*-1,4 polymerization of butadiene.

It has been demonstrated by E. O. Fischer (64) that the complex obtained in this reaction can be formulated as

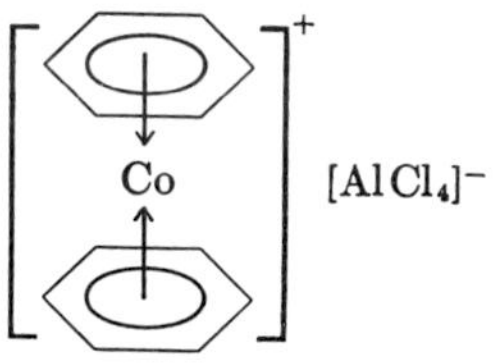

Therefore it contains monovalent Co just as the complex obtained from $AlEt_2Cl$ and $CoCl_2$. By taking into account that the $[(arene)_2Co]^+$ cation is formed in the reaction between $AlEt_2Cl$ and a Co compound in an aromatic solvent, as stated above, the only difference between the complex obtained from $AlEt_2Cl + CoCl_2$ and $AlCl_3 + Al + CoCl_2 + C_6H_6$, respectively, seems to be that the former contains the anion $AlEt_2Cl_2^-$, and the latter the anion $AlCl_4^-$.

More recently, however, it was shown that the simple complex obtained from $AlCl_3$ and $CoCl_2$ (65) (or other Co compounds such as $Co(acac)_2$ (66)), in the absence of Al, can yield *cis*-1,4 polybutadiene. The complex formed from $AlCl_3$ and $CoCl_2$, which was formulated as $CoCl_2{\cdot}2AlCl_3$, is active, both in benzene and in cyclohexane (65). In complexes of this type the Co present is divalent. Consequently, the existence of Co(I) is not a necessary condition for the formation of a catalyst for the *cis*-1,4 polymerization of butadiene.

During the discussion on the mechanism of polymerization by Co catalysts (Sec. I–F-1), attempts will be made to show that the two types of catalysts, i.e., those containing Co(I) and Co(II), respectively, may belong to the same class.

D. Synthesis of the Polymers

1. *Butadiene Polymers*

By the use of anionic catalysts based on transition metals it has been possible to obtain from butadiene all four conceivable types of stereoregular polymers, i.e., *trans*-1,4; *cis*-1,4, 1,2 isotactic, and 1,2 syndiotactic.

In addition to these highly regular, and hence highly crystalline or crystallizable, stereoisomers, several other polybutadienes have been obtained with less regular structures. These polymers show only a low degree of crystallinity or are amorphous by x-rays.

Some of the polybutadienes obtained by transition metal catalysts have practical significance. The most important of these is the *cis*-1,4 polybutadiene, which exhibits excellent elastomeric properties.

The preparation of stereoregular polymers of butadiene by coordination catalysts based on transition metals will now be reviewed.

a. *Cis*-1,4 Polybutadiene. The first announcement of the synthesis of a polybutadiene having at least 85% *cis*-1,4 content occurred in a patent of April 1956 (47). A later patent of July 1956 reported the isolation of polybutadienes with high *cis*-1,4 structure obtained by the $AlEt_3$–$TiCl_4$ catalyst system. These high *cis*-1,4 polybutadienes crystallized on stretching at room temperature (67). The structure of crystalline *cis*-1,4 polybutadiene, determined on samples obtained by the $AlEt_3$–$TiCl_4$ system, was published shortly thereafter (68).

New catalyst systems for *cis*-1,4 polybutadiene, based on metals of group VIII, i.e., Co, Ni, Pd, Pt, were discovered later (53–55, 69–72). Among these catalysts, those based on Co seem to be the most important.

In this section we will examine the *cis*-1,4 polymerization of butadiene by the following systems: (1) $AlEt_3$–$TiCl_4$; (2) AlR_3–TiI_4 and related systems; and (3) cobalt catalysts.

Only the systems 2 and 3 are of industrial interest.

(1) Polybutadienes by the AlR_3–$TiCl_4$ *Systems.* A vast patent literature exists on the polymerization of butadiene by $TiCl_4$-based catalysts (23,41,67,74,80); however, this topic has been examined in but a few papers (27,81,82).

Catalysts prepared by gradual addition of AlR_3 to $TiCl_4$ become active at an Al/Ti ratio of about 0.5. Upon increasing this ratio, the yield of polymer increases rapidly, reaches a maximum at a ratio of about 1, then decreases rapidly (27,82). At an $AlR_3/TiCl_4$ ratio of 3, only a small amount of solid polymer is obtained, together with a large amount of oily products.

The nature of the polybutadienes obtained depends on the $AlR_3/TiCl_4$ ratio (Table II).

1. At an Al/Ti ratio of ~0.5, a powder is obtained which exhibits a much lower than theoretical degree of unsaturation due to cyclization and crosslinking; however, x-ray analysis shows a low degree crystallinity due to *trans*-1,4 sequences. This powder is practically insoluble in benzene and other hydrocarbon solvents.
2. The product obtained at an Al/Ti ratio of about 1 (at this ratio the system is actually $AlR_2Cl + \beta\text{-}TiCl_3$) is an amorphous rubbery polymer consisting of *cis*-1,4 and *trans*-1,4 units, with a very low percentage of 1,2 units (max. 4%). These polymers have the highest *cis*-1,4 content obtainable with this system at different Al/Ti ratios. Their composition was at first reported to be (27): 50–60% *cis*-1,4; 35–45% *trans*-1,4; 2–4% 1,2. These data later proved to be incorrect because of an inaccurate analytical method. The authors of this chapter reexamined the composition of these products by a more precise analytical method (83) and obtained the following values: 75–78% *cis*-1,4; 21–23% *trans*-1,4; 1–2% 1,2. These data are in agreement with those reported by other authors (82). Fractionation of these products is of interest and can be performed by a rapid method as follows: the polymer is dissolved in benzene (in which it is 90–95% soluble) until a solution with a maximum concentration of about 2% is obtained. The benzene solution is

TABLE II
Polymerization of Butadiene by the $Al(C_2H_5)_3$–$TiCl_4$ System in *n*-heptane[a]

Run no.	Catalyst[b] $TiCl_4$ mmoles	Catalyst[b] Al/Ti molar ratio	Monomer, g	Polymerization Temp., °C	Polymer g	Polymer IR analysis, % cis	Polymer IR analysis, % trans	Polymer IR analysis, % 1,2	Polymer X-ray examination
1	10	1.1	100	0	35[c]	75	18	2	Amorphous
2	10	1	100	0	34[e]	78	21.5	1.5	Amorphous
3	10	1.3	100	0	38[e]	78	21	1	Amorphous
4	20	2.0	150	13	60[d]	42	51	7	Crystalline[e]
5	20	2.1	150	13	56[d]	46	48	6	Crystalline[e]
6	20	2.3	150	15	63[d]	41	50	9	Crystalline[e]

[a] Solvent 400 ml; polymerization time: 40 min.

[b] Catalyst prepared by introducing slowly a solution of $Al(C_2H_5)_3$ in 50 ml of *n*-heptane into a solution of $TiCl_4$ in 350 ml of *n*-heptane, with stirring (time of addition about 20 min). In runs 1–3 liquid monomer was added about 5 min after the addition of $Al(C_2H_5)_3$ was completed. In runs 4–6 the solid catalyst was washed twice by decantation, then fresh *n*-heptane was added to reach the original volume, then liquid monomer was introduced.

[c] The polymer was fractionated by dissolving in benzene and reprecipitating with MEK. After two dissolutions and reprecipitations, the MEK insoluble fraction analyzed as follows: *cis* 87–89%; *trans* 9–14%; 1,2 ~ 1%.

[d] About 55% of the product is soluble in boiling diethyl ether. IR analysis of the diethyl ether extract, after precipitation with MEK: *cis* 85–86%; *trans* 13–16%; 1,2 ~ 1%. IR analysis of the residue after ether extraction: *trans* 90–95%.

[e] Crystallinity due to *trans*-1,4 polybutadiene.

poured into a large excess of methyl ethyl ketone (MEK), which precipitates about 80% of the dissolved polymer. This product contains 82–83% *cis*-1,4 units and about 1% 1,2 units. After two further dissolutions in benzene and reprecipitations with MEK, a product is obtained containing 87% *cis*-1,4 units and $<1\%$ 1,2 units. These results show that the products obtained at an $AlEt_3/TiCl_4$ ratio of ~ 1 consist of macromolecules with different *cis*-1,4 contents. Some of them may be even 90% *cis*-1,4. Macromolecules with lower *cis*-1,4 contents are of lower molecular weight and therefore can be removed with MEK. It is of interest that 85–87% *cis*-1,4 polybutadienes isolated by MEK precipitations have final melting temperatures slightly below 0° (about −2°C), that is, only a few degrees below the melting temperature of 99–100% *cis*-1,4 polybutadiene. The reason for this may be that long sequences of exclusively *cis*-1,4 units are present in the polymers prepared with $TiCl_4$.

3. The polymers obtained at an $AlEt_3/TiCl_4$ ratio of 2–2.2 are harder than those obtained at a ratio of 1. According to recent methods of IR analysis (83), they have the following composition: 40–42% *cis*-1,4; 56–58% *trans*-1,4; 3–4% 1,2. X-ray analysis reveals that the polymers have the crystallinity typical for *trans*-1,4 polybutadiene (27). About 35% of the product is extractable with boiling diethyl ether; this fraction is amorphous by x-rays and consists of about 80% *cis*-1,4 units. The residue after the ether extraction is a fibrous mass, which on IR analysis appears to consist of about 90% *trans*-1,4 units.

The ether extractable amorphous fraction can be purified by dissolutions in benzene and reprecipitations with MEK, as mentioned above. By this route, fractions with 91–92% *cis*-1,4 content were isolated, having melting temperatures between 0 and −1°C. These fractions contain about 2% 1,2 units.

In regard to the composition of the crude polymers Mayer and Lehr's (82) and our data are in agreement. On the other hand, Gaylord et al. (81) reported different data. These authors found maximum activity at an $AlR_3/TiCl_4$ ratio of about 2.8. Furthermore, the product obtained at an $AlR_3/TiCl_4$ ratio of ~ 1 was reported to be crystalline *trans*-1,4. This result seems rather strange in view of the fact that, as is shown in Sec. I-D-2a, at this ratio, the AlR_3–$TiCl_4$ system yields a *cis*-1,4 polymer also from isoprene. It seems improbable that the same catalyst system

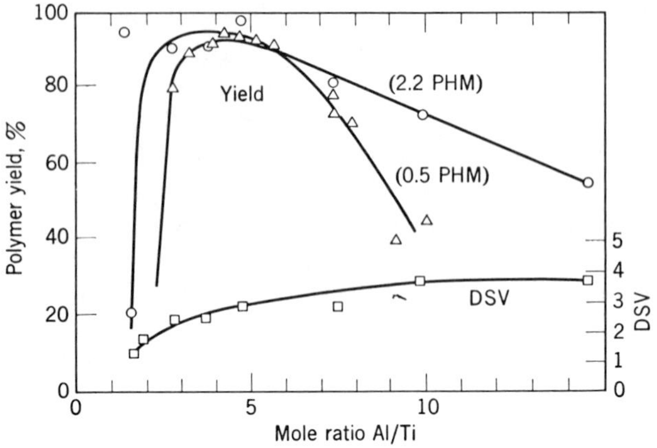

Fig. 1. Yield and dilute solution viscosity of polybutadienes prepared with the $Al(i\text{-}C_4H_9)_3$–TiI_4 catalyst. □ and ○ from Ref. 41; △ from Ref. 42. (Phm is catalyst concentration in parts by weight per 100 parts of butadiene.)

(which is actually $AlEt_2Cl$ + β-$TiCl_3$) would yield *trans*-1,4 polymers from butadiene, and *cis*-1,4 polymers from isoprene.

Polybutadienes by Titanium-Based Catalysts Containing Iodine. The characteristics of these catalysts differ from both those prepared from $TiCl_4$ described in the previous paragraph, and those prepared from Co compounds, which will be described later. In addition to several patents (45,47,84,85), various papers have been published on the polymerization of butadiene by catalysts from TiI_4 and analogous systems (42,82,86). Practically identical results are obtained by catalysts prepared from TiI_4, $TiCl_2I_2$, or $TiClI_3$.

The main features of these catalysts are as follows:

1. The catalysts become active at an AlR_3/Ti ratio of about 1 or slightly above. Yields increase rapidly upon increasing the Al/Ti ratio until a maximum is reached, then they decrease very slowly (Fig. 1). The maximum is at a ratio of 1.5–3 according to some authors (82), and around 5 according to others (42).

It should be remembered that in the case of the AlR_3–$TiCl_4$ systems the highest activity is found (24,27) at a Al/Ti ratio of about 1 (corresponding to the formation of β-$TiCl_3$); moreover in the iodine systems the activity vs Al/Ti ratio curves show a narrower peak and the decrease in activity with increasing Al/Ti ratio is much faster than in the $AlR_3/TiCl_4$ systems.

2. The *cis* content of the polymers depends on the concentration of the catalyst, and increases with decreasing concentration. At low catalyst concentrations (of the order of 1–2 mg-atoms of Ti/100 g C_4H_6, in benzene containing 10–15% of C_4H_6 by weight) the *cis* content may reach 94–95%. It does not seem that higher *cis* contents can be reached with TiI_4-based or similar catalysts. It is interesting to compare this behavior with that of the catalysts from $TiCl_4$ (Al/Ti $\sim$1), in which the *cis* content is independent of the catalyst concentration over a wide range.

3. The *cis* content is the highest at Al/Ti ratios corresponding to maximum catalyst activity, then it decreases slightly with increasing Al/Ti ratio, while simultaneously the percentage of 1,2 units increases (about 4% at an Al/Ti ratio of 5, about 10 at an Al/Ti ratio of 10). For polybutadienes obtained with $TiCl_4$, the decrease in the *cis* content with increasing Al/Ti ratio occurs considerably faster.

4. At constant monomer concentration, polymer molecular weight is highly influenced by catalyst concentration: it rapidly decreases with an increase in catalyst concentration. Depending on the conditions, polymers may have molecular weights from a few tens of thousands to about one million.

The various ternary systems exhibit similar characteristics. Catalyst activity as well as the stereospecificity vary with the molar ratio of the catalyst components, and only certain combinations produce good stereospecificity, good activity, and high molecular weights.

In the case of the ternary system $Al(i\text{-}C_4H_9)_3$–I_2–$TiCl_4$, the optimum composition was found to be (42), in mole %: $Al(i\text{-}C_4H_9)_3$, 70–75; I_2, 15–25; $TiCl_4$, 5–12. In the case of the system $AlEt_3$–$AlEt_2I$–$TiCl_4$ the optimum composition is (48) at molar ratios of 4:4:1. Considering that in the former system I_2 reacts with AlR_3 to give AlR_2I (42), it can be seen why these two compositions are equivalent.

There is some literature concerning the polymerizations by metal hydride catalysts (48–50,87). Ternary systems from $TiCl_4$ + AlI_3 and one of the following compounds: $AlHCl_2 \cdot O(C_2H_5)_2$, $AlH_2N(CH_3)_2$, $AlH_2Cl \cdot N(CH_3)_3$, $AlH_3 \cdot N(CH_3)_3$ are particularly stereospecific and active.

The *cis* content of the polymers obtained by these systems is reported to be about 95% (49,87).

It is of interest that the systems $LiAlH_4$–$TiCl_2I_2$ (Al/Ti $\geq$5) or $LiAlH_4$–I_2–$TiCl_4$ (I_2/Ti $\sim$ 0.5; Al/Ti $\geq$8) in benzene, at room temperature or slightly below, yield 93–94% *cis*-1,4 polybutadienes (50). This seems to be in contrast to some patents (41,88), according to which these catalyst systems yield *trans*-1,4 (and not *cis*) polybutadienes or polyisoprenes. This discrepancy is due to the fact that in the patents quoted an ether suspension of $LiAlH_4$ is used and the presence of ether causes the different stereospecificity. This fact will be further discussed in Section I-F, dealing with the polymerization mechanism.

As pointed out earlier, all Ti catalysts containing iodine are equivalent because the final products of the catalyst forming reaction contain all the iodine bonded to Ti. However, this equivalence can be explained only by assuming that halogen exchange among the catalyst components is faster than polymerization initiation, even with catalysts prepared in the presence of monomer (82).

The true nature of the catalyst formation in these systems is not yet clearly understood. The catalyst forming reaction yields a precipitate. Separately, the solid and the liquid phases do not exhibit any catalytic activity (42,82). This may suggest that these catalysts are heterogeneous. Evidently active heterogeneous catalytic species are present in the systems from TiI_4. For instance, the $Al(i\text{-}C_4H_9)_2I$–TiI_3 system which is moderately active and yields 85–90% *cis*-1,4 polymer, seems to be heterogeneous (82).

However, there is also evidence for the presence of active homogeneous complexes. By treating $AlEt_2I$ with $TiCl_3 \cdot \frac{1}{3}AlCl_3$ (obtained by reduction of $TiCl_4$ with Al) for 15 min at 20 to 50°C a clear solution is obtained which, after cooling and filtering, contains from 2 to 4% of the initial Ti. This solution polymerizes butadiene (48) in high yield to a polymer with up to 90% *cis* content. In addition, it has been reported (49) that the $AlHCl_2 \cdot O(C_2H_5)_2$–$AlI_3$–$TiCl_4$ system is apparently soluble when prepared in the presence of monomer.

Most probably, the catalytic species responsible for the formation of high *cis*-1,4 polymer (94–95%), in the case of Ti systems containing iodine, are homogeneous.

Two features of the polymerization support this conclusion:

1. The *cis* content of the polymer increases with decreasing Ti concentration

2. The molecular weight increases greatly with decreasing Ti concentration

These aspects are similar to those observed with the homogeneous Co catalysts, which will be discussed in the next paragraph. In contrast, these aspects differ considerably from those observed when using the heterogeneous $TiCl_4$ catalysts. The homogeneous nature of the polymerization is also indicated by kinetic studies carried out with the $Al(i\text{-}C_4H_9)_3 \cdot O(i\text{-}C_3H_5)_2$–$TiI_4$ system. The termination was found (86) to be a bimolecular process which is conceivable only in a homogeneous system.

Polybutadienes by Co Catalysts. Catalysts from Aluminum Alkyl Halides and Co Compounds. The first catalysts were prepared from heterogeneous Co compounds ($CoCl_2$, CoS, $CoCO_3$, $CoSO_4$, or $Co_3(PO_4)_2$) in combination with $AlEt_2Cl$ (51,54). In conjunction with $CoCl_2$, AlR_3 was also used (69) at a low Al/Co ratio (about 1). It soon became evident that homogeneous catalytic complexes were formed in the reaction between the alkyl aluminum and the Co compound and that AlR_2Cl was the most suitable aluminum compound for the preparation of such catalysts (51,53,55,70–73). In the system AlR_2–$CoCl_2$, Al/Co $\sim$ 1, AlR_2Cl is formed as a result of the alkylation of $CoCl_2$ by AlR_3. The only practically used Co compounds are the soluble ones.

That the Co catalysts obtained from AlR_2Cl and a Co compound are actually homogeneous is indicated by the absence of a Tyndall effect (51,89,90).

Polymerization of butadiene by the AlR_2Cl–Co compound system in benzene, yields polymers with as high as 99% or even higher *cis*-1,4 content and with molecular weights varying from about 10,000 to more than one million, depending on the experimental conditions. Co catalysts are highly stereospecific only for the polymerization of butadiene. From isoprene, they yield only about 65% *cis*-1,4 units, the remaining being predominantly 3,4 (61). From 1,3-pentadiene they give predominantly (80–90%) *cis*-1,4 polymers. This subject will be discussed later (this Section, 3b).

Since the issue of the first patents, various papers have been published on the polymerization of butadiene by Co catalysts (51,52,60, 91–94). Unfortunately, the data reported are often in disagreement. The amount of catalyst used in these polymerizations is very low (1–5 mg of Co per liter of solvent–monomer mixture) and its efficiency is influenced by electron donors, H_2O and Lewis acids. Substances of this type may be present in the solvent or in the monomer in amounts of the order of magnitude of the catalyst, and may, at least partially, be responsible for the discrepancies among the results reported by the various authors.

While the first patents and papers refer to catalyst systems obtained only from $AlEt_2Cl$ and a Co compound in an anhydrous medium, subsequent papers claim that the presence of an activator is also required. Gippin examined this particular aspect (52,92). He found that the system $AlEt_2Cl$–$CoCl_2$·py (Al/Co from 100 to 200; $CoCl_2$·py from 0.2 to 0.02 mmoles per 100 g of monomer), in benzene at about 6°C, does not yield solid polymer in 24 hr in the absence of an activator. When H_2O or O_2 was added (in amounts from 5 to 50 moles on $AlEt_2Cl$) rapid polymerization ensued and practically quantitative yields of nearly 98% *cis*-1,4 high molecular weight polybutadiene was obtained. According to Gippin, besides H_2O and O_2 other substances can also act as activators, i.e., $AlCl_3$, organic hydroperoxides, halogens, some alcohols (e.g., *t*-butyl alcohol), some organic halides (e.g., 2-chloro-ethanol, allyl chloride, isochlorobutanes), and also metallic Al. All these compounds (except metallic Al) are used in amounts corresponding to 2–10 mmoles per 20 mmoles of $AlEt_2Cl$.

It is difficult to establish whether or not the presence of an activator is absolutely necessary to obtain high molecular weight *cis*-1,4 polybutadiene with the $AlEt_2Cl$–Co compound catalyst system. This is mainly due to the fact that, unless extreme precautions are taken, trace amounts of many substances which may act as activators may be present in the solvent, in the monomer or in the reagents used to prepare the catalyst. These include H_2O, $AlEtCl_2$ (which may be present in $AlEt_2Cl$), and AlEt(OEt)Cl, which constitutes the major impurity of $AlEt_2Cl$.

Although the results obtained by the various authors in the polymerization of butadiene with Co catalysts often cannot be compared, some fundamental characteristics of this type of polymerization are now well established:

1. Conversion varies with time as shown in Fig. 2. Practically complete conversions can be obtained provided the viscosity of the solution does not become prohibitive.
2. The rate of polymerization depends on the aromatic solvent used and decreases in the order: benzene > toluene > xylene > mesitylene. In toluene, the rate is 3 to 4 times as slow as in benzene (61). The addition of hexamethylbenzene to the catalyst solution in aromatic solvent inhibits polymerization (62).
3. The Al/Co ratio does not influence stereospecificity above a mini-

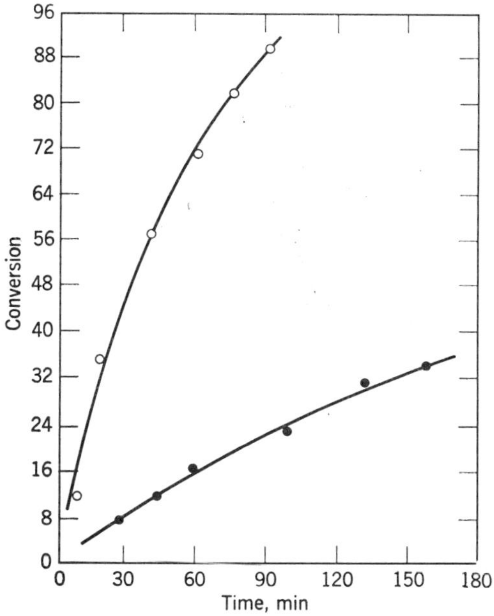

Fig. 2. Conversion vs. time curves for *cis*-1,4 polybutadiene with $AlEt_2Cl$–$Co(acac)_2$ catalyst. Solvent (sodium-dried) 250 ml (⊙ benzene; ● toluene); $AlEt_2Cl$ 2.5 ml; Co 0.5 mg; catalyst aged for 30 min at 0°C; monomer: ⊙ 10 g, ● 15 g; polymerization temperature 0°C.

mum value depending on the catalyst concentration (about 30–40 for Co concentration of 5–10 mg/liter of monomer–solvent mixture).

4. For a given set of experimental conditions, the average molecular weight of the polymers initially increases rapidly with increasing conversion; then the increase gradually becomes less rapid and, in some cases, after a certain conversion is reached, the molecular weight no longer increases and may even decrease. The behavior of the molecular weight vs amount of polymer curves depends on the nature of the solvent and on monomer concentration (Fig. 3).
5. The molecular weight increases with increasing monomer concentration (Table III and Fig. 3), while it decreases with increasing Co concentration. Zgormick et al. reported (95) that the molecular weight is approximately proportional to the inverse of [Co], at least up to $5–6 \times 10^{-4}$ moles/liter. Molecular weight, on the other hand, does not seem to be influenced by the concentration of $AlEt_2Cl$. This seems to indicate that transfer between growing

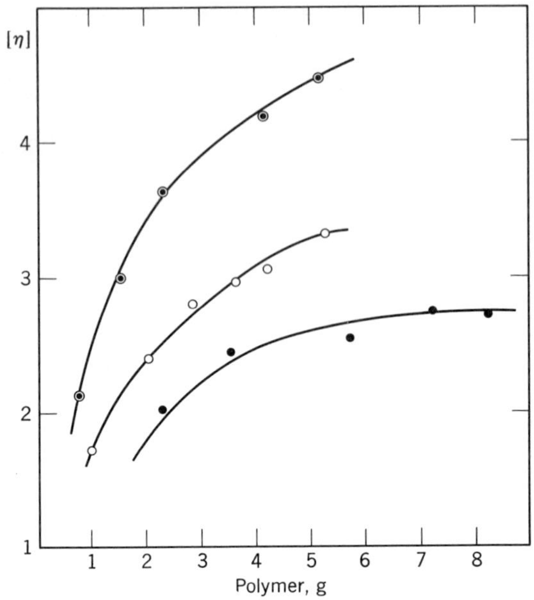

Fig. 3. Intrinsic viscosities vs. polymer curves for *cis*-1,4 polybutadiene obtained by the $AlEt_2Cl$–$Co(acac)_2$ catalyst. Solvent (sodium-dried) 250 ml (⊙, ● benzene: ○ toluene). Monomer: ⊙, ○ 20 g; ● 10 g. Other conditions as under Fig. 2.

TABLE III
Effect of Monomer Concentration on the Molecular Weight of Polybutadienes Obtained by the $Al(C_2H_5)_2Cl$–$Co(acac)_2$ System in Benzene[a] (61)

Concentration of C_4H_6 g/liter charge	Polymerization time, min	Polymer g	Polymer [η], dl g^{-1}
19.3	240	25.4	1.44
28.6	210	24.4	1.61
87	20	9.3	5.27

[a] Experimental conditions: benzene 250 ml; monomer (total amount added): 25 g; $Co(acac)_2$: 3.8×10^{-6} moles; polymerization temperature +4°C; catalysts aged for 15 min before monomer addition. The monomer concentration was kept as constant as possible by the continuous addition of fresh butadiene. Monomer consumption per unit time, under the conditions used, was known from previously determined kinetic data.

chains and $AlEt_2Cl$ is rather limited if occurring at all. On the other hand, Fig. 3 indicates that chain termination occurs. This seems to be mainly due to transfer with monomer.

6. The temperature of polymerization can be varied over a wide range, from low temperatures up to about +30°C, without influencing stereospecificity. Above about +30°C, the *cis*-1,4 content decreases, while the 1,2 content increases. The *cis* content of polymers obtained at +50°C are below 90%, and their intrinsic viscosity is less than one-half of that obtained at +5°C (51,52).
7. Monomer concentrations up to about 40 wt% do not influence the *cis* content of the polymers. At higher monomer concentrations small amounts of gel are formed and the *cis*-1,4 content decreases (52).

Various methods have been developed for regulating polymer molecular weight. This is of practical importance, since polymers of too high molecular weight are difficult to process. Hydrogen can be used as a regulator (96), as in the case of the polymerization of α-olefins. In addition to H_2, also ethylene, α-olefins, allenes (96), or some unsaturated compounds containing internal double bonds, such as cyclooctadiene (97) can be used as chain transfer agents. Data showing the influence of these agents on the molecular weight are reported in Tables IV–VI.

TABLE IV
Effect of H_2 on the Molecular Weight of *cis*-1,4 Polybutadiene Obtained by the $Al(C_2H_5)_2Cl$–$CoCl_2$·py System in Benzene[a] (96)

p_{H_2}, atm	Polymerization time, min	Conversion, %	Polymer[b] [η], dl g^{-1}	Polymer[b] mol wt[c]
0	60	99	5.50	742.000
0.39	65	100	4.17	502.000
5	60	98	2.95	316.000
10	65	100	2.65	272.000
20	60	100	1.37	109.700

[a] Experimental conditions: $Al(C_2H_5)_2Cl$, 0.036 moles; $CoCl_2$·py, 0.0925 mmoles; benzene, 1000 ml; butadiene (Phillips "pure grade"), 100 g; polymerization temp., 15°C.

[b] All the polymers obtained are reported to be at least 97.7% *cis*-1,4.

[c] Calculated from the intrinsic viscosity using the relationship $[\eta] = 3.37 \times 10^{-4} M^{0.715}$ (118).

TABLE V

Effect of Transfer Agents on the Molecular Weight of *cis*-1,4 Polybutadiene Obtained by the $Al(C_2H_5)_2Cl$–$CoCl_2$·py System in Benzene[a] (96)

$CoCl_2$ mmoles 10^3	Transfer agent mole/100 mole C_4H_6		Polymerization time, min	Conv., %	Polymer[f] [η], dl g^{-1}	Polymer[f] mol, wt[g]
92.5	C_2H_4[b]	0	60	94	5.57	759,000
92.5		0.842	60	96	4.26	519,500
92.5		2.41	65	96	2.72	282,000
92.5		5.08	60	91	1.78	156,700
90.0	C_3H_6[c]	0	60	100	5.70	776,000
90.0		72.2	60	99	3.43	389,000
90.0		137.5	70	99	2.80	292,000
77.0	C_3H_4[d]	0	75	94	6.6	968,000
77.0		0.0225	75	97	4.09	495,000
77.0		0.0930	80	98	2.63	266,000
90.0	C_4H_6[e]	0	60	100	5.95	832,000
90.0		0.090	60	98	3.12	339,000
90.0		0.233	60	96	2.10	200,000

[a] Experimental conditions: $Al(C_2H_5)_2Cl$, 0.036 moles; benzene 1000 ml; butadiene (Phillips "pure grade") 100 g; polymerization temp., 15°C.

[b] Ethylene.

[c] Propylene.

[d] Propa-1,2-diene.

[e] Buta-1,2-diene.

[f] All the polymers are reported to be at least 97% *cis*-1,4.

[g] Calculated from [η] using the relationship reported in Ref. 118.

Although the most common solvents are benzene or toluene, the use of aliphatic solvents, such as *n*-hexane, *n*-heptane or cyclohexane is mentioned in the literature (51,52). The *cis* content and the molecular weights of the polymers obtained in these solvents are lower than those obtained in benzene, although high conversions can be obtained.

The kinetics of butadiene polymerization to *cis*-1,4 polymer by Co catalysts in aromatic solvent was studied by several authors (52,60,94,95). It seems established that the polymerization is first order with respect to both monomer and Co. According to some authors, however, this first order dependence with respect to Co holds only for low Co concentrations (94). The activation energy of the polymerization process in toluene is reported to be about 11.86 kcal/mole (60).

Catalysts from $AlCl_3$ or $AlBr_3$ and Co Compounds. The polymerization of butadiene to *cis*-1,4 polymer by catalysts obtained from $CoCl_2$ and

TABLE VI
Effect of Cyclooctadiene on the Molecular Weight of *cis*-1,4 Polybutadiene Obtained by the $Al(C_2H_5)_2Cl$–$Co(acac)_2$ Catalyst System in Benzene (61)

$Co(acac)_2$, mmoles	Al/Co molar ratio	Benzene, ml	C_4H_6, g	COD, g	Polymeriz. time, min	Polymer g	Polymer [η]	Polymer mol wt[a]
5.8×10^{-3}	145	60	26	—	5	2.1	5.3	708,000
5.8×10^{-3}	145	60	26	0.26	10	8	2.07	193,000
5.8×10^{-3}	145	70	19.5	—	10	2.7	4.6	582,000
5.8×10^{-3}	145	70	19.5	0.21	20	9.1	1.81	160,000
5.8×10^{-3}	145	80	13	—	20	3.1	3.76	440,000
5.8×10^{-3}	145	80	13	0.18	40	8.7	2.24	215,000

[a] Determined from [η] using the relationship reported in Ref. 118.

$AlCl_3$ in the absence of aluminum alkyls, was reported by Scott et al. (63), O'Reilly et al. (180), and by Balas et al. (65). The use of catalysts from $AlBr_3$ and Co compounds other than $CoCl_2$ ($Co(acac)_2$, $CoCl_2{\cdot}2py$, $Co(acac)_3$, Co-octoate, etc.) was also described (66).

Scott's catalyst consists of a complex obtained from $CoCl_2$ and $AlCl_3$, having the formula $Co(AlCl_4)_2$. Solutions obtained by dissolving this complex in benzene polymerize butadiene. The addition of thiophene to the system (thiophene/$AlCl_3$ from 1 to about 5) before polymerization initiation, seems a necessary condition to obtain high conversions of a polymer with a *cis*-1,4 content of about 94–95%. In the absence of thiophene, tacky low polymers containing phenyl groups and having a *cis*-1,4 content of only 48–56% are obtained. However, in a subsequent paper, Balas and co-workers report that dilute solutions of the $AlCl_3$–$CoCl_2$ complex in benzene or even in cyclohexane (Al/Co molar ratio from 2.4 to about 12.5) can yield, even without addition of thiophene, polymers with high *cis*-1,4 content (~95%) and high molecular weight ([η] up to about 6.8).

In analogy with the catalysts obtained from aluminum alkyl halides and Co compounds, the catalysts obtained from $AlCl_3$ and $CoCl_2$ are highly stereospecific only for the polymerization of butadiene, and are far less stereospecific for the polymerization of isoprene.

b. *Trans*-1,4 Polybutadiene. The synthesis of a highly crystalline *trans*-1,4 butadiene polymer was first announced in a patent of March 1955 (98). The catalyst used was the heterogeneous $AlEt_3$–$\alpha TiCl_3$ system. Polymers of the same type were later obtained with hetero-

TABLE VII
Polymerization of Butadiene by Catalysts from $Al(C_2H_5)_3$ or $Al(C_2H_5)_2Cl$ and Vanadium Chlorides[a] (103,104)

V halide, mmoles		Aluminum compound, mmoles	Polymeriz. temp., °C	Polymeriz. time, hr	Polymer g	IR analysis cis, %	IR analysis trans, %	IR analysis 1,2, %	Diethyl ether extract,[c] %
VCl_3	3.18	6.36	25	19	26.8	—	99	1	1.8
	3.18	31.8	25	15	23.7	—	99	1	1.8
$VOCl_3$[b]	3.4	3.74	15	6	6.2	1	96	3	9.8
	3.4	6.8	15	8	18.5	1	94	5	15.6
	3.4	17	15	7	12.4	1	95	4	15.5
VCl_4[b]	3.4	5.1	15	3	15	1	97	2	7.5
	2.1	4.2	15	2	9.2	1	95	4	12.9
	2.1	6.3	15	2	14.5	1	95	4	11.6
	2.1	10.5	15	3	14	1	95	4	12

[a] Experimental conditions: solvent (*n*-heptane) 100 ml; monomer (Phillips 99%) 50 g.

[b] Catalyst prepared by introducing slowly a solution of $AlEt_3$ in *n*-heptane into a solution of VCl_4 or $VOCl_3$ in the same solvent, with stirring.

[c] Amorphous by x-ray examination. The residue after diethyl ether extraction contains 98–99% *trans*-1,4 units and has a final melting temperature of about 145°C.

geneous catalysts from $TiCl_4$ (23,27,88), TiI_4 (47), VCl_4 (76), $VOCl_3$ (99), and VCl_3 (99). More recently, 99–100% *trans*-1,4 polybutadienes were also obtained with homogeneous systems prepared from compounds of V (100) or of metals of the VIIIth group (61,102).

(*1*) *Heterogeneous Catalysts.* The most stereospecific system for the synthesis of *trans*-1,4 polybutadiene (and of *trans*-1,4 polydiolefins in general) is probably that from aluminum trialkyl and VCl_3 (103). This catalyst system yields products (Table VII) which, even in the crude state, consist of 98–99% *trans*-1,4 units. The amorphous fraction (extractable with diethyl ether) is of the order of about 2% in polymerizations carried out at room temperature or below. The residue after the ether extraction consists of 99–100% *trans*-1,4 units; vinyl groups are hardly detectable while *cis*-1,4 units seem to be completely absent.

The catalysts from VCl_4 or $VOCl_3$, combined with either AlR_3 (Al/V = 1.5–3) or AlR_2Cl (Al/V = about 5–10) are also highly stereospecific (104). The products obtained by these catalysts contain a larger amorphous fraction (up to about 10%) than the products from VCl_3 catalysts

(Table VII). However, if only the heterogeneous phase of the catalyst is used, after filtration and resuspension in fresh *n*-heptane, polymers are obtained that contain a lower amount of amorphous fraction and that differ only slightly from the products obtained by VCl_3-based catalysts. The catalysts obtained from VCl_4 or $VOCl_3$ give much higher polymerization rate than those obtained from VCl_3.

The catalysts from Ti halides are less stereospecific than those from V for the synthesis of *trans*-1,4 polybutadiene or *trans*-1,4 polydiolefins in general. The system AlR_3–$TiCl_4$, Al/Ti about 0.5, yields *trans*-1,4 polymers of low crystallinity, (23,27). Moreover, the degree of unsaturation is considerably lower than the theoretical one, due to cyclization or crosslinking. The same system, at an Al/Ti ratio of about 2, gives a mixture of amorphous (predominantly *cis*-1,4) and crystalline (predominantly *trans*-1,4) products. The *trans*-1,4 content of the latter, which can be isolated by removing the amorphous fraction with diethyl ether, is 90–95%.

Catalysts obtained from violet $TiCl_3$ are more stereospecific than those from $TiCl_4$. However, the polymers obtained with the former catalysts also contain considerable amounts of an ether-extractable amorphous fraction. The amorphous fraction can vary from about 25 to 50%, depending on the type of $TiCl_3$ used and on the polymerization conditions (38). In general, the amorphous fraction increases with increasing polymerization temperature. In runs carried out at room temperature with $TiCl_3$ prepared by reduction of $TiCl_4$ with H_2, at an Al/Ti ratio of about 1–5, polymers are obtained whose IR analysis indicates 70–88% *trans*-1,4, 3–10% *cis*-1,4, and 15–20% 1,2. About 35% of the polymer is soluble in diethyl ether. The residue after the ether extraction contains 90 to 95% *trans*-1,4 units, and shows a fair degree of crystallinity.

According to patents, predominantly *trans*-1,4 polymers of butadiene and of isoprene can also be obtained with the $LiAlH_4$–$TiCl_4$ or $LiAlH_4$–I_2–$TiCl_4$ systems (41,88). These products are probably mixtures of macromolecules with different *trans*-1,4 contents, some of which are able to crystallize. Such catalysts yield *trans*-1,4 polymers only when diethyl ether solutions or suspensions of $LiAlH_4$ are used. In the absence of ether they give predominantly *cis*-1,4 polymers.

(2) Homogeneous Catalysts. Various homogeneous catalysts are known that can give *trans*-1,4 polymers from butadiene. One of these is the system obtained by the reaction between $AlEt_2Cl$ and a soluble V compound, such as $V(acac)_3$, or complexes of VCl_3 with Lewis bases, e.g., $VCl_3 \cdot 3THF$ (100). A large excess of $AlEt_2Cl$ (Al/V molar ratio of 20–50 or even higher) is usually employed in these systems. They yield poly-

TABLE VIII

Polymerization of Butadiene, Isoprene, and 1,3 Pentadiene by the Homogeneous System $Al(C_2H_5)_2Cl$–$VCl_3 \cdot 3THF$[a] (100)

No.	Monomer	g	$VCl_3 \cdot 3C_4H_8O$, moles	Al/V molar ratio	Temperature, °C	Polymeriz. time, min	Polymer g	Polymer $[\eta]$[j] dl g^{-1}	Polymer IR exam	Polymer X-ray exam
1	Butadiene[b]	15	8×10^{-5}	30	0	30	3.6	1.5[k]	99–100% *trans*-1,4	Crystalline
2	Butadiene[b]	15	14×10^{-5}	50	−20	60	6	1.71[k]		
3	Butadiene[b]	5	11×10^{-4}	30	0	7	0.1	0.3		
4	Butadiene[b]	15	8×10^{-5}[c]	30	0	1200	Traces	—		
5	Butadiene[b]	15	8×10^{-5}[d]	30	0	1200	2.5	—		
6	Pentadiene[e]	12	4×10^{-5}	50	−15	900	2.2	0.3	*trans*-1,4 + 1,2	Amorphous
7	Pentadiene[f]	12	4×10^{-5}	30	−15	900	7	1.87		
8	Pentadiene[g]	10	4×10^{-5}	50	−15	900	6.2	1.		
9	Isoprene[h]	15	8×10^{-5}	30	−15	1440	0.1	—	*trans*-1,4 (95%)	Crystalline
10	Isoprene[i]	20	8×10^{-5}	30	−15	1800	0.4	0.3		

[a] Solvent toluene 100 ml.
[b] Phillips "pure grade" 99%.
[c] Catalyst aged for 3 days at 20°C before introducing the monomer.
[d] Catalyst aged for 3 days at −70°C before introducing the monomer.
[e] Product of Houdry Process Corp., 76% *trans* isomer.
[f] From decomposition of the sulfone; 99% *trans* isomer.
[g] Pure trans isomer, obtained by preparative gas chromatography.
[h] Phillips "polymerization grade" 99%.
[i] ~99.9% pure, obtained by gas chromatography.
[j] Determined in toluene at 30°C.
[k] Determined on the fraction soluble in toluene at 30°C.

butadienes with 99–100% *trans*-1,4 content (Table VIII) which are highly crystalline by x-rays. However, their molecular weight is lower than that of polymers obtained by VCl_3, VCl_4, and $VOCl_3$ catalysts. Polymerizations with catalysts prepared from $AlEt_2Cl$ and V compounds must be carried out at low temperatures, otherwise catalyst activity is rapidly deterioriating.

Crystalline polybutadienes with 97–99% *trans*-1,4 structures were also obtained with Co or Ni catalysts.

As discussed above the $AlEt_2Cl$–Co compound systems in benzene yield *cis*-1,4 polybutadienes. If triethyl- or trimethylamine is added to these systems, *trans*-1,4 polybutadiene is obtained (105). Thus the $AlEt_2Cl$/Co octoate/NEt_3 system, at a molar ratio of 10/1/0 gives 95% *cis*-1,4 polymer; at a ratio of 10/1/7.4 it gives 36% *cis*, 24% *trans*, 40% 1,2 polymer; at a ratio of 10/1/8.4 it gives 95% *trans* and 5% 1,2 polymer.

Polybutadienes with 97–99% *trans*-1,4 structure can also be obtained with the $AlEt_3$–$Co(acac)_2$ or $AlEt_2Cl$–$Co(acac)_2$ systems in THF solvent (61). The reaction between AlR_3 and $Co(acac)_2$ in THF gives rapidly metallic Co. However, if the reaction is carried out in the presence of monomer at 0°C or below, a *trans*-1,4 polymer is formed in low yields.

The synthesis of highly crystalline *trans*-1,4 polybutadiene by π-allyl-Ni-I has recently been reported (102). Some data concerning these polymerizations are shown in Table IX.

c. 1,2 Polybutadienes. (*1*) *1,2 Syndiotactic Polybutadiene.* The synthesis of a crystalline 1,2 syndiotactic polybutadiene was first reported in a patent of 1955 (106). Homogeneous catalysts obtained from $AlEt_3$ and either an acetylacetonate or an alcoholate of Ti, V or Cr (but only under particular conditions that will be specified later) were used. Later, it was observed that many other halogen free compounds of these metals (complexes with CO, isonitriles, nitriles, pyridines, or other Lewis bases) yield, in combination with an aluminum trialkyl, seemingly homogeneous catalysts which give 1,2 syndiotactic polybutadienes. Even some chlorinated compounds (e.g., $MoCl_5$) produce, in combination with AlR_3, catalysts yielding 1,2 syndiotactic polybutadienes (61).

A detailed study of the polymerization of butadiene by the $AlEt_3$–V-$(acac)_3$ system has been published (107). This catalyst combination yields macromolecules with varying degree of stereoregularity. The products can be separated by successive extractions with different solvents into amorphous or slightly crystalline fractions (soluble in boiling

TABLE IX
Polymerization of Butadiene by π-allyl Nickel Iodide (102,61)

					Polymerization product							
					Solid					Oil		
						IR analysis					IR analysis	
No.	Allyl Ni iodide, moles × 10^{-3}	Solvent, type	ml	Butadiene, g	g	*trans*-1,4, %	1,2, %	$\bar{M}_n$	*Tm*	mg	*trans*-1,4, %	1,2, %
1	0.4	Benzene	30	5	2.5	97.6	2.4	4016	125	70	94	6
2	0.25	Dioxane	30	7	1	97.7	2.3	3650	118	30	91	9
3	1	Ethanol	25	3	0.6	97	3.0	1900	95	100	90	10
4	0.45	THF	35	6	3.0	98	2.0	3710	120	30	94	6
5	0.3	Pentane	35	8	0.5	95	5.0	2500	100	80	90	10
6	0.5	Diethylether	30	9	0.5	94.7	5.3	1800	92	60	89.5	10.5

TABLE X
Polymerization of Butadiene by the $Al(C_2H_5)_3$–$V(acac)_3$ Catalyst System[a] (107)

Al/V molar ratio	Time of aging of the catalyst, min	Monomer,[b] g	Polymer g	IR analysis cis, %	IR analysis trans, %	IR analysis 1,2, %	Diethyl ether extract,[c] %
3.5	2	30	4.1	12.5	5.5	82	99
4	2	30	13.2	14	5	81	89
6	2	30	10.2	16	4	80	71
6	60	30	10.1	14	6	80	71
6	120	30	10.35	14	5	81	63.5
6	300	30	10.0	13	4	83	60
8	2	30	9.3	10	5	85	64
10	2	30	8.6	12.5	4.5	83	59
10	60	50	8.5	11	3	86	48
10	120	50	7.6	11	4	85	45
10	180	50	7.0	12	5	83	39.4
30	2	30	8.7	11	3	86	59

[a] Experimental conditions: $V(acac)_3$ mmoles, 1.42; solvent (benzene), 80 ml; time and temp. of polymerization: 16 hr at 15°C.
[b] From decomposition of the sulfone: >99.9% pure.
[c] Amorphous or slightly crystalline by x-rays. Residue after ether extraction: crystalline by x-rays; melting temp., 156°C; [η] (in toluene at 30°C) 2 dl g^{-1} (determined on the fraction soluble at 30°C); IR analysis: about 95–97% 1,2.

diethyl ether) and highly crystalline fractions (residue after diethyl ether extraction). Both the Al/V ratio and catalyst aging influence stereospecificity (Table X).

The catalyst from $AlEt_3$ and either $VO(OR)_3$ or $VO(acac)_2$ give analogous results to those obtained with the catalysts from $V(acac)_3$ (61).

Catalysts obtained from $AlEt_3$ and $Ti(OR)_4$ are less stereospecific than those obtained from V (108). Furthermore, they tend to give partially crosslinked products especially at high conversions, consequently, they are of little utility for preparative purposes. Among the Ti catalysts good stereospecificity is shown by the system obtained from $Ti[N(C_2H_5)_2]_4$ and $AlH_2N(CH_3)_2$ (109).

Catalysts showing good stereospecificity for the synthesis of 1,2 syndiotactic polybutadiene have been obtained from $AlEt_3$ and various molybdenum compounds i.e., $MoO_2(OR)_2$, $MoO_2(acac)_2$, $Mo(acac)_3$, and $MoCl_5$. The crystalline fraction (residue after diethyl ether extraction) can be as high as 80% (61).

It has been reported recently that 1,2 syndiotactic polybutadiene can be synthetized with catalysts obtained from soluble or insoluble Co compounds ($CoSO_4$, $CoCl_2$, $Co_3(PO_4)_2$, Co-stearate, $CoCl_2 \cdot 2py$, $Co(acac)_2$, etc.). As discussed in Section I-D-1a these Co compounds give, after reaction with AlR_2Cl, catalysts for the *cis*-1,4 polymerization of butadiene. With AlR_3, the same Co compounds give homogeneous catalysts which yield 1,2 syndiotactic polymers (110). In modifications of these catalysts, the reaction product of $AlEt_3$ and H_2O (Al/H_2O ratio = 1:0.5) or of $AlEt_3$ and a primary amine such as aniline (Al/amine ratio = 1:0.5) is used as organoaluminum compound (111). It is believed that in these reactions $Et_2{-}Al{-}O{-}Al{-}Et_2$ and $Et_2{-}Al{-}N(C_6H_5){-}Al{-}Et_2$ are formed, respectively.

The polymers obtained with the above Co systems (either from $AlEt_3$ or from the reaction product of $AlEt_3$ and H_2O or an amine) contain a small amount of amorphous (max. 10%) fraction. The residue after diethyl ether extraction is a highly crystalline white powder containing almost exclusively 1,2 units. Table XI reports data concerning the polymerization of butadiene by the homogeneous systems prepared from $CoCl_2 \cdot 2py$ and either $AlEt_3$ or the reaction product of $AlEt_3$ and H_2O.

The present authors reexamined the polymerization of butadiene by the $AlEt_3$–$Co(acac)_2$ system, but were unable to repeat the results reported in the literature. Probably the formation of 1,2 syndiotactic polybutadiene by the above system requires particular conditions, which do not seem to be completely specified in the literature. It is worth

TABLE XI
Polymerization of Butadiene to Syndiotactic Polymer by Co Catalysts[a]

				Polymer				
Al compound, mmoles	Co compound, mmoles × 10^3	Monomer, g	Polymeriz. time, hr	g	IR anal., 1,2 %	Diethyl ether insoluble fraction, %	Crystallinity, %	Ref.
$Al(C_2H_5)_3$ 33.4	$CoCl_2 \cdot 2py$ 61.5	100	15	31	98	98	76.5	110
$Al(C_2H_5)_3$ 33.4	$Co(acac)_2$ 58	100	15	14	98	90	73.5	110
$(Et_2Al)_2O$ 17.7	$CoCl_2 \cdot 2py$ 77	99	2	45	Not rep.	Not rep.	78	111
$(Et_2Al)_2O$ 21.8	$CoCl_2 \cdot 2py$ 77	100	6.5	70	Not rep.	Not rep.	68.4	111

[a] Solvent (benzene) 1000 ml.

mentioning that the $AlEt_3$–$Co(acac)_2$ system, which according to Susa yields 1,2 syndiotactic polybutadiene, according to other authors yields mainly an oligomer, 4-methyl heptatriene (112,113). Evidently, the experimental conditions which are necessary for the formation of 1,2 stereoregular polymer have not been specified sufficiently.

Finally, 1,2 polybutadienes have also been obtained by the BrMg-(C_6H_5)–$TiCl_3$ and $MoCl_5$–$Co_2(CO)_8$ systems, respectively (114,115). The latter catalyst gives an amorphous product, while nothing has been reported about the stereoregularity of the polymer obtained by the former system.

(2) 1,2 Isotactic Polybutadiene. The catalysts discussed in the preceding paragraph, prepared from AlR_3 and a Ti, V, Mo, or Co compound, have always yielded, irrespective of the conditions under which the catalyst is prepared, crystalline 1,2 syndiotactic polybutadiene.

The catalysts obtained from AlR_3 and several Cr compounds, i.e., $Cr(acac)_3$, $Cr(CNR)_6$, chromium hexacarbonyl and its derivatives, show different characteristics (116,117). These apparently homogeneous catalysts give either crystalline syndiotactic or isotactic polybutadiene or both depending on the preparation conditions of the catalyst (mainly the Al/Cr ratio and the time of aging).

Table XII shows some data concerning the polymerization of butadiene by Cr catalysts. It is seen that at low Al/Cr ratios, the unaged catalysts give crystalline syndiotactic polybutadiene, or mixtures of predominantly syndiotactic and isotactic polymers.

Upon increasing the Al/Cr ratio, the amount of isotactic polymer increases and becomes predominant at high Al/Cr ratios.

All the homogeneous AlR_3–Cr compound systems are similar with regard to the formation of syndiotactic or isotactic polybutadiene. Differences, however, exist between catalysts obtained from different chromium compounds. Thus, polymer yield and amount of crystalline fraction in the crude polymer varies depending on the particular Cr compound used.

Apparently the reaction between AlR_3 and a Cr compound proceeds stepwise leading to the formation of catalytic complexes having different stereospecificities for the polymerization of butadiene. Evidently first a complex is formed which is stereospecific for the synthesis of syndiotactic polybutadiene. After further reaction with AlR_3 this complex is transformed into a new one which is stereospecific for the synthesis of isotactic polybutadiene. This explanation accounts for the effect of aging of the catalysts on the stereospecificity and also for the effect of the Al/Cr ratio in the unaged catalysts. In fact, at high Al/Cr ratios

TABLE XII
Polymerization of Butadiene by Catalysts from $Al(C_2H_5)_3$ and Cr Compounds[a] (117)

Cr compound, mmoles		Al/Cr molar ratio	Time of aging of catalyst, min	Polymer		
					Diethyl ether insoluble fraction	
				g	%	X-ray examination
$Cr(CNC_6H_5)_6$	1.49	2	2	0.3	—	syndio
	1.49	5	2	14.5	14	syndio (>50%) + iso
	1.49	5	240	9.7	32.5	iso
	0.745	7.5	2	6.4	15.3	syndio (>50%) + iso
	0.745	7.5	120	5.15	25	iso
	0.745	15	2	7.2	13.5	iso (>50%) + syndio
	0.745	15	120	6.6	24	iso
	0.745	15	240	6.8	34	iso
$Cr(acac)_3$	1.42	3	2	6	15	syndio
	1.42	10	2	9.85	2	iso
$Cr(CO)_5py$	1.84	3	2	5.4	31	syndio + iso
	1.84	5	2	5.75	15	iso

[a] Benzene, 80 g; monomer, 30 g; 16 hr at 15°C.

the catalyst forming reaction is so much faster than at low ones that it reaches (the minimum time of aging in the runs of Table XII) an advanced stage even after only 2–3 min, which corresponds to the formation of a catalyst for isotactic polymer.

The reaction between AlR_3 and the Cr compound probably continues also during the polymerization, that is, in the presence of the monomer, although presumably much more slowly. Consequently, it is possible that when mixtures of syndio- and isotactic polymers are obtained, the former is produced mainly during the first part of the polymerization and the latter afterwards.

These data demonstrate the basic difference between the catalysts from Cr compounds and those from Ti, V, Mo, or Co compounds. The latter systems do not yield isotactic polybutadiene even at very high Al/transition metal ratios and after a long aging time.

2. Isoprene Polymers

Next to butadiene, isoprene is the monomer which has been studied most thoroughly in polymerizations with coordination catalysts. Two stereoregular polymers of isoprene have been obtained by such catalysts, one with a *trans*-1,4, the other with a *cis*-1,4 structure. These polymers are practically identical with guttapercha and natural rubber, respectively.

Another polymer obtained with these catalysts is a polyisoprene comprised almost completely of 3,4 units. This polymer, however, is amorphous by x-rays, probably due to insufficient order in the configurations of the asymmetric carbon atoms.

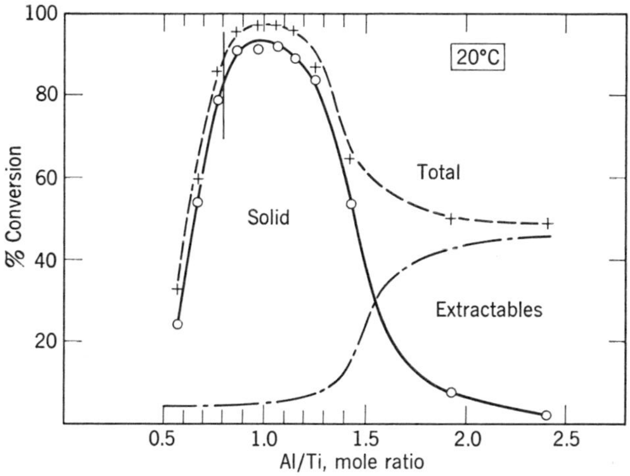

Fig. 4. Isoprene conversion to polymer as a function of the Al/Ti molar ratio. Catalyst preformed by Al to Ti addition at 20°. Polymerizations carried out at 50°C for 22 hr with a 20% solution by weight of isoprene in pentane. Ti, 0.132 mmole per 10 g of isoprene (120).

a. *Cis*-1,4 Polyisoprene. The synthesis of a polyisoprene having a structure practically identical with that of natural rubber, was first reported in a patent of Dec. 1954 (23). The AlR_3–$TiCl_4$ system was used, at an Al/Ti molar ratio of about 1 in a hydrocarbon solvent. As discussed in Sect. I-C-2, it is apparent that the actual catalyst obtained at this ratio consists of β-$TiCl_3$ with $AlEt_2Cl$.

The $AlR_3/TiCl_4$ ratio is the most important variable in this polymerization. Figure 4 shows the effect of the Al/Ti ratio on the conversion at 50°C. At an Al/Ti ratio of 0.2–0.3 the product is a crosslinked powdery substance, which is mostly insoluble in benzene. The microstructure of the polymer resembles products obtained by cationic catalysts. The highest yield is obtained at an Al/Ti ratio of about 1. The polymer obtained under these conditions is mostly (~80%) soluble in benzene and IR analysis reveals that it is 95–96% *cis*-1,4. Molecular weights are ~100,000. At higher Al/Ti ratios, the yield of solid polymer (still 95–96% *cis*-1,4) decreases rapidly and low molecular weight oily products are formed (extractables). At a ratio of 2.5 only oily polymers are formed. Thus the AlR_3–$TiCl_4$ system is highly active and stereospecific for the *cis*-1,4 polymerization of isoprene over only a narrow Al/Ti ratio range. This range corresponds to the formation of β-$TiCl_3$ (24,119–122).

The mode of reaction of $TiCl_4$ with AlR_3 influences the activity of the resulting catalysts.

Due to the industrial importance of *cis*-1,4 polyisoprene as a replacement for natural rubber, considerable work was undertaken to determine the best conditions for catalyst preparation with regard to yield, *cis*-1,4 content, molecular weight, molecular weight distribution, and gel content (122,123).

The catalyst can be prepared either by introducing AlR_3 into the $TiCl_4$ solution or vice-versa, or by simultaneous introduction of the two reagents into the polymerization solvent. Moreover, the formation of the catalyst can be carried out either in the presence (*in situ*) or in the absence ("preformed catalysts") of the monomer.

The diagram of Fig. 4 refers to preformed catalysts, prepared at 20° by introducing a solution of $Al(i\text{-}C_4H_9)_3$ into a $TiCl_4$ solution, and used 5–10 min after preparation.

Although no definitive conclusions can be drawn regarding the best method of catalyst preparation, preformed catalysts obtained by introducing AlR_3 into a $TiCl_4$ solution are generally preferred (122). The catalysts prepared by adding $TiCl_4$ to AlR_3 are less active, and yield higher gel contents. The same drawbacks are shown by catalysts prepared *in situ*, which, in addition, give less reproducible results (122).

The influence of the temperature of preparation on the catalytic properties was investigated. In the case of catalysts prepared by adding AlR_3 to $TiCl_4$, the higher the temperature the lower the activity (122).

Figure 5 shows conversion/time plots for catalysts prepared at −20, +20, and +40°C, and aged for 4 months at room temperature. Even after such a long aging, catalysts prepared at lower temperatures remain more active. Catalysts prepared at +125°C were practically inactive. For catalysts prepared at lower temperatures, the optimum Al/Ti ratio is slightly above 1 and the useful Al/Ti ratio range is rather narrow. With increasing temperature, the optimum Al/Ti ratio gradually decreases, while the Al/Ti range useful for the production of *cis*-1,4 polyisoprene increases. For example, for catalysts prepared at 90°, the optimum Al/Ti ratio is 0.6–0.7.

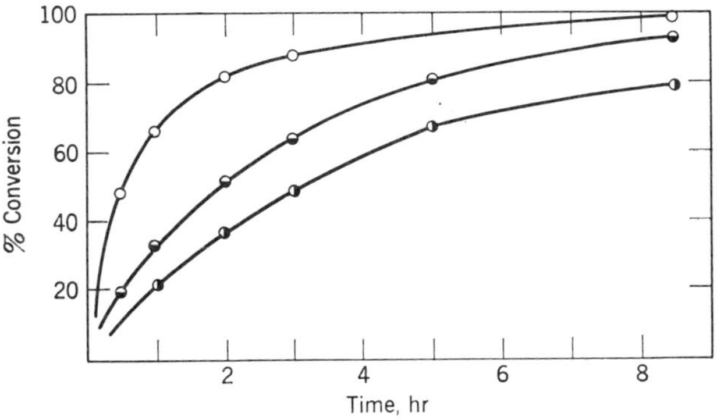

Fig. 5. Effect of catalyst preparation temperature on isoprene conversion to *cis*-1,4 polymer. Catalyst preparation temperature, °C: ○, −20; ◒, 20; ◑, 40. Al/Ti-1.0. Other conditions as under Fig. 4, except for polymerization time.

The above data on the influence of the temperature of catalyst preparation can be interpreted by considering that the optimum Al/Ti ratio corresponds to the formation of β-$TiCl_3$. This ratio is slightly higher than 1 when the reaction between AlR_3 and $TiCl_4$ is carried out at a low temperature, while it is lower than 1 when the reaction is carried out at higher temperatures.

The temperature of catalyst preparation also influences some polymers properties (Table XIII). Other conditions being constant, the catalysts prepared at higher temperatures yield polymers with higher viscosity, while the microstructure of the polymers seems to be practically independent of the temperature of catalyst preparation (122). Moreover, this variable seems to influence the amount of low molecular weight polymers formed. For example, catalysts prepared at +90°C and an Al/Ti ratio of 0.6–0.7, yield products with a high *cis*-1,4 content (96–97%) and no oils. However, as mentioned above, the activity of these catalysts is moderate.

TABLE XIII
Properties of Polymers Obtained with Catalysts Prepared by Adding AlR_3 to $TiCl_4$ at Different Temperatures (122)

Catalyst prep. temp., °C	Al/Ti	Inherent viscosity	Gel, %	*cis*-1,4, %
−20	0.98	1.8	31	96.9
	1.08	2.5	9	
0	0.98	2.8		97.4
40	0.80	2.3	9	95.5
	0.90	2.1	6	96.5
60	0.80	3.1	10	96.4
	0.90	3.0	7	96.9
	1.00	3.0	7	96.9
75	0.81	3.1	9	94.6
90	0.59	5.0	23	96.4
	0.68	5.7	12	95.0

The polymerization temperature influences only slightly the microstructure of the polymers prepared by catalysts at optimum Al/Ti ratio. Polymers with a 95% *cis*-1,4 content, in fact, can be obtained both at +70 and −30°C. Below −30° only low conversions are obtained. At such low temperatures, the polymer does not dissolve and remains attached to the catalyst, thus probably retarding the polymerization.

Molecular weight is practically independent of catalyst concentration, as indicated by the data in Table XIV. This is characteristic of polymerizations by heterogeneous catalysts. Polymerizations by homogeneous catalysts (e.g., catalysts from TiI_4 or Co compounds for *cis*-1,4 polybutadiene) show a noticeable dependence of the molecular weight

TABLE XIV
Effect of Catalyst Concentration on the Molecular Weight of the Polymer (131)

Catalyst conc., mmoles $Al(i\text{-}C_4H_9)_3$ per liter charge	DSV	Gel, %
3.10	2.91	32
5.47	2.87	29
5.97	2.46	19
11.9	2.52	26

on catalyst concentration. In addition the molecular weight is independent of conversion but dependent on the polymerization temperature (Table XV). These results suggest that polymer chain growth is rather rapid and that the molecular weights are determined by transfer with monomer or with aluminum alkyl, but do not depend on the number of catalytic centers.

The influence of the nature of aluminum alkyl on catalyst activity was recently examined by Schoenberg et al. (124). These authors examined the behavior of a series of aluminum trialkyls in preformed catalysts obtained by introducing the aluminum compound into a solution of $TiCl_4$ in heptane. The influence of the Al/Ti ratio was practically the same for all the aluminum alkyls and appeared to be similar to that reported in Fig. 4. At room temperature, the optimum ratio was about 0.9–1, except for $AlMe_3$, which is less active and requires a higher Al/Ti ratio. A slight increase in catalytic activity was observed when the

TABLE XV
Effect of Temperature of Polymerization on the Molecular Weight of Polyisoprene (131)

Temp. of polymerization, °C	DSV
0	3.9
20	3.2
40	2.5
50	2.1

alkyl chain was increased from C_1 to C_8. Higher yields at the optimum Al/Ti ratio were obtained with catalysts from aluminum alkyls containing bulky or branched alkyl groups, i.e., triisohexylaluminum and diisobutylaluminum hydride. The physical properties of the polymers obtained with different aluminum alkyls were similar.

The influence of catalyst aging on the activity was studied by several authors. Schoenberg et al. (124) found that aged catalysts gave higher yields of *cis*-1,4 solid polymer and simultaneously lower amounts of oil. Figure 6 shows results from polymerizations with aluminum trihexyl based catalysts employed 10 min., 1 week and 5 weeks after their preparation. Aged catalysts also give higher intrinsic viscosity polymers.

Adams et al. (121) state that the activity of catalysts from $AlEt_3$ or $Al(i\text{-}C_4H_9)_3$ remains unaltered after 5 days. Different results were reported by Yamazaki et al. (125) who found a rapid decrease in the activity of the $AlEt_3$–$TiCl_4$ system upon aging. It is very difficult to explain these contrasting results concerning the influence of catalyst aging.

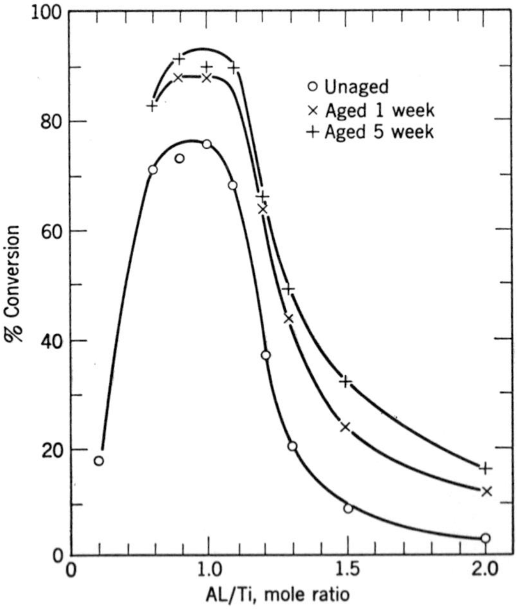

Fig. 6. Isoprene conversion to *cis*-1,4 polymer as a function of the Al/Ti ratio and catalyst aging. Triisohexylaluminum–$TiCl_4$ catalyst system. Experimental conditions as under Fig. 4.

TABLE XVI
Comparison of Catalysts Prepared from AlR_3 Complexed with $(C_6H_5)_2O$ and from Uncomplexed AlR_3 (127)

			% Yield	
Trialkylaluminum	Al/Ti	Polym. time, hr	Complexed Al–alkyl	Noncomplexed Al–alkyl
Ethyl	1.0	2.5	72	25
Propyl	1.0	2.5	88	39
Isobutyl	0.9	2.5	92	61

Good polymerization rates and polymer properties were obtained with catalysts from aluminum trialkyls complexed with a molar amount of ether, i.e., diethyl, dipropyl, diisobutyl, diphenyl ether, and anisole (126,127). Table XVI shows a comparison of the yields obtained, at a given polymerization time, with catalysts complexed with diphenyl ether and with noncomplexed ones (127).

The polymers obtained with aluminum etherates have better physical properties than those obtained with noncomplexed aluminum alkyls. The mode of action of the ethers is still obscure as is the reason why the properties of the polymers are improved. It is now accepted that all diolefin polymers obtained by coordination catalysts contain, to some extent, cyclized units* (128). It would be of interest to know whether or not the improved polymer properties obtained with etherate catalysts are due to the fact that such polymers contain lower amounts of cyclized units than polymers obtained with noncomplexed catalysts.

Data on the influence of the solvent were reported by Adams et al. (121). Aliphatic solvents, such as petroleum ether and *n*-heptane are preferred, but other solvents can also be used. Polymerizations in benzene and toluene yield polymers very similar to those obtained in heptane. In laboratory tests, ortho-di-chlorobenzene was also found to be a satisfactory solvent. The few available data indicate that the polymerization rate in this solvent is higher than in petroleum ether, but that the polymers obtained contain a slightly higher percentage of *trans*-1,4 units.

The kinetics of the polymerization of isoprene to *cis*-1,4 polymer by AlR_3–$TiCl_4$ systems were studied by Saltman (24) and Yamazaki (125).

* We wish to point out that the data reported in this chapter concerning the composition of the diolefin polymers do not take into account the presence of cyclized units. Therefore the percentages of trans-1,4, *cis*-1,4, 1,2 units, etc. reported refer only to the unsaturated units and not to the total number of monomeric units in the polymer.

The former employed $Al(i\text{-}C_4H_9)_3$, the latter $AlEt_3$. Both prepared the catalyst *in situ:* the former by separate addition of solutions of $Al(i\text{-}C_4H_9)_3$ and $TiCl_4$ to the isoprene–heptane mixture, the latter by adding $TiCl_4$ to the hexane solution of $AlEt_3$ and isoprene.

Polymerizations carried out at different initial catalyst concentrations indicated a high dependence of the polymerization rate on catalyst concentration. The rate is a function of the product of the initial concentrations of Ti and of Al. Due to the necessity of operating at a constant Al/Ti ratio, this means that the rate is proportional to both $[Al]^2$ and $[Ti]^2$.

The polymerization appears to be first order with respect to monomer. This is demonstrated by the linearity of the plots of ln M/M_0 vs reaction time. In these plots a break was found by some authors (125) who used unaged catalysts, but others who used aged catalysts found a fairly good linearity over a large interval of time (122).

The kinetic equation of the polymerization reaction can be expressed as follows:

$$-dM/dt = K[M][Ti]^2$$

where K is the rate constant. The activation energy of the overall process is 14.4 kcal/mole according to Saltman (24) and about 22 kcal/mole according to Yamazaki (125).

Monomer and catalyst concentrations influence the rate of polymerization, but not the microstructure of the polymer. The latter seems to be determined essentially by the chemical nature of the catalytic complex.

Predominantly *cis*-1,4 polyisoprene was also obtained with catalysts from $TiCl_4$ and $ZnEt_2$ (129), $CdEt_2$ (130), or complexes of the type $(CaH_2)_x \cdot (CaEt_2)_y \cdot ZnEt_2$ (129). It seems that these systems offer no advantages over those obtained from AlR_3.

Detailed data were published (39,40) on the polymerization of isoprene to *cis*-1,4 polymer by catalysts from $TiCl_4$ and various alanes (e.g., $AlHCl_2 \cdot O(C_2H_5)_2$, $AlHCl_2 \cdot N(CH_3)_3$, $AlH_2Cl \cdot N(CH_3)_3$, $AlH_3 \cdot N(CH_3)_3$, and $AlH_2 \cdot N(CH_3)_2$). These systems are used in benzene and give good yields of high molecular weight polymers with about 96% *cis*-1,4 content.

b. *Trans*-1,4 Polyisoprenes. The synthesis of an isoprene polymer having a structure practically identical with that of gutta-percha was first reported in a patent of March 1955 (98). The heterogeneous system $Al(C_2H_5)_3$–$TiCl_3$ (violet modification) was used as polymerization catalyst.

Synthetic *trans*-1,4 polyisoprene was obtained with several other catalysts, e.g., $AlEt_3$–$TiCl_4$ (Al/Ti ratio ~0.5) (23), $AlEt_3$–VCl_4 (76), $AlEt_3$–VCl_3 (99), $LiAlH_4$–TiI_4 (88).

The most suitable catalyst for the preparation of synthetic gutta-percha seems to be that obtained from an Al trialkyl and VCl_3. This system gives crude polymerization products consisting of 99–100% *trans*-1,4 units, and having a negligible amorphous fraction (103). Improvements in catalyst performance were obtained by using VCl_3 supported on an inert carrier, such as titanium dioxide, silica, alumina, and barium sulfate (132,133).

The supported VCl_3 can be easily prepared by heating (e.g., to 80°C for about 2 hr) a suspension of the carrier in an inert liquid containing dissolved VCl_4. The latter undergoes thermal decomposition, precipitating VCl_3 on the carrier. The supported catalysts gives higher efficiencies, (i.e., amount of total polymer obtained per gram of VCl_3) and higher polymerization rates.

By using the recipe: benzene 350 g; VCl_3 70–100 mg (10% by weight on TiO_2); $Al(i\text{-}C_4H_9)_3/VCl_3 = 5$; isoprene 80 g; temperature 50°C, it is possible to obtain up to 450–470 g of polymer per gram of VCl_3, with polymerization rates as high as 15–20 g of polymer/g VCl_3/hr.

Further improvements in polymerization rate and catalyst efficiency were obtained by using a homogeneous three-component system AlR_3–VCl_3–$Ti(OR)_4$ where Al/V = 10/1 and V/Ti = 2/1 (133,134). The efficiency of this homogeneous catalyst is reported to be about 50 times higher than that of the $Ti(OR)_4$ free supported catalyst. The polymerization rate can reach 600–700 g of *trans*-1,4 polyisoprene/g VCl_3/hour.

Other homogeneous catalysts for the *trans*-1,4 polymerization of isoprene were obtained from $AlEt_2Cl$ and $V(acac)_3$ or $VCl_3 \cdot 3THF$ (100). However, these systems seem to be far less efficient than the ternary one containing $Ti(OR)_4$.

The catalysts based on Ti, both the AlR_3–α-$TiCl_3$ (38) and the $LiAlH_4$ (ether suspension)–TiI_4 (88) systems, are less stereospecific than those from VCl_3. These catalysts produce in addition to pure *trans*-1,4 macromolecules, less pure polymer which, although predominantly *trans*-1,4 (>50%) contains 3,4 and *cis*-1,4 units as well.

Kinetic studies have been published on the polymerization of isoprene to *trans*-1,4 polymer with the $AlEt_3$–α-$TiCl_3$ (135) and $AlEt_3$–VCl_3 (136) systems.

c. 3,4 Polyisoprenes. 3,4 Polyisoprenes were first obtained, independently and almost simultaneously, by Wilke and by the School of Milan (106,137).

Both teams used a homogeneous catalyst system obtained from $Al(C_2H_5)_3$ and a titanium tetraalcoholate in an aromatic or aliphatic solvent (108,138). The optimum Al/Ti ratio, both with regard to the yield of polymer and 3,4 content, is about 6–7. Different titanium tetraalcoholates give practically identical results. The Al/Ti ratio strongly influences the molecular weight. This is probably due to transfer between the growing polymer chain and excess aluminum trialkyl used for catalyst preparation. This is suggested by polymerizations carried out in the presence of C^{14}-containing $AlEt_3$, which showed that the radioactivity in the polymer increased with increasing Al/Ti ratio, while the molecular weight decreased (Table XVII). This phenomenon seems to be quite similar to that observed in the polymerization of α-olefins (139).

The 3,4 content of the polymer depends on the polymerization temperature, as indicated in Table XVIII. At 20–25° and with an Al/Ti ratio of 6–7, the products contain 94–95% 3,4 units while at 0° or slightly below the 3,4 content is 97–98%.

The $AlEt_3$–$VO(OR)_3$ system also yields 3,4-polyisoprenes. These products are analogous to those obtained with the $AlEt_3$–$Ti(OR)_4$ system (61). By contrast $AlEt_3$–$V(acac)_3$ does not polymerize isoprene. The systems obtained from $AlEt_3$ and $V(acac)_3$ or $VO(OR)_3$, respectively, which are practically equivalent for the polymerization of butadiene (both yielding 1,2 syndiotactic polymers), are very different in the polymerization of isoprene. This is probably due to the fact that the ace-

TABLE XVII

Polymerization of Isoprene by the $Al(C^{14}{}_2H_5)_3$–$Ti(O\text{-}n\text{-}C_3H_7)_4$ Catalyst System[a]
Variation of Polymer C^{14} Activity on the Al/Ti Ratio (108)

Al/Ti molar ratio	Polymer[b] g	Polymer[b] [η]	Polymer activity (counts/min)
6	1.5	1.27	47
9	2.57	0.56	70
12	2.38	0.37	100
15	2.04	0.35	115

[a] Experimental conditions: 30 ml toluene; 10 ml isoprene (Phillips "polymerization grade"); 0.2 ml $Ti(O\text{-}n\text{-}C_3H_7)_4$ (isoprene was added to the toluene solution of $Al(C_2H_5)_3$, then $Ti(OR)_4$ was introduced). Polymerization 9 hr at 25°C.

[b] IR analysis: 90–95% 3,4 units.

TABLE XVIII
Influence of the Polymerization Temperature on the Structure of Polyisoprenes Obtained by the $Al(C_2H_5)_3$–$Ti(O\text{-}n\text{-}C_3H_7)_4$ System[a] (108)

Polym. temp., °C	3,4 units, %
25	94
0	97
−10	99

[a] Al/Ti molar ratio = 6.

tylacetonate groups are not completely removed from the vanadium in the reaction with aluminum alkyl at room temperature. It is possible that severe steric hindrance prevents polymerization from taking place in the case of isoprene. Information on this point is scant and further investigations would be required for clarification.

Predominantly or exclusively 3,4 polyisoprenes were recently obtained by Stolka et al. using Na, $(C_6H_5)MgBr$, $(n\text{-}C_4H_9)MgBrCo(acac)_2$ catalysts (140).

3. Piperylene Polymers

Piperylene (1,3-pentadiene) is present in the C_5 fraction from petroleum cracking and is obtained as a by-product of the industrial preparation of isoprene. The study of the polymerization of this monomer is of particular interest from the scientific point of view, due to the complex phenomena of isomerism exhibited by its polymers.

1,3-Pentadiene exists in two isomeric forms, *cis* and *trans*, which do not always exhibit identical polymerization behavior. This is disadvantageous from the practical point of view, as the separation of the two isomers is not easy on an industrial scale.

Of the numerous regular stereoisomers that can be visualized for 1,3-pentadiene polymers, four have been obtained and characterized so far: isotactic *trans*-1,4, isotactic *cis*-1,4, syndiotactic *cis*-1,4 and syndiotactic-1,2. In addition to these stereoregular polymers, various types of amorphous polymers have been obtained, containing different types of monomer units in variable proportions.

a. *Trans*-1,4 Polypentadienes. The synthesis of a crystalline isotactic *trans*-1,4 polypentadiene was first reported in a patent of 1955 (98). The heterogeneous $AlEt_3$–$TiCl_3$ (violet modification) catalyst system was used in heptane, at about 60°C. A mixture of the two isomers of pentadiene was used as the monomer. The crude polymerization product consisted of an amorphous fraction (extractable with boiling diethyl ether) and a crystalline fraction (insoluble in diethyl ether). The percentage of the latter was rather low, probably due to the low purity of the monomer used and the relatively high temperature of polymerization.

Far better results, both with regard to polymer yield and crystalline fraction in the polymer, were obtained with the heterogeneous $AlEt_3$–VCl_3 system in heptane at room temperature (103,141). Both the *cis* and the *trans* monomers are polymerized by this catalyst system, yielding practically identical results (Table XIX). The only difference observed

TABLE XIX
Polymerization of 1,3-Pentadiene with the $Al(C_2H_5)_3$–VCl_3 System[a] (141)

Monomer[b] *trans* isomer, %	Polym. time, hr	Polymer, g	Residue from ether extn., %[c]	Melting temp., °C
100	14	1.23	87	95
100	15	1.5	83.5	95
100	17	1.4	88	—
100	70	2.4	85	95
100	72	2.4	85	—
77	14	1.44	69	92
75	14.30	0.68	66	92
50	14.30	0.64	65	90
50	15	0.95	58	89
50	16	0.87	64	90
28	14.30	0.67	69	89
25	16	1.47	64	91
0	16	0.95	94	95
0	76	1.6	92	95

[a] Polymerization conditions: monomer 4 ml; VCl_3, 0.3 g.; Al/V molar ratio, 2.5; *n*-heptane, 15 ml.

[b] A mixture of pure *cis* and pure *trans* isomers was used.

[c] About 95% soluble in boiling benzene; $[\eta]$ 1.3–1.5 dl g^{-1} (determined in toluene at 30°C).

is that the product from the *cis* isomer contains a lower percentage of amorphous fraction (about 4–6% vs 12–15%). Mixtures of the two isomers yield a product containing a considerably higher percentage of amorphous fraction than that obtained from either of the two isomers. In addition, the crystalline fraction obtained from mixtures of the two isomers exhibits a final melting temperature that is a few degrees lower than that of the crystalline fraction obtained from either isomer. This seems to be due to a lower degree of steric order in the configuration of the asymmetric carbon atoms.

The amorphous fraction obtained with the $AlEt_3$–VCl_3 system consists predominantly of *trans*-1,4 units. Although this fraction is amorphous by x-ray analysis, the IR spectrum of the solid polymers shows some bands (e.g., at 12.80; 11.54 μ) that are characteristic of isotactic *trans*-1,4 polypentadiene. Although these bands are very weak, they nonetheless indicate the presence of short isotactic sequences, which are evidently insufficient to give rise to crystallinity detectable by x-rays.

The heterogeneous $AlEt_3$–VCl_3 system seems to be the most stereospecific for the synthesis of isotactic *trans*-1,4 polypentadiene. In addition to this system and to that from violet $TiCl_3$ mentioned above, other heterogeneous catalysts are known which yield crystalline *trans*-1,4 isotactic polypentadienes, e.g., systems obtained from AlR_3 and $TiCl_4$, VCl_4, and $VOCl_3$, respectively (61).

At present, no homogeneous catalyst based on transition metals is known which will give *trans*-1,4 isotactic polymers from pentadiene. The homogeneous catalysts which give highly crystalline *trans*-1,4 polymers from butadiene or isoprene do not usually give polymers with a high *trans*-1,4 content from pentadiene. Thus the systems from AlR_2Cl and $V(acac)_3$ or $VCl_3 \cdot 3THF$, already mentioned for the preparation of 99–100% *trans*-1,4 polybutadiene, yield amorphous polymers, containing about 70% *trans*-1,4 and 30% 1,2 units from pentadiene (100). This does not mean that the presence of a solid catalytic surface is necessary to obtain isotactic *trans*-1,4 polypentadiene. Polymers of this type, having a good degree of crystallinity, were also obtained by butyl lithium in *n*-heptane, from the *cis* isomer of pentadiene (7). The latter catalyst is outside the scope of this chapter, however cf. Chapter 6, p. 537.

b. Cis-1,4 Polypentadienes. (*1*) *Isotactic cis-1,4 Polypentadiene.* This polymer was prepared by homogeneous systems obtained from an aluminum trialkyl and a titanium tetraalcoholate $Ti(OR)_4$ (142,143). Data concerning the polymerization of both the *cis* and the *trans* isomers of pentadiene by these systems are shown in Table XX. The optimum

Al/Ti ratio, both with regard to polymer yield and the stereoregularity, was found to be about 7. Although both the *trans* and the *cis* isomers can be polymerized, the polymers obtained from the *trans* isomer are far more stereoregular than those obtained from the *cis* one. The *trans* isomer gives products that appear crystalline by x-rays, even in the crude state. From these, it is possible to separate an amorphous fraction (about 60% of the total product) and a fraction exhibiting a high degree of crystallinity. The latter fraction has 85–90% *cis*-1,4 units and a melting temperature of about 45°C. The *cis*-1,4 content in the amorphous fraction is lower (about 60–70%).

The products obtained from the *cis* isomer have a *cis*-1,4 content practically identical with that of the polymers obtained from the *trans* isomer (about 80–85% in the crude polymerization products). However, they are amorphous by x-rays, and only after careful fractionation was it possible to isolate a small fraction exhibiting low crystallinity of the isotactic type. However evidence exists that the fraction appearing amorphous by x-rays exhibits a certain degree of stereoregularity of the isotactic type (62).

It was observed that the AlR_3–$Ti(OR)_4$ catalyst can isomerize the *cis* isomer of 1,3-pentadiene to the *trans* isomer. This was demonstrated by terminating polymerizations of the pure *cis* isomer at 10–15% conversion: the recovered unconverted monomer was a mixture of the *cis* and *trans* isomers, the latter being the predominant one. It is not known whether the polymerization occurs only with the *trans* monomer obtained by ismerization, or with both the *trans* and *cis* monomers.

The AlR_3–$Ti(OR)_4$ catalyst systems are not the only ones able to give *cis*-1,4 isotactic polypentadienes. Polymers that show crystallinity by x-ray and IR analysis due to isotactic *cis*-1,4 sequences were also obtained with the heterogeneous $AlEt_3$–$TiCl_4$ system from the *trans* isomer of pentadiene (61). The polymers obtained at an Al/Ti ratio of about 1 exhibit weak crystallinity but those obtained at a ratio of 2 appear as crystalline as the polymers obtained with the AlR_3–$Ti(OR)_4$ system. The products obtained with the $TiCl_4$ catalysts, even the purest fractions isolated, have a *cis*-1,4 content not higher than about 70%. Therefore, crystallinity in these products indicates that they contain sufficiently long *cis*-1,4 sequences interspersed with other units.

(2) Syndiotactic cis-1,4 Polypentadiene. Syndiotactic *cis*-1,4 polymers of 1,3-pentadiene were obtained with homogeneous catalysts prepared from an aluminum alkylhalide and a Co compound in aromatic solvent (144,145). These catalysts are the same as those used for the *cis*-1,4

TABLE XX

Polymerization of 1,3-Pentadiene by Catalysts Obtained from Aluminum Alkyls and Titanium Alkoxides[a] (143)

Run	Aluminum alkyl	10^3 moles	Ti compound	Al/Ti, molar ratio	Monomer,[b] g	Polymerization Temp, °C	Polymerization Time, hr	Crude polymer Yield, g	Crude polymer IR analysis,[d] % cis	Crude polymer IR analysis,[d] % trans	Crude polymer IR analysis,[d] % 3,4	MEK insoluble fraction[c] IR analysis,[d] % cis	MEK insoluble fraction[c] IR analysis,[d] % trans	MEK insoluble fraction[c] IR analysis,[d] % 3,4	MEK insoluble fraction[c] X-ray exam
1	$Al(C_2H_5)_3$	4.2	$Ti(O\text{-}n\text{-}C_4H_9)_4$	3	5	0	26	0.2	66	25	9	—	—	—	—
2	$Al(i\text{-}C_4H_9)_3$	12	$Ti(O\text{-}i\text{-}C_3H_7)_4$	4	5.5	0	40	5.1	67	24	9	82	11	7	Cryst.
3	$Al(C_2H_5)_3$	6	$Ti(O\text{-}n\text{-}C_4H_9)_4$	5	14	0	30	1.0	70	20	10	85	10	5	Cryst.
4	$Al(CH_2\text{–}CH(CH_3)\text{–}(CH_2)_2\text{–}CH_3)_3$	7	$Ti(O\text{-}n\text{-}C_4H_9)_4$	5	15	−15	45	6.9	78	16	6	87	9	4	Cryst.
5	$Al(C_2H_5)_3$	8	$Ti(O\text{-}n\text{-}C_4H_9)_4$	5	16	0	35	6	80	14	6	85	10	5	Cryst.
6	$Al(CH_3\text{-}CH(CH_2)\text{–}(CH_2)_2\text{–}CH_3)_3$	6.4	$Ti(O\text{-}n\text{-}C_4H_9)_3$	5	18	0	70	2.2	77	17	6	81	13	6	Cryst.
7	$Al(C_2H_5)_3$	15	$Ti(O\text{-}i\text{-}C_5H_{11})_4$	7	12	0	14	5	70	23	7	81	13	6	Cryst.
8	$Al(C_2H_5)_3$	20	$Ti(O\text{-}n\text{-}C_4H_9)_4$	7	10	0	40	4.6	54	30	16	60	25	15	Amorph.
9	$Al(C_2H_5)_3$	14	$Ti(O\text{-}n\text{-}C_4H_9)_4$	10	14.5	0	26	4.6	55	34	11	71	17	12	Cryst.
10	$Al(C_2H_5)_3$	7	$Ti(O\text{-}n\text{-}C_4H_9)_4$	5	17.5	0	60	1.5	75	15	10	79	13	8	Amorph.
11	$Al(C_2H_5)_3$	16	$Ti(O\text{-}n\text{-}C_4H_9)_4$	7	11.2	−15	30	1.2	76	15	9	84	10	6	Trace of crystal

[a] Solvent (benzene) 100 ml; in runs 3, 5, 6, 10 the catalyst was aged at room temperature for about 20 min; in the other runs the monomer was added immediately after catalyst formation.

[b] Run 1–7, 9: *trans* isomer (98–99 %); run 8: mixture of *trans* (50 %) and *cis* (50 %) isomers; run 10–11: *cis* isomer (99.9 %).

[c] 30–35 % of the crude polymer; [η] 5–7 dl/g (100 ml/g; in toluene at 30°C).

[d] According to NMR analysis the *trans* double bonds are partly *trans*-1,4 and partly 1,2, while the *cis* double bonds are almost exclusively *cis*-1,4.

polymerization of butadiene. In the case of pentadiene, they polymerize only the *trans* isomer and not the *cis* form. The latter seems to remain unchanged (62).

The characteristics of the polymerization of pentadiene by Co catalysts are similar to those of the polymerization of butadiene. In the polymerization of butadiene the Co catalysts can be prepared in combination with $AlEt_2Cl$, $AlCl_2Et$, and $Al_2Et_3Cl_3$. Differences among the catalysts obtained from the various aluminum alkyls affect the kinetics of the polymerization and the molecular weights, but not the stereospecificity of the process. With pentadiene the catalysts from $AlEt_2Cl$ yield predominantly *cis*-1,4 polymers, while those from $AlEtCl_2$ or $Al_2Cl_3Et_3$ yield low molecular weight cationic polymers predominantly consisting of 1,2 units. These polymers are identical with those obtained from $AlEtCl_2$ alone in the absence of Co compound. The different behavior of pentadiene in comparison with butadiene is due to its much higher reactivity under cationic conditions.

However, by adding a Lewis base, such as thiophene or pyridine to $AlEtCl_2$, catalysts are obtained that yield high *cis*-1,4 polypentadienes.

Some data on the polymerization of pentadiene by the $AlEtCl_2$·thiophene–Co(acac)$_2$ and $AlEtCl_2$·pyridine–Co(acac)$_2$ systems are shown in Table XXI. In these systems, the thiophene/aluminum ratio can be varied within fairly wide limits, from 5 to about 0.5, while the pyridine/aluminum ratio can be varied within a narrower range, from about 0.5 to 0.9. This is related to the different basicities of the two electron donors. The crude polymers obtained by these two systems contain about 75–80% *cis*-1,4 units and show a fairly good degree of crystallinity by x-rays. By fractionation of the crude polymer it is possible to obtain fractions with about 85–90% *cis*-1,4 content. This means that the polymers are heterogeneous in the sense that they consist of macromolecules ranging from about 55 to about 90% *cis*-1,4. This is another difference between the polymerizations of pentadiene and butadiene by Co catalysts. *Cis*-1,4 polybutadienes obtained with these catalysts are more homogeneous and the *cis*-1,4 content in the various molecular weight fractions vary within far narrower limits. The heterogeneity of the *cis*-1,4 polypentadienes cannot be attributed to the existence of different catalytic centers, because, if this were the case, macromolecules with different *cis*-1,4 contents should be obtained also from butadiene.

c. 1,2 Syndiotactic Polypentadiene. When used in *n*-heptane or other aliphatic solvents, the catalysts prepared from AlR_2Cl and a Co compound yield polypentadienes containing predominantly 1,2 units (up to about 94%) (146).

TABLE XXI
Polymerization of 1,3-Pentadiene by Catalysts Prepared from Cobalt Diacetylacetonate, $Co(acac)_2$, and $Al(C_2H_5)Cl_2$ Complexed with Thiophene[a] or Pyridine[b]

				Polymerization		Crude polymer		MEK insoluble fraction[e]	
Run	$Co(acac)_2$[c], moles 10^5	Benzene, ml	Monomer,[d] g	Temp., °C	Time, hr	Yield, g	IR analysis *cis*-1,4, %	IR analysis *cis*-1,4, %[f]	[η], dl g^{-1}
1	5.1	350	28	20	24	23	77	84	2.8
2	1.5	50	10.5	20	6	8	72	85	—
3	0.34	15	3.1	20	12	2.3	73	83	2.9
4	0.68	30	5	0	20	4	81	86	2.3
5	0.5	30	3	20	8	2.6	77	83	1.9
6	0.15	15	3.5	0	48	3.2	71	85	—
7	0.5	30	4	20	12	3.1	69	85	2.5
8	0.5	30	3	0	12	1.7	76	86	—

[a] Runs 1–6; Al/thiophene molar ratio: 1.
[b] Runs 7 and 8; Al/pyridine molar ratio: 0.53.
[c] Al/Co molar ratio: ~500. Catalyst prepared by introducing first the Co compound and the Lewis base, then the $Al(C_2H_5)Cl_2$ and finally, after a few minutes, the monomer.
[d] *trans* Isomer, 99.5 % pure.
[e] Crystalline by x-ray examination (polymer annealed 4 hr at 35°C). [η] was determined in toluene at 30°C.
[f] The remaining units are characterized by *trans* double bonds and are probably a mixture of 1,2 and *trans*-1,4 units.

Table XXII shows data on the polymerization of pentadiene by the $AlEt_2Cl–Co(acac)_3$ system in *n*-heptane. The polymers obtained are amorphous by x-rays at room temperature. However, they crystallize on stretching and show an identity period of about 5.1 Å as measured from the fiber spectrum. On the basis of this, a 1,2 syndiotactic structure was attributed to the polymers.

It should be remembered that in the polymerization of butadiene, the $AlEt_2Cl–Co(acac)_3$ system yields predominantly *cis*-1,4 polymers even in *n*-heptane (although the *cis*-1,4 content is lower than in polymers obtained, by the same system, in benzene).

E. Properties of the Diolefin Polymers

Although a detailed examination of the physical and elastomeric properties of the polymers of butadiene, isoprene, and 1,3-pentadiene obtained with coordination catalysts is beyond the scope of this chapter, we shall discuss briefly some of the characteristics of these polymers.

TABLE XXII
Polymerization of 1,3-Pentadiene (*trans* Isomer) by Catalysts from $Co(acac)_3$ and $Al(C_2H_5)_2Cl$ in *n*-Heptane[a] (61)

			Polymerization		Polymer			
						IR analysis		
n-Heptane, ml	$Co(acac)_3$, moles 10^6	Al/Co molar ratio	Temp., °C	Time, hr	Yield, g	*cis*-1,4, %	1,2,[c] %	$[\eta]$,[b] dl g^{-1}
20	2.2	800	−10	48	1	14.5	82	2.35
20	2.03	400	0	24	3.5	4.8	91	3.2
20	3.6	400	0	24	3.5	3.5	92	2.22
20	1.2	200	0	144	1	4	92	—
30	3.65	400	24	12	3	2	94	2.12
30	3.93	5000	24	6	2.5	3	93	2.31
25	3.9	400	24	24	1.2	2	94	—

[a] Catalysts prepared by introducing first $Co(acac)_3$, then $Al(C_2H_5)_2Cl$ and finally 5 ml of pentadiene.
[b] Determined in toluene at 30°C.
[c] The remaining units are *trans*-1,4.

In general, the physical properties of a polymer from a given monomer depend on the type and degree of tacticity. Table XXIII shows melting temperatures, identity periods, and densities of the polybutadienes, polyisoprenes, and polypentadienes so far obtained.

Among the polybutadienes, the *trans*-1,4 polymer (>99% *trans*-1,4 content) melts at about 145°C. Hence this polymer has no elastomeric properties. The same holds true for the highly crystalline 1,2 isotactic and 1,2 syndiotactic polybutadienes, which melt at 127 and 156°C, respectively. However, stereoisomers of 1,2 polybutadiene are known which have such a low degree of stereoregularity that they are amorphous at room temperature by x-ray analysis. These polymers, which include the diethyl ether soluble fractions of the products described under Sect. I-D-1c, have elastomeric properties.

The high *cis*-1,4 polybutadiene melts at about +3°C, which is only slightly lower than the melting point of natural rubber. Among the butadiene polymers, only the *cis*-1,4 possesses highly satisfactory elastomeric properties.

The *cis*-1,4 and *trans*-1,4 polyisoprenes are very similar to the corresponding natural products in their properties (157,158,127,131).

Although it may have a 3,4 content as high as 97–98%, the 3,4 polyisoprene obtained so far is amorphous because of a lack or a low degree of stereoregularity.

Among the polypentadienes, the *trans*-1,4 isotactic polymer melts at about 95°C, and hence it is not an elastomer at room temperature. The isotactic and syndiotactic, *cis*-1,4 polymers, melt at about 42 and 52.5°C, respectively. These melting temperatures refer to the purest polymers (85–90% *cis*-1,4 content) obtained. Higher melting temperatures are expected for polypentadienes having a higher *cis*-1,4 content or a higher degree of stereoregularity than those obtained so far. Of the two *cis*-1,4 polypentadienes presently available, the syndiotactic shows properties which are intermediate between those of gutta-percha and

TABLE XXIII
Physical Properties of Butadiene, Isoprene, and Pentadiene Polymers Obtained with Stereospecific Catalysts

Polymer	Melting temp., °C	Identity period, Å	Density	Ref.
trans-1,4 Polybutadiene[a]	70–75° (transition temp.)	4.85 mod. I	1.02	103, 147 148, 149
	145°C (melting temp.)	4.7 mod. II	0.93	
cis-1,4 Polybutadiene	3	8.60	1.01	68, 150, 151
Isotactic 1,2 polybutadiene	128	6.5	0.96	152, 153
Syndiotactic 1,2 polybutadiene	156	5.14	0.96	154
cis-1,4 Polyisoprene	20–30	8.10	1.00	150, 155, 156
trans-1,4 Polyisoprene	65	4.77 8.75 9.2	1.04	148, 155, 160
3,4 Polyisoprene	Amorphous	—	—	
trans-1,4 Polypentadiene	95	4.82	0.98	141
Isotactic *cis*-1,4 polypentadiene	42	8.15	n.d.	142, 143
Syndiotactic *cis*-1,4 polypentadiene	52–3	8.5	n.d.	145
1,2 Polypentadiene	10–20	515	n.d.	146

[a] *trans*-1,4 Polybutadiene can exist in two crystalline modifications; one (mod. I) is stable below about 75°C, the other from 75 to 145°C. The two modifications have different identity periods and different equatorial encumberment per each chain (the latter being greater for mod. II). Only the equatorial encumberment is greater for mod. II. Identity period is greater for mod. I, as reported under the third column.

natural rubber, while the isotactic has a lower melting temperature and in general is more similar to *cis*-1,4 polybutadiene or polyisoprene.

Among the elastomeric polybutadienes, polyisoprenes, or polypentadienes, the 1,4 polymers show dynamic properties superior to those of the 1,2 polymers. These properties are better for 1,4 polybutadienes and polyisoprenes than for 1,4 polypentadienes. This is due to the higher freedom of rotation around the $—CH_2—CH{=}$ or even the $—CH_2—CH_2—$ bonds, than around the $—CH_2—\underset{\displaystyle R}{\underset{|}{CH}}—$ bonds.

From the practical point of view *cis*-1,4 polybutadiene and *cis*-1,4 polyisoprene are by far the most important of the various polydienes obtained by coordination catalysts. They are also being produced industrially. The physical properties of the elastomers derived from these two polymers have been examined in detail elsewhere (127,131, 157–159).

F. Mechanism of Polymerization

After twelve years of research on stereospecific polymerization of diolefins a great number of new polymers have been obtained, some of which have a high degree of structural regularity. The present state of knowledge concerning the mechanism of formation of these polymers will now be examined.

1. Nature of the Polymerization

The nature of the polymerizations initiated by catalysts based on transition metals has been discussed to a considerable extent. In the case of catalysts prepared from Ti, V, Cr, or Mo compounds, there is general agreement that polymerization occurs by monomer incorporation at the polarized $Me^{\delta+}—C^{\delta-}$ bond between the transition metal and the alpha carbon of the last polymerized unit. This conclusion has been reached not only from the study of the polymerization of diolefins, but also from that of ethylene and α-olefins.

For catalysts based on metals of Group VIII, in particular of Co or Ni, there is much less agreement as to the nature of the active catalyst. Therefore, the two cases will be examined separately.

a. Polymerization by Catalysts from Ti, V, Cr, or Mo. The hypotheses regarding the mechanism of these catalysts are based on the following evidence.

1. Polymerizations terminated by CH_3OH^3 give tritium-containing polymer which evidently derives, at least in part, from a reaction of the type

$$\text{Cat—CH}_2\text{—CH=CH—CH}_2\sim + \text{CH}_3\text{OH}^3 \rightarrow \text{Cat—OCH}_3 + \text{H}^3\text{CH}_2\text{—CH=CH—CH}_2\sim$$

Experiments of this type were carried out with the $AlEt_3$–$Ti(OR)_4$ catalyst system in the polymerization of isoprene or pentadiene (61) and with the $Al(i\text{-}C_4H_9)_3$–TiI_4 system in the polymerization of butadiene (161). With the latter system, the termination with $C^{14}O_2$ has also been tested and radioactive polymer was obtained (161).

2. Catalysts from $Al(C_2{}^{14}H_5)_3$ give radioactive polymer. This is due to the fact that the monomer is incorporated at the metal–$C_2{}^{14}H_5$ bond. This bond could form by reaction between $Al(C_2{}^{14}H_5)_3$ and the transition metal compound or during the polymerization by transfer between the growing polymer chain and the aluminum alkyl:

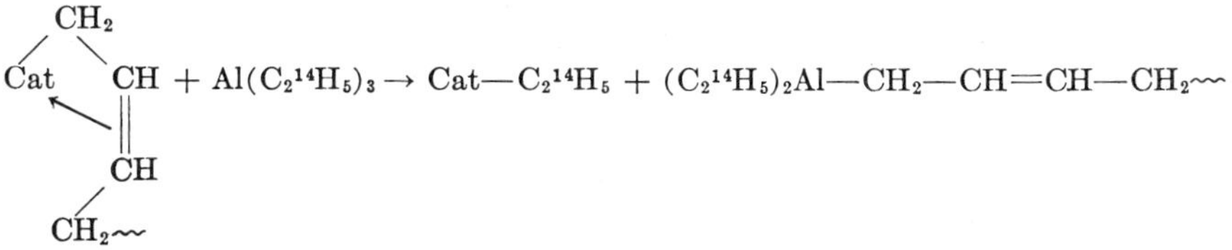

This problem has been widely discussed in connection with the polymerization of propylene by the $AlEt_3$–α-$TiCl_3$ system (139). With diolefins, transfer between aluminum alkyl and the growing chain has been observed in the polymerization of butadiene and isoprene by the $AlEt_3$–VCl_3 system (61,136); with butadiene by the $Al(i\text{-}C_4H_9)_3$–TiI_4 system (86); with 1,3-pentadiene and isoprene by the $AlEt_3$–$Ti(OR)_4$ system (61,108,143).

3. Overall activation energies of polymerization in the cases examined so far are much lower than those observed in radical polymerizations which is evidence for an ionic mechanism. Thus, for the polymerization of isoprene by AlR_3–$TiCl_4$, $E_a = 14.4$ kcal/mole (24); of butadiene by the $AlHCl_2 \cdot O(C_2H_5)_2$–$AlI_5$–$TiCl_4$ system, $E_a = 8.75$ kcal/mole (87); and of propylene by the $AlEt_3$–α-$TiCl_3$ system, $E_a = 12.4$ kcal/mole (162).

4. For some catalysts obtained from AlR_3 and Ti, V, Cr, or Mo compounds a cationic mechanism can certainly be excluded since systems like AlR_3–$Ti(OR)_4$, AlR_3–$V(acac)_3$, AlR_3–$Mo(acac)_3$ are unlikely to exhibit cationic activity. This conclusion is supported by the fact that polymerizations by these catalysts can be performed in solvents such as thiophene which destroy the activity of strong Lewis acids such as $AlCl_3$, $AlBr_3$, etc. (61). For other systems, e.g., the AlR_3–$TiCl_3$ system, this conclusion may not seem so obvious, but it seems reasonable to assume that all these catalysts belong to the same class.

Some of the findings reported in items 1–4 are not conclusive. Thus, the validity of the method of termination by CH_3OH^3 has been questioned in regard to the possibility of isotopic exchange (161). Taken as a whole, however, these arguments clearly suggest that the active catalyst site is a polarized $Me^{\delta+}$—$C^{\delta-}$ bond.

It has been discussed whether the growing polymer chain is bonded to the Al (or to another metal of Group II or III present in the alkyl metal used) or to the transition metal component. At present there is little doubt that the polymer grows on the transition metal. Evidence for this conclusion is that stereospecific catalysts have been obtained by transition metal compounds alone, in the absence of Al. For example, in the field of diolefins, $TiCl_2(CH_3)_2$ (31) gives 1,4 polybutadienes similar to those obtained with AlR_3–$TiCl_4$, Al/Ti = 2, and (π-allyl)$_3$Cr gives 1,2 polybutadienes (163), a fraction of which shows crystallinity of the syndiotactic type (61).

Commonly this type of polymerization is called "coordinated anionic." The term "anionic" may seem incorrect considering that the growing chain, at least in most of the cases, is not a free ion but is bonded to the transition metal by an essentially covalent bond. In the case of diolefins this bond is of the π-allylic type. However, this term is to be understood in the sense that in the polarized metal–carbon bond involved in the polymerization, the positive charge is on the metal and the negative on the carbon of the growing chain. The term "coordinated" is used because the monomer coordinates to the transition metal before it is incorporated into the growing chain. This topic will be discussed later (see Section V-2-a).

b. Polymerization by Co Catalysts. According to some authors the Co catalysts used for the *cis*-1,4 polymerization of butadiene are different from those examined in the previous section.

Arguments in favor of this are as follows:

1. When the growing polymer chain is terminated by CH_3OH^3, tritium is not found in the polymer.

2. The $AlEt_2Cl$–Co compound systems are inactive without the addition of an activator e.g., H_2O.

3. Catalysts obtained from $Al(C_2{}^{14}H_5)_2Cl$ yield polymers that do not contain C^{14}.

4. High *cis*-1,4 polybutadienes can also be obtained with catalysts from $AlCl_3$ and $CoCl_2$ in the absence of any metal alkyl. It seems highly improbable, according to some authors, that the polymerization by these systems proceeds by monomer incorporation at a metal–carbon bond, since bonds of this type are not present in the catalyst system.

These items will be discussed separately.

(*1*) *Termination of the Growing Chains by Labeled Alcohols.* This is a much debated point. Childers found (164) that polybutadienes initiated by $AlEt_2Cl$–Co octoate were radioactive if terminated by C^{14}-containing butanol while they were inactive if terminated by CH_3OH^3. He deduced from this that the polymerization was cationic. Cooper repeated Childers' experiments and obtained opposite results (165): he thus deduced that the polymerization was anionic. Natta and co-workers found (166) activity in the polymers terminated by CH_3OH^3 but showed that the activity is partly derived from secondary reactions. Also they cast some doubts on the validity of the method with catalysts based on metals of Group VIII. Bresler has recently reexamined (161) the problem and his data are substantially in agreement with those of Childers'.

These discrepancies demonstrate the complexities of these measurements. This is partly due to the very low amount of catalyst used and also to the possibility of secondary reactions. For instance, Cooper found (105) that upon terminating with inactive alcohol polymerizations initiated by the $AlEt_2Cl^{36}$–Co octoate–H_2O system, the polymer contained radioactive Cl^{36}. Evidently, in the termination by alcohol, HCl^{36} is evolved which may add to the polymer double bonds. Thus the polymer may become radioactive. This was probably one of the sources of contamination observed by G. Natta and co-workers in their experiments (166). It is difficult to explain why Childers and Bresler have not found radioactivity deriving from secondary reactions of this type in the polymers terminated by CH_3OH^3.

It should be added that the validity of these termination processes for the AlR_2Cl–Co compound catalyst has never been thoroughly investigated. According to the mechanism of anionic polymerizations the polymer chain is bonded to Co by a π-allylic bond. There is no experimental evidence showing that in a reaction between the catalyst complex and CH_3OH^3, the bond between Co and the last polymerized unit would react quantitatively with the alcohol according to:

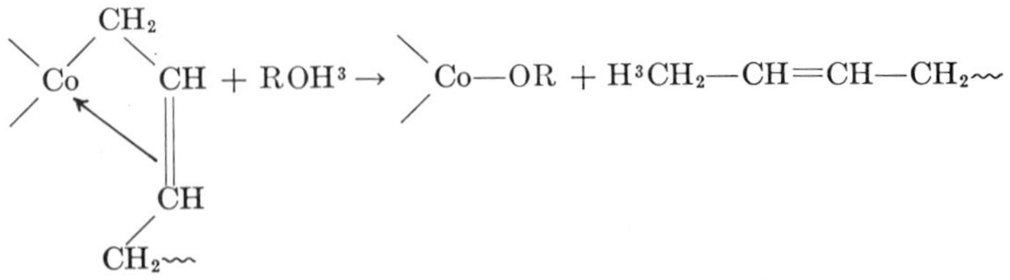

It is known that π-allyl-Ni halides are stable in alcohols and can initiate the polymerization of butadiene in alcohol solvent (102). It has been established that this polymerization is anionic in the sense discussed above. Thus termination with labelled alcohols is not of general validity, particularly when applied to the polymerization of diolefins by catalysts based on metals of the Group VIII.

These considerations cast doubt on the conclusions derived from termination experiments with CH_3OH^3.

(*2*) *Activation of the Catalysts by* H_2O. Although the question of catalyst activation for the *cis*-1,4 polybutadiene process remains controversial, it has been established that the addition of particular substances (e.g., H_2O) strongly influence both the rate of polymerization and the molecular weight. However, this is no evidence for the hypothesis that Co catalysts are of a different nature than those obtained from, e.g., $TiCl_3$, $TiCl_4$, etc.

Since H_2O is always added in small amounts with respect to the aluminum alkyl, compounds containing the $>$Al—O—Al$<$ group might arise by the following reaction:

$$2AlEt_3 + H_2O \rightarrow Et_2Al{-}O{-}AlEt_2 + 2C_2H_6$$

A possible explanation for the activation by H_2O is that compounds containing the $>$Al—O—Al$<$ group, or mixtures of such compounds with AlR_2Cl, may be much more active in the polymerization than the initial organoaluminum compounds.

(*3*) *Absence of Radioactivity in Polymers Obtained with* $Al(C_2{}^{14}H_5)_2Cl$–$Co(acac)_2$. The fact that polymers obtained with the $Al(C_2{}^{14}H_5)_2Cl$–$Co(acac)_2$ system were inactive (167) might suggest that the Co—C bond is not involved in the polymerization. This fact was considered by some authors as further evidence that the polymerization by Co catalysts is cationic (164).

Actually the absence of C^{14} in the polymer is quite consistent with the hypothesis that the polymer grows on a Co—C bond. It has been established that the reaction between $AlEt_2Cl$ and a Co compound leads to the formation of a complex which contains Co(I) (58,60). However, Co—C bonds could form by the reaction of butadiene with the complex containing Co(I), e.g.,

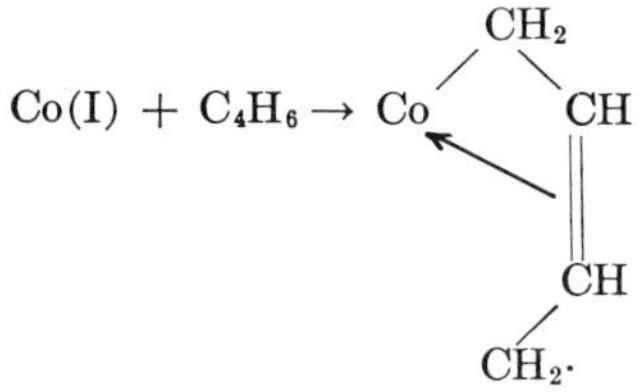

Two radicals of this type could couple rapidly giving rise to a chain growing at the two ends. Transfer reactions with monomer would lead to chains bonded only to one Co and therefore growing only at one end.

Initiation of this type takes place in the polymerization of dienes with metallic lithium (168). In this case a Li—C bond is formed (and consequently a formal oxidation from metallic lithium to Li(I) occurs) as a result of the reaction of Li with C_4H_6 (cf. Chapter 6, p. 496).

Various reactions between diolefins and transition metal compounds are known to lead to the formation of π-allyl bonds. Thus, dichloro-(dodeca-2,6,10-triene-1,2-diyl)Ru(IV) containing two π-allyl bonds was obtained from $RuCl_3$ and butadiene (169), dichloro(2,7-dimethyl-octa-2,6-diene-1,8-diyl)Ru(IV) was obtained from $RuCl_3$ and isoprene (170), and a $Rh_2Cl_4C_{12}H_8$ complex which probably contains π-allyl bonds was obtained from $RhCl_3$ and butadiene (171).

These facts indicate that the existence of a Co—C bond is not a necessary prerequisite for anionic polymerization since such a bond can be easily formed by the action of the monomer on the complex obtained from $AlEt_2Cl$ and the Co compound. This type of initiation can explain the absence of radioactivity in polymers obtained by the system Al-$(C_2{}^{14}H_5)_2Cl$–Co(acac)$_2$.

The hypothesis that the polymer chain grows on a Co—C bond is further supported by the following facts: a) cobalt–allyl–monoiodide can polymerize butadiene to a predominantly *cis*-1,4 polymer (163), b) π-allyl–Ni–Cl is capable of producing low polymers of butadiene having predominantly *cis*-1,4 structures (102,172). There is also evidence which indicates that the chain grows by incorporation of the monomer at the Ni—C bond.

(*4*) *Catalysts from* $AlCl_3$ *and* Co *Compounds.* The catalysts obtained from $AlCl_3$ (or $AlBr_3$) and Co compounds (in particular $CoCl_2$) might be considered to belong to a different class from that obtained from $AlEt_2Cl$. Here we must distinguish between the complexes obtained in the presence of metallic Al (63) and those obtained in the absence of any reducing agent (65,66). The former complexes contain Co(I) (64) and may initiate in the same way as complexes obtained from $AlEt_2Cl$.

It is conceivable that the catalysts obtained in the absence of a reducing agent, i.e., from aluminum trihalide and a Co compound, are similar to $AlEt_2Cl–CoCl_2$ systems. In other words, the active species could contain a Co—C bond formed by the reaction between the monomer and the initial complex, also in the case of the $AlCl_3·CoCl_2$ system. The complex obtained from $AlBr_3$ and $CoBr_2$ in aromatic solvent has been examined by Fisher (64). This author showed the existence of $[(arene)_2Co]^{2+}$ which under particular conditions could be isolated as a salt with the anion $(PtCl_6)^{2-}$. It is extremely interesting, however, that this cation can undergo disproportionation very easily to give the more stable monovalent cation $[(arene)_2Co]^+$. It is possible that a disproportionation of this type also occurs during the catalyst formation. If so, the initiation by these catalysts should also fall within the case examined under (*3*).

The formation of a Co—C bond via a radical anion is not the only possible explanation. For instance, it is known that the complex between butadiene and $PdCl_2$, $C_4H_6·PdCl_2$, exists in solution as

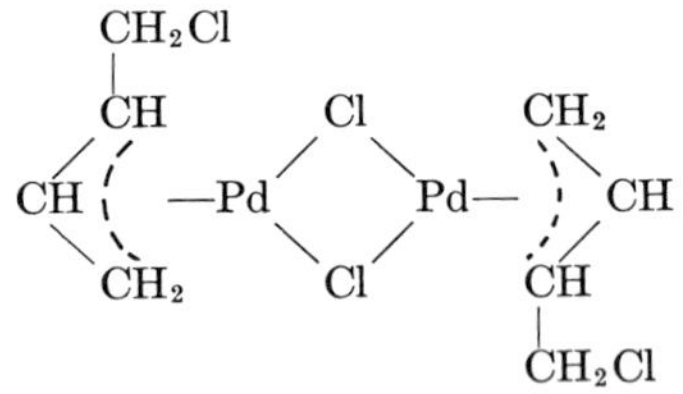

a π-allyl complex (173). Similarly, butadiene may coordinate to the Co of the $2AlCl_3·CoCl_2$ complex to form a π-allyl bond:

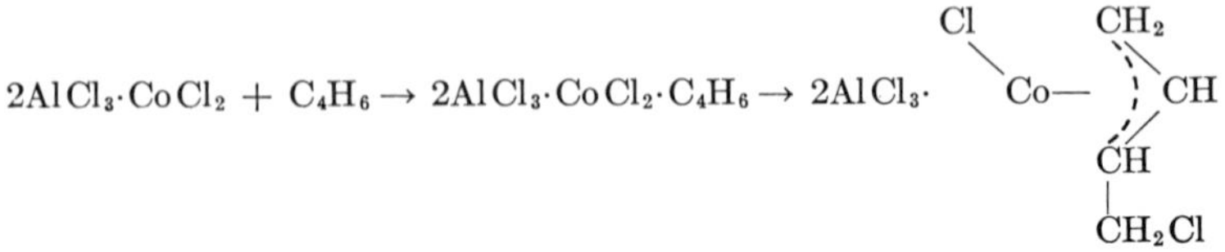

In conclusion it seems that Co catalysts also operate by a coordinated anionic mechanism, as do other catalysts obtained from aluminum alkyls and Ti, V, Cr, Mo compounds. Co-containing catalysts are probably ionic complexes in which the Al is part of an anion, and the Co is part of a cation. In the presence of the monomer the following complex can be visualized:

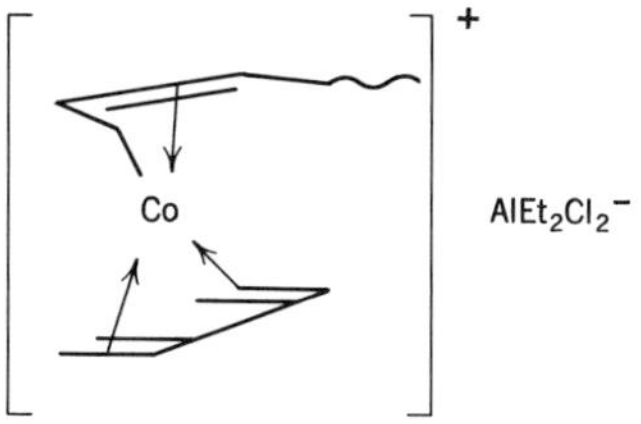

The growing chain is bonded to the Co by a π-allyl bond, while the incoming monomer is coordinated by the two double bonds. Obviously this figure is an oversimplification, as the catalyst is a rapidly changing species during polymerization and cannot be represented by a single formula or figure.

2. Factors Determining or Influencing the Type of Addition of the Monomeric Units

Although the mechanism of polymerization of conjugated diolefins by stereospecific catalysts is still rather obscure it is now possible, after twelve years of research in this field, to single out some of the factors which determine or influence the type of addition of the monomeric units. This aspect of the problem will now be examined.

a. Coordination of the Monomer to the Catalyst. It is now generally accepted that the incoming monomer coordinates to the transition metal of the catalyst before being incorporated into the growing chain. Some authors have expressed reservations with this hypothesis because of kinetic results (175) or other considerations (176). Several facts, however, indicate that coordination actually does occur. The transition metal in the catalyst complex is in a low valence state and is electron-deficient, therefore the monomer should be able to coordinate to it.

Evidence for the coordinating capability of the transition metal in the catalytic complex exists with the Co catalysts. As already mentioned (see I-C-4) $AlEt_2Cl$ and a cobalt compound in aromatic solvent give a cation, $[(\text{arene})_2Co]^+$, which can be isolated. If the arene coordinates to Co, the monomer, also an electron donor, is also expected to coordinate to Co. The coordination of the monomer evidently occurs by displacement of the arene. This explains why the addition of hexamethylbenzene to the benzene solution of the catalyst inactivates the catalyst (62). Hexamethylbenzene is a strong electron donor and therefore coordinates so strongly to Co that it cannot be displaced by the monomer.

The mode of coordination of the monomer to the transition metal may determine the type of addition of the monomer unit. If the coordination occurs through both double bonds with the monomer in the *cis* conformation, it appears plausible that a *cis*-1,4 unit will be formed. This occurs most probably in the polymerization by Co catalysts.

The formation of a 1,2 unit is probably preceded by coordination involving only one unsaturated group. That the monomer coordinates by only one unsaturated group is determined by the number of vacant coordination sites around the transition metal.

Various arguments, however, suggest that a diolefin coordinated by only one unsaturated group can lead, after incorporation, not only to 1,2 but also to *trans*-1,4 units. Evidence suggesting that in the case of homogeneous catalysts the formation of *trans*-1,4 units is preceded by a coordination of the monomer with only one unsaturated group are as follows:

1. It seems unlikely that a diolefin can coordinate to a metal with both double bonds in the *trans* conformation. No example exists in organometallic chemistry for a coordination of this type.

2. Two typical homogeneous catalysts which yield *cis*-1,4 polybutadiene in benzene, i.e., $LiAlH_4$–TiI_4 and $AlEt_2Cl$–Co compound (see I-D-1a), yield *trans*-1,4 polybutadiene when a small amount of Lewis base is added to the system (Section I-D-1b). This can be explained by assuming that the Lewis base occupies one coordination site so that the monomer can no longer coordinate through both double bonds but only by one (105).

On the other hand, if coordination by only one unsaturated group can lead to *trans*-1,4 units, it seems that at least in one case (62) this type of coordination can also lead to *cis*-1,4 units (see I-F-3).

In conclusion, while coordination through both double bonds leads to *cis*-1,4 units, coordination through only one vinyl group may lead to 1,2 as well as to *trans*-1,4 or *cis*-1,4 units. The factors determining the type of unit obtained in the latter case are in general obscure and, as we will see later, are known only in particular cases.

b. Effect of the Chemical Structure of the Catalyst. 1,2 vs. 1,4 Polybutadienes. In general, catalysts from transition metal halides yield 1,4 polymers from butadiene while those halogen free compounds yield 1,2 polymers. Thus, catalysts from AlR_3 and $TiCl_4$, VCl_4, $TiCl_3$, or VCl_3 yield 1,4 polymers, whereas those from AlR_3 and $Ti(OR)_4$ or $V(acac)_3$ yield 1,2 polymers. However, catalysts from AlR_2X (X = halogen) and halogen free transition metal compounds, such as $Ti(OR)_4$, $V(acac)_3$, $Co(acac)_2$ also give 1,4 polymers. This is due to the fact that the groups bonded to the transition metal are replaced by the halogen of the Al compound. The two systems AlR_3–$MoCl_5$ and AlR_3–$CoCl_2$, which are prepared from halogen containing compounds but yield 1,2 polymers (Section I-D-1c), may appear to be exceptions. However, in these systems practically all the chlorine is removed from the transition metal during the reaction with AlR_3.

In some cases the formation of 1,4 units is favored by catalyst heterogeneity. For example, the heterogeneous AlR_3–VCl_3 system, gives 95–98% *trans*-1,4 polymers from pentadiene, while the homogeneous AlR_2Cl –VCl_3·3THF system gives about 70% *trans*-1,4 and 30% 1,2 polypentadienes (Section I-D-3a).

With homogeneous systems, however, the chemical nature of the catalytic complex determines the type of enchainment, i.e., 1,2 or 1,4. Let us consider, e.g., the two homogeneous systems AlR_3–V $(acac)_3$, which yields 1,2 polybutadiene, and $AlEt_2Cl$–$V(acac)_3$, which yields *trans*-1,4 polybutadiene. In both cases the polymer grows on an allylic bond between V and the terminal polymer unit. The mode of coordination of the monomer does not seem to be a determining factor since in both cases the monomer probably coordinates only through the vinyl group. A possible explanation for the different modes of monomer addition is that the allylic unit, depending on the nature of the groups bonded to the transition metal, can react either as I (which gives rise to 1,4 units) or as II (which gives rise to 1,2 units).

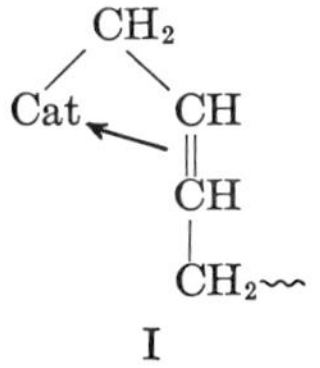

I

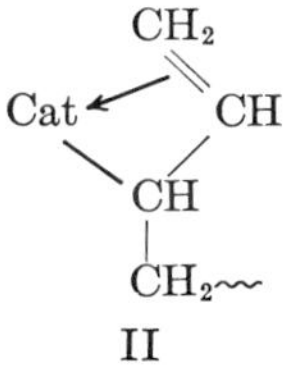

II

These questions cannot be resolved at present since very little is known about how substituents on the transition metal affect the properties of π-allyl bonds.

c. Effects of Monomer Substituents. Different monomers can yield different polymer structures by the same catalyst system. This can be

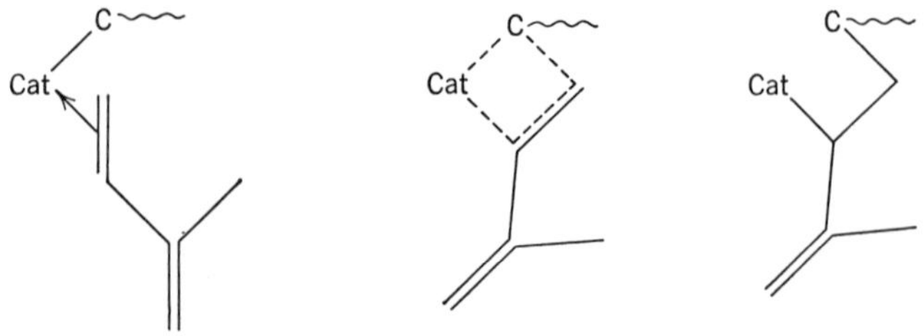

Fig. 7. Possible scheme for the formation of 3,4 units from isoprene.

explained by steric, inductive, or conformational factors depending on the nature and position of the substituents in the monomer.

(1) 1,2 Polymers from 4-Methyl-1,3-Pentadiene. 4-Methyl-1,3-pentadiene is easily polymerized by catalysts from AlR_3 and $TiCl_3$, $TiCl_4$, VCl_3, or VCl_4 to predominantly 1,2 polymers (177). The above systems give almost completely 1,4 polymers with butadiene, isoprene, or pentadiene. The different behavior of 4-methyl-1,3-pentadiene has been attributed to a steric effect due to the presence of the methyl group in the 4 position.

(2) 1,4 Polypentadienes and 3,4 Polyisoprenes by the AlR_3–$Ti(OR)_4$ *System.* The homogeneous AlR_3–$Ti(OR)_4$ system yields 1,2 polymers from butadiene (Section I-D-1c), 3,4 polymers from isoprene (Section I-D-2c) and *cis*-1,4 polymers from 1,3-pentadiene (Section I-D-3b).

The reason why 1,4 units are obtained from 1,3-pentadiene and 3,4 units from isoprene has been attributed to the different electronic distribution in the two monomers due to the different position of the methyl group. Figures 7 and 8 show possible schemes for the formation of 3,4 units from isoprene and 1,4 units from 1,3-pentadiene (62,108).

(3) 1,4 Polybutadienes and 1,2 Polypentadienes by $AlEt_2Cl$–$Co(acac)_3$ *in n-heptane.* The $AlEt_2Cl$–$Co(acac)_3$ system in *n*-heptane yields *cis*-1,4 polybutadienes (Section I-D-1a), and 1,2 polypentadienes (Section I-D-3c).

These facts may be explained as follows. With Co catalysts, a *cis*-1,4 unit is obtained presumably by a coordination of the monomer to Co through both double bonds. Such coordination probably occurs in two steps: first, coordination through only one of the two double bonds and, second, coordination with the other. There is some experimental evidence in support of this hypothesis. $PdCl_2$ forms a complex with 1,5-cyclooctadiene, $C_8H_{12}\cdot PdCl_2$, and also with butadiene, $C_4H_6\cdot PdCl_2$.

In these complexes the diolefin is coordinated to Pd by both double bonds. When operating at low temperatures, however, an intermediate has been observed in which the diolefin is coordinated to Pd by only one double bond (179).

Thus it is suggested that the mechanism of the formation of a *cis*-1,4 unit by Co catalysts is that shown by route I in Fig. 9. Coordination through only one of the vinyl groups leads to a 1,2 unit by route II. According to this scheme the structure of the polymer is determined by the relative rates of the reactions by routes I and II. With $AlEt_2Cl$–$Co(acac)_3$ in *n*-heptane, 1,3-pentadiene would react faster by route II, while butadiene would react faster by route I.

(4) 1,4 Polypentadienes by AlR_3–$TiCl_4$ *Catalyst.* Polypentadienes obtained by this system have predominantly *trans*-1,4 structures when prepared from the *cis* isomer, and predominantly *cis*-1,4 structures when prepared from the *trans* isomer (61). This is probably due to conformational factors relating to the monomer. The *trans* isomer can assume both the *trans* and the *cis* conformation and yields *cis*-1,4 polypentadiene with this catalyst, which preferentially yields *cis*-1,4 polymers. For steric reasons the *cis* isomer cannot assume the *cis* conformation and therefore polymerizes to a predominantly *trans*-1,4 polymer.

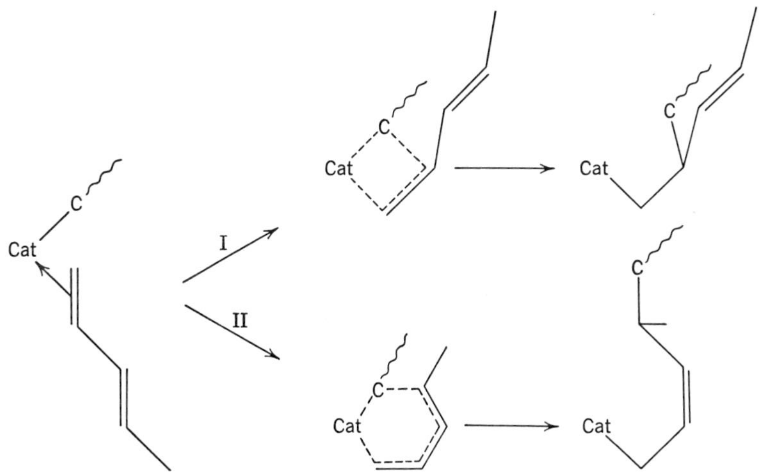

Fig. 8. Possible scheme for the formation of *cis*-1,4 (II) or 1,2 (I) units from 1,3-pentadiene.

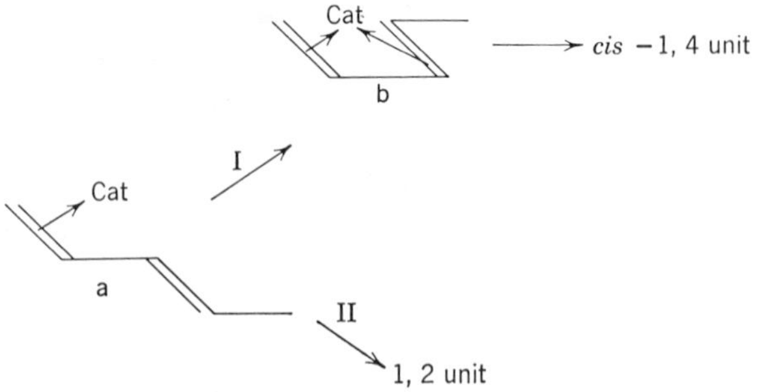

Fig. 9. 1,2 versus *cis*-1,4 polymerization of 1,3-pentadiene.

3. Forces of Stereoregulation

Five of the polymers previously discussed exhibit configurational regularity with respect to the asymmetric carbon atoms in the chain, namely isotactic and syndiotactic 1,2 polybutadiene, isotactic and syndiotactic *cis*-1,4 polypentadiene, and isotactic *trans*-1,4 polypentadiene. All these polymers can be obtained by homogeneous catalysts. Thus with diolefins, a solid catalytic surface is not a necessary condition for stereoregulation. This has been clearly recognized since 1955–1956, when the first isotactic and syndiotactic 1,2 polybutadienes were obtained with homogeneous catalysts. Although the presence of a solid catalytic surface is not necessary it can influence the stereospecificity. Thus, isotactic *trans*-1,4 polypentadiene obtained with $AlEt_3$–VCl_3 is more crystalline (and of higher molecular weight) than that obtained with butyl lithium in a homogeneous phase. Furthermore, isotactic *cis*-1,4 polypentadiene obtained with the hetereogeneous $AlEt_3$–$TiCl_4$ system (Al/Ti $\sim$2; *trans* isomer of pentadiene) exhibits higher crystallinity (61) than polymers obtained with the homogeneous $AlEt_3$–$Ti(OR)_4$ system, although the latters have higher *cis*-1,4 contents. Evidently, the polymers obtained with the heterogeneous $AlEt_3$–$TiCl_4$ system contain more stereoregular isotactic sequences than those obtained with the homogeneous system.

In the case of diolefin polymerization, the catalytic complex (which, for simplicity, we shall consider as symmetric) and the terminal monomer unit constitute an asymmetric system, independently of the nature of the diolefin (butadiene, isoprene or pentadiene) and of the structure of the terminal unit (1,2, *trans*-1,4, or *cis*-1,4). In fact, a system consisting of a diene bonded to a metal by a π-allylic bond does not have a plane of symmetry. The formation of a stereoregular sequence by the incorporation of the coordinated monomer into the Me—C bond (Me = transition metal) is determined by two factors: (1) the relative configuration assumed by the incoming monomer with respect to the asymmetric system consisting of the catalytic center and the terminal monomer unit; (2) the mode of monomer incorporation, i.e., *cis* or *trans* opening of the double bonds.

Provided the chemical nature of the catalyst remains the same during polymerization, the mode of the double bond opening also remains the same throughout the process. Since the latter should remain the same as long as the chemical nature of the catalyst does not change, it may be concluded that point (*1*) determines the formation of a stereoregular sequence.

Little is known about the factors that determine the configuration of the incoming monomer with respect to the asymmetric system consisting of the transition metal and the terminal monomer unit. The only case for which plausible hypotheses have been put forward is that of the polymerization of 1,3-pentadiene to isotactic and syndiotactic *cis*-1,4 polymers.

In the schemes proposed (Figs. 10 and 11) pentadiene coordinates through the vinyl group only in the AlR_3–$Ti(OR)_4$ system, while it coordinates through both double bonds in the $AlEt_2Cl$–$Co(acac)_2$ system. Figs. 10(a) and 11(a) show the transition metal with the terminal monomer unit bonded to it, and a coordinated monomer molecule; Figs. 10(b) and 11(b) represent the transition state; Figs. 10(c) and 11(c) show the transition metal with the monomer that was coordinated in (a) already incorporated, and a new coordinated monomer molecule. It can easily

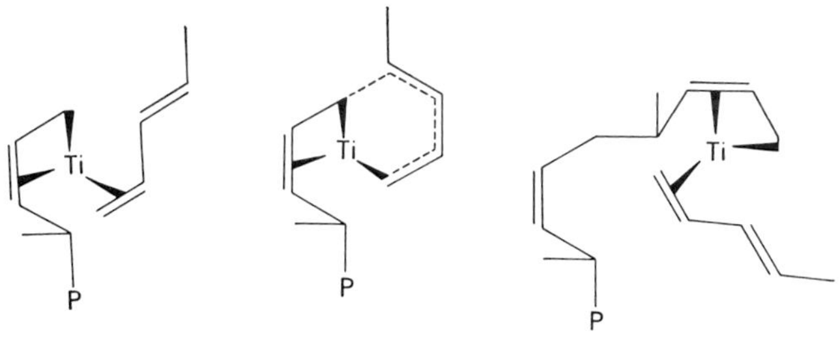

(*a*) (*b*) (*c*)

Fig. 10. Possible scheme for the formation of *cis*-1,4 isotactic polypentadiene.

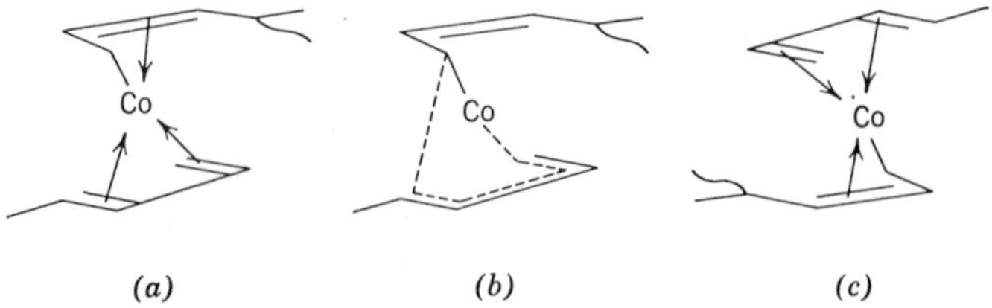

Fig. 11. Possible scheme for the formation of *cis*-1,4 syndiotactic polypentadiene.

be seen that Fig. 10(c) represents a situation identical to that shown in Fig. 10(a). Therefore, after incorporation, the coordinated monomer in (c) will give a unit with the same configuration as the preceding one. By this mechanism, *cis*-1,4 isotactic sequences will be formed.

On the other hand, Fig. 11(c) shows a situation that is enantiomorphous to that depicted in Fig. 11(a). Therefore, after incorporation, the coordinated monomer in (c) will give a unit with configuration opposite to the preceding one. Hence, *cis*-1,4 syndiotactic sequences will be formed by this mechanism. Obviously, these schemes are grossly oversimplified and the phenomena actually occurring during polymerization are much more complex.

II. COPOLYMERS OF BUTADIENE, ISOPRENE, AND PIPERYLENE

A. Introduction

Most studies of the polymerization of conjugated diolefins with catalysts based on transition metals have been concerned with the preparation of homopolymers. Relatively little effort has been devoted to the copolymerization of diolefins. Apart from disclosures in the patent literature, information is available concerning the following types of copolymers:

1. Butadiene–2-phenyl-butadiene copolymers obtained with Ti catalysts containing iodine (181).
2. Butadiene–pentadiene copolymers, obtained (*a*) with the heterogeneous $AlEt_3$–VCl_3 system (182), and (*b*) with the homogeneous $AlEt_2Cl$–$V(acac)_3$ system (182,183).

3. Butadiene–isoprene copolymers, obtained (*a*) with the AlR_3–$TiCl_4$ system (184,185), and (*b*) with the alkylaluminumchloride–Co compound system (184,186).

The copolymerization of conjugated diolefins with ethylene and/or α-olefins has been investigated extensively, but this subject falls outside the scope of this chapter.

B. Copolymers of Butadiene and 2-Phenyl-Butadiene

Copolymers of butadiene and 2-phenyl-butadiene have been prepared with the $AlHCl_2 \cdot O(C_2H_5)_2$–$AlI_3$–$TiCl_4$ system ($AlHCl_2/AlI_3/TiCl_4$ molar ratio = 5:1:1). This catalyst yields homopolymers with predominantly *cis*-1,4 structure from both butadiene and 2-phenyl-butadiene. In the copolymers both monomer units have *cis*-1,4 structure. The formation of true copolymers has been confirmed through fractionation, solvent extraction, and determination of glass transition temperatures. The copolymers are apparently random.

The reactivity ratios were found to be

$$r_{C_4} = 1.85\text{–}1.90 \qquad r_{PhC_4} = 2.58\text{–}2.6$$

Technological evaluation showed that the copolymers possess outstanding elastomeric properties. Greatly improved stress-strain properties, tear strengths and friction coefficients have been demonstrated. The introduction of up to about 25% by weight of 2-phenyl-butadiene into the *cis*-1,4 polybutadiene chain showed only a slight influence on the heat build-up. Thus butadiene–2-phenyl-butadiene copolymers (181), show particularly interesting properties for general purpose elastomer applications.

C. Copolymers of Butadiene and Piperylene

1. Copolymers Obtained with the Heterogeneous $AlEt_3$–VCl_3 *System*

The heterogeneous $AlEt_3$–VCl_3 system yields butadiene-1,3-pentadiene copolymers in which both the butadiene and the pentadiene units have a *trans*-1,4 structure (182). It is known (see Sections I-D-1b and I-D-3a) that the homopolymers of both butadiene and pentadiene obtained with the same system also have a 99–100% *trans*-1,4 structure. Either the *trans* or the *cis* isomer of pentadiene can be used as the comonomer.

TABLE XXIV
Melting Temperatures of *trans*-1,4-Butadiene-Pentadiene Copolymers (182)

Copolymer composition, C_4, mole %	T_m, °C
100	145
86	130
63	128
46	107
33	99
23	97
0	95

trans-1,4 Butadiene-pentadiene copolymers obtained with the $AlEt_3$–VCl_3 catalyst are crystalline over the whole composition range examined (from about 20 to 100% C_4). The final melting temperatures (T_m) are between those of the homopolymers over the entire composition range (Table XXIV). The type of crystallinity in the copolymers depends on their composition. Copolymers rich in butadiene (85–100%) exhibit crystallinity typical of modification I of *trans*-1,4 polybutadiene, while copolymers having lower butadiene content exhibit the crystallinity typical of modification II of *trans*-1,4 polybutadiene.

Copolymers properties have been explained by assuming that, due to the pendant methyl groups, the *trans*-1,4 pentadiene units are not (or only to a slight extent) isomorphous with the butadiene units of mod. I of *trans*-1,4 polybutadiene while they are isomorphous with mod. II, which is characterized by a higher equatorial encumberment for each chain.

2. Copolymers Obtained with the Homogeneous $AlEt_2Cl$–$V(acac)_3$ *System*

In copolymers obtained with the homogeneous $AlEt_2Cl$–$V(acac)_3$ catalyst, the butadiene units have *trans*-1,4 structure while the pentadiene units are partly *trans*-1,4 and partly 1,2. Only the *trans* isomer of pentadiene can be polymerized by this catalyst (182,183).

In these copolymers the melting temperature (T_m) decreases rapidly with increasing pentadiene content. The transition temperature (T_t) from mod. I to mod. II also decreases, but much less rapidly than T_m. Table XXV shows the values of T_m and T_t for various copolymers as a function of composition.

The difference in properties between these butadiene-pentadiene copolymers and those obtained with the $AlEt_3$–VCl_3 catalyst have been attributed to the side chains of the 1,2 pentadiene units which prevent the former copolymers from being isomorphous with mod. II of *trans*-1,4 polybutadiene (and, hence, even less with mod. I).

As shown by the data in Table XXV, a relatively small amount of C_5 units strongly decreases the T_m. This is due to the low enthalpy of fusion of mod. II of *trans*-1,4 polybutadiene, which is about 1000 cal/monomer unit (188).

The properties of the copolymers depend on the composition. Copolymers with a low pentadiene content and hence a high melting temperature are plastomers. On the other hand, copolymers which have a T_m close to room temperature are elastomeric. Thus, a continuous spectrum of products can be obtained by incorporating varying amounts of pentadiene into the *trans*-1,4 polybutadiene chain.

The elastomers obtained from the copolymers with T_m about 20°C have good hysteresis properties and are also able to crystallize on stretching. The type of crystallinity appearing on stretching at room temperature is that of mod. II of *trans*-1,4 polybutadiene (i.e., the modification of pure *trans*-1,4 polybutadiene which is stable above ~75°C).

The capacity of these copolymers to crystallize on stretching is therefore related to the isomorphism in *trans*-1,4 polybutadiene. More precisely, it is due to the existence of mod. II, which is characterized by an irregular chain conformation and therefore can exist even when a certain number of extraneous units have been introduced into the chains (183).

TABLE XXV
Transition and Melting Temperatures of Butadiene-Pentadiene Copolymers Obtained with the Homogeneous $Al(C_2H_5)_2Cl$–$V(acac)_3$ and $Al(C_2H_5)_2Cl$–$VCl_3 \cdot 3THF$ Systems (183)

Copolymer composition, C_5, mole %	T_t, °C	T_m, °C
0	75	145
5	65	120
10	53	95
13	47	81
15	40	67
19	27	46
22	—	20

D. Copolymers of Butadiene and Isoprene

1. Copolymers Obtained with the Heterogeneous AlR_3–$TiCl_4$ *System*

Butadiene-isoprene copolymerization by the AlR_3–$TiCl_4$ catalysts has been studied by Bresler et al. (184) and by Suminoe et al. (185). It is known (see Sections I-D-1a and I-D-2a) that such catalysts are highly stereospecific for the polymerization of isoprene, yielding polymers with 95–97% *cis*-1,4 content, while they are considerably less stereospecific for the polymerization of butadiene, giving only about 70% *cis*-1,4 addition.

In the copolymers obtained either with $Al(i\text{-}C_4H_9)_3$–$TiCl_4$ (Al/Ti molar ratio 1.1:1) or with $Al(C_2H_5)_3$–$TiCl_4$ (Al/Ti molar ratio: 1.5:1), both the isoprene and the butadiene units have the same structure as in the homopolymers. That true copolymers, rather than mixtures of homopolymers, have been obtained was demonstrated by fractionation and by determination of the glass transition temperature (T_g). The latter varies linearly with composition from about −72°C to about −110°C for copolymers containing from 0 to 100% butadiene.

The reactivity ratios for the two monomers are $r_{C_4} = r_{C_5} = 1$. Hence, the composition of the copolymers corresponds exactly to the composition of the monomer charge.

2. Copolymers Obtained with the Homogeneous AlR_2Cl–Co *Compound System*

These types of copolymers have been studied by Bresler et al. (184), and by Pasquon et al. (186). The former authors (184) used $Al(i\text{-}C_4H_9)_2$-Cl–$CoCl_2 \cdot C_2H_5OH$ in benzene, the latter (186) $AlEt_2Cl$–$Co(acac)_2$ in toluene. It is known (see Section I-D-1a) that these systems are highly stereospecific for the polymerization of butadiene, yielding polymers with 97–98% *cis*-1,4 content, while they are less stereospecific for the polymerization of isoprene, yielding polymers with about 65–70% *cis*-1,4 units, the remaining ones being 3,4.

In the copolymers the microstructure of the butadiene and isoprene units depends on the copolymer composition. The ratio of *cis*-1,4 isoprene units/total C_5 units increases with increasing butadiene content, while the amount of 3,4 isoprene units simultaneously decreases. On the other hand, the ratio *cis*-1,4 butadiene units/total C_4 units decreases with increasing amounts of isoprene in the copolymer, while the 1,2

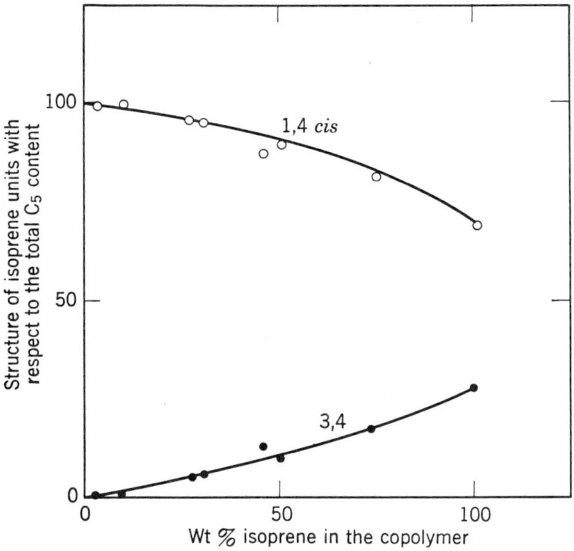

Fig. 12. Structure of isoprene units as a function of copolymer composition.

butadiene units simultaneously increase (Figs. 12 and 13). These facts suggest that the structure of a new unit is, at least in part, influenced by the nature and structure of the terminal monomer unit. Phenomena of this type have been observed in other types of copolymers (189).

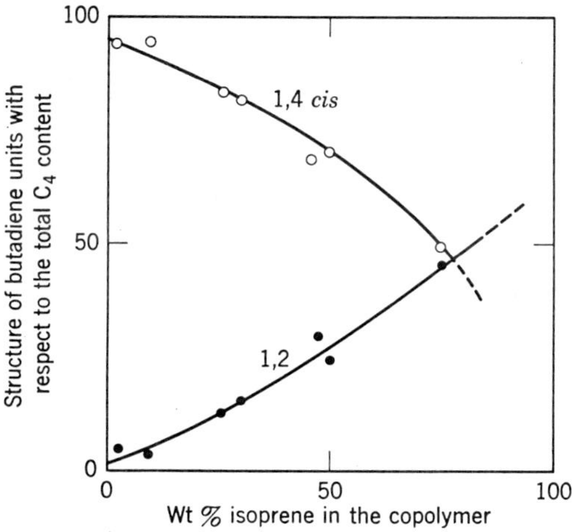

Fig. 13. Structure of butadiene units as a function of copolymer composition.

The reactivity ratios for the two monomers are $r_{C_4} = r_{C_5} = 1$ for copolymerization in toluene by $AlEt_2Cl$–$Co(acac)_2$, and $r_{C_4} = 2.3$, $r_{C_5} = 1.15$ for copolymerization in benzene by $Al(i\text{-}C_4H_9)_2Cl$–$CoCl_2\cdot$-C_2H_5OH.

The physical properties of the copolymers are determined by the composition. In particular, the melting temperature (which is about +3°C for 99% *cis*-1,4 polybutadiene) decreases with increasing isoprene content. These copolymers are therefore elastomers which may be suitable for low temperature applications.

References*

1. A. W. Meyer, R. R. Hampton, and J. A. Davison, *J. Am. Chem. Soc.*, **74,** 2294 (1952); *Rubber Chem. Technol.*, **26,** 522 (1953).
2. C. E. Schildknecht, *Polymer Processes,* Interscience, New York, 1956, p. 227.
3. G. S. Whitby, *Synthetic Rubber,* Wiley, 1954, pp. 734, 755, 959.
4. Firestone Tire & Rubber Co., Ital. Pat. 559704 (Sep. 19, 1955).
5. F. W. Stavely, et al., *Ind. Eng. Chem.*, **48,** 778 (1956).
6. H. Morita and A. V. Tobolski, *J. Am. Chem. Soc.*, **79,** 5853 (1957).
7. L. Porri, M. C. Gallazzi, and G. Natta, *Rend. Accad. Naz. Lincei,* (8) **36,** 752 (1964).
8. C. S. Marvel, R. Gilkey, C. R. Morgan, J. F. Noth, R. D. Rands, Jr., and C. H. Young, *J. Polymer Sci.*, **6,** 483 (1951).
9. W. S. Richardson, *J. Polymer Sci.*, **13,** 325 (1954).
10. J. L. Binder, *Ind. Eng. Chem.*, **46,** 1727 (1954).
11. K. E. Beu, W. B. Reynolds, C. F. Fryling, and H. L. McMurry, *J. Polymer Sci.*, **3,** 465 (1948).
12. W. S. Richardson and A. Sacher, *J. Polymer Sci.*, **10,** 353 (1953).
13. J. T. Maynard and W. E. Mochel, *J. Polymer Sci.*, **13,** 235 (1954).
14. J. T. Maynard and W. E. Mochel, *J. Polymer Sci.*, **13,** 251 (1954)
15. A. A. Morton, *J. Am. Chem. Soc.*, **68,** 68, 93 (1946); **69,** 160, 161, 167, 172, 950, 1657 (1947); **70,** 3132 (1948); **71,** 481, 487 (1949); **72,** 3785 (1950); *Ind. Eng. Chem.* **42,** 1488 (1950); *Rubber Chem. Technol.*, **24,** 35 (1951).
16. A. A. Morton, F. H. Bolton, F. W. Collins, and E. F. Cluff, *Ind. Eng. Chem.*, **44,** 2876 (1952).
17. J. D. D'Janni, F. J. Naples, and J. E. Field, *Ind. Eng. Chem.*, **42,** 95 (1950).
18. R. A. Stewart and H. Leverne Williams, *Ind. Eng. Chem.*, **45,** 173 (1953).
19. M. Farina, M. Peraldo, and G. Natta, *Angew. Chem., Intern. Ed.*, **4,** 107 (1965).
20. P. Pino, *Advan. Polymer Sci.*, **4,** 393 (1966).
21. C. L. Arcus, in P. B. De La Mare and W. Klyne, Eds., *Progress in Stereochemistry,* Butterworths, London, 1962, p. 264.
22. M. L. Huggins, G. Natta, V. Desreux, and H. Mark, *J. Polymer Sci.*, **56,** 153 (1962).
23. Goodrich-Gulf Chem., Inc., Eng. Pat. 827365 (Dec. 2, 1954, Apr. 21, 1955, Apr. 21, 1955). Inventors: S. E. Horne, F. Gibbs, and E. J. Carlson.
24. W. M. Saltman, W. E. Gibbs, and J. Lal, *J. Am. Chem. Soc.*, **80,** 5615 (1958).

* The date reported for each patent is the priority date in the country of origin.

25. M. L. Cooper and J. B. Rose, *J. Chem. Soc.*, 795 (1959).
26. P. H. Mayer, *J. Polymer Sci.*, *A*, **3**, 209 (1965).
27. G. Natta, L. Porri, A. Mazzei, and D. Morero, *Chim. Ind.*, **41**, 398 (1959).
28. G. Natta, P. Pino, G. Mazzanti, and P. Longi, *Gazz. Chim. It.*, **87**, 549 (1957).
29. H. N. Friedländer and K. Oita, *Ind. Eng. Chem.*, **49**, 1885 (1957).
30. H. Martin and J. Stedefeder, *Ann.*, **618**, 17 (1958).
31. C. Beerman and H. Bestian, *Angew Chem.*, **71**, 618 (1959).
32. M. H. Jones, U. Martins, and M. P. Thorne, *Can. J. Chem.*, **38**, 2303 (1960).
33. A. Simon and G. Ghymes, *J. Polymer Sci.*, **53**, 327 (1961).
34. R. J. Kern and H. G. Hurst, *J. Polymer Sci.*, **44**, 272 (1960).
35. Y. P. Tepenitsyna, M. I. Faberov, A. M. Kutin, and G. S. Sevskaia, *Vysokomolek. Soedin.*, **1** (8), 1148 (1959).
36. F. Böck and L. Moser, *Monatsh.*, **33**, 1407 (1912); *ibid.*, **34**, 1825 (1913).
37. G. Natta, P. Corradini, I. W. Bassi, and L. Porri, *Rend. Accad. Naz. Lincei*, (8) (**24**), 121 (1958).
38. G. Natta, L. Porri, and L. Fiore, *Gazz. Chim. It.*, **89**, 761 (1959).
39. W. Marconi, A. Mazzei, S. Cucinella, and M. De Maldè, *Makromol. Chem.*, **71**, 118 (1964).
40. W. Marconi, A. Mazzei, S. Cucinella, and M. De Maldè, *Makromol. Chem.*, **71**, 134 (1964).
41. Phillips Petr. Co., Belg. Pat. 551851 (Oct. 17, 1955; Apr. 16, 1956; Apr. 20, 1956; Apr. 30, 1956). Inventors: R. P. Zelinski and D. R. Smith.
42. W. M. Saltman and T. H. Link, *Ind. Eng. Chem., Prod. Res. Dev.*, **3**, 199 (1964).
43. Polymer Corp. Ltd., Belg. Pat. 610400 (Nov. 19, 1960). Inventor: J. Darcy.
44. Farbenfabriken Bayer, Belg. Pat. 612732 (Jan. 18, 1961; July 22, 1961). Inventors: G. Pampus, H. Gröne, and J. Witte.
45. Phillips Petroleum Co., Brit. Pat. 865337 (Nov. 8, 1958). Inventors: J. R. Hooton and F. E. Naylor.
46. Phillips Petroleum Co., Brit. Pat. 910216 (Aug. 8, 1960). Inventors: R. C. Farrar and F. E. Naylor.
47. Phillips Petroleum Co., U.S. Pat. 3,050,513 (Apr. 20, 1956). Inventors: R. P. Zelinski and D. R. Smith.
48. W. Marconi, M. Araldi, A. Béranger, and M. De Maldè, *Chim. Ind.*, **45**, 522 (1963).
49. W. Marconi, A. Mazzei, M. Araldi, and M. De Maldè, *J. Polymer Sci.*, *A*, **3**, 735 (1965).
50. W. Marconi, A. Mazzei, M. Araldi, and M. De Maldè, *Chim. Ind.*, **46**, 245 (1964).
51. C. Longiave, R. Castelli, and G. F. Croce, *Chim. Ind.*, **43**, 625 (1961).
52. M. Gippin, *Ind. Eng. Chem., Prod. Res. Dev.*, **1**, 32 (1962).
53. Montecatini S.p.A., Ital. Pat. 587968 (Feb. 11, 1958). Inventors: G. Marullo, A. Baroni, U. Maffezzoni, C. Longiave, and E. Susa.
54. Montecatini S.p.A., Ital. Pats. 592477 (Dec. 6, 1957) and 588825 (Dec. 24, 1957). Inventors: C. Longiave, G. F. Croce, and R. Castelli.
55. Montecatini S.p.A., Ital. Pat. 594618 (Apr. 24, 1958). Inventors: G. Marullo, U. Maffezzoni, A. Baroni, C. Longiave, and E. Susa.
56. De Bataafsche Petr. Maat., Brit. Pat. 911947 (Apr. 25, 1958). Inventor: E. A. Youngman.
57. Chemische Werke Hüls, Brit. Pat. 905001 (May 24, 1960).

58. Goodrich-Gulf Chem., Inc., Brit. Pat. 916384 (Dec. 19, 1958). Inventor: H. Scott.
59. L. Porri and A. Carbonaro, *Makromol. Chem.*, **60,** 236 (1963).
60. C. E. H. Bawn, *Rubber Plastics Age*, **46,** 510 (1965).
61. Unpublished results from authors' laboratory.
62. G. Natta and L. Porri, *Advan. Chem. Ser.*, **52,** 24 (1966).
63. H. Scott, R. E. Frost, R. F. Belt, D. E. O'Reilly, *J. Polymer Sci., A*, **2,** 3233 (1964).
64. E. O. Fischer and H. H. Lindner, *J. Organomet. Chem.*, **1,** 307 (1964).
65. J. G. Balas, H. E. De la Mare, and D. D. Schissler, *J. Polymer Sci., A*, **3,** 2243 (1965).
66. Montecatini S.p.A., Ital. Pat. 679829 (Dec. 12, 1962). Inventors: G. Natta, A. Carbonaro, and L. Porri.
67. Montecatini S.p.A., Ital. Pat. 566940 (July 31, 1956). Inventors: G. Natta, L. Porri, and P. Corradini.
68. G. Natta and P. Corradini, *Angew. Chem.*, **68,** 615 (1956).
69. De Bataafsche Petr. Maat., Brit. Pat. 906052 (Nov. 6, 1957). Inventors: J. G. Balas, L. M. Porter, and R. J. Renolds.
70. Goodrich-Gulf Chem., Belg. Pat. 575671 (Feb. 13, 1958). Inventor: H. Tucker.
71. De Bataafsche Petr. Maat., Brit. Pat. 906053 (Feb. 28, 1958). Inventors: A. J. Canale, J. G. Balas, and C. H. Wilcoxen, Jr.
72. Montecatini S.p.A., Ital. Pat. 587976 (Feb. 26, 1958). Inventors: G. Natta, L. Porri, and L. Fiore.
73. Du Pont, Brit. Pat. 776326 (Aug. 16; Aug. 19; Oct. 15; Nov. 22, 1954).
74. Monsanto Chem. Co., Brit. Pat. 795350 (Apr. 18, 1955). Inventors: C. A. Hochwalt and R. J. Slocombe.
75. Badische A.S.F., Brit. Pat. 798447 (Sep. 9, 1955).
76. Imperial Chem. Ind., Belg. Pat. 547669 (May 10, 1955; Dec. 9, 1955; Feb. 8, 1956; Apr. 18, 1956). Inventors: J. W. C. Crawford and M. F. Vincent.
77. Badische A.S.F., Brit. Pat. 807178 (Dec. 28, 1955). Inventors: H. Spänig and H. R. Heusel.
78. Goodrich-Gulf Chem., U.S. Pat. 2,977,349 (Nov. 7, 1956). Inventors: C. E. Brockway and A. F. Ekar.
79. Chemische Werke Hüls, Ital. Pat. 577790 (Sep. 26, 1956).
80. Goodrich-Gulf Chem., Brit. Pat. 835584 (Jan. 18, 1956). Inventors: W. L. Beears, M. R. Frederick, L. C. Kreider, and M. E. Roha.
81. N. G. Gaylord, T. K. Kwei, and H. F. Mark, *J. Polymer Sci.*, **42,** 417 (1960).
82. P. H. Moyer and M. H. Lehr, *J. Polymer Sci., A*, **3,** 217 (1965).
83. D. Morero, A. Santambrogio, L. Porri, and F. Ciampelli, *Chim. Ind.*, **41,** 758 (1959).
84. Polymer Corp. Ltd., Brit. Pat. 917401 (June 19, 1959). Inventors: L. A. McLeod and R. A. Stewart.
85. Firestone Tires & Rubber Co., Brit. Pat. 904421 (Apr. 13, 1959). Inventors: R. S. Stearns and A. Fono.
86. J. F. Henderson, *J. Polymer Sci., C*, **4,** 233 (1964).
87. A. Mazzei, M. Araldi, W. Marconi, and M. De Maldè, *J. Polymer Sci., A*, **3,** 753 (1965).
88. Phillips Petr. Co. Brit. Pat. 906266 (July 7, 1960). Inventor: R. C. Farrar.

89. B. A. Dolgoplosk, B. L. Erussalimskii, E. N. Kropatsheva, and E. I. Tinyakova, *J. Polymer Sci.*, **58**, 1333 (1962).
90. V. N. Zgonnik, B. A. Dolgoplosk, V. A. Kropatchev, and N. I., Nikolaiev, *Vysokomolekul. Soedin.*, **4**, 1000 (1962).
91. A. Guyot, M. Rochina, and Y. Trambuze, *Bull. Soc. Chim. France*, **1962**, 1893.
92. M. Gippin, *Ind. Eng. Chem., Prod. Res. Rev.*, **4**, 160 (1965).
93. E. I. Tinyakova, B. A. Dolgoplosk, T. K. Vydrina, and A. V. Alferov, *Dokl. Akad. Nauk SSSR*, **152** (6) 1376 (1963).
94. A. I. Diaconescu and S. S. Medvedev, *J. Polymer Sci.*, *A*, **3**, 31 (1965).
95. V. N. Zgonnik, B. A. Dolgoplosk, N. I. Nikolaiev, and V. A. Kropachev, *Vysokomolekul. Soedin*, **7** (2), 308 (1965).
96. C. Longiave, R. Castelli, and M. Ferraris, *Chim. Ind.*, **44**, 725 (1962).
97. Montecatini S.p.A., Ital. Pat. 687758 (Feb. 12, 1963). Inventors: E. Giachetti and W. Bortolini.
98. Montecatini S.p.A., Ital. Pat. 545952 (Mar. 12, 1955). Inventors: G. Natta, L. Porri, and M. Mazzanti.
99. Montecatini S.p.A., Ital. Pat. 553904 (Dec. 22, 1955). Inventors: G. Natta and L. Porri.
100. G. Natta, L. Porri, and A. Carbonaro, *Rend. Accad. Naz. Lincei*, **31** (8), 189 (1961).
101. L. Porri, G. Natta, and M. C. Gallazzi, *Chim. Ind.*, **46**, 428 (1964).
102. L. Porri, G. Natta, and M. C. Gallazzi, *J. Polymer Sci.*, *C*, **16**, 2525 (1967).
103. G. Natta, L. Porri, P. Corradini, and D. Morero, *Chim. Ind.*, **40**, 362 (1958).
104. G. Natta, L. Porri, and A. Mazzei, *Chim. Ind.* **41**, 116 (1959).
105. W. Cooper, G. Degler, D. E. Eaves, R. Hank, and G. Vaughan, *Advan. Chem. Ser.* **52**, 1966, page 46.
106. Montecatini S.p.A., Belg. Pat. 549544 (July 15, 1955). Inventors: G. Natta and L. Porri.
107. G. Natta, L. Porri, G. Zanini, and L. Fiore, *Chim. Ind.*, **41**, 526 (1959).
108. G. Natta, L. Porri, and A. Carbonaro, *Makromol. Chem.*, **77**, 126 (1964).
109. A. Mazzei, S. Cucinella, W. Marconi, and M. De Maldè, *Chim. Ind.*, **45**, 528 (1965).
110. E. Susa, *J. Polymer Sci.*, *C*, **4**, 399 (1964).
111. C. Longiave, and R. Castelli *J. Polymer Sci.*, *C*, **4**, 387 (1964).
112. D. W. Wittenberg, *Angew. Chem.*, **75**, 1124 (1963).
113. T. Saito, T. Ohno, Y. Uchida, and A. Misono, *J. Chem. Soc. Japan (Ind. Chem. Sect.)*, **66**, 1094 (1963).
114. De Bataafsche Petr. Maat. Brit. Pat. 837689 (Jan. 20, 1958). Inventor: L. M. Porter.
115. S. Otsuka and M. Kawakami, *Angew. Chem.*, **75**, 858 (1963).
116. Montecatini S.p.A., Ital. Pat. 563507 (Apr. 14, 1956). Inventors: G. Natta, L. Porri, and A. Palvarini.
117. G. Natta, L. Porri, G. Zanini, and A. Palvarini, *Chim. Ind.*, **41**, 1163 (1959).
118. F. Danusso, G. Moraglio, and G. Gianotti, *J. Polymer Sci.*, **51**, 475 (1961).
119. S. E. Horne, J. P. Kiehl, J. J. Shipman, V. L. Folt, C. F. Gibbs, E. A. Willson, E. B. Newton, and M. A. Reinhart, *Ind. Eng. Chem.*, **48**, 784 (1956).
120. R. H. Mayor, W. M. Saltman, and R. M. Pierson, *Rubber Plastics Age*, **39**, 938 (1958).

121. H. E. Adams, R. S. Stearns, W. A. Smith, and J. L. Binder, *Ind. Eng. Chem.*, **50,** 1507 (1958).
122. E. Schoenberg, D. L. Chalfant, and R. H. Mayor, *Rubber Chem. Tech.*, **37,** 103 (1964).
123. W. M. Saltman, *J. Polymer Sci.*, *A*, **1,** 373 (1963).
124. E. Schoenberg, D. L. Chalfant, and T. L. Hanlon, *Advan. Chem. Ser.*, **52,** 6 (1966).
125. N. Yamazaki, T. Suminoe, and S. Kambara, *Makromol. Chem.*, **65,** 157 (1963).
126. E. Schoenberg, D. L. Chalfant, J. B. Pyke, and R. H. Mayor, Paper presented at the Division of Ind. & Eng. Chemistry, A.C.S. New York Mtg, 1963.
127. J. D. D'Ianni, Communication at the Intern. Rubber Conference, Munich, June 1965.
128. J. L. Binder, *Polymer Letters*, **4,** 19 (1966).
129. W. Marconi, A. Mazzei, S. Cucinella, and M. De Maldè, *Chim. Ind.*, **44,** 121 (1962).
130. J. Furukawa, T. Tsuruta, T. Saegusa, A. Onishi, A. Kawasaki, and T. Fueno, *J. Polymer Sci.*, **28,** 450 (1958).
131. C. F. Gibbs, S. E. Horne, Jr., J. H. Macey, and H. Tucker, *Rubber World*, **144,** 69 (1961).
132. U.S. Rubber Co., Belg. Pat. 587628. Inventor: J. S. Lasky.
133. J. S. Lasky, H. K. Garner, and R. H. Ewart, *Ind. Eng. Chem.* (*Prod. Res. Dev.*), **1,** 82 (1962).
134. U.S. Rubber Co., U.S. Pat. 3,114,744 (Oct. 20, 1960). Inventor: J. S. Lasky.
135. Ye.V. Zabolotskaya, V. A. Khodzhemirov, A. R. Gantmakher, and S. S. Medvedev, *Polymer Sci. USSR*, **6** (1), 88, 94 (1964).
136. W. Cooper, D. E. Eaves, G. D. T. Owen, and G. Vaughan, *J. Polymer Sci., C*, **4,** 211 (1963).
137. G. Wilke, *Angew. Chem.*, **68,** 306 (1956).
138. H. Breil, P. Heinbach, M. Kröner, H. Müller, and G. Wilke, *Makromol. Chem.*, **69,** 18 (1963).
139. G. Natta, I. Pasquon, and E. Giachetti, *Chim. Ind.*, **40,** 97 (1958); G. Natta, I. Pasquon, E. Giachetti, and G. Pajaro, *Chim. Ind.*, **40,** 267 (1958).
140. M. Stolka, J. Vodelnal, and I. Koessler, *Coll. Czech. Chem. Commun.*, **28,** 1535 (1963); *Chem. Abstr.*, **59,** 5343 d (1963).
141. G. Natta, L. Porri, P. Corradini, G. Zanini, and F. Ciampelli, *J. Polymer Sci.*, **51,** 463 (1961).
142. G. Natta, L. Porri, G. Stoppa, G. Allegra, and F. Ciampelli, *J. Polymer Sci.*, *B*, **1,** 67 (1963).
143. G. Natta, L. Porri, A. Carbonaro, and G. Stoppa, *Makromol. Chem.* **77,** 114 (1964).
144. Montecatini S.p.A., Ital. Pat. 659704 (May 13, 1961). Inventors: G. Natta, L. Porri, A. Carbonaro, and G. Stoppa.
145. G. Natta, L. Porri, A. Carbonaro, F. Ciampelli, and G. Allegra, *Makromol. Chem.*, **51,** 229 (1962).
146. G. Natta, L. Porri, and G. Sovarzi, *European Polymer J.*, **1,** 81 (1965).
147. G. Natta and P. Corradini, *Nuovo Cimento, Suppl.* **15,** Ser. X, 32 (1960).
148. G. Natta, P. Corradini, and L. Porri, *Rend. Accad. Nazl. Lincei*, **20** (8), 728 (1956).
149. G. Natta and G. Moraglio, *Rubber Plastics Age*, **44,** 42 (1963).

150. G. Natta and P. Corradini, *Nuovo Cimento, Suppl.*, **15**, Ser. X, 111 (1960).
151. G. Crespi, U. Flisi, and A. Arcozzi, *Chim. Ind.*, **44**, 627 (1962).
152. G. Natta, L. Porri, P. Corradini, and D. Morero, *Rend. Accad. Nazl. Lincei*, **20** (8), 560 (1956).
153. G. Natta, P. Corradini, and I. W. Bassi, *Rend. Accad. Nazl. Lincei*, **23** (8), 363 (1957).
154. G. Natta and P. Corradini, *J. Polymer Sci.*, **20**, 251 (1956).
155. C. W. Bunn, *Proc. Royal Soc. (London) A*, **180**, 40, 82 (1942).
156. S. C. Nyburg, *Acta Cryst.*, **7**, 385 (1954).
157. W. Cooper, Communication presented at the 15th Congress on Plastics, Turin, Italy, Sept. 1963.
158. K. W. Scott, G. S. Trick, R. H. Mayor, W. M. Saltman, and R. M. Pierson, *Rubber Plastics Age*, **42**, 175 (1961).
159. G. Crespi, G. Guzzetta, S. Leghissa, and F. Sabbioni, *Rubber Plastics Age*, **42**, 402 (1961).
160. G. A. Jeffrey, *Trans. Faraday Soc.*, **40**, 517 (1944).
161. L. S. Bresler, I.Ya. Poddubnyi, and V. N. Sokolov, *J. Polymer Sci., C.*, **16**(8), 4339 (1969).
162. G. Natta, I. Pasquon, and E. Giachetti, *Angew. Chem.*, **69**, 213 (1957); *Makromol. Chem.*, **24**, 258 (1957); G. Natta, and I. Pasquon, *Advan. Catalysis*, **11**, 1 (1959).
163. G. Wilke, B. Bagdanovic, P. Hardt, P. Heimback, W. Keim, M. Kröner, W. Oberkirch, K. Tanaka, E. Steinrücke, D. Walter, and H. Zimmermann, *Angew. Chem., Int. Ed.*, **5**, 151 (1966).
164. C. W. Childers, *J. Am. Chem. Soc.*, **85**, 229 (1963).
165. W. Cooper, D. E. Eaves, and G. Vaughan, *Makromol. Chem.*, **67**, 229 (1963).
166. G. Natta, L. Porri, A. Carbonaro, and A. Greco, *Makromol. Chem.*, **71**, 207 (1964).
167. G. Natta, L. Porri, and A. Carbonaro, *Rend. Accad. Nazl. Lincei*, **29** (8), 491 (1960).
168. A. V. Tobolski and D. J. Kelley, *J. Am. Chem. Soc.*, **81**, 1597 (1959); J. E. Mulvaney, C. G. Overberger, and A. M. Schiller, *Advan. Polymer Chem.*, **3**, 106 (1961).
169. J. E. Lydon, J. K. Nicholson, B. L. Shaw, and M. R. Truter, *Proc. Chem. Soc., (London)*, (**1964**) 421.
170. L. Porri, M. C. Gallazzi, A. Colombo, and G. Allegra, *Tetrahedron Letters*, **47**, 4187 (1965).
171. J. Powell and B. L. Shaw, *Chem. Commun.*, **1966**, 323.
172. B. D. Babitskii, B. A. Dolgoplosk, V. A. Kormer, M. I. Lobak, E. I. Tinyakova, and V. A. Yakovlev, *Dokl. Akad. Nauk SSSR*, **161**, 583 (1965).
173. S. D. Robinson and B. L. Shaw, *J. Chem. Soc., (London)*, **1963**, 4806.
174. H. Scott, *J. Polymer Sci., B*, **4**, 105 (1966).
175. C. E. H. Bawn, A. M. North, and J. S. Walker, *Polymer*, **5**, 419 (1964).
176. M. Roha, *Advan. Polymer Sci.*, **4**, 353 (1966).
177. L. Porri and M. C. Gallazzi, *European Polymer J.*, **2**, 189 (1966).
178. E. G. See, G. E. Coates, and F. Glocking, in H. Zeiss, *Organometallic Chemistry*, Reinhold, New York, 1960, page 451.
179. M. Donati and F. Conti, *Tetrahedron Letters*, **11**, 1219 (1966).

180. D. E. O'Reilly, C. P. Poole, R. F. Belt, and H. Scott, *J. Polymer Sci., A*, **2,** 3257 (1964).
181. W. Marconi, A. Mazzei, G. Lugli, and M. Bruzzone, *J. Polymer Sci., C*, **16,** 805 (1967).
182. G. Natta, L. Porri, A. Carbonaro, and G. Lugli, *Makromol. Chem.*, **53,** 52 (1962).
183. L. Porri, A. Carbonaro, and F. Ciampelli, *Makromol. Chem.*, **61,** 90 (1963).
184. L. S. Bresler, B. A. Dolgoplosk, M. F. Kolechkova, and E. N. Kropacheva, *Rubber Chem. Technol.*, **1963,** 121.
185. T. Suminoe, K. Sasaki, N. Yamazaki, and S. Kambara, *Chem. High Polymers Japan*, **21,** No. 225, 9–16 (1964).
186. I. Pasquon, L. Porri, A. Zambelli, and F. Ciampelli, *Chim. Ind.*, **43,** 509 (1961).
187. G. Natta, L. Porri, P. Corradini, and D. Morero, *Chim. Ind.*, **40,** 362 (1958).
188. G. Natta, G. Moraglio, *Rubber Plastics Age*, **44,** No. 1, 42 (1963).
189. A. V. Tobolsky and C. E. Rogers, *J. Polymer Sci.*, **38,** 205 (1959).

CHAPTER 7

ELASTOMERS BY COORDINATED ANIONIC MECHANISM

B. Ethylene-Propylene Rubbers

Giulio Natta, Alberto Valvassori, and Guido Sartori*

Istituto di Chimica Industriale del Politecnico and Istituto Ricerche "G. Donegani," Montecatini S.p.A., Milano, Italy

Contents

I. Introduction 680
II. Ethylene-Propylene Copolymers 682
A. Synthesis 682
B. Influence of Operating Conditions on Copolymer Composition 684
C. Reactivity Ratios in Ethylene-Propylene Copolymerization 686
D. Intrinsic Viscosity of Ethylene-Propylene Copolymers 687
1. Polymerization Time 687
2. Temperature 688
3. Catalyst Concentration 688
4. Monomer Concentration 688
5. Ethylene-Propylene Molar Ratio in the Reacting Phase 688
6. Nature of the Alkyl Aluminum Compound 688
7. Alkyl Aluminum Compound/Transition Metal Compound Molar Ratio 688
8. Aging of the Catalyst 689
E. Kinetics of Ethylene-Propylene Copolymerization in the Presence of the Catalyst System $VCl_4 + Al(C_6H_{13})_3$ 689
F. Ethylene-Propylene Copolymerization Rate in the Presence of Different Catalyst Systems 691
III. Ethylene-Propylene Terpolymers 693
IV. Determination of the Composition of Ethylene-Propylene Copolymers 697
A. Radiochemical Method 697
B. IR Spectrographic Method 698
C. Mass Spectrographic Analysis of Products Obtained by Pyrolysis 699
D. Relationship between the Composition of Ethylene-Propylene Copolymers and the Temperature of Minimum Rebound 699

* Present address: Esso Research S.A., Brussels, Belgium.

V. Determination of the Composition of Ethylene-Propylene Terpolymers.... 700
A. Propylene Content........ 700
B. Unsaturation Content........ 700
1. Iodometric Method........ 700
2. Infrared Method........ 701
References........ 701

I. INTRODUCTION

Copolymers and terpolymers containing ethylene and α-olefins are of particular interest for many reasons. The most important of these are: (*1*) low cost of the lower olefins relative to diolefins as raw materials; (*2*) practically unlimited availability of the olefins; (*3*) absence of unsaturation or low content of unsaturated groups, which increases the chemical resistance and the resistance toward aging in comparison with the traditional unsaturated rubbers.

The only low unsaturation hydrocarbon rubber known for several decades is butyl rubber, a copolymer of primarily isobutylene with small amounts of isoprene. The incorporation of the latter monomer introduces a small amount of double bonds into the polymer and makes the product vulcanizable with traditional vulcanization systems based on sulfur and accelerators. The presence of two methyl side groups for each isobutylene monomer unit has a detrimental effect on the dynamic properties of the rubber thus obtained, owing to the steric hindrance caused by these groups and the resulting slowness with which a deformed product tends to regain its initial shape after the stress has ceased. As a consequence, high mechanical hysteresis will accompany every temporary deformation process of such a rubber.

This is the reason why the interest in butyl rubber is practically limited to those fields in which its high chemical resistance and in particular its very low permeability to gases are especially important (e.g., use in inner tubes for tires); however, butyl rubber is less suitable for those applications which involve frequent and rapid deformation under high stress (e.g., use as treads for tires).

As described in other chapters of this volume dealing with hydrocarbon polymers (e.g., polyalkenamers and polydiolefins), good elastic and dynamic properties can be expected only when long macromolecules exhibit high flexibility as a consequence of low hindrance to rotation of part of the macromolecule around carbon to carbon bonds in the main chain.

This is the case of the $=CH—CH_2—$ bonds in some diolefin polymers with 1,4 arrangement. Low steric hindrance, although slightly higher than the previous case, is shown by the $—CH_2—CH_2—$ bonds of polyethylene.

The high crystallinity and high melting temperature of linear polyethylene prevent its practical use as an elastic rubber, since polyethylene behaves as an excellent rubber above its melting temperature ($\sim$130°C).

The production of synthetic rubbers from polyethylene (e.g., Hypalon by DuPont) dates far back in time. The introduction of chemical irregularities (such as the random introduction of Cl atoms or of sulfonic groups) by chlorination or sulfochlorination of linear polyethylene prevents its crystallization. However, the required introduction of Cl atoms (at least 28–30%) causes a considerable decrease in the chain flexibility. An even greater decrease in flexibility is observed when sulfonic groups are present, because of their tendency to associate.

The discovery of the coordinated ionic polymerization processes made it possible to produce long linear polymers of α-olefins, which are crystalline only when stereoregular and otherwise amorphous.

By means of nonstereospecific catalysts acting through a coordinated anionic mechanism, it was possible to produce amorphous linear polymers of α-olefins, which are of interest as elastomers from a dimensional point of view, having low elastic moduli, but which present poor dynamic properties owing to the deficient flexibility of the main chain caused by the presence of side groups. This is the reason why poly-α-olefins by themselves are not suitable for the production of elastic rubbers of good dynamic properties.

As the crystallinity of polyethylene can be prevented by the introduction of irregularities (20–30%), the authors of this article visualized already in 1955 the copolymerization of ethylene with α-olefins as a process for the production of very valuable hydrocarbon rubbers. To this end, they studied the copolymerization of ethylene with α-olefins, and in particular with propylene, so as to obtain the most suitable compositions and structures. First of all they observed that not all Ziegler-Natta type catalysts are suitable for the production of homogeneous polymers. The best known coordinated anionic catalysts obtained by reaction between Ti halides and Al alkyls present the disadvantage of being heterogeneous and of containing active centers exhibiting not only different catalytic activities, but also different reactivity ratios.*

* The reactivity ratios referred to in this chapter correspond to those defined for the butadiene-acrylonitrile system in the chapter by Hofmann on nitrile rubber in this volume (Part I, page 192). The reader further interested in the general mathematics of copolymerization may refer to one of the comprehensive treatises on this subject, e.g., *Copolymerization,* G. E. Ham, Ed., Interscience, New York, 1964.

For instance, some of the centers present on the surface of the solid phase can polymerize ethylene with a higher relative rate than the others. Different types of macromolecules are therefore formed: some contain polyethylenic chain segments that are long enough to give rise to crystallinity of the polyethylenic type and a worsening of the elastomeric properties, which can be corrected only partly by increasing the proportion of copolymerized propylene, which in turn causes a decrease in the flexibility of the chains.

The problem of obtaining amorphous homogeneous products by the use of the lowest possible amount of α-olefin was solved by the authors through the discovery of suitable catalysts, particularly of the homogeneous type.

First of all we shall describe the preparation of the most effective copolymerization catalysts; then we shall report on the variations in the properties of the copolymers resulting from variation of their composition.

II. ETHYLENE-PROPYLENE COPOLYMERS

A. Synthesis

The best anionic coordinated catalysts for the synthesis of ethylene-propylene copolymers are those obtained by reaction of alkyl aluminum compounds (e.g., $Al(i\text{-}C_4H_9)_3$, $Al(C_2H_5)_2Cl$, $Al_2(C_2H_5)_3Cl_3$, $Al(C_2H_5)Cl_2$, $Al(C_6H_{13})_3$) with hydrocarbon soluble vanadium compounds (e.g., $VOCl_3$, VCl_4, V = trisacetylacetonate (VAc_3), alkyl esters of vanadic or chlorovanadic acid). Other transition metals, such as niobium, titanium, and chromium, can be substituted for vanadium; beryllium, zinc, and alkali metals can be used instead of aluminum. However, the copolymers obtained in the presence of aluminum- and vanadium-based catalysts are by far the best as regards elastomeric properties, amorphousness and absence of homopolymer fractions.

As in the case of propylene homopolymerization, it has been established also for ethylene-propylene copolymerization (1,2) that at least one of the reagents employed in the catalyst preparation must contain a halogen, something that is not required for ethylene homopolymerization. The reaction is usually carried out in the presence of a solvent. Aliphatic, cycloaliphatic, and aromatic hydrocarbons, as well as some of their halogenated derivatives (e.g., methylene chloride, chlorobenzene, tetrachloroethylene) have been claimed useful.

In order to control the copolymer composition, the ethylene/propylene ratio in the liquid phase must be kept as constant as possible throughout the polymerization.

To this end, a gaseous ethylene-propylene mixture, whose composition can be calculated from the desired ethylene to propylene ratio in the reacting liquid phase and the partition coefficients of the two olefins, is continuously fed through the polymerization system at such a high rate that the conversion of ethylene, which is the more reactive monomer, is kept at a low value (e.g., under 5%) (3).

According to another procedure, an ethylene–propylene mixture, the composition of which is calculated as described above, is fed through the diluent before the copolymerization (i.e., before the catalyst is added) until saturation is reached. After the copolymerization has started, an ethylene–propylene mixture having the same composition as the copolymer being formed is fed without any exit gas being discharged (4). A combination of the two systems has also been suggested (5).

In order to control the monomer composition (and also the average molecular weight of the copolymer, as explained below) during the copolymerization the temperature must be very carefully controlled. As the copolymerization is exothermic, cooling must be provided (5). To avoid a large, uncontrollable increase in temperature, the addition of large amounts of catalyst should be avoided.

To maintain equilibrium between the gaseous and the liquid phases and to keep a constant temperature throughout the reaction mass, sufficient agitation must be provided. As the reaction progresses, the mass becomes more and more viscous and it becomes more and more difficult to maintain saturation. Mass and heat transfer phenomena can exert a certain influence on the composition and properties of the product and on the course of the polymerization.

Particularly high copolymer yields can be obtained if the copolymerization is carried out without an inert solvent, i.e., with liquid propylene acting as solvent (6). Since the copolymer being formed is insoluble in the reaction mixture, there is no appreciable increase in viscosity during the reaction and high copolymer yields per unit volume can be attained without any particular stirring problems.

If the copolymerization is carried out batchwise or with an insufficient supply of olefins, copolymers whose composition varies with time are formed (diagonal copolymers (1,7)). Since ethylene is more reactive than propylene, the copolymer formed at the beginning of the copolymerization has the highest content of ethylene, whereupon its propylene content increases with time.

B. Influence of Operating Conditions on Copolymer Composition

In order to determine the influence of the ethylene/propylene ratio in the reacting phase on the copolymer composition, one has to be able to eliminate the influence of some parameters connected with the preparation of the catalyst and the polymerization procedure.

It has been established (3,8) that if the catalyst is the same, the copolymer composition is independent of the following factors: (*1*) polymerization time; (*2*) catalyst aging time (time elapsed between catalyst preparation and use); (*3*) catalyst concentration; and (*4*) alkyl aluminum to transition metal compound molar ratio. The last factor has little or no influence on the copolymer composition when aliphatic hydrocarbons are used as solvents; if benzene or tetrachloroethylene is used, the Al/V ratio influences the copolymer composition within a certain range (8). Experiments carried out in cyclohexane have also shown a certain dependence of monomer reactivities on Al/V ratio (9). If the catalyst system $HCl_2Al{\cdot}O(C_2H_5)_2 + VCl_4$ is used in benzene, an increase in Al/V ratio favors the relative reactivity of ethylene (10).

The nature of the organometallic compound plays only a minor role as regards the relative reactivities of the monomers in the presence of a certain transition metal compound. In experiments with VCl_4 it has been shown (11) that the relative reactivities do not change significantly if $Zn(C_2H_5)_2$, $Zn(n\text{-}C_4H_9)_2$ or CH_3TiCl_3 are substituted for $Al(i\text{-}C_4H_9)_3$.

If $Al(i\text{-}C_4H_9)_3$ is used as the alkyl aluminum and the transition metal compound is varied, the relative reactivity of propylene increases in the order $HfCl_4 < ZrCl_4 < TiCl_4 < VOCl_3 < VCl_4$, that is with increasing electronegativity of the transition metal (11).

In the presence of certain vanadium compounds, e.g., VCl_4 and $VOCl_3$, a certain decrease in the relative reactivity of ethylene is noticed if $Al_2(C_2H_5)_3Cl_3$ or $Al(C_2H_5)Cl_2$ are substituted for $Al(C_2H_5)_3$ or $Al(C_2H_5)_2Cl$ (7).

These results disagree in part with those obtained by Ichikawa (8) in experiments with different mixtures of $Al(C_2H_5)_2Cl$ and $Al(C_2H_5)Cl_2$ together with $VOCl_3$.

According to Junghanns, the aluminum compounds having the larger number of Cl atoms, i.e., $Al_2(CH_5)_3Cl_3$ and $Al(C_2H_5)Cl_2$, show the higher tendency to give completely amorphous copolymers in the compositional range of 65 to 75 mole % of ethylene (7). If larger groups are substituted for ethyl, no difference is noticed.

The dependence of the copolymer composition on the ethylene-propylene ratio in the reaction phase in the presence of different catalyst systems is shown in Figs. 1 and 2.

It has been shown (12) that if the catalyst $Al(C_2H_5)_3 + VCl_4$ is prepared in the presence of propylene alone and then used in the copolymerization, the copolymer formed is richer in propylene than when the catalyst is prepared in the presence of the ethylene-propylene mixture. By contrast, the copolymers obtained with a catalyst prepared in the presence of either ethylene alone or both monomers together have the same composition.

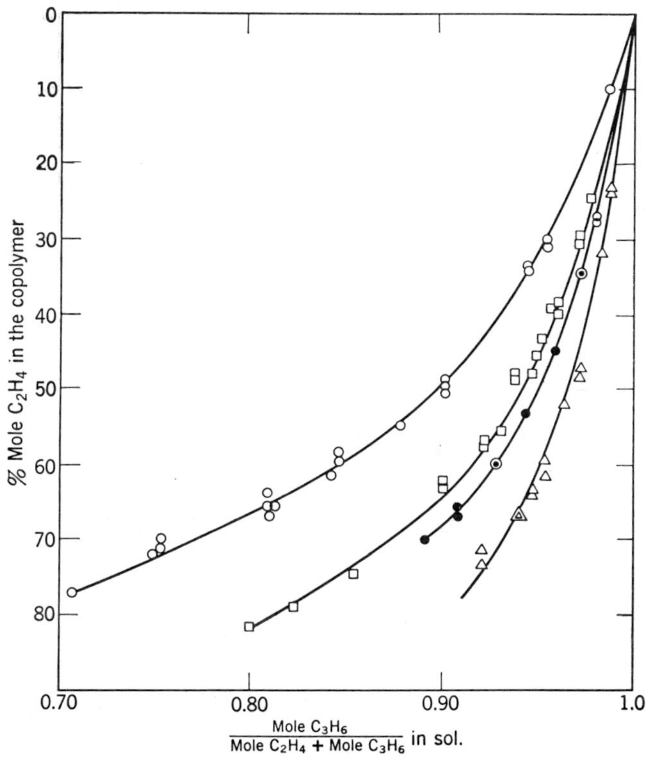

Fig. 1. Composition of ethylene-propylene copolymers plotted against the mole fraction of propylene in the total dissolved monomer for different catalyst systems prepared from hydrocarbon soluble transition metal compounds. ○, $VCl_4 + AlR_3$; □, $VOCl_3 + AlR_3$; ●, $VAc_3 + AlR_2Cl$; △, $TiCl_4 + AlR_3$.

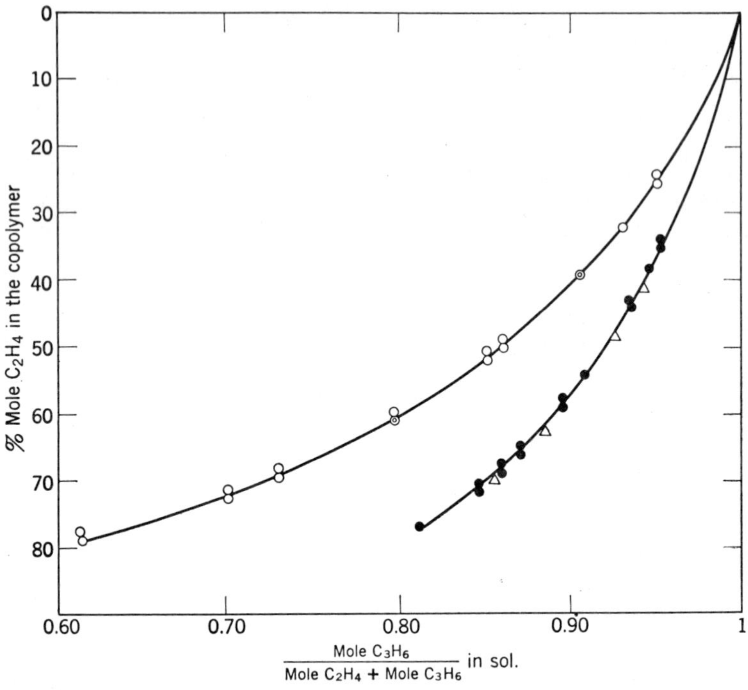

Fig. 2. Composition of ethylene-propylene copolymers plotted against the mole fraction of propylene in the total dissolved monomer for different catalyst systems prepared from hydrocarbon insoluble transition metal compounds. ○, $VCl_3 + AlR_3$; ●, $TiCl_3 + AlR_3$; △, $TiCl_2 + AlR_3$.

C. Reactivity Ratios in Ethylene-Propylene Copolymerization

In the study of the reactivity ratios in ethylene-propylene copolymerization, the influence of the penultimate monomer unit on the reactivity of the chain end is generally neglected.

Table I shows the values of the reactivity ratios for ethylene-propylene copolymerizations in the presence of different catalyst systems. In every case the reactivity ratio of ethylene is much higher than that of propylene, as may be expected for anionic copolymerization. The product of the reactivity ratios is in many cases close to unity, as generally happens in ionic copolymerizations.

In the series of catalysts made from $VOCl_3$, VCl_4, and VCl_3, the relative reactivity of ethylene generally decreases with decreasing vanadium valence. The same happens for catalysts based on $TiCl_4$ and $TiCl_3$. In the presence of the latter compounds, the relative reactivity of ethylene is higher than in the presence of the corresponding vanadium compounds (VCl_4 and VCl_3, respectively) under otherwise identical conditions.

The reactivity ratios have been shown to be practically independent of temperature in the range of −20 to 75°C (14,2).

D. Intrinsic Viscosity of Ethylene-Propylene Copolymers

Many factors influence the intrinsic viscosity of ethylene-propylene copolymers. The most important ones are examined below.

1. *Polymerization Time*

The intrinsic viscosity of ethylene-propylene copolymers increases with time in the presence of some catalyst systems, e.g., $VAc_3 + Al(C_2H_5)_2Cl$

TABLE I
Monomer Reactivity Ratios for Ethylene-Propylene Copolymerization in the Presence of Different Catalyst Systems

Catalyst system	$r_{C_2H_4}$	$r_{C_3H_6}$	Ref.
$VOCl_3 + Al(C_6H_{13})_3$	17.95	0.065	13
$VCl_4 + Al(C_6H_{13})_3$	7.08	0.088	14
$VCl_3 + Al(C_6H_{13})_3$	5.61	0.145	15
VAc_3[a] + $Al(C_2H_5)_2Cl$	15.0	0.04	2
$TiCl_4 + Al(C_6H_{13})_3$	33.36	0.032	16
$TiCl_3 + Al(C_6H_{13})_3$	15.72	0.110	16
$TiCl_2 + Al(C_6H_{13})_3$	15.72	0.110	16
$VO(OR)Cl_2 + AlC_2H_5Cl_2$	17.5	0.05	1
$VO(OR)_3$, $VO(OR)_2Cl$, $VO(OR)Cl_2$ + AlR_2Cl, $AlRCl_2$[b]	17–28	—[c]	5
$VOCl_3$, VCl_4 + AlR_3, AlR_2Cl, $AlRCl_2$[b]	17–28	—[c]	5
$VO(O\text{-}n\text{-}C_4H_9)_3 + Al(i\text{-}C_4H_9)_2Cl$	22.00	0.046	17
$VO(OC_2H_5)_2Cl + Al(i\text{-}C_4H_9)_2Cl$	18.90	0.056	17
$VO(OC_2H_5)Cl_2 + Al(i\text{-}C_4H_9)_2Cl$	16.80	0.055	17
$VO(OC_2H_5)_3 + Al(i\text{-}C_4H_9)_2Cl$	15.00	0.070	17
$VCl_4 + HCl_2Al\cdot O(C_2H_5)_2$	10.7	0.022	10

[a] VAc_3 = vanadium trisacetylacetonate.
[b] Any combination of an aluminum and vanadium compound.
[c] The product $r_{C_2H_4} \cdot r_{C_3H_6}$ is equal to 1.

(2), $VOCl_3$ + alkyl aluminum dichloride or sesquichloride (7,18), $VOCl_2(OR)$ + $AlRCl_2$ or VCl_4 + AlR_2Cl (18).

In the presence of other catalyst systems, such as $Al(C_6H_{13})_3 + VCl_4$ aged at 60°C for 30 minutes and employed at 25°C (19), the copolymerization time hardly influences the intrinsic viscosity.

2. Temperature

Other factors being the same, the intrinsic viscosity of ethylene-propylene copolymers increases with decreasing polymerization temperature (7).

3. Catalyst Concentration

Other factors being the same, the intrinsic viscosity of the copolymer decreases when the catalyst concentration is increased (see e.g., Ref. 2), a fact that agrees with the existence of transfer processes involving the catalyst.

4. Monomer Concentration

Other factors being the same, the intrinsic viscosity of the copolymer decreases with increasing monomer concentration.

5. Ethylene-Propylene Molar Ratio in the Reaction Phase

Other factors being the same, the intrinsic viscosity of the copolymer increases when the molar ratio of ethylene to propylene in the reacting phase is increased (see e.g., Ref. 1, 12).

6. Nature of the Alkyl Aluminum Compound

In the presence of some vanadium compounds, e.g., VCl_4 and $VOCl_3$, at room temperature, the highest viscosities are obtained in the presence of $Al(C_2H_5)_3$, $Al_2(C_2H_5)_3Cl_3$, and $Al(C_2H_5)_2Cl$ (7). These results have been confirmed by Ichikawa (8) using mixtures of $Al(C_2H_5)_2Cl$ and $Al(C_2H_5)Cl_2$ with $VOCl_3$ at a constant Al/V molar ratio of 20.

7. Alkyl Aluminum Compound/Transition Metal Compound Molar Ratio

In the presence of some catalyst systems, such as $Al(C_2H_5)_2Cl + VAc_3$ (2) or $Al(C_6H_{13})_3 + VCl_4$, aged at 60°C for 30 min and employed at 25°C, and with the concentration of the vanadium compound and other factors being kept constant, the intrinsic viscosity decreases when the molar ratio of alkyl aluminum compound to vanadium compound is increased.

In the presence of the catalyst system $Al(C_2H_5)Cl_2 + VOCl_3$, and $Al_2(C_2H_5)_3Cl_3 + VOCl_3$ (20), the intrinsic viscosity increases when the Al/V ratio increases up to 15. If this ratio is further increased, the intrinsic viscosity decreases in the case of the first catalyst system but remains constant in the case of the second.

If $Al(C_2H_5)_2Cl$–$Al(C_2H_5)Cl_2$ mixtures are employed at a constant Al/V ratio of 20, the intrinsic viscosity of the copolymers is lower than that obtained from employing $Al(C_2H_5)_2Cl$ or $Al(C_2H_5)Cl_2$ alone.

When tetrachloroethylene is used as solvent and $VOCl_3 + Al(i\text{-}C_4H_9)_3$ or $VOCl_3 + Al(C_2H_5)_2Cl$ as the catalyst, an increase in Al/V ratio has no influence on the intrinsic viscosity (8). In heptane, on the other hand, an increase in $Al(i\text{-}C_4H_9)_3/VOCl_3$ ratio increases the intrinsic viscosity.

In hexane and benzene, maxima in intrinsic viscosity are observed for $Al(C_2H_5)_2Cl/VOCl_3$ ratios of 5 and 15, respectively.

In the presence of the catalyst system $HCl_2Al{\cdot}O(C_2H_5)_2 + VCl_4$ in benzene, the intrinsic viscosity increases as the Al/V ratio is increased from 3 to 10.

8. Aging of the Catalyst

Other factors being constant, for some catalyst systems, such as $Al(C_6H_{13})_3 + VCl_4$, aging does not exert any influence on the intrinsic viscosity of the copolymer.

For other catalyst systems, such as $Al(C_2H_5)_2Cl + VAc_3$ (2) or $VOCl_3$ + alkyl aluminum dichloride or sesquichloride (7), the intrinsic viscosity of the copolymer increases when the aging time of the catalyst is increased.

E. Kinetics of Ethylene-Propylene Copolymerization in the Presence of the Catalyst System $VCl_4 + Al(C_6H_{13})_3$

A systematic kinetic study of the ethylene-propylene copolymerization in the presence of catalysts prepared from $Al(C_6H_{13})_3$ and VCl_4 was carried out by Natta and co-workers (19).

When low monomer and catalyst concentrations were used so that the effects of mass and heat transfer phenomena could be neglected, the following results were obtained:

1. The activity of the catalyst decreases with time. However, if the catalyst is aged in the absence of monomer for a certain period of time (30 min) at 60°C, further aging in the temperature range of 0–40°C does not influence the activity (Fig. 3).

2. The activity of the stabilized catalyst depends on the molar ratio

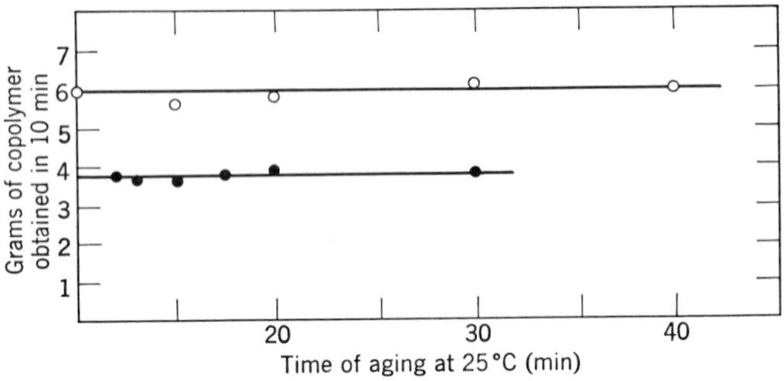

Fig. 3. Independence of activity with time for $Al(C_6H_{13})_3$–VCl_4 catalysts aged at 60°C for 30 min. Polymerization temperature = 25°C; absolute pressure = 1 atm; solvent: *n*-heptane, 410 cm³; $Al(C_6H_{13})_3/VCl_4$ mole ratio = 2.5; C_3H_6/C_2H_4 mole ratio in the gaseous feed = 2.15. ●, V (g vanadium present in the catalytic system) = 0.0299; polymerization time = 10 min; ○, V = 0.0449; polymerization time = 6 min.

between the two reagents used for its preparation. The highest activity is obtained for a molar ratio $Al(C_6H_{13})_3/VCl_4$ of about 2.5.

3. At constant ethylene-propylene ratio, the copolymerization rate is first order with respect to catalyst and overall monomer concentration.

4. The overall monomer concentration being constant, the polymerization rate increases very rapidly with increasing ethylene concentration.

5. The activation energies of the four elementary copolymerization reactions are practically the same (6600 cal/mol).

In some copolymerizations carried out with the aid of catalysts acting through an anionic coordinated mechanism (e.g., copolymerization of propylene with butene-1 (21), of some vinylaromatic monomers (22), of ethylene with propylene in the presence of catalysts prepared from solid halides of Ti or V), r_1 (or the reciprocal of r_2)* is almost equal to the ratio between the homopolymerization rates of monomers 1 and 2. This relationship is not observed for the corresponding polymerizations of ethlene and propylene in the presence of the catalyst system $Al(C_6H_{13})_3$ + VCl_4. In this case the ratio between the homopolymerization rates of ethylene and propylene is much higher than the reactivity ratio of ethylene. Neither this fact nor the considerable increase in the copolymerization rate obtained by increasing the ethylene/propylene ratio in reacting phase can be explained only on the basis of the values of the

* See footnote on page 681.

propagation constants. It is, therefore, also necessary to take into account that a variation in the total number of growing chains may result from a variation in the ethylene propylene ratio. This variation in the number of growing chains can be explained as the consequence of the existence of active centers capable of homopolymerizing ethylene, but which are rather inert as soon as a propylene unit has been added (23). In the latter case the activity will not be lost irreversibly, but propagation will occur at such a slow rate as to be practically negligible. Propylene will be able to add to growing chains formed by such centers only when the monomer unit added immediately before is ethylene.

This phenomenon has also been confirmed by direct measurement of the number of active centers (capable of originating growing chains) present in the homopolymerization of ethylene and propylene with the catalyst systems $VCl_3 + AlR_3$ and $TiCl_4 + AlR_3$. Further proof is given by the possibility of preparing ethylene-propylene copolymers with catalysts that cannot start the homopolymerization of propylene but are active in the homopolymerization of ethylene.

By recognizing the variation in the number of the growing chains as indicated above and relating the polymerization rates to the same concentration of growing chains, the ratio between the homopolymerization rates of ethylene and propylene is almost the same as the reactivity ratio for ethylene.

F. Ethylene-Propylene Copolymerization Rate in the Presence of Different Catalyst Systems

Using catalyst systems prepared from VOC_3 and alkyl aluminum dichloride or sesquichloride, Junghanns and co-workers (7) have studied the influence of different parameters connected with the catalyst preparation on the copolymerization rate. A loss in activity with time occurs both when the catalyst is prepared in the presence of the monomers and when it is kept some time under nitrogen before being added to the monomers. The loss in activity is faster in the former case, however. In the absence of the monomers, the catalyst activity decreases more slowly if the A/V ratio is increased from 5 to 40. As the catalyst activity decreases, a corresponding decrease in the vanadium valence also takes place.

The temperature scarcely influences the rate of decrease in activity, at least not between 20 and 40°C.

The polymerization rate increases if the ethylene-propylene ratio increases. If the monomer concentrations are kept constant, an increase in temperature causes an increase in polymerization rate. An increase in total monomer concentration at constant monomer ratio increases the polymerization rate.

In the presence of $VOCl_3$-based catalysts and with $Al(i\text{-}C_4H_9)_3$ or $Al(C_2H_5)_2Cl$ as the alkylaluminum (8), an increase in yield calculated on $VOCl_3$ is always observed if the Al/V ratio is increased from 1 up to a certain maximum value that varies with the nature of the catalyst and the solvent. Beyond that value, no further increase in yield is observed.

Using the catalyst systems $Al(C_2H_5)Cl_2 + VOCl_3$ or $Al_2(C_2H_5)_3Cl_3 + VOCl_3$, Kelly and co-workers (20) found that an increase in the Al/V molar ratio causes an increase in the catalyst efficiency. If the Al/V ratio is kept constant at 20 and $Al(C_2H_5)_2Cl$–$Al(C_2H_5)Cl_2$ mixtures of different composition are employed, a maximum catalyst efficiency is found for an $Al(C_2H_5)_2Cl:Al(C_2H_5)Cl_2$ molar ratio of 2/3.

If mixtures of trialkyl aluminum compounds and $AlBr_3$ are employed in the preparation of the catalyst, the molar ratio of $AlBr_3/AlR_3$ must not exceed 2:1, otherwise very poor copolymer yields are obtained (20). An increase in propylene content in the feed at constant total monomer concentration causes a decrease in the polymerization rate and in the intrinsic viscosity of the copolymer. Similar results have been obtained by Ichikawa (8).

When copolymerizations are carried out with the catalyst system $VAc_3 + Al(C_2H_5)_2Cl$ at 25°C (2), the overall polymerization rate depends on the molar ratio of the two catalyst components, and the highest activity is found for $Al(C_2H_5)_2Cl/VAc_3$ ratios close to 3.5.

The catalyst ages, both if it is employed in the copolymerization and if it is kept at 25°C under nitrogen for some time before being added to the monomer mixture.

If the preparation of the catalyst and the copolymerization are carried out at temperatures below 0°C, the catalyst activity decreases much more slowly than at 25°C.

When the catalyst activity is plotted versus the $Al(C_2H_5)_2Cl/VAc_3$ molar ratio for experiments carried out at −20°C, no definite maximum is noticeable in contrast to what is observed at 25°C. The catalyst activity increases considerably if the $Al(C_2H_5)_2Cl/VAc_3$ molar ratio is increased from 3 to 4, and increases slightly if the same ratio is varied from 4 to 20.

At −20°C, the copolymer yields obtained in a given time and with catalysts aged under the same conditions are directly proportional to the catalyst concentration, i.e., the copolymerization rate is first order with respect to the catalyst concentration.

If the C_3H_6/C_2H_4 ratio and other factors are kept constant, the copolymerization rate is first order with respect to the monomer concentration.

All other conditions being equal, the copolymerization rate increases remarkably if the C_2H_4/C_3H_6 molar ratio in the feed is increased.

III. ETHYLENE-PROPYLENE TERPOLYMERS

Ethylene-propylene copolymers cannot be vulcanized by the conventional processes used for diene rubbers or for butyl rubber because of the absence of groups that can react with sulfur.

Since the hydrogen atom of the tertiary carbon atoms is particularly reactive toward free radicals, ethylene-propylene copolymers can be vulcanized with organic peroxides. Crosslinking takes place by combination of free radicals belonging to different polymer chains (see e.g., Ref. 24 and literature cited there).

As rubber users are traditionally accustomed to vulcanize with recipes based on sulfur and accelerators, many investigators (of which the authors of this chapter were among the first) have studied the introduction of double bonds into every copolymer molecule during the polymerization. In this way terpolymers containing a small amount of double bonds capable of being vulcanized with traditional methods used for low unsaturation rubbers (such as butyl rubber) are obtained.

Although many linear or cyclic diolefins may be copolymerized with ethylene and propylene, not all of them are suitable for producing good synthetic rubbers. First of all, they must be able to polymerize is such a manner that the distribution of the double bonds becomes random. This is probably one of the reasons why conjugated diolefins give terpolymers whose vulcanizates generally exhibit modest properties.

The use of acetylene and its homologs as termonomers does not give good results owing to the tendency of these monomers to react with alkylaluminums and thus deactivate the catalyst.

In order to avoid the formation of branches or crosslinks during or after the terpolymerization, the residual double bond of the diene entering the polymer chain should not react further during the polymerization and the subsequent polymer recovery steps.

A number of classes of nonconjugated polyenes suitable for the synthesis of ethylene-propylene terpolymers have been found (Fig. 4) (25–29).

The factors regulating the intrinsic viscosity of ethylene-propylene

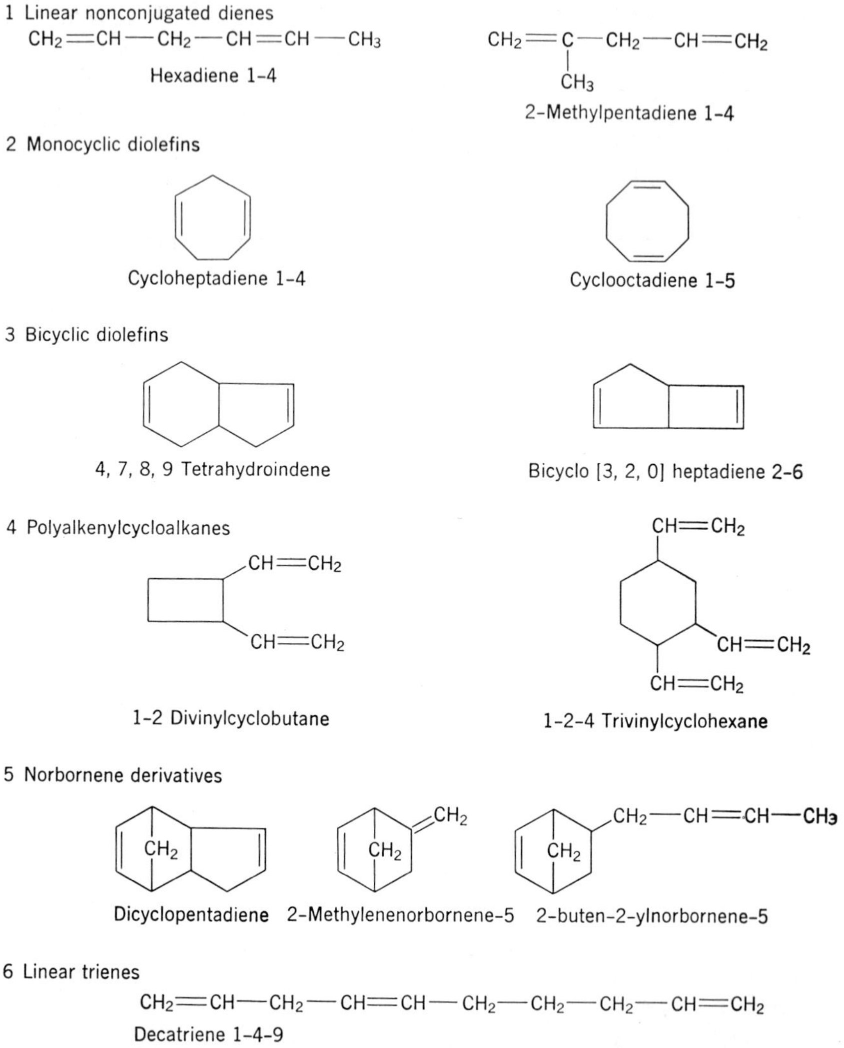

Fig. 4. Classes of termonomers suitable for making ethylene-propylene terpolymers.

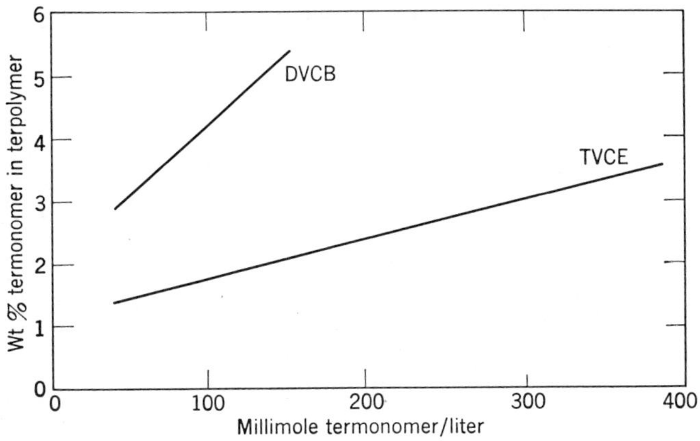

Fig. 5. Weight percentage of *trans*-1,4 divinylcyclobutane (DVCB) and 1,2,4 trivinylcyclohexane (TVCE) in terpolymer as a function of termonomer concentration in the liquid phase.

terpolymers are the same as for the binary copolymers. The rate of terpolymerization is generally lower than that of the diene-free copolymerization (4). The content of termonomer in the terpolymer increases, as can be predicted, if its relative concentration in the reacting phase is increased (Fig. 5).

Whereas monoolefins are generally fed continuously throughout the terpolymerization, all the termonomer can often be added at the beginning of it, depending on its low rate of conversion.

However, if the termonomer is particularly reactive, continuous or periodic addition of it throughout the polymerization may be desirable or even necessary to prevent undesirably high termonomer conversions (4).

It has often been observed that, if the concentrations of ethylene and propylene in the feed are kept constant and the diene termonomer concentration is increased, unlike in the case when the termonomer is another alpha-olefin, e.g., butene-1, the ethylene to propylene ratio in the terpolymer increases. This phenomenon has been observed in the case of linear, non-conjugated diolefins (25), 1,5-cyclooctadiene (26) (Fig. 6) and dicyclopentadiene (25,30). However, the way in which the monomers are added can limit the extent to which it appears (4).

The termonomer most studied is dicyclopentadiene (25,4,30,31). As the norbornene-type double bond is the more reactive, the monomer unit is

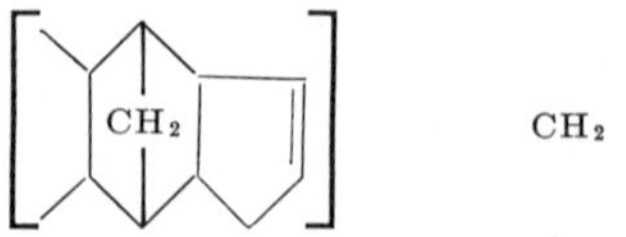

(25,30). However, in some cases the second double bond reacts, too (31), giving rise to branching.

The monomer unit formed from a certain termonomer in terpolymerization is often different from that formed in its homopolymerization. This is for example the case for 1,5-cyclooctadiene (32,26), 2-methylene-5-norbornene (cationic systems) (33,33a), and 1-methyl-1,5-cyclooctadiene (34) (Fig. 7).

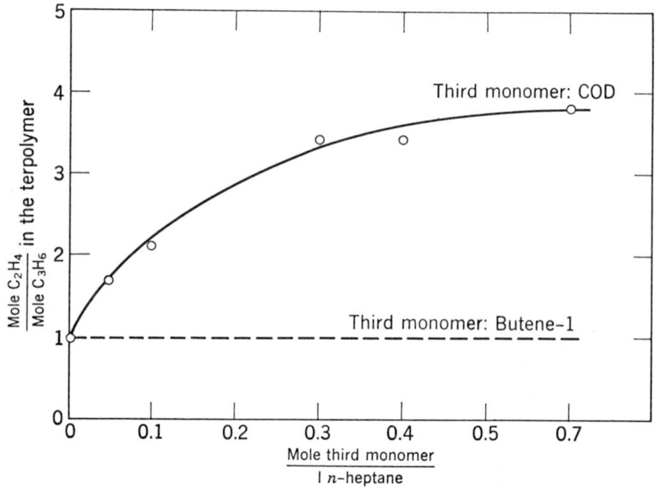

Fig. 6. Copolymerization of ethylene and propylene with a third monomer. Dependence of C_2H_4/C_3H_6 molar ratio in the terpolymer on the concentration of the third monomer in the reacting phase. Solid line: ethylene-propylene-cyclooctadiene-1.5 terpolymerization. Experimental conditions: polymerization temperature = −10°C; abs. pressure = 1 atm; solvent, *n*-heptane; C_3H_6/C_2H_4 mole ratio in the gaseous feed = 2; VCl_4 = 0.5 mmole/1; $Al(C_2H_5)_2Cl/VCl_4$ mole ratio = 5; dotted line: ethylene-propylene-butene-1 terpolymerization. Experimental conditions: polymerization temperature = 25°C; abs. pressure = 1 atm; solvent, *n*-heptane; C_3H_6/C_2H_4 mole ratio in the gaseous feed = 2; VCl_4 = mmole/1; $Al(C_6H_{13})_3/VCl_4$ mole ratio = 2.5.

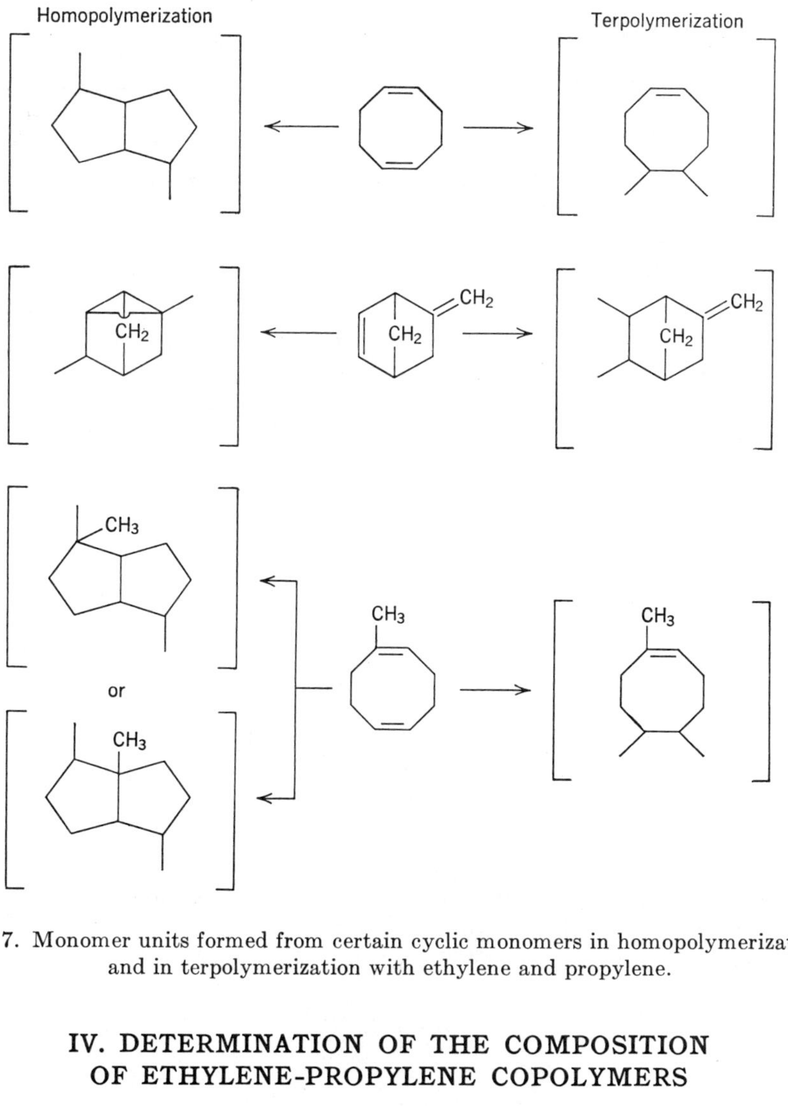

Fig. 7. Monomer units formed from certain cyclic monomers in homopolymerization and in terpolymerization with ethylene and propylene.

IV. DETERMINATION OF THE COMPOSITION OF ETHYLENE-PROPYLENE COPOLYMERS

A. Radiochemical Method

When radioactive ethylene (3) is used in ethylene-propylene copolymerization, the ethylene weight percentage in the copolymer is given by the ratio of the specific activity of the copolymer to that of the polyethylene obtained from the same ethylene.

B. IR Spectrographic Method

When adopting this method, which is the most general and important one for determination of the copolymer composition, one must distinguish between two cases depending on whether the copolymer is or is not soluble in solvents suitable for IR spectroscopic examination (e.g., carbon tetrachloride).

In the former case, the analysis is rather simple (3); measurement of the optical density of the absorption band at 7.25 μ, due to methyl groups, makes it possible to calculate the amount of propylene units present. The value of the extinction coefficient used is the average of the values obtained from measurement on various solutions of atactic polypropylene.

A limitation to this method is that ethylene-propylene copolymers sometimes give rise to seemingly homogeneous solutions, which, however, also contain swollen copolymer particles. In such cases, the measurement should be carried out in the solid state (i.e., on pieces of thin film obtained by molding the copolymer).

According to the method proposed by Gössl (35), the ratio

$$R = \frac{E13.9}{E8.6}$$

between the extinction coefficients at 13.9 μ and 8.6 μ, respectively, is used. The band at 13.9 μ is attributed to sequences of methylene groups from ethylene units and the band at 8.6 μ to methyl groups from propylene units.

The calibration curve was obtained from measurements on samples completely soluble in carbon tetrachloride, whose propylene content could be determined with the help of the band at 7.25 μ.

The method proposed by Wei (36) uses the ratio:

$$R' = \frac{E8.7}{E13.9}$$

The logarithm of this ratio is a linear function of the mole percent of propylene in the copolymer.

The method proposed by Ciampelli and co-workers (37) uses the ratio between the intensities of the bands at 8.6 μ, whose intensity is proportional to the propylene content, and 2.32 μ, whose intensity is proportional to the number of carbon–hydrogen bonds present in the copolymer and therefore practically proportional to the thickness of the film under examination regardless of its composition. The calibration curve was obtained with samples containing C^{14}-ethylene.

A near infrared method proposed by Bucci and Simonazzi (38) uses the intensity ratio between the shoulder at 1692 μ attributable to the methyl groups, and the maximum at about 1764 μ, attributable to the methylene groups. The ratio is a linear function of the copolymer composition.

C. Mass Spectrographic Analysis of Products Obtained by Pyrolysis

Bua and Manaresi (39) set up an analytical method based on the pyrolysis of ethylene-propylene copolymers followed by mass spectrographic analysis of the products thus obtained. A drawback of this method is the considerable length of time required for the analysis. Its possible field of application is rather limited, therefore.

D. Relationship between the Composition of Ethylene-Propylene Copolymers and the Temperature of Minimum Rebound

The methylene sequences in ethylene-propylene copolymers constitute the most flexible part of the amorphous macromolecule; while the propylene sequences by contrast are the least flexible ones. By increasing the ethylene content in amorphous copolymers, one increases the flexibility of the macromolecule; thus a higher rebound is obtained at any given temperature.

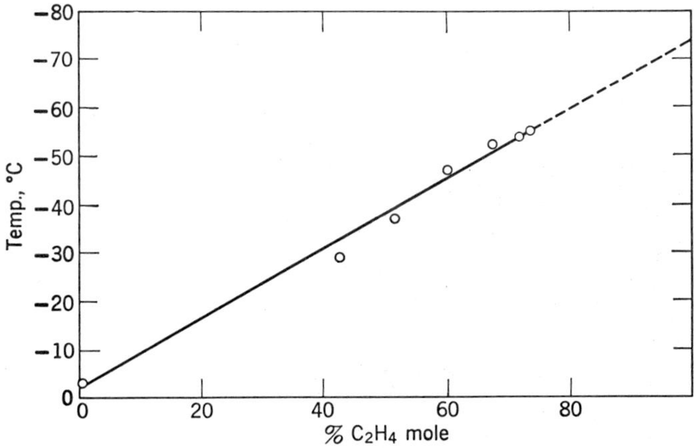

Fig. 8. Temperature of minimum rebound as a function of ethylene content for ethylene-propylene copolymers of varying composition.

A quantitative relationship between the ethylene content of the copolymer and the rebound value at or slightly below room temperature cannot be obtained easily, especially with uncured samples. In fact, the rebound value can be influenced by the viscosity of the copolymer, which is, in turn, a function of the average molecular weight.

At temperatures much below room temperature, the influence of the molecular weight becomes negligible; therefore, the rebound value is a function only of the copolymer composition. If the temperature of minimum rebound is used as a variable, it appears to be a linear function of the ethylene content (Fig. 8) (40).

V. DETERMINATION OF THE COMPOSITION OF ETHYLENE-PROPYLENE TERPOLYMERS

A. Propylene Content

Although no detailed study of the determination of the propylene content in ethylene-propylene terpolymers has been published, it may be assumed that the determination can be carried out by using the same bands and the same techniques as in the case of binary ethylene-propylene copolymers.

B. Unsaturation Content

1. Iodometric Method

The determination of unsaturation in ethylene-propylene terpolymers by the ICl method has been thoroughly described by Hank (41) and Tunnicliffe and co-workers (42). According to the first author, an excess of ICl is added to a CS_2 or CCl_4 solution of the terpolymer. After about 1 hr, KI and water are added. Iodine formed in the reaction between KI and unreacted ICl is titrated with sodium thiosulfate.

$$\sim CH{=}CH\sim \xrightarrow{ICl} \sim CHI{-}CHCl\sim$$

$$ICl + KI \rightarrow I_2 + KCl$$

As a blank, an ethylene-propylene copolymer solution is employed. Two side reactions may take place: HI elimination (1) and substitution (2):

$$\sim CHI{-}CHCl\sim \rightarrow \sim CH{=}CCl\sim + HI \tag{1}$$

$$\sim CHR{-}CH_2\sim + ICl \rightarrow \sim CRCl{-}CH_2\sim + HI \tag{2}$$

HI then reacts with excess ICl to give iodine:

$$HI + ICl \rightarrow I_2 + HCl$$

While the first reaction does not disturb the determination of unsaturation, the second reaction gives too high unsaturation values. The extent of the two side reactions can be judged by titration of I_2 with KIO_3:

$$KIO_3 + 2I_2 + 6HCl \rightarrow KCl + 5ICl + 3H_2O$$

To determine the reliability of the ICl method, terpolymers containing radioactive dicyclopentadiene were prepared. The iodometric values agreed well with those obtained by the radiochemical method.

According to the related method of Tunnicliffe et al. (42), measured portions of a CCl_4 solution of terpolymer containing excess ICl are removed at regular intervals and titrated as described above. The values so obtained are then extrapolated to zero time. Also in this case a control should be carried out with terpolymers containing labeled dicyclopentadiene.

The ICl method is suitable also for the analysis of 1,4-hexadiene terpolymers, but not for 1,5-cyclooctadiene terpolymers, in which extensive HI elimination and further ICl addition takes place.

2. *Infrared Method*

The unsaturation content of dicyclopentadiene terpolymers can be determined (41) from the intensity ratio between the band at 6.22 μ, due to the double bond contained in the cyclopentene ring, and the band at 2.32 μ, proportional to the thickness of the terpolymer film. Calibration curves can be obtained with the help of terpolymers whose unsaturation content has been established by other methods, e.g., by the ICl method.

References

1. G. Bier, *Angew. Chem.*, **73**, 186 (1961).
2. G. Natta, G. Mazzanti, A. Valvassori, G. Sartori, and D. Fiumani, *J. Polymer Sci.*, **51**, 411 (1960).
3. G. Natta, G. Mazzanti, A. Valvassori, and G. Pajaro, *Chim. Ind.* (*Milan*), **39**, 733 (1957).
4. R. German, R. Hank, and G. Vaughan, *Kautschuk Gummi*, **19**, 67 (1966).
5. C. A. Lukach and H. M. Spurlin, in *Copolymerization*, G. Ham, Ed., Interscience, 1964, p. 115.
6. Ital. Pat. 581,418, pr. 12.12.1957 (Montecatini).
7. E. Junghanns, A. Gumboldt, and G. Bier, *Makromol. Chem.*, **58**, 18 (1962).
8. M. Ichikawa, *J. Chem. Soc. Japan, Ind. Chem. Sect.*, **68**, 535 (1965); *Intern. Chem. Eng.*, **5**, 724 (1965).
9. F. J. Karol and W. L. Carrick, *J. Am. Chem. Soc.*, **83**, 2654 (1961).
10. W. Marconi, S. Cesca, and G. Della Fortuna, *Chim. Ind.* (*Milan*), **46**, 1131 (1964).
11. W. L. Carrick, F. J. Karol, G. L. Karapinka, and J. J. Smith, *J. Am. Chem. Soc.*, **82**, 1502 (1960).
12. T. Suminoe, N. Yamazaki, and S. Kambara, *Chem. High Polymers Japan*, **20**, 461 (1963).

13. G. Mazzanti, A. Valvassori, and G. Pajaro, *Chim. Ind. (Milan)*, **39,** 743 (1957).
14. G. Mazzanti, A. Valvassori, and G. Pajaro, *Chim. Ind. (Milan)*, **39,** 825 (1957).
15. G. Natta, G. Mazzanti, A. Valvassori, and G. Sartori, *Chim. Ind. (Milan)*, **40,** 717 (1958).
16. G. Natta, A. Valvassori, G. Mazzanti, and G. Sartori, *Chim. Ind. (Milan)*, **40,** 896 (1958).
17. R. D. Bushick, *J. Polymer Sci.*, **A3,** 2047 (1965).
18. G. Bier, A. Gumboldt, and G. Schleitzer, *Makromol. Chem.*, **58,** 43 (1962).
19. G. Natta, G. Mazzanti, A. Valvassori, G. Sartori, and A. Barbagallo, *J. Polymer Sci.*, **51,** 429 (1961).
20. R. J. Kelly, H. K. Garner, H. E. Haxo, and W. R. Bingham, *Ind. Eng. Chem. Prod. Res. Devel.*, **1,** 210 (1962).
21. G. Mazzanti, A. Valvassori, G. Sartori, and G. Pajaro, *Chim. Ind. (Milan)*, **42,** 468 (1960).
22. D. Sianesi, G. Pajaro, and F. Danusso, *Chim. Ind. (Milan)*, **41,** 1176 (1959).
23. A. Valvassori, G. Sartori, G. Mazzanti, and G. Pajaro, *Makromol. Chem.*, **60,** 46 (1963).
24. G. Natta, G. Crespi, A. Valvassori, and G. Sartori, *Rubber Chem. Technol.*, **36,** 1583 (1963).
25. E. K. Gladding, B. S. Fisher, and J. W. Collette, *Ind. Eng. Chem. Prod. Res. Devel.*, **1,** 65 (1962).
26. G. Natta, G. Mazzanti, G. Crespi, A. Valvassori, G. Sartori, *Rubber Chem. Technol.*, **36,** 988 (1964).
27. G. Natta, G. Crespi, A. Valvassori, G. Sartori, N. Cameli, and V. Turba, *Rubber Plastics Age*, **46,** 683 (1965).
28. J. J. Van Schooten and K. Evenhuis, *Polymer*, **6,** 561 (1965).
29. G. Sartori, A. Valvassori, G. Mazzanti, *Mater. Plast. Elastom.*, **32,** 3 (1966).
30. G. Sartori, A. Valvassori, and S. Faina, *Atti Acc. Naz. Lincei, Ser. VIII*, **35,** 565 (1963); *Rubber Chem. Technol.*, **38,** 620 (1965).
31. R. E. Cunningham, *J. Polymer Sci.*, **A3,** 3157 (1965); *ibid.*, **A4,** 1203 (1966).
32. B. Reichel, C. S. Marvel, and R. Z. Greenley, *J. Polymer Sci.*, **A1,** 2835 (1963).
33. G. Sartori, A. Valvassori, V. Turba, and M. P. Lachi, *Chim. Ind. (Milan)*, **45,** 1529 (1963).
33a. J. P. Kennedy and H. S. Makowski, *J. Macromol. Sci. (Chem.)*, **A1,** 345 (1967).
34. A. Valvassori, G. Sartori, V. Turba, and M. P. Lachi, *J. Polymer Sci.*, **C16** (1), 23 (1967).
35. T. Gössl, *Makromol. Chem.*, **42,** 1 (1960).
36. P. E. Wei, *Anal. Chem.*, **33,** 215 (1961).
37. F. Ciampelli, M. Bucci, M. Simonazzi, and A. Santambrogio, *Chim. Ind. (Milan)*, **44,** 489 (1962).
38. G. Bucci and T. Simonazzi, *Chim. Ind. (Milan)*, **44,** 262 (1962).
39. E. Bua and P. Manaresi, *Anal. Chem.*, **31,** 2022 (1959).
40. G. Natta and G. Crespi, *Chim. Ind. (Milan)*, **41,** 123 (1959); *Rev. Gen. Caoutchouc*, **37,** 1003 (1960).
41. R. Hank, *Kautschuk Gummi*, **18,** 295 (1965).
42. M. E. Tunnicliffe, D. A. Mc. Killof, and R. Hank, *European Polymer J.*, **1,** 259 (1965).

CHAPTER 7

ELASTOMERS BY COORDINATED ANIONIC MECHANISM

C. Elastomers from Cyclic Olefins

GIULIO NATTA
Istituto di Chimica Industriale del Politecnico, Milano, Italy
AND
GINO DALL'ASTA
Societá Montecatini, Edison, Milano, Italy

Contents

I. Relationships between Structure and Elastomeric Properties in Stereoregular Polyalkenamers 704
II. Catalysts for the Stereospecific Polymerization of Cycloolefins 713
III. Mechanism of the Ring Opening Polymerization of Cycloolefins 717
References 724

This chapter deals with the synthesis and the properties of a new class of linear unsaturated hydrocarbon elastomers called polyalkenamers.* Before going into the details, we should like to review some of the more important features which render a polymer elastomeric.

1. Essentially linear structure.
2. High molecular weight which enables the macromolecules to resist extensive permanent viscous flow when oriented in parallel by stretching, thus conferring reversibility to the deformation process.
3. A flexible structure, i.e., one in which the rotation around the bonds in the polymer backbone is opposed only by low potential barriers.

* According to the IUPAC nomenclature (1).

4. Possibility to hinder irreversible viscous flow by chemical vulcanization or by physical phenomena having analogous effects, e.g., crystallization of macromolecules oriented under high load. The vulcanization may be facilitated by the presence of reactive chemical groups along the chains.

Considering the modest limitations thus imposed on elastomers from a chemical standpoint, it is not surprising that elastomers of greatly different chemical nature are known. However, they still appear few if the wide possibilities of modern macromolecular chemistry are considered. Especially in the field of polymers having chemical and steric regularity, a deeper study will permit us to single out many new elastomeric products. Low cost and low density have so far assured hydrocarbon polymers a preeminent position among synthetic elastomers. The polyalkenamers described here belong also to this class.

I. RELATIONSHIPS BETWEEN STRUCTURE AND ELASTOMERIC PROPERTIES IN STEREOREGULAR POLYALKENAMERS

The polymethylene chain is one of the more flexible ones. This property results above all from the absence of bulky side groups that might hinder free rotation around the bonds linking the methylene groups. In fact, linear polyethylene, when employed above its melting temperature, is an excellent elastomer (2).

Linear polyethylene, however, does not exhibit elastomeric properties at room temperature, mainly because of its great tendency to crystallize. Yet, the introduction of chemically different groups in the polymethylene chain is sufficient to decrease the melting temperature; when the number of such groups exceeds 25% and when their distribution along the chain is random, crystallization generally becomes impossible as a consequence of the chemical disorder in the chain. Since such chains, in particular when the side groups are not very bulky, substantially maintain good flexibility, polymers of this type can exhibit excellent elastomeric properties. As examples can be mentioned the ethylene-α-olefin random copolymers (3) and sulfochlorinated polyethylene (4).

When these chemically different groups are regularly introduced into the polymethylene chain so that a definite number of methylene groups is followed by a given group having a different chemical structure, a new type of order rather than disorder is established in the chains.

Therefore, these chains will still be crystallizable. Being a new and defined chemical substance, such a polymer has its own melting point which is generally different from that of polyethylene. If this melting point is sufficiently low (room temperature or below), the product may be an elastomer, provided that the other requirements mentioned above are satisfied.

Stereoregular 1,4 polybutadiene has a structure that corresponds to this concept. In fact, it contains a chemically different group, —HC=CH—, after every two methylene groups:

$$((\text{—}CH_2)_2\text{—}CH\text{=}CH\text{—})_p \qquad (1)$$

In this case the unsaturated groups satisfy three requirements: (*1*) they modify the chemical structure giving rise to a new chemically and sterically regular substance; (*2*) they introduce the sites that are necessary for the vulcanization; and (*3*) they allow the chains to maintain a high flexibility, in that the rotation around the —C—C= single bond is even more easy than around the —C—C— bond.

The crystallizability of 1,4 polybutadiene obviously depends also on the degree and the type of the steric regularity of the double bonds (*cis* or *trans*). The melting temperature of the crystalline stereoregular 1,4 polybutadienes varies with the type of double bonds: *cis*-1,4 polybutadiene melts below room temperature (+1°C), hence it is an excellent elastomer (5); on the other hand, *trans*-1,4 polybutadiene finally melts (6) at a higher temperature (145°C) than polyethylene (130°C), therefore it does not exhibit elastomeric properties in the temperature range of the usual applications.

From the general point of view just described, elastomeric properties could also be expected for other stereoregular polymers containing double bonds regularly inserted between methylene sequences of a given length, but different from two. Polymers having the general structure:

$$((\text{—}CH_2)_n\text{—}CH\text{=}CH\text{—})_p \qquad (2)$$

(where n is an integer and p the degree of polymerization) are to be called "polyalkenamers" (1). None of these polymers, except 1,4 polybutadienes (where $n = 2$), had been known until a few years ago. Only recently, mostly thanks to research initiated by Montecatini S.p.A. with the cooperation of G. Natta (7–9), a series of stereoregular polyalkenamers was obtained in which n corresponds to different values. Some of these polymers exhibit excellent elastomeric properties.

The general reaction according to which polyalkenamers were obtained is a ring opening polymerization of unsubstituted cycloolefins with retention of the double bond:

$$p \begin{array}{c} HC = CH \\ \diagdown \quad \diagup \\ (CH_2)_n \end{array} \rightarrow ((-CH_2)_n-CH=CH-)_p \qquad (3)$$

Thus it was possible to polymerize all the cycloolefins so far examined in which $n \geq 2$, except cyclohexene, in which $n = 4$. The polyalkenamer corresponding to the latter cycloolefin, i.e., polyhexenamer, was obtained by Natta et al. (10) by alternating copolymerization of ethylene with butadiene:

$$pCH_2=CH_2 + pCH_2=CH-CH=CH_2 \rightarrow (-CH_2-CH_2-CH_2-CH=CH-CH_2-)_p \qquad (4)$$

The polymerization of cycloolefins to polyalkenamers can be carried out in a stereoregular manner. It is therefore possible to prepare polyalkenamers in which all or a predominant part of the double bonds are either *cis* or *trans*. Usually, the *trans* polyalkenamers can be obtained more easily; we shall consider them first.

Table I lists some of the most characteristic *trans* polyalkenamers, including polyacetylene and polyethylene which can be considered as the extreme members of the series. All the *trans* polyalkenamers (reported in Table I) in which the content of *trans* double bonds exceeds 70% of the total unsaturation can be made to crystallize at room temperature. However, polyalkenamers with a *trans* double bond content of 85% and, in many cases even of 95%, can be easily obtained. As already mentioned, the elastomeric properties of a polymer depend to a large extent on its melting temperature. If the latter occurs in the range between room temperature and slightly below, the polymer is usually amorphous at room temperature in the unstretched state, while it will crystallize when subjected to stretching. This is the case for natural rubber (melting temperature +13°C (11)) and of *cis*-1,4 polybutadiene (+1°C).

In order to know within what limits a polymer can exhibit elastomeric properties, it is necessary to know its melting temperature. Figure 1 reports the melting temperatures of *trans* polyalkenamers vs. the length n of the methylene sequence between two subsequent double bonds. As can be noticed, the melting temperatures decrease regularly with decreasing length of the methylene sequence, from the value of normal linear polyethylene (130°C), to that of *trans* polypentenamer ($n = 3$), which has the lowest melting temperature (23°C) of the whole homologous series. Surprisingly, the curve ends with *trans* polypentenamer, in that

TABLE I

Trans Polyalkenamers and Methods for Their Preparation

Trans Polyalkenamers	Length n of the methylene sequence according to $((CH_2)_n—CH{=}CH—)_p$	Melting temp., °C[a]	Method of preparation	Ref.
Polyacetylene	0	—[b]	Polymerization of acetylene	12
Polypropenamer•	1	—	Still unknown	—
Polybutenamer (1,4 polybutadiene)	2	145 (96)	1,4 Polymerization of butadiene or ring opening polymerization of cyclobutene	4, 5, 7
Polypentenamer	3	23	Ring opening polymerization of cyclopentene	8
Polyhexenamer	4	61 (41)	Alternating ethylene-butadiene copolymerization	10
Polyheptenamer	5	51	Ring opening polymerization of cycloheptene	9
Polyoctenamer	6	67 (62)	Ring opening polymerization of cyclooctene	9
Polydodecenamer	10	80	Ring opening polymerization of cyclododecene	9
Polyethylene	∞	130	Low pressure polymerization of ethylene	13–15

[a] Two melting temperatures refer to two different crystalline modifications.

[b] Decomposes before melting.

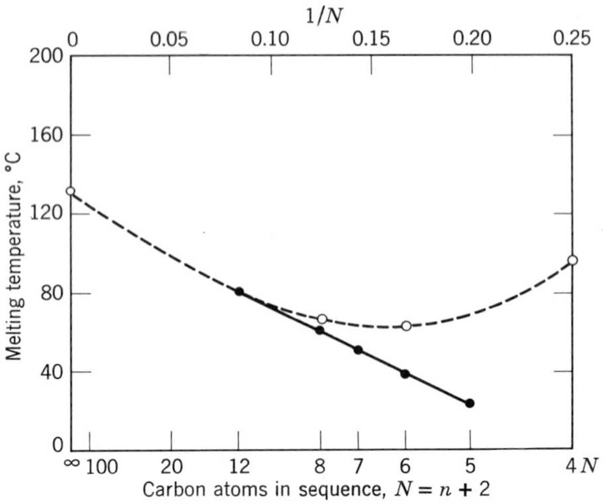

Fig. 1. Variation in melting point for the homologous series of *trans* polyalkenamers $((\text{—CH}_2)_n\text{—CH═CH—})_p$. ($N$ = total number of carbon atoms in the sequence ($N = n + 2$).)

the lower members of the series (*trans*-1,4 polybutadiene and *trans* polyacetylene) behave in a manner quite different from that of the other homologs. Actually, polybutadiene presents a far higher melting temperature than could be expected from this simple correlation. However, another correlation exists between *trans* polybutadiene and polyalkenamers, and we will deal with it later. With regard to *trans* polyacetylene, what causes this polymer not to melt before decomposition is probably the conjugation of the chain double bonds. It is of interest to point out a phenomenon that could not be foreseen: excluding the first members of the series (polybutadiene and polyacetytene), the lowest among the remaining members, i.e., *trans* polypentenamer, combines the highest double bond content with the lowest melting point and the best elastomeric properties at room temperature.

Although an essentially *trans* unsaturated stereoregular polymer with good elastomeric properties, i.e., *trans* poly-2-chlorobutadiene (polychloroprene), was already known in the past (16), it was a widely held opinion that primarily the unsaturated *cis*-tactic polyhydrocarbons had a chain flexibility high enough to promote good elastomeric properties. This was probably due to the fact that the best known stereoregular hydrocarbon elastomers are essentially *cis* unsaturated: *cis*-1,4 polyisoprene (natural rubber), *cis*-1,4 polybutadiene and isotactic *cis*-1,4 polypentadiene (17). In the case of *trans* polyalkenamers, and *trans* polypentenamer in particular, we can now visualize an unsaturated *trans*-tactic polymer that can compete very well as to the elastomeric properties with the best stereoregular, *cis*-tactic elastomers (Table II). From this it can be deduced that the flexibility given to the chain by a single bond adjacent to a double bond does not differ considerably in the case of a *trans* from that of a *cis* double bond.

As to the higher *trans* polyalkenamers following polypentenamer, the progressive increase in melting temperature impairs the elastomeric properties at room temperature. However, up to polyoctenamer (T_m = 67°C) the melting temperature is still low enough to allow the unstretched vulcanized product to have a predominantly amorphous structure and to give it elastomeric properties, since the vulcanization causes a further lowering of the crystallization temperature. Moreover, in these cases, said properties can be improved by a method that has already given good results for *trans*-1,4 polychloroprene (18). This polymer melts at about 80°C. Commercial products, which contain a certain amount of steric and chemical irregularities (80 or 91.5% *trans*-1,4 units) show crystalline melting temperatures of 30 and 55°C, respectively (19). The decrease in melting temperature together with a lowered ability to crystallize during stretching, improves the elastomeric properties of this polymer. Analogously, it is possible to improve some elastomeric properties of higher *trans* polyalkenamers by using products containing a certain amount of *cis*-1,4 units, which cause a decrease in the melting temperature of the polymer.

The good elastomeric properties of the *trans* polyalkenamers also derive from another structural factor that characterizes these polymers. For reasons that will be discussed in the section dealing with the polymerization mechanism of the cycloolefins, polyalkenamers do not contain any branching, unlike the polymers derived from conjugated dienes, which always contain a certain amount of 1,2 or 3,4 added monomer units (20). The elastomeric properties are worsened more by the presence of such groups than by steric irregularities (*cis*-1,4 in a *trans*-1,4 polymer or vice versa), as they hinder the free rotation around the single bonds of the chain, thus reducing its flexibility. Furthermore, the crystallizability of the chains upon stretching is reduced less if the irregularities are due to the type of double bond rather than to the presence of side groups.

Analysis of the crystal structure of *trans* polyalkenamers has revealed the existence of polymorphism. *Trans* polyalkenamers having an odd number of methylene groups between two subsequent double bonds

TABLE II
Some Elastomeric Properties of Vulcanized *Trans* and *Cis* Polypentenamers

(Vulcanization conditions: 150°C × 40 min; vulcanizing agents: sulfur + accelerators; properties determined at 23°C)

Poly-pentenamer	Mooney plasticity ML(1 + 4) at 100°C	Carbon black filler	Tensile strength, kg/cm²	Elongation at break, %	Elasticity modulus, kg/cm² at 200%	at 300%	at 500%	Rebound (μRE), %	Tear resistance, kg/cm
Trans	30	Absent	140	750	11	—	20	n.d.	n.d.
	155	Absent	180	750	15	—	33	80	n.d.
	30	50 parts HAF	280	400	75	170	—	70	50
	100	50 parts HAF	315	370	110	230	—	n.d.	55
Cis	35	50 parts HAF	150	430	—	93	—	74	n.d.

usually exhibit a chain conformation with S $(2/1)m$* symmetry and pack into an orthorhombic crystal lattice (8,22,25) which is quite analogous to that of the usually stable modification of polyethylene. This is the main reason for the phenomenon observed in Fig. 1; i.e., the melting temperatures of *trans* polyalkenamers drop regularly with decreasing methylene sequence length *n* from the value for polyethylene to that for *trans* polypentenamer. The crystallographic repeat distance in these polymers always occurs after two chemical structural units.

In the case of *trans* polyalkenamers having an even number of methylene groups between two subsequent double bonds, only one chain conformation can be foreseen in the crystalline state. It is characterized by a *ti* symmetry* and contains only one structural unit in the crystalline repeat distance (9). However, these chains can pack in at least two different manners, characterized, respectively, by a monoclinic unit cell with a main spacing of 4.13 Å and by a triclinic unit cell with two main spacings of 4.48 and 3.83 Å. The first mode of packing of the even numbered *trans* polyalkenamers (modification IV) is quite analogous to that of the odd series of *trans* polyalkenamers and of the orthorhombic modification of polyethylene (9,24). This is the reason why the melting temperatures of the even numbered *trans* polyalkanemers in the monoclinic modification IV appear on the straight line in Fig. 1 that connects polyethylene with *trans* polypentenamer (lower curve).

The triclinic modification of the *trans* polyalkenamers of the even series (modification III) is characterized, especially for the lower members, by considerably higher melting temperatures. The difference between the melting points of the two crystalline modifications increases with decreasing monomer size. The mode of packing of modification III is very different from that of the odd *trans* polyalkenamers and of modification IV of the even series (9,25), but it shows analogies to that of the normally unstable triclinic modification of polyethylene (26). Very low energy minima have been calculated (27) for the triclinic modification of even numbered *trans* polyalkenamers as well as for the normally stable modification of *trans*-1,4 polybutadiene, characterized by the same chain conformation (28) but by different modes of packing (29). As expected, the entropies of fusion of both polymers are comparably low (30). For these reasons we have correlated the melting points of *trans* polyoctenamer and *trans* polyhexenamer in modification III with that of *trans*-1,4 polybutadiene (upper curve of Fig. 1). With regard to

* According to the nomenclature proposed by Corradini (21).

trans-1,4 polybutadiene, a melting point of 96°C was assumed in Fig. 1. This was deduced (31) by extrapolation from thermodynamic measurements. It is actually known that the normally stable modification of *trans*-1,4 polybutadiene does not melt directly, but that it undergoes an isophasic first order transition at 76°C to another modification which finally melts at 145°C, the crystal structure of which has not been completely elucidated (31–33).

Polyalkenamers having double bonds either exclusively or predominantly of the *cis* type were also obtained in our laboratories by polymerization of cycloolefins via ring opening. Although this homologous series of polymers is presently far less known than the *trans* series, some general remarks can be made. The *cis* polyalkenamers prepared so far always exhibit far lower melting temperatures than the corresponding *trans* isomers. Also in this case a phenomenon occurs which is often observed in ethylenically unsaturated hydrocarbon polymers (Table III); namely, that *trans*-tactic isomers generally exhibit melting temperatures that are at least 50°C higher than those of the corresponding *cis* isomers. This phenomenon is observed also for low molecular weight hydrocarbons, but it is enhanced in polymers. The exact melting temperatures of the *cis* polyalkenamers could not be determined yet, both because they are quite low and because of the remarkable difficulties encountered in preparing the pure *cis* isomers of polyalkenamers except in the case of polypentenamer.

With regard to the elastomeric properties of *cis* polyalkenamers (Table II) just the opposite of what is usually observed in unsaturated hydrocarbon polymers occurs: the *cis* isomer, though presenting fairly good

TABLE III
Comparison between the Melting Temperatures of Some Unsaturated *Cis* and *Trans* Hydrocarbon and Chlorinated Polymers

	Melting temperature, °C		
Unsaturated hydrocarbon polymers	*Cis* isomer	*Trans* isomer	Ref.
1,4 Polybutadiene	1	145	5, 6
1,4 Polyisoprene	13	74	11, 34
1,4 Poly-2,3-dimethyl-butadiene	192	272	35, 36
Isotactic 1,4 polypentadiene	44	95	17, 37
1,4 Poly-2-chloro-butadiene	70	80	38, 18
Polypentenamer	<-40	23	8

TABLE IV
Second Order Transition Temperatures of Some Elastomers

Elastomer	T_g, °C
trans-1,4 Polychloroprene	−45
Ethylene-propylene copolymer	−50
SBR	−65
Natural rubber	−70
Butyl rubber	−70
Propylene oxide rubber	−75
trans Polypentenamer	−95
cis-1,4 Polybutadiene	−115
Silicon rubber	−120
cis Polypentenamer	−140

elastic properties, exhibits much poorer mechanical properties than the *trans* isomer at room temperature. This confirms the general principle stated above, i.e., that the practically important elastomeric (especially dynamic) properties of polymers having the same basic chemical structure are better in those that have the melting point closer to room temperature. A very low melting polymer, like *cis* polypentenamer, can hardly crystallize at normal temperatures, even if subjected to elongations above 500%. However, all-*cis* polypentenamer has a second order transition temperature at about −140°C, which is exceptionally low even if compared with other low temperature elastomers (Table IV). Consequently, the range in which all-*cis* polypentenamer shows excellent elastomeric properties is that of very low temperatures (−50 to −90°C). Good elastomeric properties even at room temperature should be found in the higher members of the *cis* polyalkenamers, which, on the basis of the general rule already observed for the *trans* series, should melt at temperatures which are somewhat higher and closer to room temperature (Table IV).

II. CATALYSTS FOR THE STEREOSPECIFIC POLYMERIZATION OF CYCLOOLEFINS

The study of the stereospecific polymerization of cycloolefins via ring opening by the authors of this article started from the investigation of the polymerization of cyclobutene (7,39–40). It was found that cyclobutene can be polymerized by four different groups of catalysts to stereoregular polymers having four different types of structure:

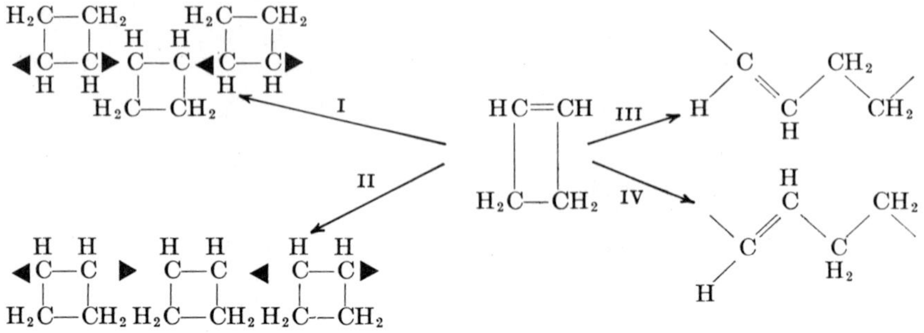

(5)

I	*erythro*-diisotactic polycyclobutene*
II	*erythro*-disyndiotactic polycyclobutene*
III	*cis* polybutenamer (corresponding to *cis*-1,4 polybutadiene)
IV	*trans* polybutenamer (corresponding to *trans*-1,4 polybutadiene)

* The assignment of the type of stereoregularity is only tentative until further experimental evidence has been obtained (38).

Table V shows some of the most significant catalyst systems, and the types of polymer they yield in the polymerization of cyclobutene. As can be seen, the type of polymerization depends first of all on the nature of the transition metal. Two classes can be distinguished among the catalysts of the system first described by Ziegler which are prepared from transition metal compounds of groups IV, V, and VI of the periodic system and organoaluminum compounds:

1. Catalysts containing chromium or vanadium, i.e., the more electronegative among these metals. These catalysts polymerize cyclobutene almost exclusively via opening of the double bond.
2. Catalysts containing titanium, molybdenum, or tungsten, i.e., the more electropositive among the metals examined. These catalysts polymerize cyclobutene primarily via ring opening to polymers having 1,4 polybutadiene structure.

(The classification of the transition metals according to their electronegativity is made following the rule that in a given period of the periodic table of elements the electronegativity increases with increasing atomic number, and in a given group with decreasing atomic weight.)

Among the catalysts made from compounds of noble metals of group

TABLE V
Catalyst Systems for the Polymerization of Cyclobutene

Catalyst system	Predominant structure of the polymer	Ref.
$CrO_2Cl_2/Al(C_2H_5)_2Cl$/toluene	Only I crystalline	39
Cr(acetylacetonyl)$_3$/$Al(C_2H_5)_2Cl$/toluene	Only I crystalline	39
$VCl_4/Al(C_2H_5)_3$/*n*-heptane	Only I crystalline	7, 39
V(acetylacetonyl)$_3$/$Al(C_2H_5)_2Cl$/toluene	Only II crystalline	7, 39
V(acetylacetonyl)Cl_2/$Al(C_2H_5)_2Cl$/toluene	Only I crystalline	39
$VO(OC_4H_9)_3/Al(C_2H_5)_2Cl$/toluene	Only II crystalline	39
$TiCl_4/Al(C_2H_5)_3$/*n*-heptane	Predom. III amorphous	7
$TiCl_4/Al(C_2H_5)_3$/toluene	Predom. IV crystalline	39
$TiCl_3xAlCl_3/Al(C_2H_5)_2Cl$/toluene[a]	Predom. IV crystalline	7, 39
$MoCl_3/Al(C_2H_5)_3$/toluene	Predom. III amorphous	39
$MoCl_5/Al(C_2H_5)_3$/toluene	I + III + IV	39
MoO_2(acetylacetonyl)$_2$/$Al(C_2H_5)_2Cl$/toluene	III + IV	39
$WCl_6/Al(C_2H_5)_3$/toluene	I + III + IV	39
π-Allyl-Ni-bromide/C_2H_5OH	Only I crystalline	42
$RhCl_3/H_2O$	Only I crystalline	40
$RuCl_3/H_2O$	III + IV amorphous	41
$RuCl_3/C_2H_5OH$	Only IV crystalline	41

[a] $TiCl_4$ reduced with Al and activated.

VIII and protic solvents in the absence of organometallic compounds, an analogous distinction can be made:

3. Catalysts containing the more electronegative metals, nickel and rhodium, which polymerize cyclobutene exclusively via opening of the double bond.

4. Catalysts containing the more electropositive ruthenium which polymerize cyclobutene exclusively via ring opening.

The behavior of the higher cycloolefin homologs toward the catalysts mentioned above also shows many analogies with what has just been described for cyclobutene; the catalysts containing the more electronegative transition metals tend to polymerize higher cycloolefins via opening of the double bond while those containing the more electropositive ones tend to do it via ring opening (8). As our present interest is especially focused on the methods that lead to elastomeric products, we shall disregard those catalysts which polymerize cycloolefins via opening of the double bond, since they yield polymers that do not show interesting

TABLE VI

Efficiency of Various Catalyst Systems in the Polymerization of Cyclopentene (Polymerization conditions: 4 hr at $-30°C$; molar ratio of transition metal to $Al(C_2H_5)_3$ and $Al(C_2H_5)_2Cl$ = 1:2.5 and 1:5, respectively; molar ratio of monomer to transition metal = 500:1; polymerization in the absence of diluent except for the run with $RuCl_3$ which was carried out in ethanol at 20°C)

Catalyst system	Polymer yield, %	Polymer structure	Intrinsic visc. in toluene at 30°C, dl/g	Internal double bonds *Cis*, %	Internal double bonds *Trans*, %
$TiCl_4/Al(C_2H_5)_3$	<1	Polypentenamer	n.d.	<5	>95
$ZrCl_4/Al(C_2H_5)_3$	<1	Polypentenamer	n.d.	7	93
$CrO_2Cl_2/Al(C_2H_5)_3$	0	—	—	—	—
$MoCl_5/Al(C_2H_5)_3$	27	Polypentenamer	1.6	99	1
$WCl_6/Al(C_2H_5)_3$	30	Polypentenamer	3.3	15	85
$WCl_6/Al(C_2H_5)_2Cl$	53	Polypentenamer	2.6	12	88
$UO_2Cl_2/Al(C_2H_5)_2Cl$	0	—	—	—	—
$RuCl_3/C_2H_5OH$	0	—	—	—	—

elastomeric properties, and we shall only consider the catalysts of classes *2* and *4*, i.e., those that cause formation of polyalkenamers. The results obtained with such catalysts in the polymerization of cyclopentene are summarized in Table VI.

Cyclopentene shows a higher selectivity with regard to catalysts than cyclobutene. In fact, catalysts based on halides of group VIII metals (ruthenium) in protic solvents do not polymerize cyclopentene. The organometal type catalysts containing transition metals of group IV (titanium, zirconium) and group VI (molybdenum, tungsten) polymerize cyclopentene to polypentenamer, i.e., exclusively via ring opening (8). But, while the former exhibit a very modest catalytic activity, the latter allow us to obtain high yields of polypentenamer. With regard to stereospecificity, the titanium- or zirconium-containing catalysts yield almost exclusively *trans*-tactic polypentenamers; those based on molybdenum pentachloride yield all-*cis* polypentenamer. Oxygen containing compounds, especially peroxides, hydroperoxides, and alcohols were reported to act as cocatalysts enhancing the activity of the catalysts prepared from tungsten halides and organoaluminum compounds (43,44).

Among the catalysts prepared from Group VIB metal salts and organoaluminum compounds only the tungsten and molybdenum catalysts induce the polymerization of cyclopentene to polypentenamer. This is surprising in view of both the high reactivity of these catalysts and a du Pont patent (45) stating that cyclopentene and cyclohexene can be polymerized, though in very low yields and with less stereospecificity, via ring opening with activated chromium or molybdenum oxide supported on aluminum oxide as the catalyst. The latter seems to be the first recognized case of a ring opening polymerization of a low-strained cycloolefin described in the literature. More recently Ziegler-Natta catalysts containing niobium or tantalum pentachloride as the transition metal salt were also reported to be active in the ring opening polymerization of cycloolefins, but their activity seems to be limited to cyclopentene (46). The polypentenamer thus obtained is built up from 60–65% *trans* and 30% *cis* units. Due to this low stereoregularity, the elastomeric properties of this polymer are poor at room temperature. The best catalysts for the preparation of *trans* polypentenamer presently known with respect to both catalytic activity and the elastomeric properties of the polymer are those based on WCl_6. The ability of the niobium and tantalum catalysts to polymerize cyclopentene via ring opening, unlike analogous vanadium catalysts which exclusively polymerize cycloolefins via opening of the double bond, is in line with the above reported rule that the tendency toward ring opening polymerization increases with increasing electropositivity of the transition metal.

The polymerization of cycloolefins higher than cyclopentene to stereoregular polyalkenamers (Table VII) appears even more selective with regard to the catalyst system (9). Contrary to what is observed with cyclopentene, the catalysts based on transition metals of the group IV appear ineffective and those based on molybdenum exhibit little activity. The catalysts based on tungsten halides, however, are very active and stereospecific in the polymerization of this group of cycloolefins. In general, tungsten catalysts yield all-*trans* polyalkenamers from higher cyclolefins. Also the $MoCl_5/Al(C_2H_5)_3$ system, which in the case of cyclopentene yields pure *cis* polypentenamer, polymerizes higher cycloolefins essentially to *trans* polyalkenamers. Cyclohexene behaves very differently in that it never yields high polymers, not even in traces, with any of these catalysts (Table VII).

III. MECHANISM OF THE RING OPENING POLYMERIZATION OF CYCLOOLEFINS

In order to establish the mechanism of polymerization of cycloolefins to polyalkenamers, a series of runs were carried out with representative examples of various classes of catalysts. The $CuCl_2/Al(C_2H_5)_3$ catalyst system, which gives rise to the formation of a great number of free

TABLE VII

Polymerization of Higher Cycloolefins in the Presence of Catalysts Based on Metals of Goups IV and VI (Polymerization conditions: 5 hr at $-30°C$, then 20 hr at $+20°C$; molar ratio of transition metal to $Al(C_2H_5)_3$ and $Al(C_2H_5)_2Cl$ = 1:2.5 and 1:5, respectively; molar ratio of monomer to transition metal = 500:1; polymerization in the absence of diluent)

Cycloolefins	Catalyst system	Conversion, %	$[\eta]$ dl/g[a]	Polymer structure	Internal double bonds *Cis*, %	Internal double bonds *Trans*, %	X-ray exam.
Cyclohexene	$MoCl_5/Al(C_2H_5)_3$	0	—	—	—	—	—
Cyclohexene	$WCl_6/Al(C_2H_5)_2Cl$	0	—	—	—	—	—
Cycloheptene	$TiCl_4/Al(C_2H_5)_3$	0	—	—	—	—	—
Cycloheptene	$MoCl_5/Al(C_2H_5)_3$	5	n.d.	Polyheptenamer	7	93	Crystalline
Cycloheptene	$WCl_6/Al(C_2H_5)_2Cl$	18	1.1	Polyheptenamer	9	91	Crystalline
cis- Cyclooctene	$WCl_6/Al(C_2H_5)_3$	23	2.4	Polyoctenamer	15	85	Crystalline
Cis/trans(1:2) Cyclododecene	$WCl_6/Al(C_2H_5)_2Cl$	34	2.2	Polydodecenamer	6	94	Crystalline

[a] Intrinsic viscosity in toluene at 30°C.

radicals, does not polymerize either cyclobutene or cyclopentene. Similarly, the organometallic compounds alone (e.g., $Al(C_2H_5)_3$, $Al(C_2H_5)_2Cl$, $Li{\cdot}n\text{-}C_4H_9$) do not polymerize these monomers. The same is the case for some typical cationic catalysts, such as $AlCl_3$, $TiCl_4$, and CrO_2Cl_2. Among such catalysts, only WCl_6 can polymerize cyclopentene, though in extremely low yield (a few percent conversion after some weeks of contact) to low molecular weight, essentially atactic polyalkenamers. This means that the situation is similar to that observed in the case of α-olefins. Thus, for example, propylene can be polymerized, though in low yield, by titanium halides ($TiCl_2$ (47) or $TiCl_3{\cdot}xAlCl_3$ (48)) to polymers of low stereoregularity. However, for both propylene and cycloolefins, only the presence of an organometallic compound, such as an aluminum alkyl, in addition to the transition metal, makes it possible to obtain a high polymerization rate and a high stereospecificity.

The inefficiency of other catalyst systems and the analogy with the behavior of α-olefins suggest that the polymerization of cycloolefins via ring opening also takes place by a coordinated anionic mechanism. It can also be concluded that tungsten, among all transition metals, presents the highest tendency to coordinate with cycloolefins; this enables it to polymerize these monomers even by itself in the absence of an organometallic compound.

The polymerization of cycloolefins to polyalkenamers differs from a thermodynamic point of view from the usual polymerization of vinyl monomers. In the polymerization of the vinyl monomers, the transformation of a double bond in the monomer into two single bonds in the polymer chain is thermodynamically favored by a high exothermicity (about 20 kcal/mole). In the ring opening polymerization, the bonds contained in the monomer are exactly the same as those appearing in the corresponding segment of the resulting polymer chain, both with respect to number and type. No enthalpy factor resulting from bond transformation is to be considered, therefore. Thus, the thermodynamic factor that mainly favors the ring opening polymerization is the release of the ring strain energy. This energy greatly varies with the ring size of the cycloolefin (Table VIII). In cyclopropene (49,50) and cyclobutene (51) it is even higher than the heat of reaction of a normal vinyl polymerization, which explains the great tendency of these monomers to polymerize in the presence of a great number of catalysts. By contrast, in cyclopentene (52), cycloheptene (54), and *cis* cyclooctene (54) the ring strain energy is rather low. This may explain why only a few catalysts are able to polymerize them to polyalkenamers. The low heat

TABLE VIII
Ring Strain in Several *Cis* Cycloolefins

Cycloolefin	Ring strain expressed as $\Delta H°_f$(g) exp. − $\Delta H°_f$(g) calc. kcal/mole[a]	Ref.
Cyclopropene	∼54.5	49, 50
Cyclobutene	>26.1	51
Cyclpentene	4.9	52
Cyclohexene	0.8	53
Cycloheptene	∼5	54
Cis cyclooctene	∼6	54

[a] The calculated value refers to a corresponding open chain.

of reaction involved in their polymerization also accounts for the rapidly reached polymerization-depolymerization equilibrium. In addition to the ring strain, an enthalpy factor also seems to favor the ring opening polymerization of cycloolefins. In cyclohexene the ring strain is extremely low (53) since the conformation of a six-membered ring is nearly equivalent to that of the corresponding open chain. This explains why cyclohexene shows no tendency to polymerize via ring opening not even with formation of low molecular weight polymers.

Polymerization via ring opening has been generally observed only in unsubstituted cycloolefins and not in alkyl substituted ones. The alkyl substituted cyclopentenes could not be polymerized via ring opening with the catalysts described above, independent of the position of the substituent, whereas 3-methyl- as well as 3-phenylcyclooctene have recently been reported (55) to polymerize, although in significantly lower yield than cyclooctene, via ring opening in the presence of the above tungsten-based Ziegler-Natta catalysts. This decrease in reactivity is also caused by thermodynamic factors (56). It has been observed in ring opening polymerizations of cyclic ethers, too. Thus, while for instance tetrahydrofuran can be easily polymerized via ring opening (57), its alkyl substituted derivatives are not polymerizable (58–61). In the case of a four-membered ring, the stabilizing effect of the alkyl substituent is insufficient from an energetic point of view to balance the high ring strain. Thus, 3-methylcyclobutene can be converted by all the catalysts reported above to polymers having polypentadiene structure, though at a far lower rate than in the case of cyclobutene (41):

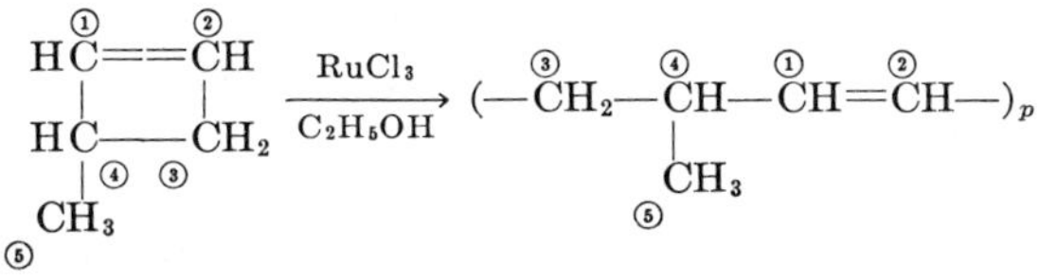

(6)

This reaction can be stereospecific with regard to the double bond. For instance, the system $RuCl_3/C_2H_5OH$ yields a polypentadiene having exclusively *trans* double bonds. However, the reaction is not stereospecific with respect to carbon atom 4, not even with the catalysts prepared from Ti alkoxides and organoaluminum compounds or from $VCl_3 + Al(C_2H_5)_3$, which polymerize pentadiene to polymers that exhibit stereoregularity both with respect to the double bonds and the tertiary carbon atoms. This demonstrates how much the mechanism of the ring opening polymerization of cycloolefins differs from that of the conventional polymerization of conjugated dienes, although in many cases the reaction products are the same.

A modest energy gain in the polymerization of cycloolefins via ring opening may result also from the transformation of the *cis* double bond, which characterizes most cycloolefins, into a *trans* double bond in the polymer chain. This is probably the reason why the higher members of the cycloolefin series have a greater tendency to form all-*trans* polyalkenamers than *cis* isomers. Cycloolefins up to the seven-membered ring are known only in the *cis* form. From cyclooctene onward the *trans* isomer is also known. Relative stability of the *trans* isomer increases with increasing ring size. In cyclododecene at equilibrium, the *trans-cis* ratio is 2:1. If such a mixture is used in a polymerization, both isomers polymerize to the same *trans* polydodecenamer, but the more energetic *cis* isomer seems to polymerize more rapidly than the *trans* isomer.

The ease by which the *cis* double bond of the cycloolefin is transformed into a *trans* double bond in the polymer is one of the phenomena suggesting that the site of the opening of the cycloolefin is one of the single bonds adjacent to the double bond. It has been ascertained that the catalysts that polymerize olefins via ring opening do not isomerize the double bond of the monomer. Therefore it seems very unlikely that the site of ring opening is a single bond far from the double bond; because if that were the case the monomer unit in the polymer should contain *cis* internal double bonds just as the monomer itself. By contrast, ring opening at a bond adjacent to the double bond gives rise to a monomeric unit with a terminal double bond, which when inserted in the polymer chain, can easily assume either *cis* or *trans* configuration, depending on the properties of the active center and on the thermodynamics of the reaction.

The site at which the cycloalkene rings open is still a matter of discussion. Three possibilities can be visualized: (a) at the single bond in alpha position with respect to the double bond, (b) at the one in beta position, and (c) at the double bond itself. The schemes of classical organic chemistry are in favor of (b). It is actually known that cyclobutene may be transformed at high temperature to butadiene via opening of the single bond in beta position (62). However, in that case the reaction is thermal and proceeds through a radical mechanism, in contrast with the present polymerizations which are ionic and involve a coordination mechanism. The ease by which the *cis* double bond of the cycloolefins is transformed into a *trans* double bond in the polymer along with the established lack of isomerization of the double bond in any cycloolefin polymerization with the above catalysts favors hypotheses (a) and (c) over (b). If the single bond in beta position opened, the polymer should preferably contain *cis* internal double bonds just as the monomer. By contrast, ring opening at the bond adjacent to the double bond gives rise to a monomeric unit with a terminal double bond, which, when inserted into the polymer chain, can easily assume either *cis* or *trans* configuration, depending on the active center and on the thermodynamics of the reaction.

Other strong evidence against (b) is the structure of the polymers obtained in the ring opening polymerizations of norbornene (63), of bicyclo[4,2,0]oct-7-ene (64), and of bicyclo[3,2,0]hexa-2,6-diene (64). In these monomers the single bond in beta position is a part of a further ring, which is retained in the polymer, as illustrated for norbornene:

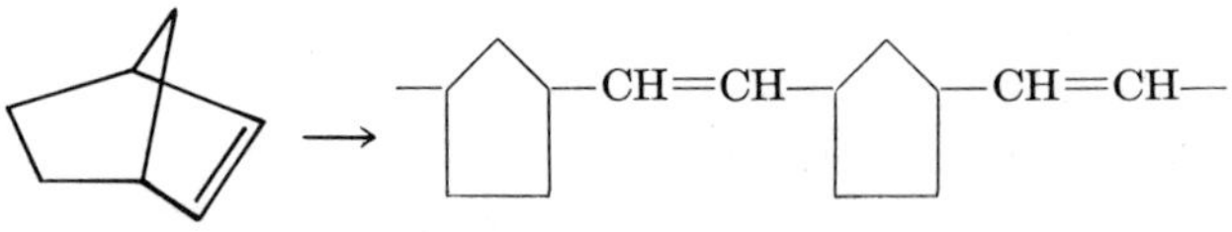

(7)

The choice between hypotheses (a) and (c) is harder to make at present. In our earlier publications we favored (a) over (c) mainly on the basis of the vinyl endgroups that characterize especially the lower molecular weight polymers of unsubstituted cycloolefins and the vinylidene endgroups exhibited by the ring opening polymers of 3-methylcylobutene (40). More recently, evidence in favor of hypothesis (c) has been furnished by the so-called olefin metathesis, a dismutation reaction of alpha-olefins as well as of internal olefins by the action of a $WCl_6/AlEtCl_2/C_2H_5OH$ catalyst (65,66). As an example, metathesis of 2-pentene produces essentially a 1:2:1 mixture of 2-butene, 2-pentene, and 3-hexene. This reaction can be interpreted on the basis of an eight electron transposition:

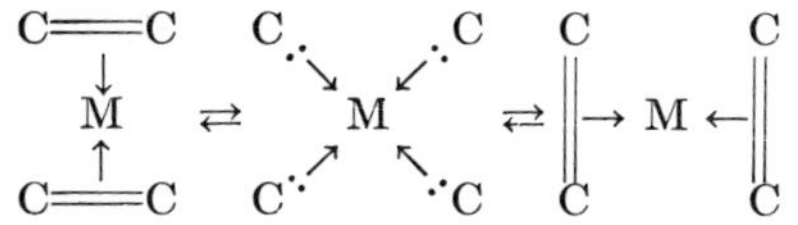

(8)

It can be traced back to an early observation made in our laboratory that propylene is partially dismutated to ethylene and 2-butene during its polymerization in the presence of supported molybdenum catalysts, yielding ethylene-propylene copolymers (67), as well as to the Phillips propylene dismutation process, which yields equimolecular amounts of ethylene and butenes (68,69). This reaction has been extended to cyclo-olefins. A Phillips patent (70) reports the synthesis of 1,6-heptadiene from cyclopentene and ethylene and of 1,7-nonadiene from cyclohexene and propylene.

An eight electron transposition (metathesis) has recently been proposed (71) also for the ring opening polymerization of cycloolefins with tungsten halide catalysts on the basis of the formation of a ring structure (macrocycle) containing the polyalkenamer thus obtained. This result appears in contrast with the above reported experimental evidence for the presence of vinyl endgroups in such polymers. Experimental work is now in progress in various laboratories in order to establish whether the cycloolefin polymerization proceeds through pathway (a) or (c).

The fact that cycloolefins open at only one definite site accounts for the perfect linearity of the polyalkenamers obtained with organometallic catalysts acting through a typically anionic coordinate mechanism. Analysis of the structure of high molecular weight polyalkenamers has actually demonstrated the absence of monomeric units of the type resulting from 1,2 polymerization of conjugated dienes (8). Saturated monomer units stemming from the opening of the double bond are equally absent. Their presence would have implied a "copolymerization" of monomeric units derived from the same cycloolefin via ring cleavage and via opening of the double bond. However, even if such a reaction is possible in principle, it must be ruled out on the basis of experimental evidence. In fact, when attempting to copolymerize cyclopentene with ethylene in the presence of a typical ring opening catalyst at low temperature, only polypentenamer completely free of monomeric units derived from ethylene is obtained.

References

1. Report on Nomenclature in the Field of Makromolecules, IUPAC, *J. Polymer Sci.*, **8,** 257 (1952).
2. A. Ciferri, C. A. Hoewe, and P. Flory, *J. Amer. Chem. Soc.*, **83,** 1015 (1961).
3. See this book, chapter by G. Natta, A. Valvassori, and G. Sartori on "Propylene-Ethylene Rubbers," p. 679.
4. See this book, chapter by H. S. Makowski on "Chlorination, Grafting and Related Techniques," p. 905.
5. G. Natta and P. Corradini, *Nuovo Cimento,* **15,** *Nuovo Cimento Suppl.*, **1,** 111 (1960).
6. G. Natta and P. Corradini, *Atti Accad. Nazl. Lincei, Rend., Classe Sci. Fis., Mat. Nat.*, **19,** 229 (1955); G. Natta, L. Porri, P. Corradini, and D. Morero, *Chim. Ind (Milan),* **40,** 362 (1958).
7. G. Dall'Asta, G. Mazzanti, G. Natta, and L. Porri, *Makromol. Chemie,* **56,** 224 (1962).
8. G. Natta, G. Dall'Asta, and G. Mazzanti, *Angew. Chem.*, **76,** 765 (1964); *Angew. Chem. Internat. Edit.*, **3,** 723 (1964).
9. G. Natta, G. Dall'Asta, I. W. Bassi, and G. Carella, *Makromol. Chemie,* **91,** 87 (1966).
10. G. Natta, A. Zambelli, I. Pasquon, and F. Ciampelli, *Makromol. Chemie,* **79,** 161 (1964).
11. W. Cooper, *J. Polymer Sci.*, **A1,** 159 (1963).
12. G. Natta, G. Mazzanti, and P. Corradini, *Atti Accad. Nazl. Lincei, Rend., Classe Sci. Fis., Mat. Nat.*, **25,** 3 (1958).
13. K. Ziegler, E. Holzkamp, H. Breil, and H. Martin, *Angew. Chem.*, **67,** 541 (1955).
14. Phillips Petroleum Co., Belg. Pat. 530,617 (1953).
15. Standard Oil Company of Indiana, U.S. Pat. 2,658,059 (1951).
16. See this book, chapter by C. A. Hargreaves on "Neoprene," p. 227.
17. G. Natta, L. Porri, G. Stoppa, G. Allegra, and F. Ciampelli, *Polymer Letters,* **1,** 67 (1963).
18. I. Maynard and W. E. Mochel, *J. Polymer Sci.*, **13,** 235; 251 (1954).
19. R. Nagao, *Polymer,* **9,** 517 (1968).
20. P. J. Flory, *Principles of Polymer Chemistry,* Cornell Univ. Press, Ithaca, N.Y., 1953, p. 238–246.
21. P. Corradini, *Atti Accad. Nazl. Lincei, Rend., Classe Sci. Fis., Mat. Nat.*, **28,** 1 (1960).
22. G. Natta and I. W. Bassi, *Atti Accad. Nazl. Lincei, Rend., Classe Sci., Fis., Mat., Nat.*, **38,** 315 (1965); *J. Polymer Sci. Part C,* **16,** part **5,** 2551 (1967).
23. G. Natta and I. W. Bassi, *European Polymer J.*, **3,** 31 (1967).
24. G. Natta and I. W. Bassi, *European Polymer J.*, **3,** 43 (1967); G. Natta, I. W. Bassi, and G. Fagherazzi, *ibid.*, **3,** 339 (1967).
25. G. Fagherazzi and I. W. Bassi, *European Polymer J.*, **4,** 151 (1968).
26. A. Turner-Jones, *J. Polymer Sci.*, **62,** 53 (1962).
27. Private communication of P. Corradini.

28. G. Natta, P. Corradini, L. Porri, and D. Morero, *Chim. Ind. (Milan)*, **40,** 362 (1958).
29. S. Iwayanagi, H. Nakane, and I. Sakurai, Paper presented at the Intern. Sympos. on Macromol. Chem., Tokyo 1966, preprint 2-4-11.
30. N. Calderon and M. C. Morris, *J. Polymer Sci. A-2,* **5,** 1283 (1967).
31. G. Moraglio, G. Polizzotti, and F. Danusso, *European Polymer J.*, **1,** 183 (1965).
32. G. Natta, M. Pegoraro, P. Cremonesi, and A. Pavan, *Chim. Ind. (Milan)*, **47,** 716; 722 (1965).
33. G. Natta and G. Allegra, Paper presented at the Intern. Sympos. on Macromol. Chem., Tokyo 1966.
34. L. Mandelkern, *Chem. Rev.*, **56,** 903 (1956).
35. T. F. Yen, *J. Polymer Sci.*, **35,** 533 (1959).
36. T. F. Yen, *J. Polymer Sci.*, **38,** 272 (1959); J. F. Brown Jr. and D. M. White, *J. Amer. Chem. Soc.*, **82,** 5671 (1960).
37. G. Natta, L. Porri, P. Corradini, G. Zanini, and F. Ciampelli, *J. Polymer Sci.*, **51,** 463 (1961).
38. C. A. Aufdermarsh, Jr. and R. Pariser, *J. Polymer Sci.*, **A2,** 4727 (1964).
39. G. Natta, G. Dall'Asta, G. Mazzanti, and G. Motroni, *Makromol. Chemie,* **69,** 163 (1963).
40. G. Natta, G. Dall'Asta, and G. Motroni, *J. Polymer Sci. B,* **2,** 349 (1964).
41. G. Natta, G. Dall'Asta, and L. Porri, *Makromol. Chemie,* **81,** 253 (1965).
42. L. Porri, G. Natta, and M. C. Gallazzi, *Chim. Ind. (Milan)*, **46,** 428 (1964).
43. G. Dall'Asta and G. Carella (to Montecatini Edison), Ital. Pat. 778,370 (1965).
44. G. Dall'Asta and R. Manetti, *European Polymer J.*, **4,** 145 (1968).
45. H. Soura Eleuterio (to E. I. du Pont de Nemours), U.S. Pat. 3,074,918 (1957).
46. C. A. Uranek and W. J. Trepka (to Phillips), U.S. Pat. Appl. filed 1966, Serial No. 589,855.
47. C. J. K. Benning, W. R. Wszolek, and F. X. Werber, Abstracts of Papers, Meeting Polymer Div. Am. Chem. Soc. Washington D.C., March 1962, Vol. 3, 138; Polymer Preprint, **1,** 122; 138 (1965).
48. J. Boor, Jr. and E. A. Youngman, *J. Polymer Sci. B,* **2,** 265 (1964).
49. J. W. Knowlton and F. D. Rossini, *J. Res. Natl. Bur. Std.*, **A43,** 113 (1949).
50. K. B. Wiberg, W. J. Bartley, and F. P. Lossing, *J. Am. Chem. Soc.*, **84,** 3980 (1962).
51. S. Kaarsemaker and J. Coops, *Rec. Trav. Chim.*, **71,** 261 (1952).
52. F. D. Rossini, K. S. Pitzer, R. L. Arnett, R. M. Braun, and G. C. Pimentel, *Selected Values of Physics and Thermodynamics of Hydrocarbons and Related Compounds,* Carnegie Press, Pittsburgh, 1953.
53. H. A. Skinner, *J. Chem. Soc.*, **1962,** 4396.
54. J. D. Cox, *Tetrahedron,* **19,** 1175 (1963).
55. N. Calderon, E. A. Ofstead, and W. A. Judy, *J. Polymer Sci. A-1,* **5,** 2209 (1967).
56. F. S. Dainton, T. R. E. Devlin, and P. A. Small, *Trans. Faraday Soc.*, **51,** 1710 (1955).
57. H. Meerwein, Ger. Pat. 741,478 (1939).
58. H. Meerwein, *Angew. Chem.*, **59,** 168 (1957); K. Hamann, *Angew. Chem.*, **63,** 231 (1951).
59. P. A. Small, *Trans. Faraday Soc.*, **51,** 1717 (1955).
60. C. L. Hamermesh and E. V. Hanry, *J. Org. Chem.*, **26,** 4748 (1962).
61. S. C. Temin, *J. Polymer Sci.*, **62,** S91 (1962).

62. E. Vogel, *Angew. Chem.*, **72,** 21 (1960).
63. W. L. Truett, D. R. Johnson, I. M. Robinson, and B. H. Montague, *J. Amer. Chem. Soc.*, **82,** 2337 (1960).
64. G. Dall'Asta and G. Motroni, *J. Polymer Sci. A-1*, **6,** 2405 (1968).
65. N. Calderon, H. Y. Chen, and K. W. Scott, *Tetrahedron Letters*, **1967,** 3327.
66. N. Calderon, E. A. Ofstead, J. P. Ward, W. A. Judy, and K. W. Scott, *J. Amer. Chem. Soc.*, **90,** 4133 (1968).
67. Private communication of G. Mazzanti.
68. R. L. Banks and G. C. Bailey, *Ind. Eng. Chem., Prod. Res. Dev.*, **3,** 170 (1964).
69. C. P. C. Bradshaw, E. J. Howman, and L. Turner, *J. Catalysis*, **7,** 269 (1967).
70. G. C. Ray and D. L. Crain (to Phillips), French Pat. 1,511,381 (U.S. Prior. 1966).
71. K. W. Scott, N. Calderon, E. A. Ofstead, W. A. Judy, and J. P. Ward, 155th Meeting A. C. S., San Francisco, 1968, preprint 54.
72. N. Calderon, Proc. 11th Intern. Conf. Coord. Chem., Haifa 1968, preprint p. 38.

CHAPTER 8

ELASTOMERS BY CONDENSATION POLYMERIZATION

A. Polyurethane Elastomers

J. H. Saunders

Mobay Chemical Company,
Pittsburgh, Pennsylvania

Contents

I. Introduction 727
II. Chemistry of Polyurethane Elastomer Formation 729
A. Raw Materials 729
B. Polymer Formation 735
III. Preparation 737
A. Cast Elastomers 738
1. Prepolymer Formation 738
2. The Curing of Prepolymers 739
3. One-Shot Method 740
B. Millable Gums 741
C. Thermoplastic Types 742
D. Miscellaneous Elastomers 743
E. Relations Between Structure and Properties 745
IV. Properties 753
A. Mechanical Properties 753
B. Environmental Resistance 755
V. Spandex Elastic Fibers 759
VI. Low Modulus Elastomers 760
References 762

I. INTRODUCTION

The polyurethane elastomers are a family of elastic polymers containing urethane groups:

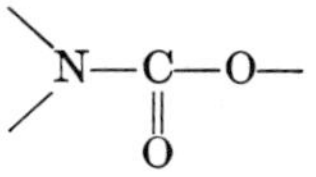

They are most frequently prepared by combining diisocyanates with linear polyesters or polyethers, often with an additional curing agent such as a glycol or diamine. These polymers are generally characterized by outstanding properties, and are finding commercial use in a variety of specialized areas.

Pinten, in Germany, prepared the first highly elastic urethane rubbers (1) with high tensile strength but poor tear resistance. Bayer and coworkers were the first to obtain polyurethane elastomers with the outstanding properties normally expected today (2). These were prepared from poly(ethylene adipate), 1,5-naphthalene diisocyanate, and curing agents such as water or, later, diamines and glycols (3). Similar polyurethanes were investigated in England, using polyesteramides (4), and in the United States, based on polyesters (5) and poly(1,4-oxybutylene) glycol (6,7). Many other reactive components have also been used in recent years, replacing the polyester component.

This family of elastomers is particularly versatile in the range of components used in preparation, and also in the methods of manufacture. In one method, known as the "casting process," components are mixed in the liquid state, poured into a mold, and cured in place. This procedure is especially suitable for those applications requiring large parts which are not produced in great numbers. A second method utilizes the preparation of a linear "millable gum" which is mixed with curing agents and crosslinked or vulcanized similar to hydrocarbon rubbers. This procedure uses conventional rubber machinery in the final mixing and curing steps. In recent years a third variety of polyurethanes has also become available, which can be processed by thermoplastic techniques such as injection molding and extrusion.

The polyurethanes are normally formulated to offer tensile strengths of 5000 psi or higher, elastic elongations above 400%, any desired hardness in the range of about 80 Shore A to 55 Shore D, all with excellent resistance to tear, abrasion, and oils. Other modifications outside this hardness range are also available, but usually with some loss in properties, such as lower elongation at greater hardness, and lower tear strength in softer types.

The primary applications of the polyurethanes most frequently utilize the toughness and high load-bearing properties, as in solid tires, shoe heels, cable jacketing, and metal forming dies. A new type of elastic fiber called "spandex" is based on polyurethanes due to the high modulus and toughness of these polymers, thus permitting the use of finer deniers.

In addition to the almost classical polyurethanes with very high property levels—and relatively high costs—more recent studies have included many lower cost systems with properties also at lower levels. These materials are suitable for uses such as potting, caulks, sealants, shoe soles, etc.

The urethane elastomers with outstanding properties are prepared from prepolymers or other components costing about one dollar or more per pound. Consumption of these materials in the United States was about six million pounds in 1963 (8), not counting spandex. Costs may be expected to come down as volumes increase. The lower property level elastomers are usually prepared from cheaper components such as tolylene diisocyanate and polyethers or castor oil, often filled and extended with cheaper components, so that raw material costs may be below twenty-five cents per pound. The use of these lower cost systems will likely soon exceed that of the more expensive types.

The polyurethane elastomers were reviewed extensively by Saunders and Frisch (9). Reference is made to those books for the details of early research, many properties of specific systems, structure:property relationships, processing techniques, and applications. Other recent reviews of importance include those of Müller (10). The thermal decomposition of elastomeric and other polyurethanes has been reviewed by Saunders and Backus (11). This chapter outlines the basic chemistry of polyurethane elastomers and emphasizes the currently available products which have evolved from the earlier research.

II. CHEMISTRY OF POLYURETHANE ELASTOMER FORMATION

A. Raw Materials

The raw materials most frequently used in preparing the urethane elastomers are tolylene diisocyanate (TDI) or 4,4′-diphenylmethane diisocyanate (MDI), a polyol such as a linear polyester or polyether, and simple glycols, triols, or diamines as curing agents. The preparations and reactions of these components have been reviewed in detail (9b). The most important aspects will be summarized briefly.

Tolylene diisocyanate is produced in largest volume as an 80:20 mixture of the 2,4 and 2,6 isomers, the isomer distribution which results from the conventional nitration of toluene. The following reactions indicate the commercial process:

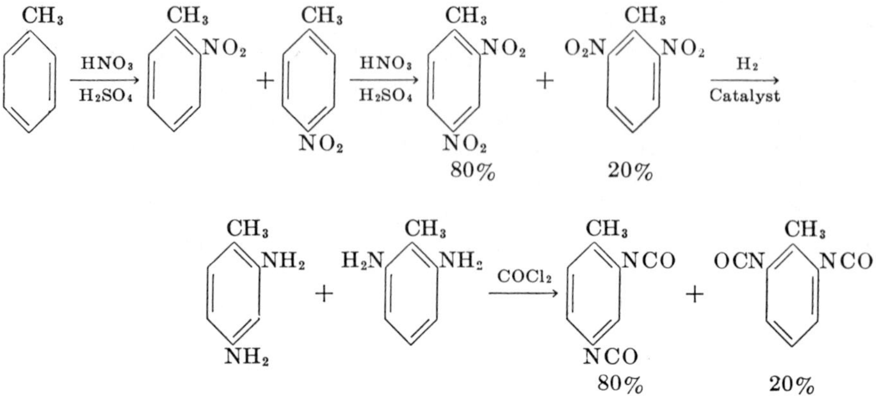

If one wishes to produce a different isomer ratio, a separation may be made at the mononitro stage, e.g., *para*-nitrotoluene on further nitration gives only the 2,4 isomer. Subsequent reduction and phosgenation give pure 2,4-tolylene diisocyanate. A separation of the 2,4-TDI can also be made by crystallization from the 80:20 mixture, leaving a 65:35 or other desired isomer ratio.

Diphenylmethane diisocyanate is prepared by the reaction sequence shown below:

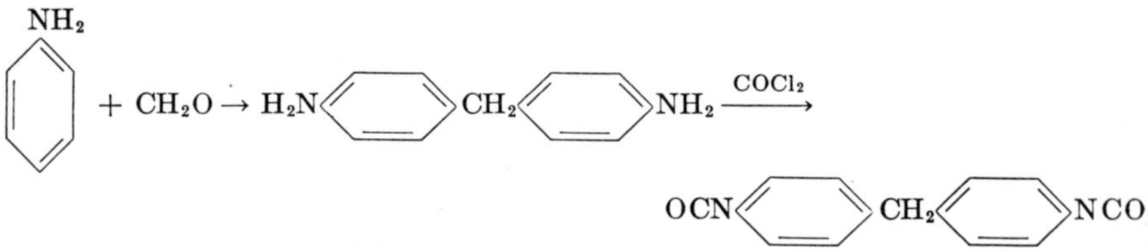

The proper control of the amine preparation leads to pure 4,4′-diamine, so that the MDI in turn is essentially free from other isomers and from either mono- or triisocyanates. This purity is highly desirable if one wishes to obtain the best elastomer properties.

The polyesters used in elastomer production are usually prepared from adipic acid and simple glycols such as ethylene, propylene, butylene, or diethylene glycol. An excess of glycol is present initially, and the esterfication is completed by distilling out glycol until the desired molecular weight is reached:

$$HOOC(CH_2)_4COOH + HOCH_2CH_2OH \xrightarrow{150°C}$$
$$HOCH_2CH_2OCO(CH_2)_4COOCH_2CH_2OH + H_2O \xrightarrow[\text{vacuum}]{200°C}$$
$$HO[CH_2CH_2OCO(CH_2)_4COO]_nCH_2CH_2OH + HOCH_2CH_2OH$$

Usually a molecular weight of about 1000–2000 is preferred, depending on the properties desired in the elastomer. The condensation is made so that the terminal groups are essentially all hydroxyl, and residual water and glycol are kept to a very low level. Other dibasic acids may be used in preparing the polyesters, of course, as well as lactones such as ε-caprolactone.

Polyethers are also used as the polyol components of urethanes. These may be obtained by polymerizing ethylene oxide or propylene oxide with water or a glycol, with a basic catalyst:

$$CH_3\overset{O}{\widehat{CHCH_2}} + HO\underset{CH_3}{\underset{|}{CH}}CH_2OH \xrightarrow{NaOR} HO\underset{CH_3}{\underset{|}{CH}}CH_2\left[OCH_2\underset{CH_3}{\underset{|}{CH}}\right]_n OH$$

The terminal groups are largely secondary hydroxyls, with smaller amounts of primary hydroxyl and traces of unsaturation when propylene oxide is used. Polyethers may also be obtained by the polymerization of tetrahydrofuran.* Lewis acid catalysts such as $SnCl_4$ are generally used for this polymerization:

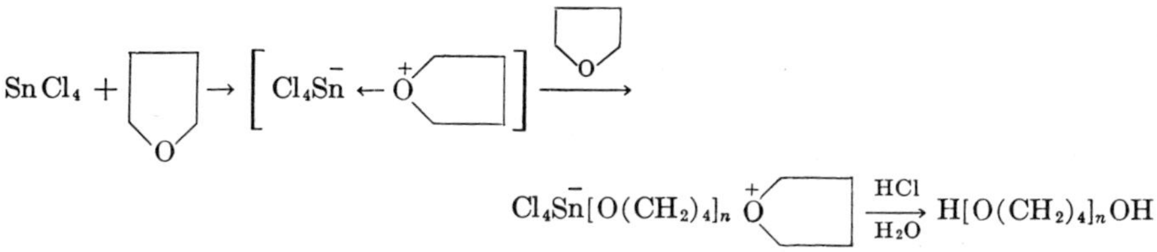

As with the polyesters, molecular weights of 1000–2000 and very low water contents are usually preferred.

Since the primary reactants are diisocyanates and polyols, the reaction between isocyanate and hydroxyl is of prime importance in elastomer formation:

$$RNCO + R'OH \rightarrow RNH\overset{O}{\overset{\|}{C}}OR'$$

* For more on the polymerization of tetrahydrofuran see the chapter by Ledwith and Fitzsimmonds, Part I, page 377.

The product, a urethane, gives the family of polymers its generic name. Most compounds containing a hydrogen replaceable by sodium react similarly, at least initially:

$$\mathrm{RNCO + HA \rightarrow RN(H)\overset{O}{\overset{\|}{C}}{-}A}$$

This addition product may be quite stable, or in some cases may decompose readily. The most important reactions for elastomer preparation, in addition to urethane formation, are indicated below.

Water, which may be an unwanted impurity in a polyol, or which may purposely be included at a carefully controlled level, initially gives a carbamic acid, ultimately a disubstituted urea and carbon dioxide:

$$\mathrm{RNCO + H_2O \rightarrow \left[RNH\overset{O}{\overset{\|}{C}}OH\right] \rightarrow RNH_2 + CO_2}$$

$$\mathrm{RNCO + RNH_2 \rightarrow RNH\overset{O}{\overset{\|}{C}}NHR}$$

The carbamic acid usually decomposes in the temperature range of 20–50°C. Primary and secondary amines, sometimes used as curing agents, react rapidly at room temperature, giving ureas, as indicated above.

Both ureas and urethanes, containing hydrogen bound to nitrogen, may react further to give a biuret and an allophanate, respectively:

$$\mathrm{R'NCO + RNHCONHR \rightarrow RN(CONHR')CONHR} \quad \text{biuret}$$

$$\mathrm{R'NCO + RNHCOOR \rightarrow RN(CONHR')COOR} \quad \text{allophanate}$$

These reactions, which may be desired for crosslinking, are usually quite slow at temperatures below 80–100°C, and may be reversed in the range of 150–200°C.

In addition to reactions with active hydrogens in the elastomer system, isocyanates may react with themselves to give dimers, trimers, and carbodiimides. These are usually undesired side reactions.

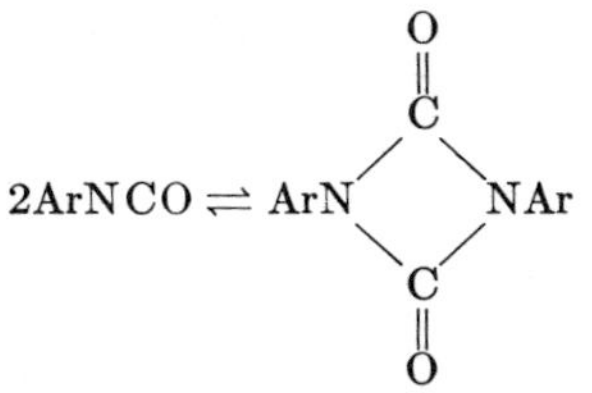

dimer

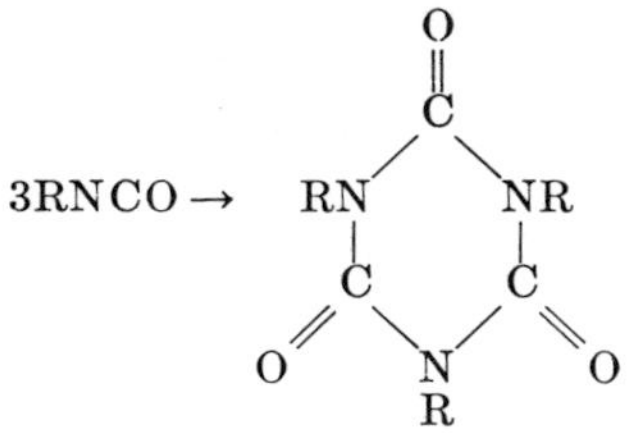

trimer

$$2RNCO \rightarrow RN{=}C{=}NR + CO_2$$

carbodiimide

The dimers have been obtained only from aromatic isocyanates. These are not stable thermally, but usually regenerate the monomer at temperatures of 150°C or higher. Pure trimers and carbodiimides may be obtained from both aliphatic and aromatic isocyanates, and are relatively stable at temperatures of 200°C and above.

All these reactions, and particularly the catalysis of the reactions, may be better understood if one considers the resonance structures possible for the NCO group:

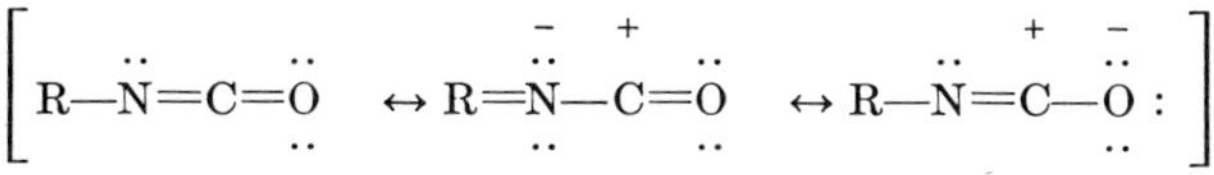

Reactions of the isocyanates normally may be considered to involve attack of a nucleophilic agent on the carbon:

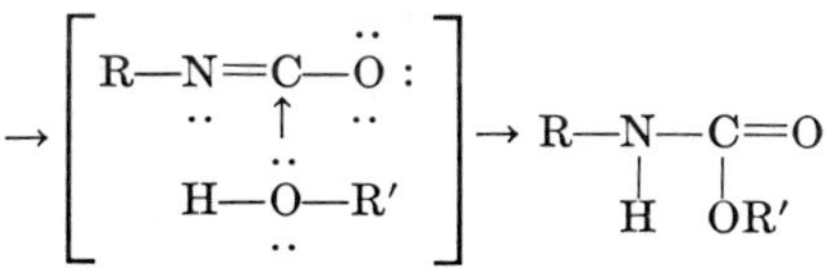

Thus, factors increasing the positive nature of the carbon or the basicity of the nucleophilic agent should increase the rate of reaction. Indeed, increasing the electron withdrawing power of R (p-NO_2–$C_6H_4 \gg C_6H_5 >$ p-$CH_3C_6H_4$) and the base strength of the attacking agent (aliphatic amines > aromatic amines > alcohols $\sim$ water > ureas > urethanes)

increase the rate of addition to isocyanates. Steric hindrance plays its expected role in these reactions, with hindrance in either reactant reducing the rate.

Both acids and bases serve as catalysts, apparently enhancing charge distribution by coordination with oxygen or carbon, respectively:

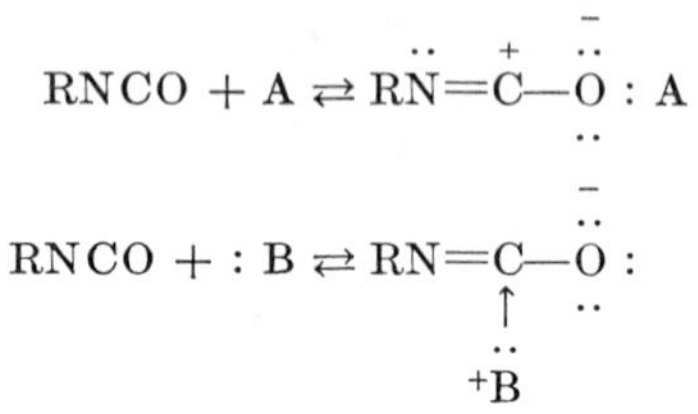

Such isocyanate:catalyst complexes may then be attacked by the active hydrogen compounds or by another isocyanate, respectively.

Many polyvalent metal atoms which are soluble in the reactants and have at least two coordination sites open are amazingly powerful catalysts for isocyanate reactions, often with considerable selectivity. Evidence supports the belief that both the isocyanate and active hydrogen compound coordinate with the metal atom, perhaps in a form such as indicated below:

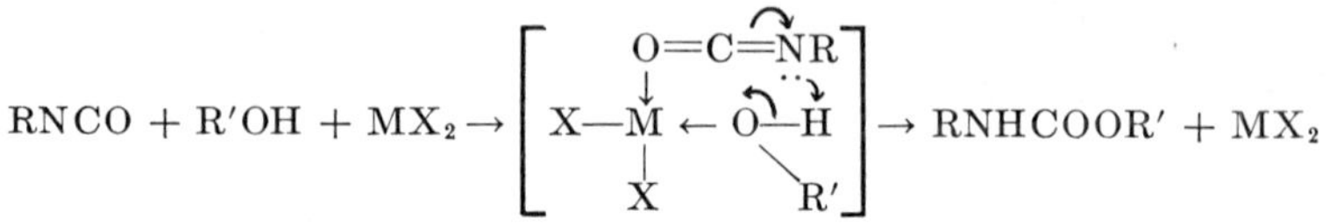

To illustrate the effect of various catalysts on the reaction of phenyl isocyanate with methanol in dibutyl ether at 30°C, 1 mole % of triethylamine increases the rate to 10 times that of the reaction without added catalyst, while the same mole percent of a strong base, benzyl trimethyl ammonium hydroxide, increases the rate sixtyfold. An equal concentration of dibutyltin dilaurate increases the rate by a factor of 37,000! The dibutyltin salts are somewhat selective, promoting the isocyanate–alcohol reaction more strongly than the isocyanate–water reaction, which in turn is promoted more than the isocyanate–urea reaction. Apparently this catalyst does not promote dimerization, trimerization, or carbodiimide formation significantly.

A very wide range of rate studies has been reported in the literature, as have many catalyst evaluations. Reference is made to a recent survey for the many and complex details of these reports (9b). With the proper choice of reactants, temperature, and catalysts one can usually control the isocyanate reactions in the desired manner.

B. Polymer Formation

The polyurethane elastomers are generally block copolymers, combining a relatively flexible or "soft" segment with a stiffer or "hard" segment. Elasticity, elongation, and a low glass transition temperature are usually provided by a polyether or polyester soft segment of molecular weight in the range of 1000–2000. The hard segment is usually a polyurethane block from an aromatic diisocyanate and a glycol, or a mixed polyurea–urethane block when a diamine or water has been used as a curing agent. Hydrogen bonding and van der Waals attractions between hard segments add greatly to the modulus and tear resistance of the polymer, and even serve as physical crosslinks. Primary crosslinks may be included if desired, using some components with a functionality greater than 2, or with a slight excess of isocyanate groups.

Structures of the indicated type may be prepared in several ways. One procedure which offers selective control of the polymerization steps is the "prepolymer process." In this the hydroxyl-containing polyether, polyester, or other resin is first reacted with an excess of diisocyanate to give an intermediate molecular weight adduct or "prepolymer":

$$2R(NCO)_2 + HO{\sim}OH \rightarrow OCN{-}R{-}NHCOO{\sim}OCONH{-}R{-}NCO$$

This prepolymer can then be cured with water, glycols, diamines, and similar reactive agents. When water is used prepolymer chains are joined together with urea links, and carbon dioxide is evolved:

$$2{\sim}OCONH{-}R{-}NCO + H_2O \rightarrow {\sim}OCONH{-}R{-}NHCONH{-}R{-}NHCOO{\sim} + CO_2$$

The use of glycols gives chain lengthening, with more urethane groups being formed, without gas evolution:

$$2{\sim}OCONH{-}R{-}NCO + HO{-}R'{-}OH \rightarrow {\sim}OCONH{-}R{-}NHCOO{-}R'{-}OCONH{-}R{-}NHCOO{\sim}$$

Diamines similarly give chain lengthening, with urea group formation:

$$2{\sim}OCONH{-}R{-}NCO + H_2N{-}R'{-}NH_2 \rightarrow {\sim}OCONH{-}R{-}NHCONH{-}R'{-}NHCONH{-}R{-}NHCOO{\sim}$$

One can obtain primary crosslinks by the use of some triol or other trifunctional material in the curing step. Crosslinks may also be obtained by regulating the ratio of prepolymer to curing agent so that a slight excess of —NCO is present. This excess may react with urea groups in the chain to give biuret branch points:

$$\sim\!\text{NHCONH}\!\sim\; + \;\sim\!\text{NCO} \rightarrow \;\sim\!\underset{\displaystyle\overset{|}{\text{CONH}\!\sim}}{\text{N}}\text{CONH}\!\sim$$

or if no urea groups are present, with urethane groups to give allophanate branch points:

$$\sim\!\text{NHCOO}\!\sim\; + \;\sim\!\text{NCO} \rightarrow \;\sim\!\underset{\displaystyle\overset{|}{\text{CONH}\!\sim}}{\text{N}}\text{COO}\!\sim$$

Urea groups are normally much more reactive toward isocyanate groups than are urethane groups, so where urea groups are present, biuret crosslinking will be favored over allophanate crosslinking.

In addition to the prepolymer route, where the reaction of isocyanate with polyether or polyester resin is completed before the curing agent is added, all components may be mixed simultaneously in a so-called "one-shot" process. This method is generally satisfactory when all active hydrogens react at about the same rate, as when all contain hydroxyl groups as the only reactive sites. When a diamine curing agent is included the procedure is usually successful only if special catalysts are added to selectively catalyze the reaction with hydroxyl groups, so that their reactivity becomes similar to that of the amine groups. Otherwise the diamine reacts first, building a polyurea which separates from the reaction mixture. Certain tin catalysts such as dibutyltin dilaurate and stannous octoate are most frequently used for this purpose.

The prepolymer or one-shot process is normally used in making "cast" elastomers. The components are mixed as liquids, poured into a mold of the desired shape, and polymerization proceeds. After about 10–60 min, depending on the system used, the polymer has enough strength for demolding. It is removed from the mold and cured further, e.g., for several days at room temperature or for several hours at an elevated temperature.

Similar reactions are employed in preparing "millable gums." In this case a slight excess of hydroxyl component is used so that a soluble polymer terminating in hydroxyl groups is obtained, e.g.,

$$\text{HO}\!\sim\!\left[\text{O}\underset{\underset{\text{O}}{\|}}{\text{C}}\text{NHRNH}\underset{\underset{\text{O}}{\|}}{\text{C}}(\text{OR}'\text{O}\underset{\underset{\text{O}}{\|}}{\text{C}}\text{NHRNH}\underset{\underset{\text{O}}{\|}}{\text{C}})_x\text{O}\!\sim\right]_n\text{OH}$$

This polymer can be cured with a polyisocyanate to give a crosslinked structure. The polyisocyanate may be added to the solid gum on a rubber mill, along with other additives, such as carbon black. The compounded stock is then cured at elevated temperatures, under pressure, with conventional rubber techniques. The compounded stock is not permanently stable, and must be cured soon after compounding. In addition, variations in moisture content of the gum, due to absorption of water from the air, may result in poor reproducibility of cure.

In efforts to avoid the limited stability of the stock, and the variable effect of moisture content, gums containing unsaturation or other points suitable for free radical cure have been developed. These gums are cured with a conventional sulfur system or with peroxides. Unsaturation may be built into the gum with reactants such as maleic anhydride in the polyester, or the monoallyl ether of glycerine. Peroxide cure can also be obtained with certain adipate polyesters reacted with MDI, apparently involving radical attack on the methylene carbon in the MDI unit:

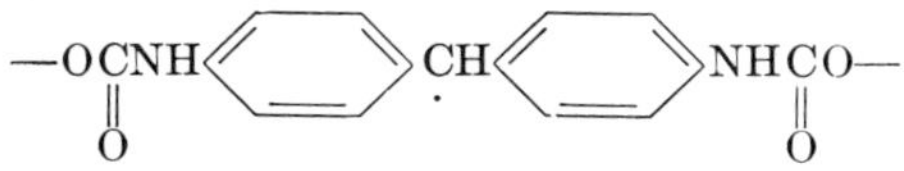

When desired, the millable gums can be used in solution, for coating purposes. The curing agent is added to the solution, the mixture is applied to a substrate such as fabric, and heat is applied to insure good curing.

Urethane elastomers processable by thermoplastic means can also be prepared by the same reactions, with very precise control of reactant ratios. The hydroxyl terminated gum indicated above may be suitable for thermoplastic use if its molecular weight is high enough to insure good properties. Similarly, the systems utilized for casting pass through a thermoplastic stage just prior to crosslinking. If no trifunctional reactant is used, and only a slight excess of isocyanate is present, these systems may be stopped at the thermoplastic state, by cooling the polymer at the appropriate time. Either approach to the thermoplastics requires very close process control to insure high molecular weight without crosslinking.

III. PREPARATION

The preparation of urethane elastomers appears deceptively simple. The major reactions are well characterized and understood, but the effects of trace impurities are not always understood and are frequently overlooked in practice. The preparation of each major type is outlined, with emphasis on variables in prepolymer preparation and curing.

These same variables are important in the other systems as well. Reference is made to earlier publications for background in isocyanate reactions, catalysis, and more details of preparative methods (9b,d).

A. Cast Elastomers

1. Prepolymer Formation

The preparation of prepolymers for foams has been reported in much more detail than that for prepolymers for elastomers. The basic principles are applicable in both cases, but some differences frequently exist in objectives. For elastomer preparation one usually prefers a minimum viscosity, and often wants a minimum vapor hazard. In the case of prepolymers from TDI, this latter consideration leads to a need for less than about 1% free, monomeric TDI in the prepolymers. The free monomer content in prepolymers from high boiling isocyanates such as MDI is not so critical with regard to vapor hazard.

The prepolymer is normally prepared by adding the dry polyol to the desired excess of isocyanate, to which has been added a trace of acid or acid chloride, such as 0.03% of benzoyl chloride. Good agitation is used, and the polyol addition is made at such a rate that the exotherm does not carry the reaction temperature above the desired limit. The reaction is continued until analysis shows the calculated NCO content, whereupon the mixture is cooled. For best stability of the prepolymer an additional 0.03% of acid chloride may be added before packaging (12). The time–temperature cycle may be adjusted according to the individual system used and processing requirements. Typical foam prepolymer sequences have been reported to be about 2 hr at 90°C, or 1.25–1.5 hr at 110°C in uncatalyzed preparations, or about 0.5 hr at 115–120°C with 0.025% of tertiary amine catalysts (9d). Similar times should be applicable for most elastomer prepolymers.

The essential features of preparing low viscosity prepolymers include the following:

(*a*) Use difunctional reactants at an NCO:OH ratio of 2.0 or higher. Increased functionality and lower NCO:OH ratios will lead to higher viscosity.
(*b*) Maintain the water content of the resin as low as possible, below 0.1%. Higher water contents normally lead to higher viscosity due to the hydrogen bonding of the substituted urea groups, and

also because the urea groups may react to form biuret branch points, thus increasing the molecular weight.

(*c*) Use only hydroxyl terminated active hydrogen reactants, since the resulting urethane groups are much less reactive with isocyanates than others, such as urea (as noted above), and amide groups.

(*d*) Avoid all catalytic impurities, intentionally added or otherwise. The prepolymer formation is normally fast enough without catalysts, and side reactions such as trimerization of isocyanate, allophanate, and carbodiimide formation are easily minimized if no catalysts are present.

(*e*) Add a trace of an acid such as hydrogen chloride, or an acid chloride, as a safety measure. Such acids will neutralize many catalytic impurities which may be present in unknown amounts.

The formation of prepolymers of minimum vapor hazard usually involves one of two approaches: the use of an isocyanate having low vapor pressure at temperatures up to about 100°C, such as MDI, or the removal of monomeric isocyanate from the prepolymer. The use of low NCO:OH ratios favors low monomeric isocyanate content, but even when this ratio is 2.0, several percent of free TDI would be present in prepolymers from it. The statistics of the molecular weight distribution are even less favorable when a diisocyanate having groups of equal reactivity is used. Consequently removal of the monomer by some means such as selective extraction or flash distillation may be necessary. When the monomer content is low it may be reduced below 1% by selective reaction with glycols after prepolymer formation, at least in some cases (13).

2. The Curing of Prepolymers

Prepolymers may be cured with reactants such as glycols, diamines, aminoalcohols, higher molecular weight resins, or even water, as may be desired. The processing conditions which may be used and the final polymer properties will govern the choice of curing agent. In most cases the prepolymer is heated to a temperature which will be above the melting point of the curing agent and which will reduce the prepolymer viscosity to a few hundred or at most a few thousand centipoise, to aid in mixing and prevent solidification of the curing agent. The curing agent is usually heated above its melting point, also. A few examples of mixing prepolymers with finely powdered solid curing agents have been reported, but this technique is not usually desirable.

The mixing of the prepolymer with curing agent is a critical step, and agitation should be excellent. Both machine and manual mixing may be done, but machine mixing is generally more reliable. Care should be used, especially at this step, to be sure that personnel are not exposed to hazardous fumes. If a TDI system is used the free TDI concentration and ventilation should be such that the worker does not expose himself to more than 0.02 ppm of TDI in the air. Consequently, a hood is normally preferred for such systems.

Glycol curing agents are normally satisfactory with MDI–polyester elastomers, with excellent properties being obtained. These systems offer the advantage of minimum vapor hazard. With TDI–polyether systems, aromatic diamines are usually required to give high modulus polymers with good tear strength. The curing agent:prepolymer ratio is selected to give the desired balance between NCO and active hydrogen groups, e.g., 1.03–1.10 for $NCO:(NH_2 + OH)$ would be a normal range. The prepolymer and curing agent are mixed, e.g., for about 2 sec with a suitable machine, and the liquid mixture is poured into the desired mold. After 10–60 min at 100–140° in the mold, most systems have polymerized enough for removal from the mold. The part may then be cured for several hours at 100–120°C, in an oven. In some cases adequate properties are obtained without the additional oven cure. Typical properties from several prepolymer–curing agent combinations are given later in Sections III-E and IV.

Some selected references are indicated for the use of 1,5-naphthalene diisocyanate–adipate polyester prepolymer systems (3,10,14), 4,4′-MDI–adipate polyester types (15–17), the use of a 90:10 isomer mixture of MDI (18,19), diamine-cured polyester systems (20), ε-caprolactone polyester types (21,22), TDI–poly(1,4-oxybutylene) glycol–MOCA (3,3′-dichloro-4,4′-diaminodiphenylmethane) systems (23,24), TDI–poly(oxypropylene)glycol–MOCA systems (25), and TDI–poly(oxypropylene) glycol–triol polymers (26).

3. One-Shot Method

Elastomers are also prepared by the "one-shot" method, where all components are mixed at once. In general, properties will be very close to those obtained by the prepolymer route if the exotherm is properly controlled and if the relative rates of reactions of all components are adjusted to be nearly the same. This method of necessity has a considerable amount of monomeric diisocyanate present at casting, and so presents a vapor hazard if volatile isocyanates are used.

The preparation of the softer urethane elastomers from diisocyanates and polyols is relatively straightforward, because exotherms are not high and the hydroxyl components generally react at about the same rates. This method has been used with polyethers, polyesters, and castor oil systems (27,28). Mixing and curing cycles are similar to those used with prepolymer systems. When active hydrogen reactants of widely different reactivity are used, selective catalysis must be employed to regulate the reactivities. Thus, if one mixes TDI, a polyether glycol, and an aromatic diamine in a one-shot system the TDI and diamine rapidly form a polyurea which solidifies while the polyether is still only partially reacted. A two-phase polymer results which has inferior properties. Axelrood et al. (29,30) found that, as in foam formation, the tin catalysts would selectively catalyze the NCO—OH reaction so that homogeneous polymers were obtained from TDI, MOCA, and polyethers with catalytic amounts of stannous octoate. Similar one-shot polyether systems have been reported by Berger and Szukiewicz (31).

B. Millable Gums

Millable gums may be prepared by prepolymer or one-shot methods. In either case, a slight excess of active hydrogen component is used.

The discovery of the high-property urethane elastomers by Bayer and co-workers (2) was made using the millable gum approach. This elastomer, called Vulkollan, was first prepared in the following way, using water as the chain extender: poly(ethylene adipate) of 2000 mol wt, hydroxyl number approximately 56, was dehydrated at 120°C. This polyester was reacted with 1,5-naphthalene diisocyanate at an NCO:OH ratio of 1.3, at 100–130°C. The reaction was complete within a few minutes. The prepolymer was placed in a heavy duty mixer and 0.4–1.4 parts of water per 1000 parts of prepolymer was added. Reaction was continued until the polymer broke into a crumbly mass. This polymer contained enough unreacted NCO groups that it had limited stability, tending to polymerize further on standing. When fresh, it could be cured in molds for 10–15 min at 150–170°C and 700–2800 psi.

In later developments, water was eliminated and polyester–glycol mixtures (32–34), polyesters without added glycols (35–37), polyesteramides (38–41), and poly(1,4-oxybutylene) glycols (42–44) were used in preparing Vulkollan, Chemigum SL (Goodyear), Vulcaprene A (later Daltoflex 1) (ICI), and Adiprene B and C (du Pont), respectively. In each case an NCO:OH ratio somewhat less than 0.99 was used, giving a stable polymer with terminal hydroxyl groups. These millable gums

TABLE I
Adiprene C: Comparison of Sulfur and Peroxide Cures[a]

Composition	A	B
Adiprene C	100	100
EPC carbon black	30	30
MBTS	3	
MBT	1	
Activator, RCD–2098	0.35	
Sulfur	1.5	
DiCup 40C[b]		2.5
Cure 60 min at 153°C		
Properties		
300% Modulus, psi	2975	2975
Tensile, psi	5000	4975
Elongation, %	450	450
Hardness, Shore A	71	69
Compression set, ASTM D 395–55, Method B		
22 hr at 70°C	20	18
70 hr at 100°C	80	45

[a] Data from Ref. 44.
[b] 40% Dicumyl peroxide, Hercules Powder Co.

were cured with more diisocyanate, or in the case of Vulcaprene A, formaldehyde could also be used. Adiprene C contained some unsaturation, and could be cured with sulfur or peroxide systems. Numerous other millable gum polymers have appeared on the market since these early developments. The data in Table I illustrate the formulation of Adiprene C for cure with either sulfur or peroxide (44).

C. Thermoplastic Types

Elastomers having polyurethane or polyurea–urethane segments with very strong interchain attractions often have properties which would be expected if those "hard blocks" formed crystallites which serve as physical crosslinks. These crosslinks exist in a mechanical sense at temperatures below their "melting points," but above the melting point the polymer will melt and will be able to flow without degradation. Consequently, it is possible to design polymers which can be processed by thermoplastic means and yet behave like crosslinked elastomers at the use temperature.

The main problem is to develop a high enough molecular weight without introducing primary crosslinking to the extent that thermoplastic processing is no longer possible.

Müller and co-workers (32,33) first prepared thermoplastic urethane elastomers by stopping the polymerization before crosslinking became significant. They reacted a polyester, 1,5-naphthalene diisocyanate, and 1,4-butanediol in the usual way, except that the polymer was cooled before it became crosslinked. This product, still containing unreacted isocyanate groups, was molded or extruded after a short time, and heat cured to a crosslinked state.

Three somewhat different approaches have been reported in the United States. In developing Estane, Schollenberger and co-workers (45–47) prepared the polymer using a slight excess of hydroxyl component. The Texin polymers are prepared with a controlled excess of isocyanate reactant (48–49). And, finally, Acterhoff et al. have reported that certain polyurethanes can be molded like a thermoplastic even when crosslinked (50). This may be due to the thermal instability of the allophanate crosslink at the molding or extruding temperature.

When processing any of the thermoplastic types one must use care to keep the polymer dry, below 0.1% water. Otherwise hydrolysis of the polymer will occur during processing, and both bubbling and property loss may occur. The loss of properties may become particularly noticeable if regrind is used. It is especially important to avoid "flow aids," which are really hydrolysis catalysts, such as zinc stearate (51). Typical molding conditions for Estane polymers are shown in Table II, and for extrusion of Texin resins in Table III. The molding conditions for Texin polymers are similar to those for Estanes, and extrusion conditions for Estanes are similar to those for Texin resins.

D. Miscellaneous Elastomers

In addition to the polyesters and polyethers which have been discussed as the resin components of primary interest for urethane elastomers, many others have been used to varying extents. These include castor oil and various derivatives of castor oil (27,54), polyesters from dimerized fatty acids (55), polythioethers (56,57), polyacetals (56,58), and thiopolyacetals (59). These and others have been reviewed recently (9e,i). A more recent group of resins which has aroused considerable interest as a urethane intermediate is the hydroxy terminated butadiene polymer and related copolymers with styrene or acrylonitrile (60,61). Properties

TABLE II
Molding Conditions for Estane Thermoplastic Polyurethanes[a]

Molding conditions	Estane 5740X1[b]	Estane 5740X7[b]
Injection molding		
Stock temperature, °C (°F)	177 (350)	182 (191)
Barrel temperatures		
Rear, °C (°F)	121 (250)	132 (270)
Front, °C (°F)	177 (350)	182 (360)
Nozzle temperature, °C (°F)	177 (350)	182 (360)
Ram pressure, psi	20,000	20,000
Cycle time, sec	30–90	30–90
Mold temperature, °C (°F)	38 (100)	38 (100)
Mold shrinkage, in./in.	0.009	0.008
Compression molding		
Stock temperature, °C (°F)	177 (350)	182 (360)
Mold temperature		
Initial, °C (°F)	177 (350)	182 (360)
Final, °C (°F)	38 (100)	38 (100)
Cycle time		
Preheat, min	5	5
Mold hot, min	5	5
Mold cold under pressure, min	5	5
Pressure on stock, psi	500–1500	500–1500

[a] Data from Ref. 52.
[b] Lubricated with 1 part of barium stearate per 100 parts of resin.

TABLE III
Operating Conditions for Texin Urethane Elastomer Extrusion[a]

Conditions	192A	480A	355D
Temp., °C (°F)			
Zone 1	121 (250)	127 (260)	121 (250)
2	135 (275)	127 (260)	149 (300)
3	149 (300)	132 (270)	163 (325)
4	163 (325)	149 (300)	177 (350)
Melt	154 (310)	152 (305)	185 (365)
Die	154 (310)	104 (220)	166 (330)
Pressure, psi	2100	3400	500 to 700

[a] Data from Ref. 53.

of selected elastomers prepared from some of these resins are given in Section VI.

E. Relations between Structure and Properties

The properties of polymers are governed by characteristics such as molecular weight, crosslinking, intermolecular forces, the stiffness of chain units, the ease of rotation of chain segments, and crystallization. The urethane elastomers are almost unique in that these variables can be changed with remarkable control, either for theoretical studies or to design polymers with specific properties. A brief discussion of this subject is essential to understanding the proper selection of reactants and reactant ratios.

The urethane elastomers may be considered to be composites of relatively stiff segments of polyurethane or polyurethane-urea structure, and of more flexible segments such as polyester or polyether. This may be represented simply by the following sketch:

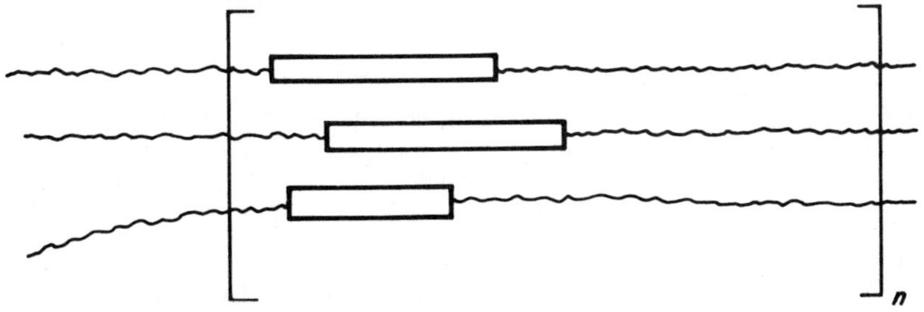

The structure and length of the hard segment may be controlled by the amount and type of diisocyanate and chain extender or curing agent used. Similarly, the structure and length of the flexible segment may be controlled by the molecular weight and type of hydroxyl-containing resin used. The hard segment may be designed to form crystallites, especially when elongated, serving as physical crosslinks. The strength of the crystallite (melting point, heat of fusion, resistance to stress) will increase with increased length, symmetry, and "fit" of the hard segments, as well as the intermolecular attractions between segments. Thus symmetrical diisocyanates and unbranched glycols may be preferred for this segment. When the isocyanate is not symmetrical some compensation may be necessary, such as the substitution of a symmetrical aromatic diamine for the glycol.

It is interesting to speculate that one should be able to evaluate the contribution of a hard segment by studying the pure polymer corresponding to that segment structure. Thus a pure $(AB)_n$ polymer will have a characteristic relation between melting point and molecular weight. This relation should serve as a guide to the maximum melting point which could be expected of an $(AB)_n$ segment as the hard segment in the urethane elastomer. It is to be expected that the crystallite in the urethane block copolymer will have poorer "fit" (as indicated in the sketch above) than in the pure $(AB)_n$ polymer, however, so that the melting point relation in the pure polymer will not quite be reached in the copolymer. Nevertheless, in urethane elastomers without primary crosslinks this should be a guide to the high temperature behavior of the polymer. Ellegast has published preliminary data indicating this to be true (62).

In addition to physical crosslinks, primary crosslinks may easily be introduced into the urethane polymers. For maximum control of the structure, these crosslinks are usually built into the hard segment by including a small amount of trifunctional reactant in the curing agent or by using excess isocyanate. They may also be included in the soft segments, e.g., when using castor oil or polyether triols as the hydroxyl-containing resins. Maximum mechanical properties have usually been obtained when the crosslinks were built into the hard segments, but this choice does not seem to be essential for the attainment of maximum properties. In those cases where the branch points have been in the resin, poorer properties may have resulted because too much crosslinking was used, or because the hard segments did not have optimum design. Data illustrating the relations between structure and properties have been reviewed extensively (9c,63). A limited selection will illustrate many of the primary variables.

Pigott and co-workers prepared a series of polyester-urethane elastomers, illustrating the effect of the polyester structure, the diisocyanate, the glycol curing agent, the degree of crosslinking (17), and the length of the polyurethane hard segment (15). Data are shown in Table IV for elastomers prepared from 0.1 equivalent of poly(ethylene adipate) of mole wt 2000, 0.2 equivalent of 1,4-butanediol, and 0.32 equivalent of diisocyanate. It can be seen that large and rigid aromatic ring structures (NDI, TODI), symmetrical structure (NDI, PDI, MDI, TODI), and the absence of methyl substituents (as in TDI, DMDI, DIPDI) favor high modulus, tear strength, and hardness.

When the polyester was changed, as shown in Table V, property changes were large. In these experiments, all polyesters were at 2000 mole wt, MDI was used, other factors were the same as for Table IV. Again, methyl substituents, which would push chains apart, reducing the

TABLE IV
Physical Properties of Cast Urethane Elastomers as Influenced by Diisocyanate

Diisocyanate[a]	Tensile strength, psi	Elongations %	Elongations Set, %	Modulus, psi, 300% elongation	Tear strength,[b] lb/in.	Hardness, Shore B
NDI	4300	500	85	3000	200	80
p-PDI	6400	600	25	2300	300	72
TDI	4600	600	1	350	150	40
MDI	7900	600	10	1600	270	61
DMDI	5300	500	0	600	40	47
DIPDI	3500	700	10	300	90	56
TODI	4000	400	10	2300	180	70

[a] NDI, 1,5 naphthalene diisocyanate; *p*-PDI, *p*-phenylene diisocyanate; TDI, 2,4-tolylene diisocyanate; MDI, 4,4′-diphenylmethane diisocyanate; DMDI 3,3′-dimethyl-4,4′-diphenylmethane diisocyanate; DIPDI, 4,4′-diphenylisopropylidine diisocyanate; TODI, 3,3′-dimethyl-4,4′-diphenyl diisocyanate.
[b] Split sample, FTMS-601/M4221 method. Data from Ref. 17.

possibility of van der Waals attractions, lowered the tensile, modulus, tear, and hardness. Poor fit, as from the use of an odd carbon glycol, had a similar effect on tear and hardness. The Clash-Berg torsional modulus of certain of these elastomers, as shown in Fig. 1, clearly shows the favorable effect of reduced ester group concentration on lowering the

TABLE V
Physical Properties of Cast Urethane Elastomers as Influenced by Polyester

Polyester	Tensile strength, psi	Elongation %	Elongation Set, %	Modulus, psi, 300% elongation	Tear strength,[a] lb/in.	Hardness, Shore B
Ethylene adipate	6900	590	15	1550	240	60
1,4-Butylene adipate	6000	510	15	1900	280	70
Pentamethylene adipate	6300	450	10	1800	60	60
1,3-Butylene adipate	3200	520	15	1100	100	58
Ethylene succinate	6800	420	40	3200	200	75
2,3-Butylene succinate	3500	380	105	—[b]	520[c]	85
Neopentyl succinate	2600	400	70	2000	230	67

[a] Split sample, FTMS–601/M4221 method.
[b] Exhibited cold drawing.
[c] Because of cold drawing this result is probably not a true tear value. Data from Ref. 17.

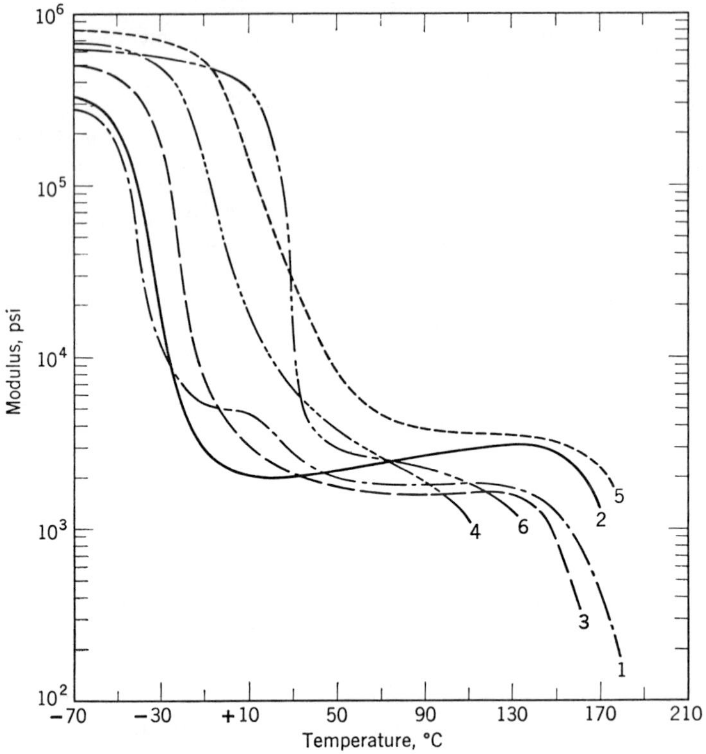

Fig. 1. Effect of polyester on Clash-Berg torsional modulus of polyester-urethane elastomers. System: polyester–diphenylmethane diisocyanate–1,4-butanediol. Polyesters: (*1*) poly(1,4-butylene adipate); (*2*) poly(1,5-pentamethylene adipate); (*3*) poly(ethylene adipate); (*4*) poly(neopentyl succinate); (*5*) poly(2,3-butylene succinate); (*6*) poly(ethylene succinate). Data from Ref. 17.

glass transition temperature. Varying the glycol chain extender had less effect than changes in isocyanate or polyester, though the use of glycols containing aromatic rings did increase hardness and modulus. Introducing crosslinking into a poly(ethylene adipate)-MDI-1,4-butanediol polymer by replacing the butanediol progressively with trimethylolpropane had the effects shown in Table VI. The weight per crosslink was calculated from the triol content. Solvent swelling in dimethylacetamide increased almost linearly with M_c values, as expected.

Decreased M_c values in the range of 21,000–5300 resulted in decreased hardness, tensile, elongation, modulus, and tear strength, but increased elasticity and reduced creep as indicated by lower elongation set and compression set. These observations are contrary to results of similar work with hydrocarbon elastomers, where increased crosslinking results in increased physical properties, especially modulus. In the case of the polyester-urethane elastomers, it appears that increased chemical crosslinking actually causes a general weakening of the polymer. This is believed due to a reduction of orientation of chains and hence a reduction in probability of obtaining hydrogen bonding and benefit of other intermolecular attractive forces. In other words, with increased chemical crosslinking, there is obtained a spatial separation of chains which reduces effective intermolecular attractions. This observation, in part, confirms the belief that a major portion of the strength of urethane elastomers is due to forces other than primary valence bonding. In this series, in the M_c range of 5300–2100 the modulus increased with lower M_c values, indicating the primary crosslinks eventually became dominant in controlling modulus.

Properties also could be varied widely by changing the length of the hard segment. This was done by using in each case 0.1 equivalent of

TABLE VI
Physical Properties of Cast Urethane Elastomers as Influenced by Chemical Crosslinking

M_c	Tensile strength,[a] psi	Elongation %	Elongation Set, %	Modulus at 100% elong.,[a] psi	Tear,[b] lb/in.	Hardness,[c] Shore B	Compression,[d] set, %
2,100	1800	170	0	570	30	57	1.5
3,100	1750	200	0	420	25	53	16
4,300	1450	280	0	300	30	49	10
5,300	2800	350	0	270	30	46	5
7,100	4500	410	0	330	40	51	25
10,900	5600	490	5	460	60	55	40
21,000	5500	510	10	500	140	56	45
—	6750	640	15	630	300	61	55

[a] Tensile strength, elongation, elongation set, and modulus, ASTM 412.
[b] Tear strength measured with a split sample, FTMS-601/M4221.
[c] Hardness, ASTM 676.
[d] Compression set, ASTM 395, method B, 70°C, for 22 hr. Data from Ref. 17.

poly(ethylene adipate) of mole wt 2000, with MDI and 1,4-butanediol in increasing amounts, with 0.02 equivalent of MDI always in excess. The weight percents of aromatic and of urethane are plotted against properties in Fig. 2 for this series (9c).

These data, and many others from both ether and ester based urethanes, lead to reliable generalizations relating structure to properties (63). Changes in effective intermolecular forces may be expected to show the trends illustrated in Fig. 3. The term "effective intermolecular force"

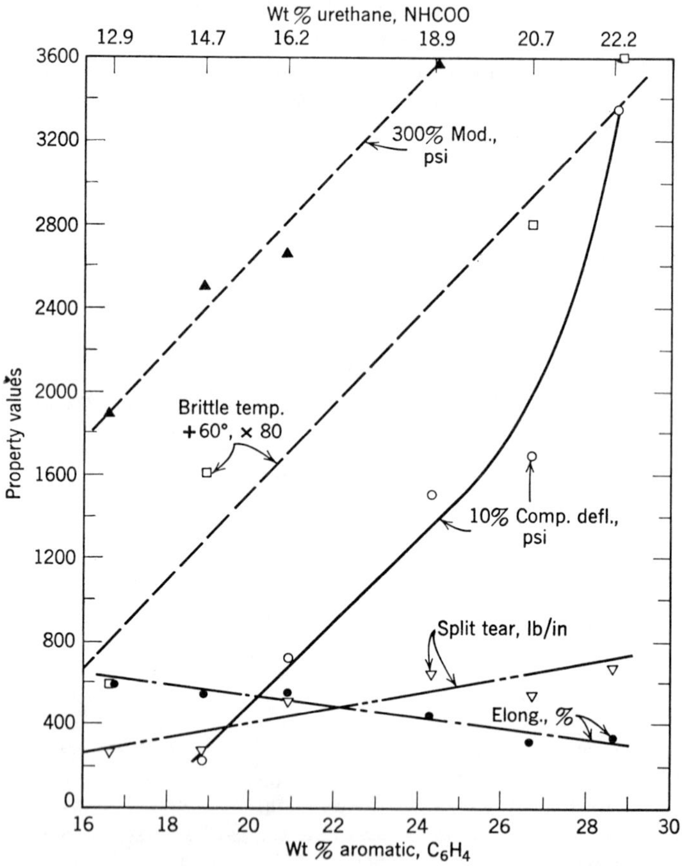

Fig. 2. Relation between properties of certain polyester-urethane elastomers and aromatic plus urethane content. Data from Ref. 15.

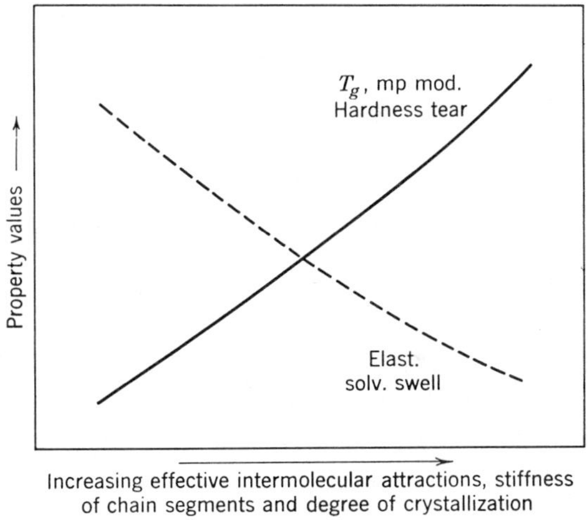

Fig. 3. Relation between urethane properties and effective intermolecular attractions, stiffness of chain segments, and degree of crystallization for polymers with no or only slight crystallization. Data from Ref. 63.

is used to indicate a combination of the intermolecular attractive forces which are possible for the structural groups present, combined with the geometrical structure or "fit" which regulates the extent to which these forces can operate.

Modulus (tensile and compression), tear strength, hardness, melting point, and glass transition temperature have been shown to increase with increasing effective intermolecular forces. For example, the effect on modulus, tear, and hardness was illustrated here with polyester elastomers, where the effectiveness of intermolecular forces was controlled by controlling the degree of crosslinking. The elasticity and solvent swelling will be reduced as the effective intermolecular forces increase. The role of fillers is normally that of increasing intermolecular attractions (filler-to-polymer). Thus relatively little advantage is realized by adding fillers to polyester-urethane elastomers with strong intermolecular attractions, but much more to other elastomers with weak intermolecular attractions. An increase in stiffness of chain segments and in the degree of crystallization may be expected to have the same effect as would increases in effective intermolecular attractions. Examples illustrating all of these features have been given previously (63).

Changes in the degree of crosslinking do not affect properties in all

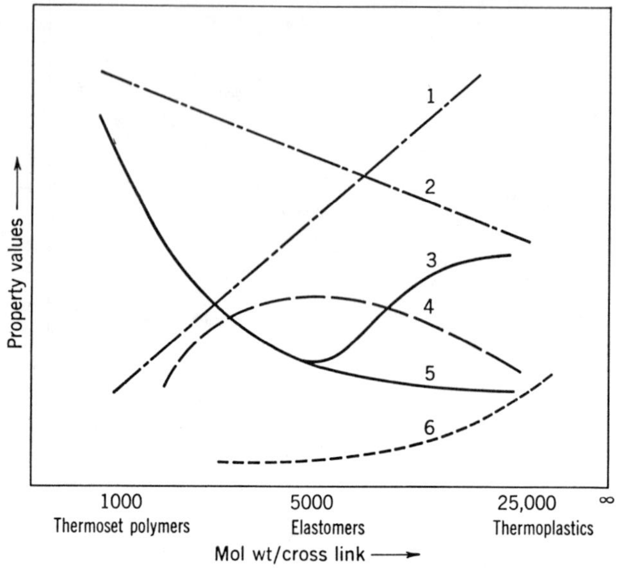

Fig. 4. Properties of urethanes related to molecular weight per crosslink for amorphous polymers. Curve 1, solvent swelling, elongation, and tear strength; curve 2, glass transition temperature and melting point; curve 3, modulus and hardness for polymers with high intermolecular attractions; curve 4, elasticity; curve 5, modulus and hardness for polymers with relatively low intermolecular attractions; curve 6, creep and compression set. Data from Ref. 63.

urethane polymers in the same way. In those noncrystalline polymers having a high degree of effective intermolecular forces, e.g., the polyester-urethane elastomers, increases in crosslinking first serve to reduce the effective intermolecular forces by reducing the fit. As M_c values decrease those forces eventually become relatively weak so that further changes in M_c values result in changes which might be predicted for hydrocarbon elastomers. This effect of small increases in crosslinking at high M_c values in polyester-urethane elastomers is analogous to the effect of introducing crosslinking into crystalline polymers.

In noncrystalline urethane polymers having relatively lower degrees of effective intermolecular forces, e.g., polyether elastomers and foams, the effects of changes in the degree of crosslinking are generally analogous to most other polymers. As crosslinking increases progressively the polymer changes from a linear, thermoplastic, soluble form to an elastomer with moderate crosslinking, and finally with further increases, to a thermoset, rigid structure. General trends are illustrated in Fig. 4.

Crystallites may also serve as crosslinks, being effective until the temperature approaches their melting points. After melting and cooling these crystallites may form again, thus serving as thermally reversible crosslinks.

IV. PROPERTIES

A. Mechanical Properties

With conventional elastomers one must usually choose between elasticity and hardness, but the urethanes retain good elasticity and elongation over a very wide range of hardness. In addition, they are characterized by remarkable toughness and abrasion resistance, and good resistance to oil. While there are several types of urethane elastomers in use, many have numerous properties in common. Table VII illustrates typical properties for several types (64).

The unusual position of the urethane elastomers in the spectrum of polymer properties is further illustrated by Fig. 5, which shows the relation between Young's modulus and tensile strength for several polymers (65). The urethanes here typified by the Vulkollans, are unique in bridging the gap between hydrocarbon rubbers and plastics. (The material called "polyurethane" in Fig. 5 refers to the thermoplastic from hexamethylene diisocyanate and 1,4-butanediol.) It is not surprising that the urethanes are replacing plastics in some applications, as well as other elastomers.

The urethanes, especially those based on linear polyesters and on polyether–diamine combinations, have exceptional tear strength. The test values may vary considerably, depending upon the method used. The FTMS-601M-4221 method, utilizing a rectangular sample which is split and then torn "like a pair of pants," is believed to give more nearly a true tear value than other methods. This "split tear" method usually gives lower values than the ASTM methods, especially with polyether elastomers. By this method the tear strength of the urethanes ranges from about 200 to 800 lb/in. (Table V), compared to about 40–110 lb/in. for hydrocarbon rubbers (15).

As would be expected from the high tear strength, the abrasion resistance of the urethanes is excellent. While laboratory test methods usually show urethanes abrading about one-third as readily as natural rubber, field applications often find the urethanes wearing only one-tenth

TABLE VII
Typical Properties of Urethane Elastomers[a]

Property	Cast elastomers		Millable gums[d]	Thermo-plastic types[e]
	Polyester[b]	Polyether[c]		
Hardness, Shore	A65–D70	A75–D70	A62–95	A83–D60
Tensile, psi	6000–4500	4500–7000	3000–5500	6000–5000
Elongation, %	650–350	600–300	450–500	500–400
100% Modulus, psi	250–1600	700–3700		600–2600
300% Modulus, psi	600–3000	1100–4400	1700–3200	1000–4000
Elongation set, %	5–80			15–60
Compression set, 22 hr, 70°C ASTM D 395 Method B	10–25	7–40	20–50	40–25[f]
Tear strength, lb/in.				
Graves, ASTM D 624	400–700	200–700	250–400	300–700
Split, FTMS 601-M-4221	200–700			300–800
Resilience rebound, %	45–50	42–48	60–70	

[a] Data from Ref. 64 and current trade literature.

[b] Data cover Vulkollans, (Farbenfabriken Bayer), Multrathanes (Mobay Chemical Co.), Vibrathanes (U.S. Rubber) and Cyanaprene (American Cyanamid).

[c] Data cover Adiprenes (du Pont) and Solithanes (Thiokol).

[d] Data cover Adiprene C (du Pont), Genthane S (General Tire), Vibrathane (U.S. Rubber), Elastothane (Thiokol), Chemigum SL (Goodyear), and Urepan (Farbenfabriken Bayer); includes black reinforced polymers.

[e] Data cover Estane (B. F. Goodrich), Texin (Mobay Chemical Co.), Roylar (U.S. Rubber), and Desmopan (Farbenfabriken Bayer).

[f] Data apply to Texin polymers, may not be typical of others, e.g., Estane gives 65–87% set at Shore A 85–88 hardness.

as fast. The unusual abrasion resistance is limited to moderate temperatures, however. At about 70–80°C the abrasion resistance is frequently little better than that of natural rubber.

While the elasticity of the urethanes is good, their hysteresis is generally higher than that of natural rubber. As a result the urethanes develop heat faster on flexing. Because of this one often finds that a part geometry designed for natural rubber may not be satisfactory in urethane if rapid flexing is encountered. Because of the urethane's greater strength the part is often redesigned to have thinner sections in the urethane, thus giving faster heat dissipation, and permitting the designer to utilize the oil resistance, abrasion resistance, and general toughness of the urethane polymer.

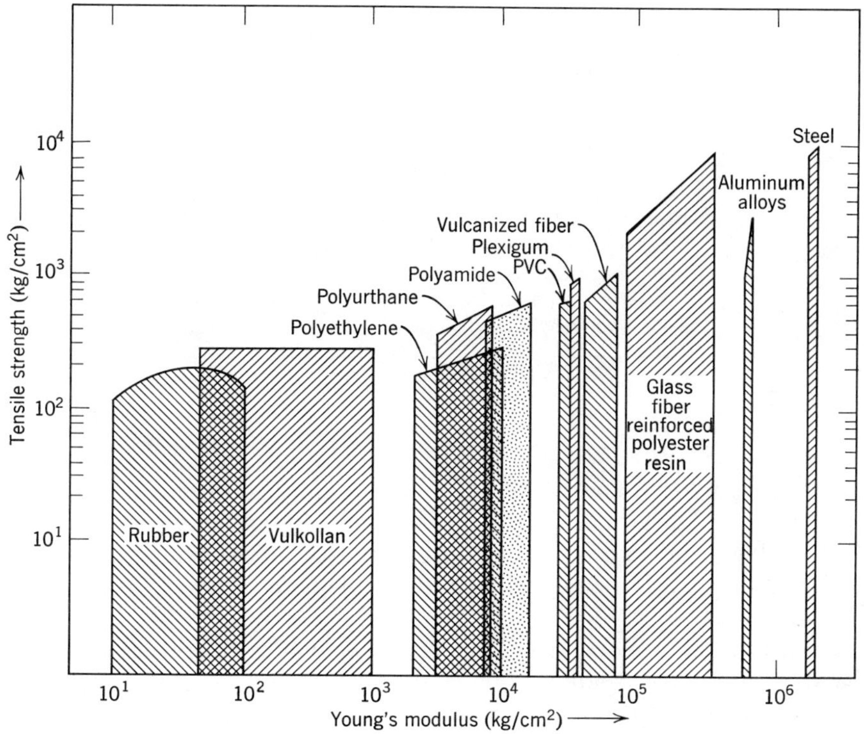

Fig. 5. Tensile strength and Young's modulus of various materials. Data from Ref. 65.

B. Environmental Resistance

The good properties of the urethanes are generally exhibited throughout moderate temperature ranges, in oil and in oxidative atmospheres. They are not outstanding at high temperature or in an atmosphere where hydrolytic action may be strong. The elevated temperature resistance depends upon the service conditions and the type of urethane used. For continuous use for moderate times in air the upper limit may be about 90–100°C, while in nonreactive oils it may be about 110–120°C. The harder grades usually are somewhat better than the softer grades in this respect, and the polyester types often are a little better than the polyether types. The effect of temperature on several properties of water-cured Vulkollan is shown in Table VIII (2). The properties of many elastomers at temperatures up to 288°C have been reported by Smith (66).

TABLE VIII
Temperature Resistance of Vulkollan[a]

Property	Temperature, °C	
	20	70
Tensile, psi	4400	2700
Elongation, %	765	765
300% Modulus, psi	1110	670
Shore hardness, A scale	69	64
Elasticity, rebound, %	64	58
Tear strength, lb/in.	2500	1780

[a] Data from Ref. 2.

The three polyurethanes tested all lost essentially all mechanical strength at 200°C. Pigott and coworkers, however, found that the use of trimethylolpropane as a curing agent reduced the room temperature compressive strength but retained a considerable percentage of that strength at 200°C (67).

Many urethane elastomers have very good low temperature flexibility. Gradual stiffening usually occurs as the temperature is reduced, until the glass transition temperature is reached, with many types retaining toughness as low as −70°C. Certain elastomers with unusually good symmetry may show a tendency to crystallize when stored for long times below about −20 to 0°C. Plasticizers sometimes improve low temperature flexibility.

As was shown earlier in Section III-E the ester group concentration in polyester-urethanes, and the aromatic–urethane block length have a considerable effect on the glass transition temperature and low temperature flexibility. Figure 6 illustrates the Clash-Berg torsional stiffness behavior of a polyester-urethane system designed for good overall properties, compared to several other urethanes and some conventional rubbers (15). The solenoid brittle point of the R-144/MDI/butanediol elastomer was below −70°C, compared to −56°C for the natural rubber, −30°C for the Neoprene GN, and −50°C for the SBR–1500 samples.

The oxygen and ozone resistance of many urethanes is excellent in accelerated tests. The weathering resistance is not always as good as would be expected unless special formulations are used. Both ultraviolet light and degradation by microorganisms sometimes complicate the weathering performance. Polyester based systems usually are better than polyether systems in the various forms of oxidation resistance.

The weathering of an Estane polymer was studied in detail by Schollenberger and co-workers (45,47). This polymer, being linear and of relatively low molecular weight, may be expected to show a somewhat faster property loss than a polymer of comparable segmental structure but crosslinked, but the study is of real value in understanding the weathering behavior. The need for protection by additives, as in other elastomer systems, is clearly demonstrated.

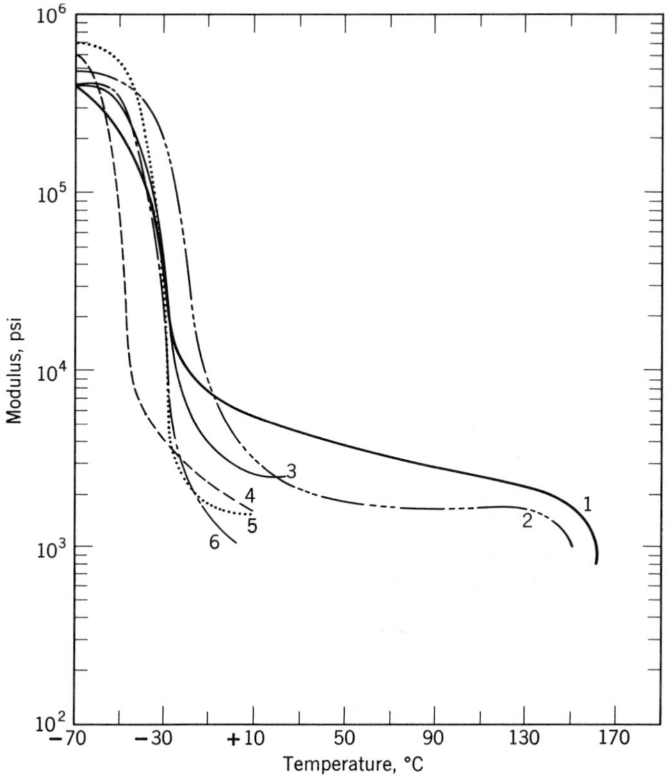

Fig. 6. Clash-Berg torsional stiffness of polyester-urethane elastomers of 80–85 Shore A hardness and conventional elastomers. Curve 1, MDI/Multron R-144/butane diol elastomer; curve 2, poly(ethylene adipate)/MDI/butane diol; curve 3, poly-(ethylene adipate)/NDI/butane diol; curve 4, natural rubber; curve 5, neoprene GN; curve 6, SBR 1500. Data from Ref. 15.

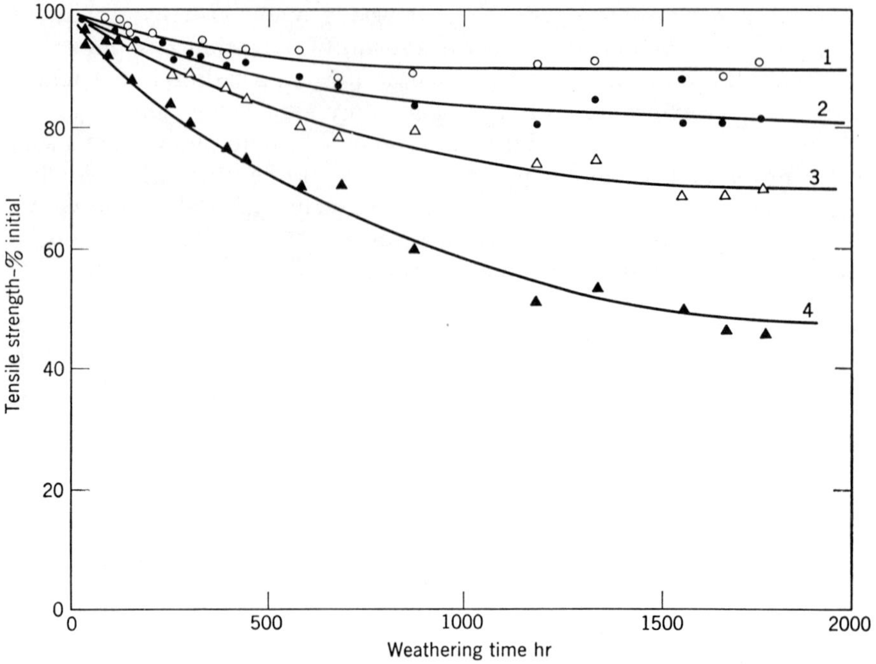

Fig. 7. Change of tensile strength of Estane polyurethane elastomer after outdoor exposure. Curve 1, 1 pph Antioxidant 425; curve 2, 1 pph Age-Rite Stalite S; curve 3, 3 pph Cyasorb 24; curve 4, unprotected polyurethane elastomer. Data from Ref. 68.

The changes in tensile strength of the Estane, with and without additives, are shown in Fig. 7 (68). Carbon black was also found to offer good protection against weathering. Infrared and ultraviolet analyses were in agreement with a proposed initial attack as indicated below:

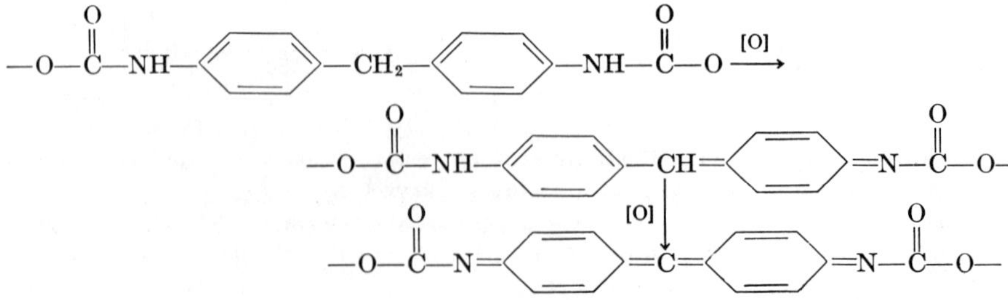

Polyurethanes are susceptible to hydrolysis by acids and alkalies, and by hot water. Properly formulated polyether systems are usually superior to polyester systems in this respect. Failure in outdoor exposure, sometimes attributed to hydrolysis, may actually be due to a combination of hydrolysis, ultraviolet catalyzed oxidation, and microbial attack. Stabilizers against all of these types of degradations have been found.

With regard to accelerated hydrolysis resistance, Harrington found that exposing samples to boiling water for 1000 hr caused a 27–100% loss in hardness of a variety of urethanes (69). Among those tested, the polyether based samples were more resistant than the polyester types. A similar comparison, favoring the polyether types, was also reported by Athey (70). The polyester types, however, may be protected against accelerated hydrolysis by sterically hindered carbodiimides, as shown by Neumann and co-workers (71). Apparently the carbodiimides function by reacting with carboxylic acid groups, which are catalytic for the hydrolysis. Outdoor exposure of urethanes, especially in tropical climates, has resulted in rapid loss of properties due to microbial attack (72). Certain antimicrobial additives such as pentachlorophenol improved this exposure, however.

For maximum service life polyether based urethanes need to be protected against ultraviolet light, oxygen, and microbes, thus requiring additives such as carbon black, UV absorbers, antioxidants and antimicrobial agents. Polyester based systems in addition need an antihydrolytic agent such as a carbodiimide. Specific additives should be tested in the system which will be used, to be sure of effectiveness, and that the additive is not also catalyzing an undesired side effect. It is quite possible, for example, that the sodium salt of a substituted phenol, or a heavy metal compound, might be a good additive to kill microbes, but might catalyze hydrolysis.

V. SPANDEX ELASTIC FIBERS

Early in the development of urethane elastomers Müller and co-workers recoginized that fibers could be spun from the Vulkollan elastomer systems (32), but no commercial use of this possibility was made until du Pont announced their "Lycra" fiber in 1958. Numerous other elastic fibers of the urethane type have since been introduced, such as Vyrene (U.S. Rubber), Blue C (Chemstrand), Stretchever (International Latex), Spandelle (Firestone), and Glospan (Globe Mfg.). The generic term "spandex" has been selected for these fibers, designating elastomeric fibers derived from a long chain polymer consisting of at least 85%

segmented polyurethane. Chemically the spandex fibers are quite similar to many of the urethanes already described, being a combination of polyether or polyester soft segment and a polyurea–urethane or polyurethane hard segment. Design considerations emphasize minimum stress relaxation, high elongation, good temperature resistance, and resistance to discoloration. This last property usually depends upon the presence of suitable additives.

Spandex fibers can be produced by a variety of methods such as dry spinning, solvent (wet) spinning, melt extrusion, or slitting of elastomer sheets. Polymerization may be completed before spinning, as in the melt extrusion of a thermoplastic type. The polymerization may also be completed at the time of spinning, as in the processing of a solution of a prepolymer to which a curing agent has been added. Rinke has reviewed these processes in detail (73), as have Britain (74), and Saunders and Frisch (9h). Specially designed linear polyesters and poly(1,4-oxybutylene) glycols appear to be the favored polyols, MDI and to a lesser extent TDI are the isocyanates of choice, and symmetrical diamines, hydrazine or certain glycols are used as curing agents (9h,73–75). The properties of the urethanes are largely responsible for the replacement of rubber threads by spandex. The unusually high modulus and tear resistance permit the satisfactory use of much finer denier threads from spandex than from rubber. Thus garments or fabrics designed for a specific purpose may be much lighter when made from spandex. Although spandex appears to be competitive in oxidation resistance and light stability, and adequate in hydrolysis resistance, improvements may be expected in these areas. Typical physical properties of Lycra spandex fiber are shown in Table IX (76).

Spandex fibers are generally not used alone in garments, but are combined with other fibers. In some cases, a monofilament of spandex is covered with nylon to provide a yarn. In others, a multifilament yarn of spandex is combined with other fibers before knitting or weaving. The blending of spandex staple with other synthetics to produce yarns with controlled elasticity is also under evaluation. The primary uses for spandex are currently in foundation garments such as girdles and bras, in swimsuits, and in hosiery. Many other possible uses, especially in fiber blends, are being evaluated.

VI. LOW MODULUS ELASTOMERS

The urethane elastomers described thus far have been characterized by unusually high mechanical properties such as modulus, tensile, and

TABLE IX
Physical Properties of Lycra Spandex Fiber[a,b]

Deniers available	70, 140, 280, 420, 560
Break tenacity, g/denier	0.6–0.8
Break elongation, %	520–610
Power at 50% elongation, g/denier	0.03–0.04
Power at 200% elongation, g/denier	0.10–0.12
Stress decay, 1 min at 50% elongation, %	6–8
Tensile recovery from 50% elongation, %	93.5–96
Moisture regain at 21°C, 65% R.H., %	1.3
Specific gravity	About 1.0
Abrasion resistance	Good
Flex life	Good
Color	White
Luster	Dull
Fume oven exposure, 16 hr	Moderate yellow
Color change	None
Physical property change	None to slight
Fade-ometer exposure, 16 hr	
Color change	None
Physical property change	None to slight
Resistance to heat	Yellows and degrades over 150°C
Melting point, °C	250
Sticking temperature, °C	175

[a] Taken from Ref. 76.
[b] As shipped, less finish.

tear strength. It is also possibe to prepare urethane elastomers which are soft and have lower levels of the usual mechanical properties. These are normally prepared from polyols which are not linear or are characterized by a low order of interchain attractions or unusual chain flexibility, such as castor oil, poly(oxyethylene) glycols, poly(oxypropylene) glycols, or hydroxyl-containing butadiene polymers. In addition, the "hard segment" is usually of minimum length and rigidity. Quite often the diisocyanate is combined with the hydroxyl-containing resin at an NCO:OH ratio of about 1.05, without any chain extender such as glycol or diamine. This group of elastomers can be prepared by the same techniques as are used for the types described previously, but are most often produced by a casting process. Batch mixing is often utilized, and machine mixing is becoming of more commercial interest as better machinery becomes available and as the volume of operations increases. A summary of some typical polyol:TDI combinations and their properties is given in Table X (27).

TABLE X
Typical Low Durometer Urethanes[a]

Resin components, parts by wt	TDI, parts by wt	Hardness, Shore A	Tensile, psi	Elongation, %
Multron R-16[b] (100)	7.84	53	880	970
Castor oil[c] (57), Flexricin 9[c] (43)	38.9	55	2460	260
PPG-400[d] (68.1)	31.9	53	1000	650
Pluronic L-44[e] (100), water (0.17)	9.97	34	600	1100
Pluronic L-44[e] (100), TMP, (0.85)	9.97	22	170	730
Pluronic L-61[e] (100), water (0.15)	14.25	7	310	1100

[a] Data from Ref. 27.
[b] Mobay Chemical Co.
[c] Baker Castor Oil Co.
[d] Polypropylene glycol, 400 mol wt.
[e] Wyandotte Chemicals Corp.

Some recent data on polymers of similar properties, but prepared from TDI and a hydroxyl terminated butadiene resin have been reported (61). The resin had an hydroxyl number of 53 and an average molecular weight of 2200–2500, with a functionality slightly greater than 2. It was reacted with 80:20-TDI at an NCO:OH ratio of 1.1, with and without carbon black and oil extenders. This resin is an interesting addition to the selection of products available for polyurethane formation.

The low durometer urethanes are used for a variety of applications, including printing rolls, potting compounds, caulks, sealants, and binders for solid fuels for rockets (9i).

References

1. H. Pinten, Ger. Pat. Appl. D-90,260 (March, 1942) (Dynamit Nobel A.G.); see O. Bayer, *Angew. Chem.*, **A59**, 275 (1947).
2. O. Bayer, E. Müller, S. Petersen, H. F. Piepenbrink, and E. Windemuth, *Angew. Chem.*, **62**, 57 (1950); *Rubber Chem. Technol.*, **23**, 812 (1950).
3. E. Müller, O. Bayer, S. Peterson, H. F. Piepenbrink, F. Schmidt, and E. Weinbrenner, *Angew. Chem.*, **64**, 523 (1952); *Rubber Chem. Technol.*, **26**, 493 (1953).
4. D. A. Harper, W. F. Smith, and H. G. White, *Rubber Chem. Technol.*, **23**, 608 (1950).
5. R. P. Dinsmore, "The New Goodyear Rubber, Chemigum SL," Address before the Washington Rubber Group, Washington, D.C., March 18, 1953.
6. F. B. Hill, C. A. Young, J. A. Nelson, and R. G. Arnold, *Ind. Eng. Chem.*, **48**, 927 (1956).
7. J. S. Rugg and G. W. Scott, *Ind. Eng. Chem.*, **48**, 930 (1956).

8. *Chem. Eng. News,* **43,** No. 3, 25 (1965).
9. (a) J. H. Saunders and K. C. Frisch, *Polyurethanes, Chemistry and Technology. I. Chemistry,* Interscience, New York, 1962, Chapter 1; (b) ibid., Chapters 2, 3 and 4; (c) ibid., Chapter 6; (d) *Polyurethanes, Chemistry and Technology. II. Technology,* 1964, Chapter 7, p. 8–43; (e) ibid., Chapter 9; (f) ibid., Chapter 10, p. 587–601; (g) ibid., Chapter 11, p. 651–652; (h) ibid., Chapter 12, p. 694–712; (i) ibid., Chapter 13, p. 770–784.
10. E. Müller, *Kautschuk Gummi,* **18** (2), 67 (1965).
11. J. H. Saunders and J. K. Backus, *Rubber Chem. Technol.,* **39** (2) 461 (1966).
12. W. R. McElroy, Mobay Chemical Company bulletin, *The Techniques of Prepolymer Preparation.*
13. J. C. Lorenz, U.S. Pat. 3,188,302 (June 8, 1965) (to duPont).
14. E. Müller, *Kunststoffe,* **50,** 437 (1960).
15. K. A. Pigott, R. J. Côté, K. Ellegast, B. F. Frye, E. Müller, W. Archer, K. R. Allen, and J. H. Saunders, *Rubber Age (NY),* **90,** 629 (1962).
16. K. A. Pigott, B. F. Frye, K. R. Allen, T. H. Cleveland, C. D. Nolen, and J. H. Saunders, *Rubber Age (NY),* **90,** 618 (1962).
17. K. A. Pigott, B. F. Frye, K. R. Allen, S. Steingiser, W. C. Darr, J. H. Saunders, and E. E. Hardy, *J. Chem. Eng. Data,* **5,** 391 (1960).
18. K. W. Rausch, R. F. Martel, and A. A. R. Sayigh, *Ind. Eng. Chem., Prod. Res. Develop.,* **3**(2), 125 (1964).
19. K. W. Rausch, Jr. and A. A. R. Sayigh, *Ind. Eng. Chem., Prod. Res. Develop.,* **4**(2), 92 (1965).
20. C. F. Blaich, Jr., and A. J. Sampson, paper presented to the Division of Rubber Chemistry, 138th Meeting, American Chemical Society, New York, N.Y., September, 1960, p. 30.
21. C. H. Smith, *Ind. Eng. Chem., Prod. Res. Develop,* **4**(1), 9 (1965).
22. G. Magnus, *Rubber Age (NY),* **98,** No. 4, 86 (1965).
23. R. J. Athey, *Rubber Age (NY),* **85,** No. 1,77 (1959).
24. A. J. Sampson and C. F. Blaich, Jr., *Rubber Age (NY),* **89,** 263 (1961).
25. S L. Axelrood and K. C. Frisch, *Rubber Age (NY),* **88,** 465 (1960).
26. H. R. Bylsma, *Ind. Eng. Chem., Prod. Res. Develop.,* **3,** 204 (1964).
27. H. L. Heiss, *Rubber Age (NY),* **88,** 89 (1960).
28. T. L. Smith and A. B. Magnusson, *J. Polymer Sci.,* **42,** 391 (1960).
29. S. L. Axelrood, C. W. Hamilton, and K. C. Frisch, *Ind. Eng. Chem.,* **53,** 889 (1961).
30. S. L. Axelrood, L. C. Smith, and K. C. Frisch, *Rubber Age (NY),* **96,** 233 (1964).
31. S. E. Berger and W. Szukiewicz, *Ind. Eng. Chem., Prod. Res. Develop.,* **3,** 129 (1964).
32. E. Müller, F. W. Schmidt, E. Weinbrenner, and H. F. Piepenbrink, U.S. Pat. 2,729,618 (to Farbenfabriken Bayer) (Jan. 3, 1956).
33. E. Weinbrenner, *Kautschuk Gummi,* **5,** wt 49 (1952).
34. E. Müller, H. F. Piepenbrink, F. Schmidt, and E. Weinbrenner, Ger. Pat. 831,772 (Farbenfabriken Bayer) (Feb. 18, 1952).
35. T. G. Mastin and N. V. Seeger, U.S. Pat. 2,625,535 (Jan. 13, 1953) (to Wingfoot).
36. N. V. Seeger, U.S. Pat. 2,625,531–32 (Jan. 13, 1953) (to Wingfoot).
37. N. V. Seeger, T. G. Mastin, E. E. Fauser, F. S. Farson, A. F. Finelli, and E. A. Sinclair, *Ind. Eng. Chem.,* **45,** 2538 (1953).
38. D. A. Harper, *Trans. Inst. Rubber Ind.,* **24,** 181 (1948).

39. B. J. Habgood, D. A. Harper, and R. J. W. Reynolds, U.S. Pat. 2,424,883 (to ICI) (July 29, 1947).
40. J. T. Watts, *Rubber Plastics Age,* **38,** 129 (1957).
41. J. M. Buist, G. P. Crowley, H. France, and G. Trappe, *Proc. Rubber Technol. Conf., 4th, London,* **1962** (45), 18 pp.; *Chem. Abstr.*, **60,** 14709 (1964).
42. F. B. Hill, C. A. Young, J. Q. Nelson, and R. G. Arnold, *Ind. Eng. Chem.*, **48,** 927 (1956).
43. J. S. Rugg and G. W. Scott, *Ind. Eng. Chem.*, **48,** 930 (1956).
44. W. G. Ogden, *Rubber World,* **136,** 537 (1957).
45. C. S. Schollenberger and K. Dinbergs, *Soc. Plastics Engrs. Trans.*, **1,** No. 1, 31 (1961).
46. C. S. Schollenberger, L. G. Pappas, J. C. Park, and V. V. Vickroy, Jr., *Rubber World,* **142,** No. 6, 81 (1960).
47. C. S. Schollenberger, H. Scott, and G. R. Moore, *Rubber World,* **137,** 549 (1958).
48. K. A. Pigott, J. W. Britain, W. Archer, B. F. Frye, R. J. Côté, and J. H. Saunders, *Ind. Eng. Chem. Prod. Res. Develop.*, **1,** No. 1, 28 (1962).
49. J. H. Saunders and K. A. Pigott, U.S. Pat. 3,214,411 (Oct. 26, 1965) (to Mobay Chem. Co.).
50. M. Achterhoff, M. Q. Felterman, N. L. Havens, and J. F. McWhorter, U.S. Pat. 3,192,185 (June 29, 1965) (to Eagle-Picher).
51. K. A. Pigott, C. L. Gable, W. Archer, E. C. Haag, and S. Steingiser, *Soc. Plastics Engrs. J.*, **19,** 1281 (1963).
52. C. A. Waugaman, *Mod. Plastics,* **39,** No. 2, 146 (1961).
53. K. A. Pigott, W. Archer, C. L. Gable, and S. Steingiser, *Mod. Plastics,* **40,** No. 4, 117 (1962).
54. T. C. Patton, A. Ehrlich, and M. K. Smith, *Rubber Age (NY),* **86,** 639 (1960).
55. J. C. Cowan, D. H. Wheeler, H. M. Teeter, R. F. Paschke, C. R. Scholfield, A. W. Schwab, J. E. Jackson, W. C. Bull, F. R. Earle, R. J. Foster, W. C. Bond, R. E. Beal, P. S. Skell, I. A. Wolff, and C. L. Mehltretter, *Ind. Eng. Chem.*, **41,** 1647 (1949).
56. O. Bayer and E. Müller, *Angew. Chem.*, **72,** 934 (1960).
57. H. Holtschmidt, Ger. Pat. 1,039,232 (Sept. 18, 1958) (to Farbenfabriken Bayer).
58. E. Schonfeld, *J. Polymer Sci.*, **49,** 277 (1961).
59. E. Schonfeld, *J. Polymer Sci.*, **59,** 87 (1962).
60. K. Hayashi and C. S. Marvel, *J. Polymer Sci.*, **A2,** 2571 (1964).
61. Sinclair Petrochemicals, Inc., Product Data Bulletin No. 505, *Hydroxyl Terminated Poly B-D Liquid Resins in Urethane Systems,* May 1, 1965.
62. K. Ellegast, *Kunststoffe,* **55,** 306 (1965).
63. J. H. Saunders, *Rubber Chem. Technol.*, **33,** 1259 (1960).
64. M. W. Riley, *Mater. Design Eng.*, **50,** No. 4, 92 (1959).
65. Farbenfabriken Bayer bulletin, *Vulkollan as a Construction Material for Mechanical Engineering,* July, 1959; see also *Bayer Plastics,* 3rd edit., 1963.
66. F. M. Smith, *Rubber World,* **139,** No. 4, 533 (1959); **139,** No. 5, 699 (1959).
67. Mobay Chemical Co., Technical bulletin TIB 33-V12, *The Improvement of High Temperature Resistance and Compression Set of Multrathane Elastomers,* Oct. 12, 1959.
68. D. Satas, *Rubber Age (NY),* **93,** 758 (1963).
69. R. Harrington, *Rubber Age (NY),* **84,** 798 (1959).

70. R. J. Athey, *Rubber Age (NY)*, **96**(5), 705 (1965).
71. W. Neumann, J. Peter, H. Holtschmidt, and W. Kallert, *Proc. Rubber Technol. Conf., 4th, London,* **1962** (59), 14 pp.; *Chem. Abstr.*, **60,** 9456 (1964).
72. F. B. Testroet, OTS report AD 422028, 1963; *Chem. Abstr.*, **62,** 4187 (1965).
73. H. Rinke, *Angew. Chem.*, **74,** 612 (1962).
74. J. W. Britain, *Manufacture of Plastics,* Vol. I, Ch. 12, W. M. Smith, Ed., Reinhold, New York, 1964.
75. J. R. Schilit, U.S. Pat. 3,097,192 (July 9, 1963) (to duPont).
76. T. B. Marshall, *Textile Ind.*, **125,** No. 8, 75 (1961).

CHAPTER 8

ELASTOMERS BY CONDENSATION POLYMERIZATION

B. The Chemistry of Silicone Elastomers

F. M. Lewis

General Electric Laboratories
Waterford, New York

Contents

I. Introduction 767
II. Basic Structure 769
III. Synthetic Methods 773
IV. Polymerization 778
V. Silicone Copolymers 784
VI. Stability of Silicone Polymers 786
A. Thermal Stability 786
B. Oxidative Stability 789
C. Rearrangement 790
D. Hydrolytic Stability 791
E. Fuel, Oil, and Solvent Resistance 792
F. Corona Resistance 794
G. Ozone Resistance 794
H. Radiation Resistance 794
VII. Low Temperature Silicone Elastomers 795
VIII. Vulcanization or Cure of Silicone Elastomers 795
IX. Strength and Reinforcement of Silicone Rubber 801
References 802

I. INTRODUCTION

Silicone polymers are somewhat unique even when viewed against today's impressive array of synthetic polymers, and it seems worthwhile to review the history of these materials. The name silicone includes a group of structures which contain silicon—oxygen polymer backbones with organic groups attached to the silicon. The interesting and useful properties of the silicones arise from the physical and chemical characteristics that are associated with these structures.

The name silicone was coined near the beginning of this century when Professor Kipping and others who were working with these new materials thought that they had structures similar to the organic ketones and accordingly they called them "silicoketones" or "silicones" for short. Although silicon double bonds (such as would be present in a silicoketone) have been reported several times, no compound containing silicon has ever been made which has been proved to have a formal double bond to silicon.

Although silicones have become commercially important only since about the mid-1940's, the chemistry attracted investigators over 100 years ago, and it was in the same year that Kekule proposed the cyclic structure for benzene that Friedel and Crafts (1) made the first material that could be considered as a precursor for the silicones. Through the golden years of organic chemistry when dyes and other organic materials attracted a great deal of attention, silicones were investigated by only a few people. Professor F. S. Kipping summarized in a long series of papers his work on the chemistry of silicone intermediates from 1900 to 1937 (2). His interests were, however, concentrated solely on the chemistry of small molecules. He did nothing with the higher polymers which were to become so important later on. During the 1930's commercial interest in silicones began to develop in several places as candidates for high temperature insulation. Dr. J. F. Hyde at Corning Glass investigated silicon compounds containing organic groups, as did Dr. Winton Patnode at General Electric. In Russia, B. N. Dolgov and K. A. Andrianov began working in organosilicon chemistry and the first patent recognizing silicones as commercial materials was issued to Andrianov in 1939 (3). In the early 1940's commercially important silicones began to develop. Dr. E. G. Rochow discovered the so-called "direct process" and this coupled with other basic rubber technology (4) provided the groundwork for the development of commercially important silicone elastomers. Since the mid-1940's both the technology and applications of silicones have moved forward at an ever-accelerating pace and there are now between 10,000 and 15,000 publications throughout the world of which approximately half are U.S. and foreign patents. Silicones as a whole encompass a wide variety of products penetrating practically all industries, and elastomers occupy an important position in this spectrum of materials.

With such an extensive literature any attempt to include a representative bibliography would be beyond the scope of this review, and the bibliography included serves only to illustrate the points made and to provide background material for further reading. References 5–12 include a number of books on silicone technology. Some are devoted to chemistry and others are directed to technology and applications. Some of the more important patents directed to elastomers include the direct process for the manufacture of chlorosilanes by Rochow, the first patent on silicone rubber by Agens, the curing of rubber by Wright and Oliver, polymerization by Hyde, vinyl-containing silicones by Marsden, and reinforcement by fine particle silica by Warrick (4).

Silicone elastomers are generally considered as specialty rubbers, and they are mostly used for one or more of the following reasons:

1. Resistance to oxidation and the effects of heat to temperatures of 500°F and higher was the first property to be exploited.

2. To an increasing degree flexibility and ease of application is opening up new markets. For example, room temperature curing rubbers compete with organics for construction sealant markets.

3. Silicone elastomers remain flexible at temperatures down to −110F° and lower; also their properties change less with temperature than do most organics. Silicones do not stick to things unless specifically designed to do so. This makes them valuable for high temperature gaskets and similar applications.

4. Silicones are inert biologically and chemically. They resist sunlight, weathering, ozone, and, in general, conditions which would degrade most organic elastomers.

5. Silicones are not very compatible with most organic materials.

6. Silicones are excellent electrical insulators and have other good electrical properties including resistance to corona and arc.

Silicones also have distinctive surface properties, and this is usually included in a list of their properties. It is omitted in the above list since this is less important in elastomers than in other silicones.

II. BASIC STRUCTURE

In the completely inorganic siliceous minerals the structures are frequently formed as a series of tetrahedron units with four oxygen or other atoms at the corners of the tetrahedra and one oxygen atom may act as the link between two adjacent silica tetrahedra. In inorganic minerals these tetrahedra are joined in chains or sheets in many ways to form minerals ranging from silica itself to the complex siliceous minerals. In some of these structures the charges on the oxide ions may be balanced by positive ions of other metals. In silicone polymers some of this structure is retained but some oxygen atoms may be replaced by organic groups that are joined directly to the silicon atom. These inorganic–organic hybrids possess many of the properties associated with the silicones. One can visualize silica itself (or "sand") in which only a few of the oxygen atoms are replaced by, for example, methyl groups. Such a structure would be a highly crosslinked and a very rigid resinous material. This structure would be representative of certain methyl silicone resins. More and more oxygen atoms can be replaced and, in the extreme, monomeric tetraalkyl silane would be formed. These low polymers resemble oils. If we control our reactions to produce long chains of silicon and oxygen with every silicon bearing exactly two organic groups we form linear silicone elastomers. Such a structure is shown here

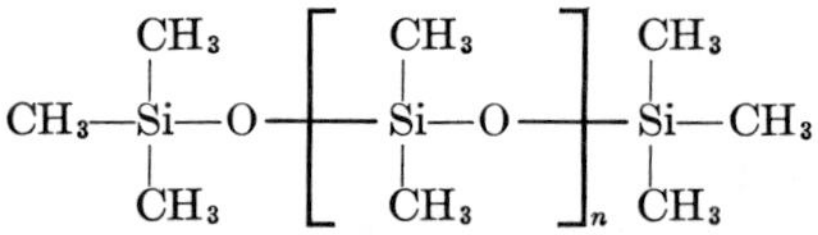

with the ends of the polymer terminated by two monofunctional units.

A formal nomenclature for organosilicon compounds has been adopted by the IUPAC Commission for the reform of organic nomenclature (13). In addition to the formal rules, workers in the field of silicone technology have adopted a number of shorthand designations for commonly recurring structures. The letters M, D, T, and Q stand respectively for mono-, di-, tri-, and tetra-functional units. Using this shorthand the structure of the rubber chain just given would be MD_nM. More complex polymers can be built up as shown in Scheme I. The shorthand for this more com-

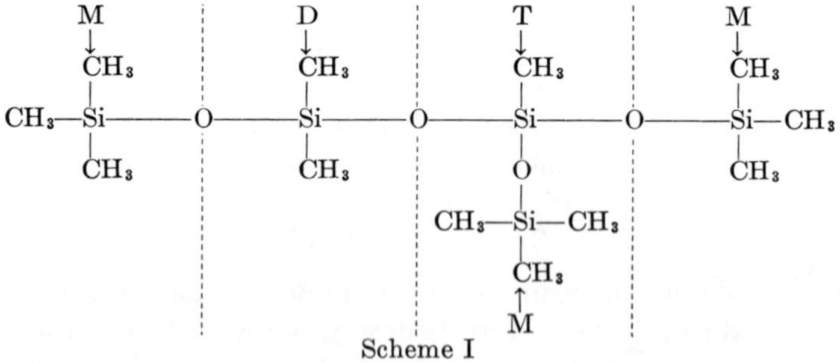

Scheme I

plex structure would be $MDTM_2$. Short, linear dimethylsilicone polymers are fluids whose viscosity depends upon the molecular weight. This relation for viscosities up to 10 million is shown in Fig. 1. When the degree of polymerization is very large, 10,000 or higher, we have polymers of the order of 30 million centistokes. It is polymers such as these on which silicone rubbers are based. It is interesting that such polymers with molecular weights over half a million will still flow very slowly although most organic polymers of this molecular weight would be quite tough.

This high fluidity is only one of the unusual properties of silicone polymers and many workers have devoted considerable attention to the measurement and interpretation of properties as a function of molecular structure. Noll and a number of other authors (14) have examined bond angles and atomic distances and have interpretated properties of silicones in terms of these parameters and the observed molecular motions. Thus the polysiloxane chain is more nearly linear with flatter bond angles than

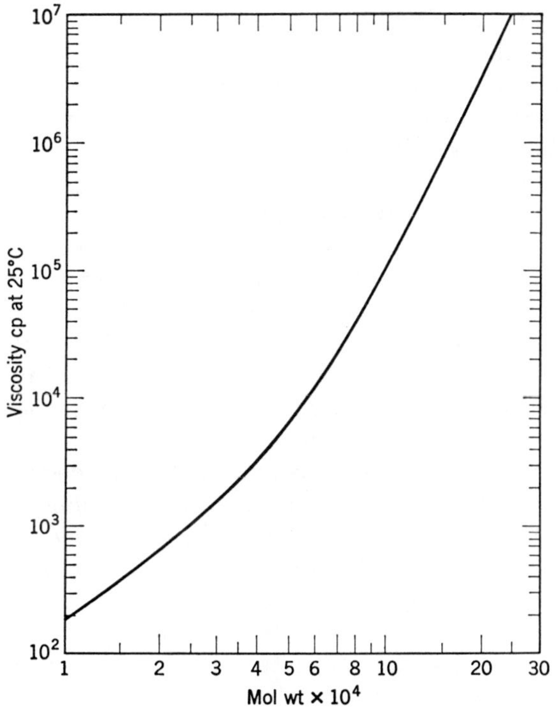

Fig. 1. Viscosity of polymethylsiloxane as a function of molecular weight.

its carbon–oxygen analogs. Noll reported 1.64 Å as the bond distance of Si—O in siloxanes and 1.88 Å for the Si—C bond distance. He also found 125–130° for the Si—O—Si bond angle, 109–115° for O—Si—O and 106–111° for the C—Si—C bond. Other authors have reported bond angles for the Si—O—Si bond up to 160°. The free rotation of the methyl group on silicon also affects the properties of siloxanes. Roth (15) determined the structure of a single crystal of a spiro silicone by X-ray Fourier analysis. He reported the methyl group rotation was so high that an electron density pattern could not be plotted for it. Several authors (16–18) have measured the methyl group rotation and found it to persist down to 77°K and have interpretated the physical properties of silicone rubber in terms of this persistent motion. These factors together with the flat bond angles and the corresponding tendency toward large ring formation have been considered by several workers to be responsible for some of the unusual physical properties, the flat temperature coefficient of viscosity, and a flat coefficeint of stress as a function of temperature. Equilibrated siloxanes are observed to have a high proportion of cyclic components and in addition many authors have proposed that this tendency toward ring formation persists even in a high polymer, giving a coiled structure with approximately seven siloxy units per turn. Wilcock (19) investigated the viscosity of siloxane fluids as a function of temperature and molecular weight and reported an activation energy of flow of 3.3 kcal/mole for low molecular weight fluids and extrapolated this to an activation energy of 3.8 kcal/mole at high molecular weight. He calculated that the unit of flow involved a group of 7.2 silicon atoms. Warrick (17) also proposed the helical structure to explain the low activation energy for viscous flow. Presumably the coiled structure unwinds as the temperature is increased and the extended molecules result in an increased viscosity offsetting the normal reduction in viscosity at higher temperatures. Fox and his associates (20) conducted experiments using a film balance and concluded that the silicone polymer can coil reversibly into helices with six monomer units at higher film pressures and that these helices uncoil as the film expands. Newing (21) made thermodynamic measurements on silicone polymers and proposed that the strong negative deviation of the free energy from ideality, even with a large positive heat of dilution, indicated a large entropy of dilution. The positive ΔH_0 indicated that the structural order in the undiluted liquid was broken up on mixing. The resulting change from order to disorder resulted in a large value of ΔS_0. He suggested the existence of a large degree of short range order at high concentrations.

Brown (22) has found additional evidence for the presence of preferentially coiled structures in cured silicone rubber.

A number of authors have examined the molecular weight and molecular weight distribution of silicone polymers prepared by different methods. A discussion of the molecular weight distribution of rings and chains will be deferred to the section on polymerization. Barry (24) did some of the earlier work on the relation between the intrinsic viscosity and the viscosity–average molecular weight of polydimethylsilicones. This relation may be expressed by the familiar equation $[\eta] = KM^{\alpha}$. Barry reported values of $K = 2 \times 10^{-4}$ and $\alpha = 0.66$. Charlesby (25) found values in agreement with these numbers. Light scattering measurements also give approximate confirmation of these values. A number of authors have subsequently made molecular weight measurements but unfortunately many of the data cannot be directly compared since all experimental details, correction for kinetic energy effects, etc. have not always been reported. These relations are approximately correct and it is beyond the scope of this brief review to discuss the subject in detail.

In summary then, the macrobehavior of silicone polymers including elastomers is related to the microstructure. The linear methyl silicones have a number of characteristics in which they differ from organic polymers. They have low energies of vaporization, low energies of viscous flow, low surface tension, and small intermolecular forces. Frisch (23) and co-workers reported approximately 1000 cal for the intermolecular attraction between two dimethyl silicon groups, roughly half that for corresponding organic structures. All this contributes to high molar volume, high compressibility and a large group and chain mobility extending down to quite low temperatures. This provides elastic behavior at temperatures below which most polymers will freeze or stiffen, and also in part explains the low tensile strength of unreinforced dimethylsilicone rubbers.

III. SYNTHETIC METHODS

The literature on silicone chemistry is very extensive. It is beyond the scope of this review to do more than touch on some of the basic methods of synthesizing silicone intermediates. For further reading Refs. 5–12 provide background in the chemistry of silicones. The text by Eaborn is one of the more comprehensive treatises on organosilicon chemistry and lists some 2,000 references. Rochow's book is a good reference for the basic chemistry of silicones. Andrianov has covered the field of organosilicon chemistry comprehensively both inside and outside

Russia. His treatise is available in English translation. Noll has treated both the technology and chemistry of silicones with many references. The volume by Meals and Lewis is concerned primarily with applications of silicones and the other references included in this series provide general coverage on silicones.

In the laboratory, organosilicon intermediates can be made in a variety of ways. For example, chlorosilicon intermediates may be reacted with organometallic reagents including organo derivatives of lithium, sodium, potassium, zinc, mercury, and magnesium (Grignard reagents), etc. The Wurtz process is also used in which an alkyl halide is reacted with a silicon chlorine bond using sodium metal as a halogen acceptor. Although a few processes exist, at least in the laboratory, for converting silica itself directly into hydrogen silanes or organosilanes, the majority of silicone intermediates are derived from metallic silicon. Of the many synthetic methods possible, only a few are important commercially. These include:

1. The "direct" process
2. The Grignard process
3. Aromatic silylation
4. Silane–olefin addition reactions
5. Redistribution reactions

The Grignard reaction is the classical method for preparing organosilanes and was the first commercially important synthetic method. Alkylation of a chlorosilicone is illustrated schematically in the following equation:

$$\equiv SiCl + RMgX \rightarrow \equiv SiR + MgClX$$

The reaction is particularly useful because of its great versatility in converting chlorosilane intermediates into other alkylated organosilane materials.

By far the most important commercial process for making organochlorosilanes is the "direct" process discovered by Rochow (4). The name derives from the fact that alkyl halides can be reacted directly with elemental silicon to produce organochlorosilanes as illustrated in the following equation:

$$MeCl + Si \xrightarrow[300°C]{Cu} \begin{cases} MeSiCl_3 \\ Me_2SiCl_2 \\ Me_3SiCl \end{cases}$$

In this reaction the difunctional chlorosilanes normally predominate although a certain amount of control can be exercised over the percentages of mono- and trichlorosilanes produced. A variety of other unwanted materials including certain hydrocarbon fractions, silicon tetrachloride and various polysilanes are produced. The desired products and the unwanted by-products must be separated, usually by distillation, into usable components. The following mechanism was suggested by Hurd and Rochow (26) based on their analysis of the reaction products and intermediates:

$$MeCl + 2Cu \rightarrow MeCu + CuCl$$
$$MeCu \rightarrow Cu + Me\cdot$$
$$CuCl + Si \rightarrow Cu + (SiCl)$$
$$Me\cdot + (SiCl) \rightarrow (MeSiCl)$$

In these equations Me represents a methyl group and Me· is a methyl radical. These authors demonstrated that copper methyl is formed in the reaction and appears to act as a carrier for methyl radicals. A number of authors have suggested alternate mechanisms (78). At this time there is still some doubt as to all of the exact processes which are taking place. The copper catalyst shown in the equation is required and there is evidence that the small percentage of the several other impurities normally present in commercial silicon markedly affect the course of the reaction.

Addition of SiH-containing silicone intermediates to unsaturated organic materials (or unsaturated organosilanes) is a very versatile and important reaction. These reactions can be catalyzed by a number of materials including platinum catalysts, either as salts or as organoplatinum complexes, organic bases, and peroxides. By the proper choice of catalyst and reaction conditions it is frequently possible to direct the reaction in the desired way. The reaction is shown schematically here:

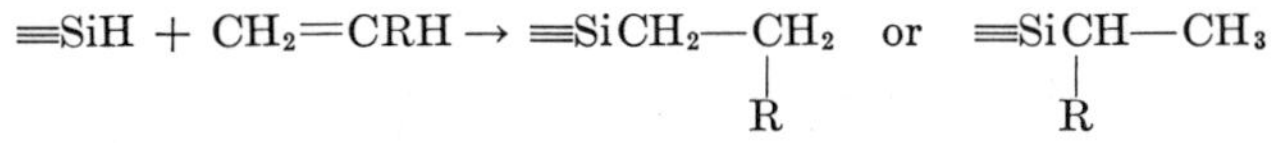

The catalyst may have an influence both on the rate of the reaction and on whether the silicon becomes attached to the α or β carbon atom. As an example, this reaction may be used to add a silane to trifluoropropene to make fluoropropyl-containing intermediates. These may be converted into high molecular weight elastomers,

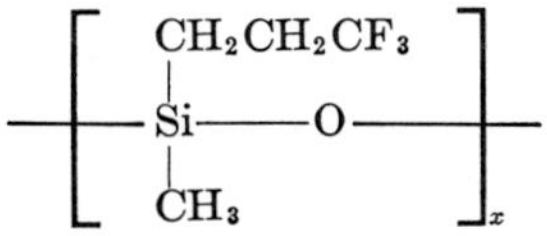

which exhibit greater resistance to swelling by solvents and fuels than dimethyl silicones.

The phenyl group attached to silicon also contributes important properties to silicone elastomers. The corresponding chlorosilanes are generally made commercially either by the direct process between chlorobenzene and silicon or by aromatic silylation. This latter reaction proceeds as follows:

$$\phi H + HSiCl_3 \rightarrow \phi SiCl_3 + H_2$$

(ϕ represents a phenyl group)

at temperatures on the order of 400°C, or at reduced temperatures in the presence of Friedel-Crafts catalysts such as aluminum chloride.

In addition to these relatively important commercial processes, there are a great many other methods of forming silicon–carbon, silicon–hydrogen, and silicon–chlorine bonds. Some of these techniques are of use in laboratory preparations, some are useful in small scale manufacture for the attainment of flexibility in achieving an optimum product mix and some may achieve commercial importance when the benefits which they provide become sufficiently important.

Only a few of these methods operate with silicon dioxide directly because of the high bond energies in this starting material. There is considerable interest in methods of forming SiH_4 because of the many potentially valuable reactions which this bond (SiH) will undergo. Some methods have been found for hydrogenating silicon dioxide directly (27) to form SiH_4; however, no method yet found is really practical. Other methods starting for example with SiF_4 (27) are more practical. Here, silicon tetrafluoride (a by-product of the fertilizer industry) reacts directly with hydrogen at high temperatures to produce a mixture of fluorosilanes which can be redistributed to produce silane itself.

An interesting method for alkylating silicon dioxide directly was reported by Anderson and Sleddon (28). Finely divided amorphous silica is used. These workers developed the following scheme:

$$3MeCl + 2Al \rightarrow Me_3Al_2Cl_3$$

$$4Me_3Al_2Cl_3 + 3SiO_2 \rightarrow 3Me_4Si + 6AlOCl + 2AlCl_3$$

$$Me_4Si + SiCl_4 \rightarrow \begin{cases} MeSiCl_3 \\ Me_2SiCl_2 \\ Me_3SiCl \end{cases}$$

The reactions are reported to go in good yield and the redistribution reactions between tetramethylsilane and silicon tetrachloride can be directed to produce greater or lesser amounts of the several methyl chlorosilanes shown.

One potentially useful technique for alkylating $SiCl_4$ with MeCl using a fused salt bath has been described by Sundermeyer (29). Fused salts were found to be excellent reaction media for reactions including quantitative electrochemical operations. The following reaction goes smoothly in a fused $NaCl–AlCl_3$ mixture:

$$3SiCl_4 + 12MeCl + 8Al \rightarrow 3Me_4Si + 8AlCl_3.$$

Subsequently, aluminum is regenerated in the form of fine, reactive crystals by electrolysis:

$$2AlCl_3 \xrightarrow{\text{Elec.}} 2Al + 3Cl_2$$

On a large scale, it would be possible to recycle the chlorine (as $SiCl_4$) as well as the aluminum.

The further conversion of the chlorosilanes to the cyclic siloxane and silanol precursors of silicone high polymers involve hydrolysis and condensation. Hydrolysis of chlorosilanes proceeds at different rates for different chlorosilanes and even for different chlorines on the same silicon. Dimethyldichlorosilane, for example, hydrolyzes in two steps which go at different rates.

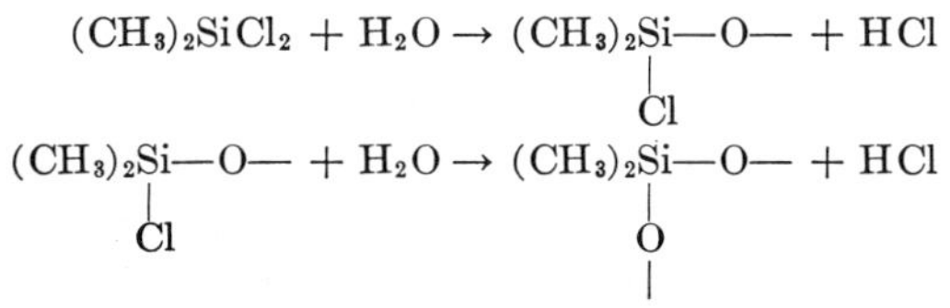

Monomeric silanols are extremely reactive and tend to condense with the elimination of water. Dihydroxydimethylsilane is so reactive that it is extremely difficult to prepare and such reactive monomers condense to higher polymers with silanol endgroups. Aromatic silanols are less reactive and diphenylsilanediol may be easily prepared. As has already been noted there is a considerable tendency for siloxanes to form cyclic structures and hydrolysis of a dichlorosilane will normally produce a mixture of cyclic siloxanes together with linear polymeric fluids with the following structures:

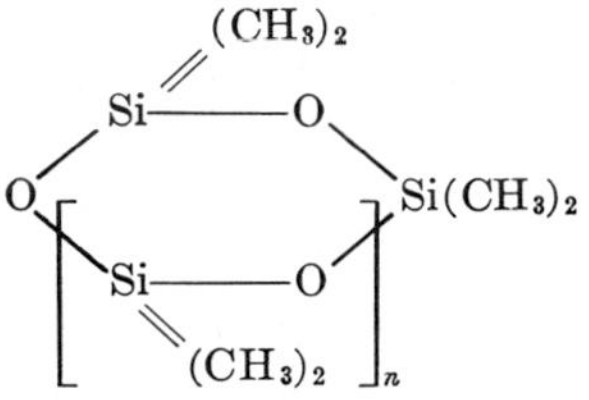

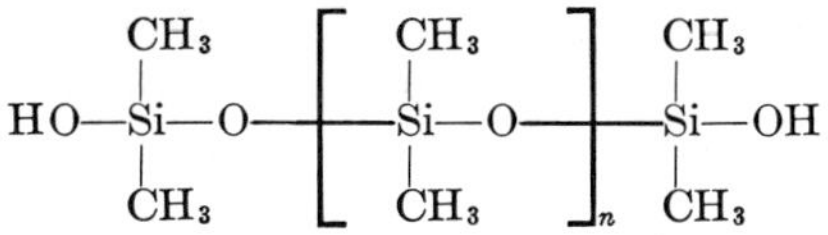

Both the cyclic siloxanes and the linear silanol-terminated polymers shown here are important starting materials for the production of the high polymers which will be used for heat-curing rubbers and for the low molecular weight starting materials for the important class of room temperature vulcanizing (RTV) elastomers. When it is desired to limit the molecular weight of the linear polymers it is customary to incorporate monofunctional silanes through the use of trimethylchlorosilane and it is of course possible to introduce branching by adding small amounts of trifunctional silanes, for example, methyltrichlorosilane to the reaction mixture. Extreme concentrations of either material may be important in fluids and resins, but for the elastomers, only very small amounts of either of these components are used.

IV. POLYMERIZATION

Except in rare cases the direct products of hydrolysis are not useful for silicone elastomers and they must be converted through polymerization and other reactions into the polymers which are the basis for silicone elastomers.

Several methods of polymerizing monomers and low molecular weight intermediates are important in the process of creating the high polymers and prepolymers that make possible heat curing and room temperature curing of silicone rubbers. In the preliminary discussion it was indicated that hydrolysis processes resulted in the conversion of chlorosilanes to higher polymers. This is an over-simplification since hydrolysis of chlorosilanes produces a mixture of cyclic siloxanes and random, linear low molecular weight siloxanes generally terminated with silanol or silanolate groups.

In the several processes of polymerization a number of reactions are important. These include base catalyzed or acid catalyzed rearrangement of cyclic siloxanes and condensation polymerization of low molecular weight monomers and oligomers to produce high polymers. In polymerization via cleavage of cyclic siloxanes the rates of polymerization and depolymerization may be such that the polymers produced do not necessarily represent equilibrium compositions but rather may be kinetically controlled.

Although some fraction of the polymerizing dimethylsiloxy units close in the form of stable cyclic structures, the linear polymer predominates. As the reacting polymer chains grow longer there is a decreasing probability of cyclizing and the resulting chains may grow to molecular weights of several million. Termination may occur by several processes.

Exhaustion of the monomer may leave reactive silanolate chain ends although these will normally react with some chain terminator or inhibitor that may be present by accident or on purpose in the reaction mixture. Traces of moisture, for example, will result in silanol endgroups. Frequently the molecular weight of the polymer may be controlled by the addition of reactive monomeric species, for example, hexamethyldisiloxane, which will react to produce trimethylsilanolate endgroups. In the absence of chain-stopping materials, molecular weights in the millions may be obtained. However, for optimum processability and physical properties, the average molecular weight of methyl silicone polymers is usually controlled to something under one million. The molecular weight distribution of a typical base catalyzed polydimethylsiloxane is shown in Fig. 2. The base catalyzed polymer has been separated (41) into 11 fractions using toluene as a solvent and methanol as a precipitant. That fraction of the polymer representing approximately 20 wt % and below 100,000 mol. wt. includes short chain linear polymers, the large ring cyclics already described and the lower cyclics which represent the volatile components of the total polymer.

The composition of the final polymer will depend upon the rates of polymerization, together with the rates of equilibration which involve polymerization, depolymerization, and ring formation.

A number of authors have studied distribution of the several species generated in polymerization and Carmichael (30) has summarized the work of previous authors and listed the distribution of the cyclic dimethylsiloxanes generated at equilibrium in the presence of potassium hydroxide

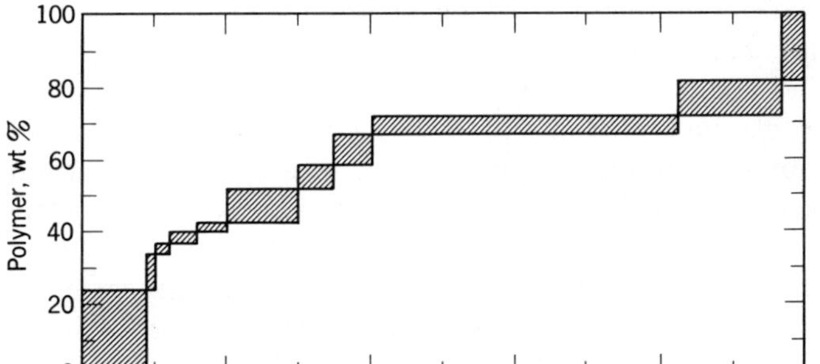

Fig. 2. Molecular weight distribution of methyl silicone gum.

TABLE I
Distribution of Cyclics, Wt %

	n =								
Temp. °C	3	4	5	6	7	8	9	10	11
25	0	5.62	4.22	1.59	0.46	0.16	0.10	0.47	trace
110	0	5.88	4.41	1.55	0.50	0.15	0.09	trace	trace
150	0	6.32	4.80	1.90	0.83	0.21	0.08	0	0
178	0.21	6.40	4.88	1.73	0.41	0.19	0.11	0.08	trace

as a rearrangement catalyst. Selected values from his experiments are shown in Table I.

In Table I *n* indicates the number of siloxane units in the several cyclics. The reactions were carried out for a time sufficient to ensure the attainment of equilibrium at the temperatures used. In all cases the cyclic tetramer is the preferred structure and as the temperature of equilibration increases the preferred ring size decreases. At temperatures in excess of 150°C the cyclic trimer starts to appear.

The relative abundance of large ring cyclics in polymerizing polydimethylsiloxanes has been further investigated by Brown and co-workers (31) who used vapor phase chromatography and gel permeation chromatography to determine quantitatively the concentrations of cyclic siloxanes in polymers formed up to a ring size of 400 units. Brown was particularly interested in the higher cyclics since these had not previously been investigated because of experimental difficulties. He reported that the macrocyclic population, which he defined as cyclics above D_{12}, was present in commercial gums or polymers to about 2–3%.

His experimental findings were that in polymerization of cyclic siloxanes the cyclic tetramer predominated in the products in greater than theoretical amounts but that beyond a ring size of 12 the concentration of higher cyclics declined in accordance with the linear relation required by the Jacobson-Stockmeyer theory (32). This constitutes the first experimental verification of that theory. Flory (31) has given an explanation for this high concentration of small-ring cyclics. The Jacobson-Stockmeyer theory postulates that the two conditions for ring closure are independent: (*1*) the termini of the closing ring must be in juxtaposition, and (*2*) the directions of the terminal bonds must be colinear. If the ring size is small the proximity of the termini is conducive to regular polygon conformation or to the puckered nonplanar analog dictated by preference for bond staggering.

Grubb and Osthoff (33) have examined the kinetics of polymerization of cyclodimethyltetrasiloxane (frequently abbreviated as methyl-tetramer) using both potassium hydroxide and potassium silanolate as catalysts. With 0.01% KOH they report an effective first order rate constant k as $\log k = 8.3042 - (4291.1/T)$ and an overall activation energy of 19.6 kcal/mole. There appears to be a threshold condition below which a given metal hydroxide will not react with a siloxane at all and above which temperature the siloxane is attacked and thenceforth polymerization involves successive reactions of metal silanolate with additional cyclic siloxanes. There is some evidence (34) that the first attack of a metal hydroxide on a siloxane is through coordinate bonding of the base to a silicon:

$$\begin{array}{c}\text{—OSiO—}\\ \uparrow\\ \text{K}\ddot{\text{O}}\text{H}\end{array}$$

followed by a rearrangement to a potassium silanolate and a silanol structure. (In this structure and in others throughout the chapter it is understood that unmarked bonds, e.g., on the silicon atom, are attached to other groups such as methyl radicals.) Thus cesium hydroxide will attack siloxanes below 100°C, potassium hydroxide will attack at 130°C or over, while sodium hydroxide requires a temperature in excess of 150°C. This is in the order of the donor abilities of the corresponding bases. Grubb and Osthoff considered the polymerization process to begin with the reaction

$$\text{KOH} + \text{SiOSi} \rightleftarrows \text{SiOK} + \text{SiOH}$$

with the equilibrium displaced far to the right. Then

$$\text{SiOK} \rightleftarrows \text{SiO}^- + \text{K}^+$$

$$K_e = \frac{[\text{SiO}^-][\text{K}^+]}{[\text{SiOK}]} = \frac{[\text{SiO}^-]^2}{[\text{SiOK}]}$$

where K_e is the equilibrium constant. The active species is then given by

$$[\text{SiO}^-] = \sqrt{K_e[\text{SiOK}]} = \sqrt{K_e[\text{KOH}]_{\text{added}}}$$

and the first order rate constant k is

$$k = A\sqrt{[\text{KOH}]_{\text{added}}}$$

A may be a function of temperature and other conditions. Accordingly the value of 19.6 kcal/mole for the overall activation energy contains the temperature dependence of K_e and is not a true activation energy. The authors found a half-order dependence of rate of polymerization on catalyst concentration and concluded that the silanolate ion was the active species in polymerization. Other workers have extended this concept and found effects of solvation of the cation, increased rates of polymerization in solvents of high dielectric constant and effects of complexing of the silanolate ion itself.

Morton (35) observed increased rates of polymerization in solvents of high dielectric constants such as nitrobenzene and Cooper and Elliott (36) found that dimethylsulfoxide caused dramatic increases in rates of polymerization in amounts well under 1%, far too low to be classed as a solvent effect. As little as 0.5% dimethylsulfoxide increased the rate of potassium hydroxide catalyzed polymerization of methyl tetramer by factors of 100–1000 and also allowed the reaction to proceed at lower than the threshold polymerization temperature in the absence of the sulfoxide. They attributed this to the solvation of the cation by the sulfoxide

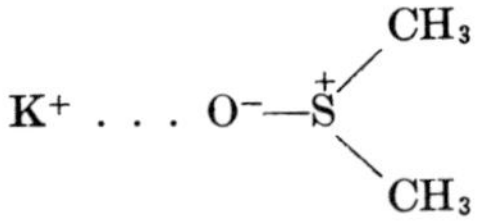

which increases the freedom and concentration of the silanolate ions, the active polymerizing species. Kucera (37) found evidence for the participation of additional complexes in polymerizing systems. He cited both kinetic and spectral evidence for the formation of complexes which may play a major role in the kinetics. When mixed bases are used as catalysts, such as a mixture of sodium and potassium hydroxide, or when certain ethers are present, Kucera found evidence for structures such as:

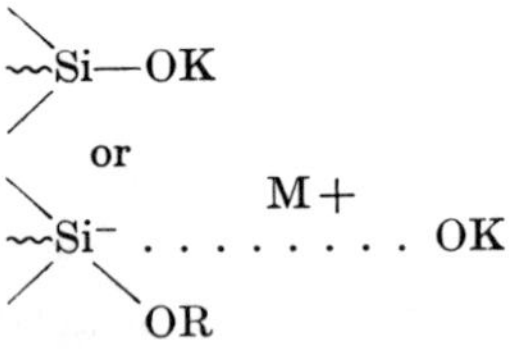

where R may be H, CH_3, or a siloxane chain and M may be Li, Na, or K. Organic ethers may form similar complexes. Observed changes in the kinetics of polymerization of methyl tetramer brought about by the presence of these complexes were in full agreement with the proposed structures.

It is apparent from these examples that a variety of reactions and structures may contribute to the detailed polymerization systems.

Coordination of the attacking base, ionization and reformation, ion pairs, complexing with free base, complexing with donor molecules, variation of dielectric constants and solvation of the cations are all factors in determining the rates and kinetics observed.

In addition to the above factors the chain structure immediately surrounding the siloxane bond being attacked is also important. The reactivities of several siloxane structures towards acids and bases has been measured by Kantor (38) who summarized them in the following order of reactivity toward bases:

$$D_3 > D_4 > MD_2M > MDM > MM$$

and the corresponding reactivity for acids:

$$D_3 > MM > MDM > MD_2M > D_4$$

Acid catalysts may also be used for polymerization. In this case the reaction generally proceeds through protonation of the oxygen of the siloxane bond rather than a base attack on silicon. It was formerly thought that aprotic acids such as ferric chloride could also attack a siloxane bond directly causing rearrangement and polymerization. More recently, however, Kendrick (39) has presented convincing evidence that the free anhydrous Lewis acids such as stannic chloride and ferric chloride are not catalysts for siloxane rearrangement but require a cocatalyst in the form of traces of water, hydrogen chloride, etc. which can form, for example, hydrogen tetrachloroferrate from hydrogen chloride and ferric chloride. Kendrick presented a complete kinetic scheme which involved successively the formation of the reactive acid, dissociation of the acid to yield protons, protonation of the siloxane bond, and propagation by ionic attack of other siloxane bonds.

In addition to polymerization reactions proceeding via rearrangement of bonds, condensation processes are also important in which labile groups attached to silicone oligomers, monomers or polymers split out small molecules and join groups of siloxanes together. Such reactions may be useful both to effect condensation polymerization and also to provide a curing process. It is frequently possible to build polymers by condensation polymerization which would not be obtainable through siloxane rearrangement. Merker (40) has described the condensation polymerization of block copolymers of dimethylsiloxane and silphenylene blocks to produce polymers with tensile strengths in the thousands of pounds range. These same polymers when equilibrated to random structures have very different properties. Merker prepared these copolymers by first forming blocks of dimethyl siloxane units containing hydroxyl endgroups and also prepared blocks of silphenylene units. These blocks were then joined together using a condensation catalyst (a substituted guanidine) which was capable of effecting silanol condensation eliminating water but was not sufficiently strong as a catalyst to cause siloxane rearrangement. The resulting block structures shown here

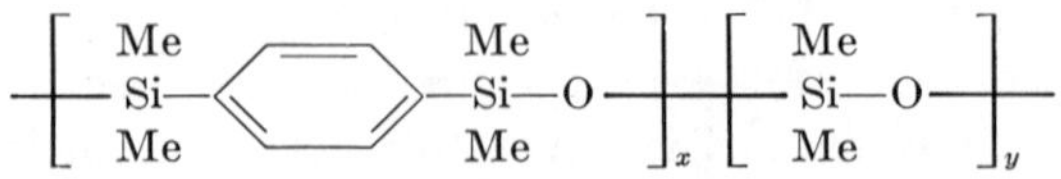

have much greater strength than from the randomly arranged units having the same average composition.

A great many cleavage reactions are possible which allow the building of molecular weight through siloxane condensation. Many of these have only limited application and are useful for certain specific polymerizations though some are more general.

Considerable attention has been focused on catalysts, reagents or reactions which will allow the generation of siloxane bonds, so as to effect polymerization, without causing the siloxane bonds already existing to rearrange. As already indicated, strong acids or bases are to be avoided. Other catalysts, for example, ferric chloride, permit the generation of desired structures without rearrangement (or with only a small amount of scrambling) when used with care:

$$\equiv SiOR + ClSi\equiv \xrightarrow{FeCl_3} \equiv SiOSi\equiv + RCl$$

However, as already pointed out if a trace of water or hydrochloric acid is present rearrangement will follow.

The reactions discussed, and many others, are useful for producing polymers and prepolymers for further conversion to cured elastomers. The specific monomer units used will vary considerably. Heat curing rubbers in general will be built from mostly difunctional units with only traces of monofunctional or end-stopping units. Polymers for special purposes such as low temperature rubbers will contain phenyl or groups other than methyl. Specific examples of special purpose polymers will be considered separately.

V. SILICONE COPOLYMERS

There are many different kinds of polymers that fall in the subject category. Variation in the substituent groups, modification of the in-chain structures, incorporation of other metals than silicon in the chain and the many structures which can be formed as block and graft copolymers provide a wide variety of polymer types. Such copolymers are important for a number of reasons. They provide variations in physical and chemical properties, greater resistance to heat, oxidation, radiation, and other severe conditions, chemical routes to different cure systems, different solubility or swelling characteristics and increased flexibility at low temperatures.

The preparation of copolymers by the polymerization of a mixture of different silicone cyclic monomers presents problems in some cases since not all cyclic monomers are attacked at the same rate by the active growing chains. Merker (42) has applied the copolymerization theory developed for free-radical copolymerization (43) to the ionic copolymerization of mixed silicone cyclics. He found that small structural changes in the reacting siloxane monomers produced very large changes in the monomer reactivity ratios. The practical result of this is that it is frequently difficult and sometimes impossible to produce useful polymers by ionic copolymerization.

Such difficulties may be circumvented in a number of ways. One method involves the formation of so-called hybrid cyclics which contain two different R groups in the same monomer (44). Another method involves condensation polymerization which has already been discussed. This is a versatile tool for making a variety of structures. A silphenylene-dimethylsiloxy example has already been described and the technique has been used to make block-block silicone copolymers, silicone-organic random and block copolymers and to distribute selected functional groups along a polymer chain.

Silicone graft copolymers have been made by swelling silicone homopolymers with a vinyl monomer followed by irradiation of the swollen polymer with gamma rays. Free radical sites generated on the homopolymer initiate polymerization of the vinyl co-monomer to produce a siloxane main chain with organic branches. A graft copolymer with acrylonitrile has produced elastomers with improved resistance to swelling by solvents.

Block copolymers have also been prepared (79) from the so-called organic "living" polymers. Monomers as styrene, isoprene and others may be polymerized with potassium naphthalene to form the "living" polymer with active anion chain ends. The subsequent addition of a cyclic siloxane results in further reaction to form a block copolymer containing groups of polysiloxane alternating with polyisoprene blocks.

A great deal of work has been done both in this country and abroad, particularly in Russia, on silicone-inorganic copolymers, in which elements such as aluminum, iron, tin, and titanium are incorporated in the polymer in a position that would normally be occupied by silicon.

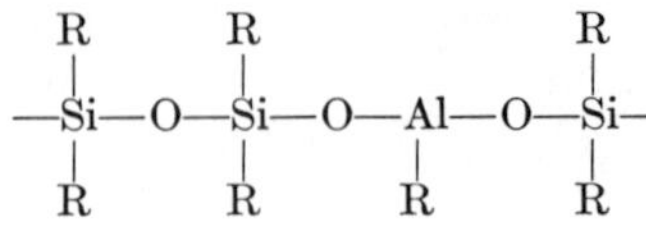

Despite the rather large volume of work, no really practical polymers have been made at this time. In general the polar nature of the bonds in the polymer backbone promote hydrolytic instability. This work has been summarized in several places. One such review is that by Andrianov (46).

Specific benefits provided by this large family of polymers are described later in this review in the sections on polymer stability, cure and low temperature elastomers. Additional details and examples will be found in Refs. 5–12.

VI. STABILITY OF SILICONE POLYMERS

The physical and chemical properties that make silicone elastomers useful have been enumerated in the introduction. Some of the factors affecting stability to environment are bond energies, oxidative stability, oxidation catalysts and inhibitors, hydrolytic stability, and thermal and catalyzed rearrangement of siloxane bonds.

High on this list of important properties is the resistance of silicone elastomers to the several degradative conditions encountered in use.

A. Thermal Stability

The term "temperature resistance" is often used in a rather loose sense. Frequently we find in the literature reports that a polymer is "resistant" to some temperature, say 400°C, without reference to time or the presence or absence of oxygen or catalysts. In considering elastomers for actual use under drastic environmental conditions it is important to put the test conditions in proper perspective.

For long-life applications such as electrical insulation it is desirable to be able to predict the useful life of an elastomer for 10 to 20 years. The relation $k = Ae^{-E/RT}$ is generally used to make such extrapolations based on degradation rates (rate constant $= k$) at elevated temperatures. Here E is an activation energy, R is a constant, A can be estimated, and T is the absolute temperature. A common and useful form is the graphical representation of log rate vs. $1/T$ and such plots are shown in Fig. 3 for three common insulation classes. Silicone elastomers are considered

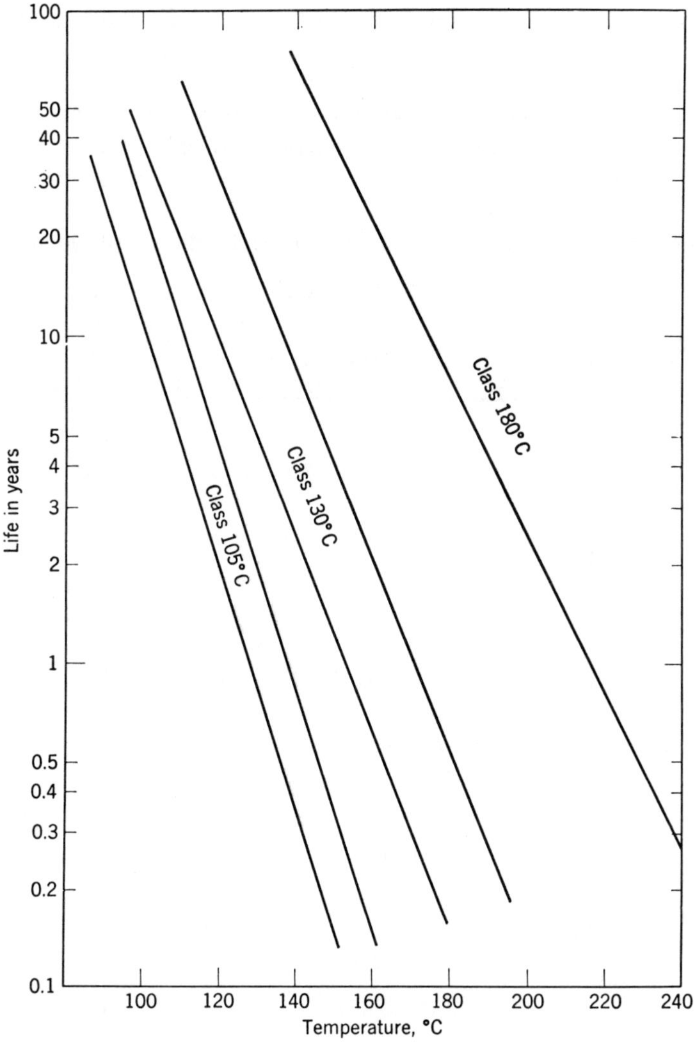

Fig. 3. Classes of insulation.

class 180°C or higher. The actual useful life will vary with composition and processing. Bobear (47) has studied the heat resistance both of standard commercial stocks and those compounded for maximum heat stability. To obtain a measure of useful life (reciprocal of rate) he used as a criterion the time for the original material to degrade to the point at which it had

50% of the initial elongation at tensile break. His data are shown in Fig. 4.

It is interesting to speculate on the ultimate thermal stability of a silicone elastomer. Tetramethyl silane has been heated (48) to 680°C before measurable decomposition occurred and calculations using bond dissociation energies as E in the Arrhenius equation suggest half lives of the order of hours at 450–600°C.

The most heat-stable elastomer reported to date (49) is made from

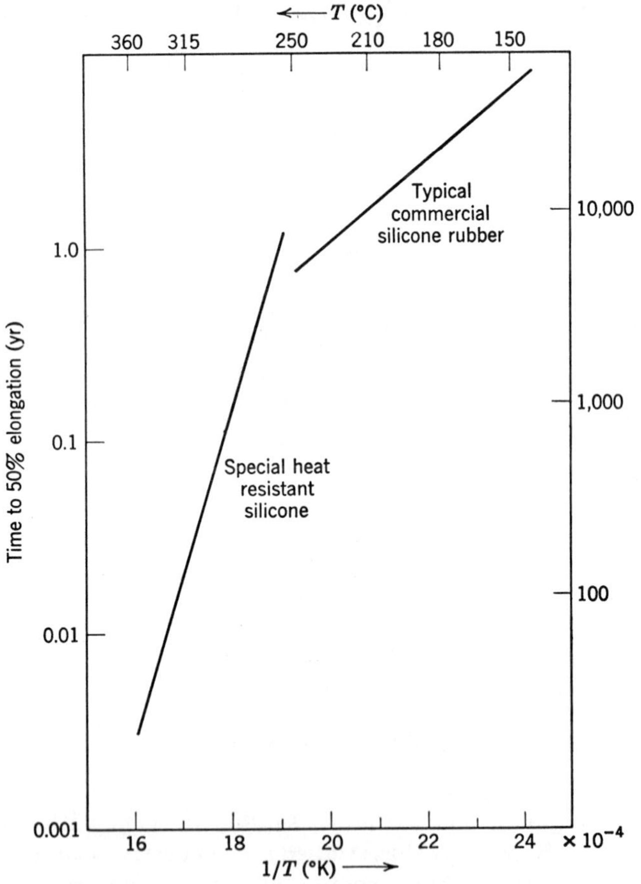

Fig. 4. Time to 50% elongation vs. temperature.

poly-*m*-carborane siloxanes with the structure:

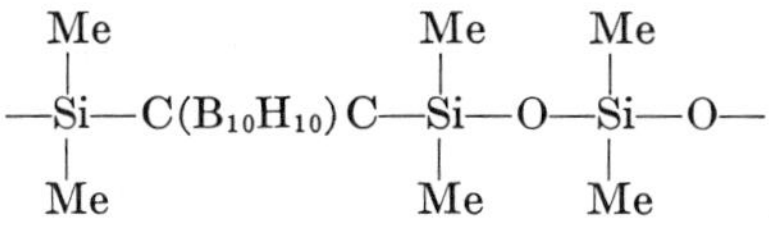

in which the —$C(B_{10}H_{10})C$— represents *m*-carborane. This extremely heat stable compound is formed by reacting acetylene with decarborane to produce a resonance-stabilized structure. Elastomers which retained over 100 psi tensile strength after 2 hr at 900°F (480°C) have been made.

B. Oxidative Stability

In addition to the thermal cleavage and rearrangement of the several bonds present in silicone polymers, reaction with atmospheric oxygen is another limiting factor in the application of silicones at elevated temperatures. A linear polydimethylsiloxane chain contains only relatively stable primary hydrogen atoms. Aromatic hydrogens (phenyl groups) are even more stable to oxidation. It is important to the high temperature stability of methylphenyl silicone elastomers that these two kinds of very stable hydrogen atoms are the only ones present. In contrast, it is difficult to prepare organic polymers which do not contain either secondary or tertiary hydrogen atoms. Russell (50) found that the initial attack of oxygen radicals on a hydrocarbon was slowest for primary hydrogen, eight times faster for secondary hydrogen, and thirteen times faster for tertiary hydrogens. Accordingly, the primary and aromatic hydrogens in the methyl-phenyl silicones provide more stable structures than are generally possible for organic elastomers. In addition to the inherent stability of a particular polymer, it is found in practice that oxidative resistance varies widely with environmental conditions. Uncompounded silicone polymers change visibly (51) in a matter of hours at 250°C, however, properly compounded and cured elastomers may give continuous service for over a year at this temperature.

The degradative reactions involved appear to be similar to those concerned in the oxidation of organic polymers. Scala (54) oxidized methylphenyl silicones at 400°C and found that water, benzene, carbon dioxide, carbon monoxide, traces of phenol, formaldehyde, methanol, and propane were produced. The small amount of oxygen consumed indicated that the polysiloxanes were quite stable to oxygen at temperatures up to 400°C. Kuz'minskii (55) examined the thermal oxidation of methyl silicone rubber at 300–400°C. He reported the formation of silanol groups and a small number of carbonyl groups. The main decomposition products were formaldehyde, water, carbon monoxide, and hydrogen, accompanied by traces of methane. Polymer changes indicated demethylation of the main chain, crosslinking and degradation.

Kuz'minskii proposed a complex series of reactions to account for the products observed. Part of this series is shown here to indicate chain initiation and possible reactions consistent with the experimental findings:

$$2SiCH_3 + O_2 \rightarrow 2SiCH_2\cdot + H_2O_2 \quad \text{(initiation)}$$

$$SiCH_2\cdot + O_2 \rightarrow SiCH_2OO\cdot \rightarrow SiOOCH_2\cdot \rightarrow SiO\cdot + CH_2O$$

$$SiCH_2OO\cdot \searrow SiCHO + \cdot OH \qquad SiOOCH_2\cdot \searrow SiO\cdot + CO + H_2$$

$$SiCH_3 + SiO\cdot \rightarrow SiOH + SiCH_2\cdot$$

$$SiOH + SiCH_3 \rightarrow SiOSi + CH_4$$

Antioxidants have not met with as much success in protecting against silicone oxidation as is the case with organic polymers. Nevertheless, certain antioxidants have improved the heat resistance of some silicones (52). It has also been found that transition elements which are capable of one-electron transfer appear to retard the oxidative attack on silicones (53). Presumably the one-electron transfer is capable of interfering with or stopping the oxidative chain reactions, for example:

$$SiO\cdot + Fe^{3+} \rightarrow SiO^- + Fe^{2+}$$

Silicone rubber protected by red iron oxide loses its red color under severe high temperature oxidation conditions at a short distance below the surface suggesting a redox reaction involving one-electron transfer between the ferrous and ferric valence states.

C. Rearrangement

The rearrangement of siloxane bonds can play a prominent part in the thermal degradation of silicone elastomers. Such rearrangement may either occur at high temperatures spontaneously or at somewhat lower temperatures in the presence of acid or base catalysts. The extent of the degradative rearrangement depends on many things including the type of the siloxane, the nature of any catalyst present, the temperature and the physical state of the polymer (e.g., the degree of crosslinking). Below a transition temperature of 600°F (approximately 320°C) rearrangement is very slow. Above this temperature rearrangement and at least some splitting out of cyclic siloxanes will proceed at a measurable rate although the rate will vary with the system and may be quite slow for heat-resistant rubber compounds.

The rate of siloxane rearrangement will also vary with the kind of substituent groups. Thus, trifluoromethylphenyl groups provide corresponding silanediols that are almost completely resistant to condensation even in contact with molten lead (327°C) which is a powerful catalyst for condensation (56). If it were possible to make high polymers with such substituents it might be anticipated that those polymers would be more resistant to heat and moisture than existing silicones.

D. Hydrolytic Stability

The degradation of silicone polymers by hydrolytic depolymerization is important in many applications. This reaction proceeds according to the equation:

$$\text{Si—O—Si} + H_2O \quad \text{SiOH} + \text{HOSi}$$

Attack of silicone rubber by water, particularly in closed spaces, is called reversion. Reversion is a controversial subject and erroneous conclusions have been reported as to the suitability of silicone elastomers for applications in sealed systems. Such tests have not always been representative of the use conditions. The polymerization and depolymerization of methyl silicone gums was studied by Martellock (57). He found that polymerization and depolymerization by hydrolytic attack of siloxane bonds, and by reversible condensation polymerization of the corresponding silanols, proceed according to the following kinetic equations:

$$\frac{-dC}{dt} = -k_0C^2\,(\text{cat}) + k_h\,\frac{C_0 - C}{2}\,P\,(\text{cat}),$$

where C = silanol concentration
C_0 = silanol in monomer
$\frac{C_0 - C}{2}$ = siloxane bond concentration
P = vapor pressure of water

The reaction is very slow in the absence of a catalyst and the closed polymer–water system does not reach equilibrium molecular weight even after 3 months at 150°C. Equilibrium conditions can be established more rapidly in the presence of either an acid or a base type of catalyst. The thermal hydrolytic cleavage was found to have an activation energy of 23 kcal/mole and a base-catalyzed activation energy of 6 kcal/mole. These compare well with values of 22.8 kcal/mole and 5.1 kcal/mole, respectively, for thermal and catalyzed stress relaxation measurements. At equilibrium in a closed system the net rate of polymerization and depolymerization is zero and the equilibrium molecular weight is represented by the expression:

$$\bar{M}_w = \frac{50,000}{P}$$

These results help to explain the long term effect of water on silicone elastomers in either closed or open systems. These and other practical design factors have been applied by Bobear (58) in the development of special rubber stocks with excellent reversion resistance for specific applications as O-rings, seals, and gaskets. The type of reinforcing filler used is important also and in this study Cab-O-Sil was found to be superior to most other fillers. Elimination of reactive catalyst residues is important and curing agents that do not leave acidic residues are preferred. Dialkyl peroxides or alkylhydroperoxides give better results than benzoyl peroxide or other peroxides which leave acidic residues. With proper preconditioning and attention to compound design details silicone rubber compounds can be produced that give satisfactory performance under environmental conditions more drastic than would be indicated by reversion tests on uncompounded gums.

E. Fuel, Oil, and Solvent Resistance

In many applications silicone elastomers are exposed to fuels, solvents and oils when used for sealing applications or in applications in which they may occasionally be splashed with such materials. Commercial and military surface and aircraft engines are operating at ever higher temperatures and fuels and hydraulic or transmission fluids generate problems when it is necessary to seal against leakage at elevated temperatures. In many cases commercial dimethyl silicone rubber swells and degrades too much to provide satisfactory performance in these sealing applications. Swelling by solvents does not permanently damage an elastomer but may only swell and tenderize it against tearing even though the rubber may regain its normal strength when the swelling fluid is removed by extraction or evaporation.

Special solvent- and fuel-resistant elastomers are required for many of these applications. There is no universally solvent-resistant elastomer and a rubber will always be attacked to a greater or lesser extent by certain solvents which more or less "resemble" it. A measure of this "likeness" of materials has been proposed by Hildebrand (59) who described chemical similarity as being measured in terms of a "solubility parameter" which is a function of internal pressure. Materials with similar solubility parameters are more compatible than those with different solubility parameters and correspondingly, elastomers are swelled more by solvents which have solubility parameters matching their own. Methyl silicone rubber swells very substantially in hydrocarbon solvents though not as much as natural rubber (Fig. 5). One might anticipate that increasing the polarity of the elastomer would result in reduced swell which is indeed the case. The gain in performance, however in gasoline or kerosene carries with it the penalty of increased relative swelling in high-polarity solvents such as a diester hydraulic fluid.

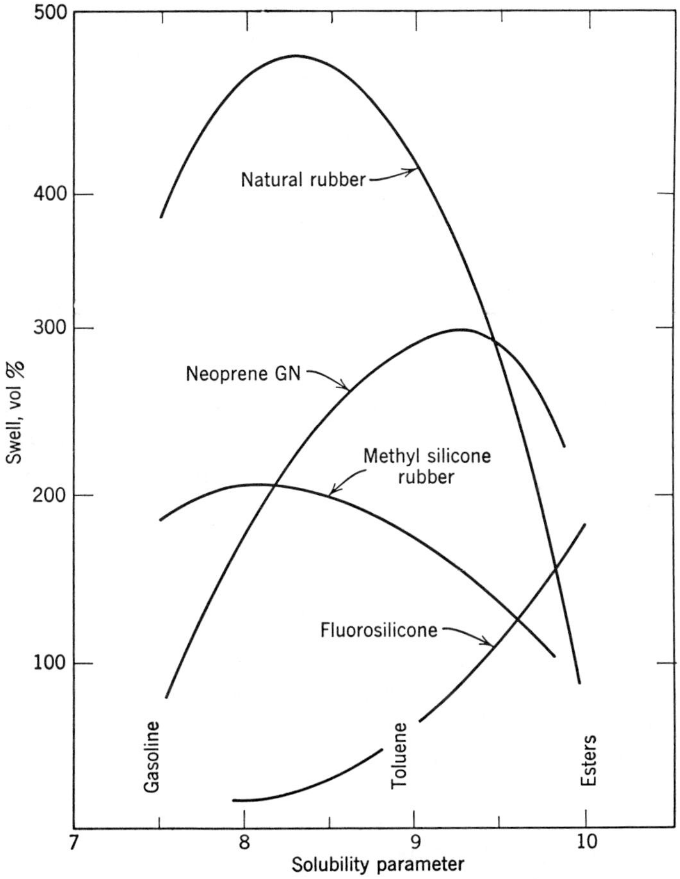

Fig. 5. The swelling of elastomers in different solvents.

Silicone elastomers with improved swelling resistance to many solvents have been made by incorporating polar groups such as cyanoethyl or trifluoropropyl groups. The swelling characteristics of dimethyl rubber and a fluorosilicone rubber with the structure

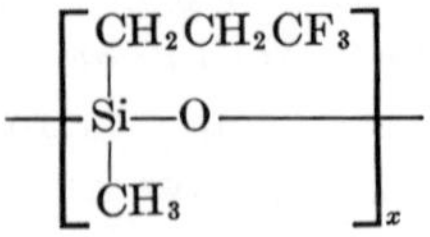

are compared (Fig. 5) with natural rubber and neoprene. It is evident from these curves that one must choose the proper elastomer according to the application and that the standard methyl silicone may actually perform better in certain hydraulic fluids with high solubility parameters than will the "solvent resistant" rubber.

F. Corona Resistance

Methyl silicone rubbers have outstanding resistance to corona and for this reason they are used in many high voltage applications in which ordinary elastomers would rapidly break down. Reynolds (60) measured the resistance of a number of materials to corona and found that silicone elastomers are nearly as resistant as mica to corona discharge.

G. Ozone Resistance

Most rubbers are attacked severely by ozone. This is especially true of those rubbers containing unsaturated groups. Silicone rubbers, which are completely saturated, can be exposed almost indefinitely to ozone under conditions that would degrade most organic rubbers. This can be important in long-life service in areas where ozone concentrations are high.

H. Radiation Resistance

Silicone polymers, in common with all organic elastomers, are degraded by ionizing radiation. This effect is important when elastomers must be used in environments subject to radiation. Two kinds of degradation are observed; chain cleavage with lowering of molecular weight and strength, and crosslinking, resulting in excessive "cure." Although some organic elastomers are mostly degraded by chain cleavage, the principal effect of radiation on methyl silicone polymers is the development of crosslinks, with very little main-chain cleavage. When methyl silicone polymers are irradiated with high-energy electrons or gamma rays, all types of bonds are cleaved to some extent; however, this cleavage is largerly restricted to the CH and SiC bonds. These reactions were studied by Kantor (61) who found that the principal new bonds formed were $SiCH_2Si$ and SiSi in the ratio 2:1. St. Pierre (62) measured the gases produced by recombination of the cleavage products and found that hydrogen, methane and ethane were the principal constituents. He reported a G value (the number of chemical events occurring per 100 eV of energy absorbed) of 2.5 and calculated an efficiency of 2.4×10^{-12} moles of crosslink/r/g for 800 keV. The phenyl group on silicon is approximately one hundred times more resistant to radiation (63) than the methyl group. Practical use is made of this fact in producing radiation resistant silicone rubber. Based on these (61–63) and other studies it does not seem probable that any organic or semiorganic elastomer will ever provide a high order of resistance to high-level radiation. High-phenyl silicones rank among the best for such applications.

VII. LOW TEMPERATURE SILICONE ELASTOMERS

Silicone elastomers remain elastic well below temperatures at which most rubbers are too stiff to be used. Weir (64) found dimethyl silicone rubber to crystallize at −66 to −67°C. He measured a second order transition at −123°C which is the lowest such value for any known elastomer.* As dimethyl silicone elastomers are cooled down they do not crystallize sharply but stiffen slowly, and in the temperature range −50 to −60°C, and at a Young's modulus of 10,000 psi, become too stiff for use as an elastic material. As discussed in the section on copolymerization it is possible to depress the melting point, and the stiffening temperatures of methyl silicone elastomers by incorporating phenyl or other organic groups in place of a portion of the methyl radicals. In this way elastomers are obtained which will remain flexible at −100°C (−150°F). It is possible to achieve improvement in low temperature properties and other desired benefits with certain other substituents. For example, incorporation of trifluoropropyl substituents will both depress the stiffening temperature of methyl rubber and at the same time impart fuel and solvent resistance.

VIII. VULCANIZATION OR CURE OF SILICONE ELASTOMERS

Silicone rubbers must be cured or vulcanized for practical use. The required crosslinked network can be developed in many ways but the

* *Editors' note added in page proofs:* The T_g of *cis*-polypentenamer has been reported to be −140°C. Cf. p. 713.

ultimate structure must always be equivalent to high molecular weight linear chains connected with chemical crosslinks so that around 200 to 600 monomer units occur between pairs of crosslinks. Such structures may be developed either by the crosslinking of initially high molecular weight chains or by building up an equivalent network from much shorter chains as is usually done in the so-called room temperature vulcanizing elastomers (RTV).

Methyl silicone rubbers were first cured by Wright and Oliver (4) with benzoyl peroxide, through reactions which have been demonstrated to proceed in the following manner:

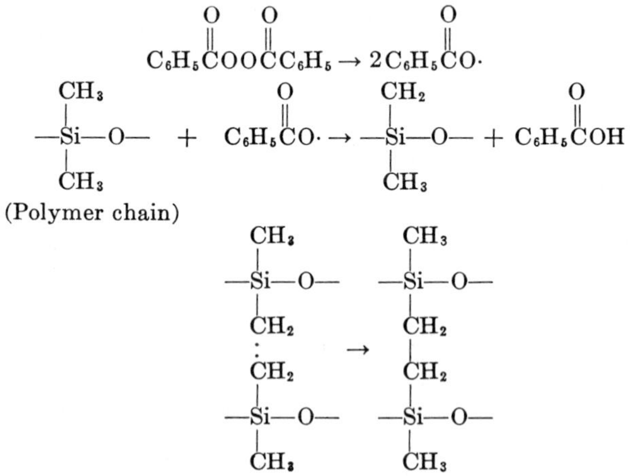

Normally substantially less than one crosslink is formed for each molecule of peroxide decomposed. Bueche (65) measured crosslink density by both tension and swelling studies. He found that the apparent efficiency of cure is a function of several variables including the type of compound, the method of sample treatment and the concentration of peroxide.

Kantor (66) presented additional evidence for the cure mechanism already outlined. He investigated the reaction of benzoyl peroxide with dimethyl polysiloxanes using model compounds. With the cyclic tetramer as a model he accounted for all of the products on a stoichiometric basis. The products in terms of moles of product per mole of peroxide decomposed are given in Table II. The term "ditetramer" in this table refers to two tetramer rings joined by an ethylene bridge via coupling of two methylene radicals as in actual cure. The isolation of this compound proves the nature of the principal cross-link structure in peroxide-cured methyl silicone rubber.

TABLE II
Reaction of Benzoyl Peroxide with Octamethylcyclotetrasiloxane

Product	Yield (moles/mole peroxide)
Benzene	0.86
Benzoic acid	0.2
Phenylbenzoic acid	0.02
Biphenyl } Phenyl benzoate }	0.175
"Ditetramer"	0.17
Residue, silicone (D_4)	0.25
Residue, organic (BPO)	0.10
Efficiencies	
H abstraction	51–55%
Ethylene bridge formation	42–44%
Stoichiometry	83% peroxide accounted for

All of the products found in this work can be explained by the following sequence of reactions:

$$
\begin{aligned}
&\phi\overset{\overset{O}{\|}}{C}OO\overset{\overset{O}{\|}}{C}\phi \text{ (benzoyl peroxide)} &&\rightarrow 2\phi COO\cdot \\
&\phi COO\cdot &&\rightarrow \phi\cdot + CO_2 \\
&\phi COO\cdot + SiCH_3 &&\rightarrow \phi COOH + SiCH_2\cdot \\
&\phi\cdot + SiCH_3 &&\rightarrow \phi H + SiCH_2\cdot \\
&2SiCH_2\cdot &&\rightarrow SiCH_2CH_2Si \text{ (cure)} \\
&2\phi\cdot &&\rightarrow \phi\phi \\
&\phi\cdot + \phi COO\cdot &&\rightarrow \phi COO\phi \\
&\phi\cdot + \phi COOH &&\rightarrow \phi H + \cdot\phi COOH \\
&\phi\cdot + \cdot\phi COOH &&\rightarrow \phi\phi COOH
\end{aligned}
$$

In this scheme a benzene ring is indicated by ϕ and the dots denote free radicals.

Peroxides are not all equally effective in curing methyl silicone elastomers. Those commonly used include benzoyl peroxide, 2,4-dichlorobenzoyl peroxide and *t*-butyl perbenzoate. Many other peroxides including alkyl hydroperoxides and dialkyl peroxides give little or no cure with methyl silicones but do cure vinyl-containing elastomers.

Marsden (4) found that by incorporating a small number of vinyl groups in a methyl rubber he could produce vulcanizates less subject to reversion and high compression set than an all-methyl silicone rubber. Such vinyl-containing polymers not only make much more efficient use of peroxides but will also cure with peroxides (hydroperoxides and dialkyl peroxides) which will not attack methyl silicone polymers. These peroxides offer an advantage in that their decomposition products do not contain acidic residues which promote degradation. The concentration of vinyl groups required to produce these beneficial effects is quite small, usually in the range 0.1–0.5 mole %. The efficiency of peroxide crosslinking as a function of vinyl group concentration has been studied by several investigators. An efficiency of 0.25 crosslinks for each molecule of *t*-butyl perbenzoate decomposed has been reported (67). With only 0.15 mole % vinyl groups the efficiency increased to 3.9. Several factors may be involved and these may include filler crosslinks, polymerization of vinyl groups, radical chain reactions and chain entanglements (77) all of which can either produce actual crosslinks or structures which act like true crosslinks.

There are several interesting aspects to the vinyl cure system. Dunham (68) confirmed that a dialkyl peroxide (e.g., *t*-butyl peroxide) does not cure methyl silicones but further noted that although vinyl groups provide an efficient cure, the vinyl structures do not have to be incorporated in the polymer itself. Even if the vinyl groups are present only in the form of low molecular weight monomers or oligomers the all-methyl chains are efficiently cured. It thus appears that there must be some kind of methyl group–vinyl group interaction in this cure. Although no mechanism has been proved, several possibilities have been proposed (67,68). One such mechanism (as shown in *1* below) not only accounts for the required interaction between vinyl and methyl groups but also accounts for a curing efficiency of over 100%. Alternatively (*2*) the RO· radical may simply add to the vinyl group followed by coupling or addition (which would also increase the cure efficiency). The RO· radi-

1. $ROOR \xrightarrow{\text{heat}} RO\cdot$

$RO\cdot + SiCH{=}CH_2 \longrightarrow Si\dot{C}HCH_2OR$

$Si\dot{C}HCH_2OR + SiCH_3 \longrightarrow SiCH_2CH_2CH_2Si + RO\cdot$

$RO\cdot \longrightarrow$ additional cure steps

Termination (by coupling of any two free radicals)

2. Alternatively,

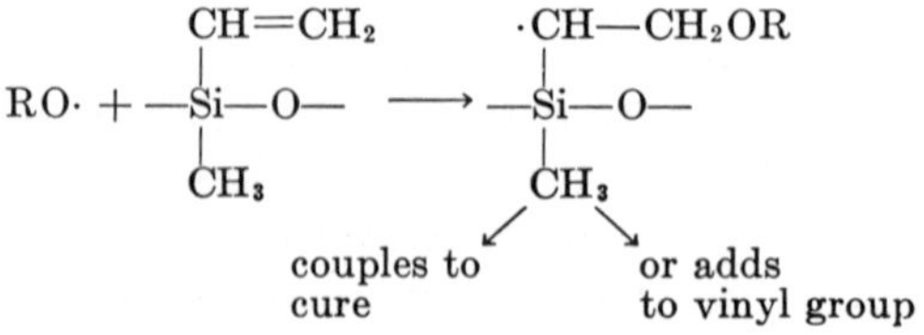

cals produced by decomposition of the peroxide would be expected to add more readily to the vinyl groups present than to extract a hydrogen from a methyl group (even to the extent of off-setting the fact that the vinyl groups are present in lower concentration). Such hydrogen abstraction evidently occurs only to a very small extent since methylene radicals which would be produced are known to couple in all-methyl curing systems when present and therefore must not be produced in any appreciable concentration by the RO· radicals.

A number of the more common peroxides used for curing silicone elastomers are shown in Table III with their structures, the temperature range used in cure and the types of curing systems for which they are suited. The only peroxide in this group suited for HAV (hot air vulcanization) is 2,4-dichlorobenzoyl peroxide. This is because of the low volatility of the decomposition products as opposed to those of most other

TABLE III
Common Silicone Curing Agents

Peroxide	Structure	Cure range, F°	Use
Benzoyl peroxide	$\phi\overset{O}{\overset{\|}{C}}O—O\overset{O}{\overset{\|}{C}}\phi$	240–260	General purpose molding and CV (continuous steam cure)
2,4-Dichloro-benzoyl peroxide	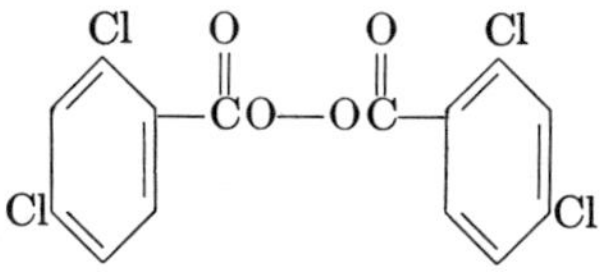	220–240	CV HAV (hot air vulcanization)
t-Butyl peroxide	$(CH_3)_3CO—OC(CH_3)_3$	320–360	Thick section, carbon black, vinyl cure
t-Butyl perbenzoate	$(CH_3)_3CO—O\overset{O}{\overset{\|}{C}}\phi$	280–320	High temperature, solutions
Dicumyl peroxide	$\phi\overset{CH_3}{\underset{CH_3}{C}}O—O\overset{CH_3}{\underset{CH_3}{C}}\phi$	300–320	Thick sections, carbon black, bonding
2,5-Dimethyl-2,5-di-*t*-butyl-peroxyhexane	$CH_3\overset{CH_3}{\underset{O—O—C(CH_3)_3}{C}}CH_2CH_2\overset{CH_3}{\underset{O—O—C(CH_3)_3}{C}}CH_3$	300–340	Thick sections, carbon black, bonding, vinyl cure

peroxides. In HAV cure the rubber compound, for example, a cable insulation, is extruded directly into a hot air chamber at atmospheric pressure. Volatile products tend to produce flaws. Most cures are carried out under pressure in a mold or autoclave.

High energy radiation in the form of either gamma rays or high-energy electrons is a convenient research tool for studying crosslinking. There are also some practical applications for this method of curing. The end results are the same for either electrons or gamma rays and in each case an absorbed dose of 3–5 million roentgens is required to achieve an optimum cure. Gamma rays have the advantage of giving deep penetration for thick section; however, the usual sources, such as a typical cobalt-60 source require several hours to deliver the required dose. 800 keV available from commercial resonance transformers as a power source for a linear accelerator can generate a curing dose in seconds (69). Due to the low penetrating power of an electron beam only a few mm deep cure can be achieved. This can, however, be an advantage for example in making semicured tapes with a tapered cure. Epstein (70) has described property advantages of radiation cure over chemical cures citing the fact that there are no by-products and that cure is completely uniform (as opposed to "clumping" of crosslinks for poorly dispersed chemical curing agents).

Cure through condensation or the splitting out of easily cleaved groups provides the important family of silicone elastomers called room temperature vulcanizing or RTV rubbers. These products are made in the form of soft compounds by mixing "endgroup reactive" fluids with reinforcing fillers to produce pastelike stocks that can be easily handled in application or in fabrication by calking or troweling operations. Berridge (71) described one such system which cures by the reaction of OH end groups on a siloxane prepolymer with silicate esters through condensation and ester interchange reactions. Nitzsche and Wick (72) made RTV rubbers which depended on the cleavage of a silane hydrogen endgroup using dibutyl tin dilaurate as a catalyst to promote cleavage. Crosslinks were established with the liberation of hydrogen gas. Another type of cure depends on the cleavage of acetoxy endgroups which split off from the terminal silicon atom by hydrolysis with water (atmospheric moisture) (73). These several systems may or may not require a catalyst to promote the condensation. Some, such as the silicate ester systems, are mixed with a catalyst such as tin octoate immediately prior to use and these are the so-called "two-package" RTV's. Others are stable in a closed container until they come in contact with atmospheric moisture and these are called "one-package" RTV's. A great many labile silicon substituents have been investigated and used for this class of silicone rubber.

IX. STRENGTH AND REINFORCEMENT OF SILICONE RUBBER

Although this is one of the most important topics in the total technology of silicones, treatment in any detail is outside the scope of this discussion which is limited to the chemistry of silicone elastomers.

Silicone polymers are very different from most other polymers which generally have much larger interchain forces. Reinforcement is important to silicones because the unreinforced methyl gum stocks are too weak to be of much use (50 psi tensile strength). This is of theoretical interest because silicone polymers are in some respect a nearly ideal model for experimental elastomer investigations. Their low chain interaction, freedom from chemical stress relaxation, nearly ideal elastic behavior, retention of molecular structure on milling, stability to oxidative degradation and their clean-cut crosslinking reactions are unique in polymer chemistry.

Silicone rubber has been shown (74) to be a nearly ideal model for the kinetic theory of rubber elasticity (75). The equilibrium stress τ is a function of ν, the number of effective chains per unit volume:

$$\tau = RT\nu \left[l/l_0 - \frac{1}{(l/l_0)^2} \right]$$

where R is the gas constant, T is the absolute temperature and l/l_0 is the ratio of the lengths of the stretched to the unstretched sample. Flory (74) has discussed three types of "imperfections" which may exist in cross-linked rubber. These include:

1. Dangling chain ends will not contribute to the equilibrium stress. This has been treated mathematically and tested experimentally for butyl rubber (76) and silicone rubber (41). This concept explains why a molecular weight of around half a million is necessary to realize a substantial fraction of the strength available from an elastomer. It also explains the structures required in the RTV rubber networks.

2. Chain entanglements will develop which resemble crosslinks and increase ν.

3. Intramolecular crosslinks that may form will produce pendant rings that decrease ν.

Until recently these several "imperfections" had not been adequately treated as a group. Bobear (77) has proposed a hypothesis that is consistent with the observed facts concerning the development of cross-links which result both from chemical combination and from chain entanglements and has quantitatively measured both. Those interested will find this treatment an interesting supplement to the chemistry of cure given here.

References

1. C. Friedel and J. M. Crafts, *Ann.*, **136**, 203 (1865).
2. F. S. Kipping, *J. Soc. Chem. Ind.*, **55**, 229T (1937).
3. K. A. Andrianov, Russ. Pat. 55,899 (1939).
4. E. G. Rochow, U.S. Pat. 2,380,995 (Aug. 7, 1945); M. C. Agens, U.S. Pat. 2,448,756 (Sept. 7, 1948); G. Wright and C. S. Oliver, U.S. Pat. 2,448,565 (Sept. 7, 1948); J. F. Hyde, U.S. Pat. 2,490,357 (Dec. 12, 1949); J. F. Hyde, U.S. Pat. 2,438,478 (March 23, 1948); J. Marsdon, U.S. Pat. 2,445,794 (July 27, 1948); E. L. Warrick, U.S. Pat. 2,541,137 (Feb. 13, 1951).
5. E. G. Rochow, *An Introduction to the Chemistry of the Silicones*, 2nd Ed., Wiley, New York, 1951.
6. H. W. Post, *Silicones and other Organic Silicon Compounds*, Reinhold, New York, 1949.
7. K. A. Andrianov, "Silicon Organic Compounds," State Scientific Technical Publishing House for Chemical Literature, Moscow, 1955, Tr. by Technical Documents Liaison Office, Wright-Patterson Air Force Base, Ohio.
8. R. N. Meals and F. M. Lewis, *Silicones*, Reinhold, New York, 1959.
9. C. Eaborn, "Organosilicon Compounds," Butterworths Scientific Publications, London, 1960.
10. W. Noll, *Chemie und Technologie der Silicone*, Verlag Chemie, GMBH, Weinheim/Bergstr., 1960
11. S. Fordham, Ed., *Silicone*, George Newnes Ltd., London, 1960; R. R. McGregor, *Silicones and Their Uses*, McGraw-Hill, New York, 1954.
12. F. G. A. Stone and W. A. G. Graham, *Inorganic Polymers*, Academic Press, 1962, Chapter 5.
13. E. J. Crane, *Chem. Eng. News*, **30**, 4517 (1952).
14. W. S. Noll, *Fortschr. Mineral.*, **34**, 63 (1956); P. J. Flory, L. Mandelkern, J. B. Kinsinger, and W. B. Schultz, *J. Am. Chem. Soc.*, **74**, 3364 (1952); R. O. Sauer and D. J. Mead, *J. Am. Chem. Soc.*, **68**, 1794 (1946).
15. W. L. Roth and D. Harker, *Acta. Cryst.*, **1**, 34 (1948).
16. E. G. Rochow and H. G. LeClair, *J. Inorg. Nucl. Chem.*, **1**, 92 (1955).
17. E. L. Warrick, M. J. Hunter, and A. J. Barry, *Ind. Eng. Chem.*, **44**, 2196 (1952).
18. H. Kusumato, *J. Chem. Phys.*, **32**, 724 (1960).
19. D. F. Wilcock, *J. Am. Chem. Soc.*, **68**, 691 (1946).
20. H. W. Fox, P. W. Taylor, and W. A. Zisman, *Ind. Eng. Chem.*, **39**, 1401 (1947).
21. M. J. Newing, *Trans. Faraday Soc.*, **46**, 613 (1950).
22. J. F. Brown, Am. Chem. Soc. Polym. Div., Polymer Preprints **2**, No. 2, 112–115 (1961).

23. H. Frisch, I. Martin, and H. Mark, *Monatsh. Chem.*, **84**, 250 (1953).
24. A. J. Barry, *J. Appl. Phys.*, **17**, 1020 (1946).
25. A. Charlsby, *J. Polymer Sci.*, **17**, 379 (1955).
26. D. T. Hurd and E. G. Rochow, *J. Am. Chem. Soc.*, **67**, 1057 (1945).
27. Jackson, H. L., U.S. Pat. 3,043,663 (July 10, 1962); N. C. Cook, J. D. Cobine, and J. K. Wolfe, U.S. Pat. 2,768,061 (Oct. 23, 1956).
28. R. C. Anderson and G. J. Sleddon, *Chem. Ind. (London)*, **1960**, 1335.
29. W. Sundermeyer, Prague Conference—International Symposium on Organometallic Chemistry, Sept. 6–9, 1965.
30. J. B. Carmichael and R. Winger, *J. Polymer Sci.*, **A3**, 971 (1965).
31. J. F. Brown and G. M. J. Slusarzuk, *J. Am. Chem. Soc.*, **87**, 931 (1965); P. J. Flory and J. A. Semlyer, *J. Am. Chem. Soc.*, **88**, 3209 (1966).
32. H. Jacobson and W. H. Stockmayer, *J. Chem. Phys.*, **18**, 1600 (1950).
33. W. T. Grubb and R. C. Osthoff, *J. Am. Chem. Soc.*, **77**, 1405 (1955).
34. D. T. Hurd, R. C. Osthoff, and M. Corrin, *J. Am. Chem. Soc.*, **76**, 249 (1954).
35. M. Morton, M. M. Deisz, and E. E. Bostick, *J. Polymer Sci.*, **A2**, 513 (1964).
36. G. D. Cooper and J. R. Elliott, *J. Polymer Sci. A-1*, **4**, 603 (1966).
37. M. Kucera, *J. Polymer Sci.*, **58**, 1263 (1962).
38. S. W. Kantor, W. T. Grubb, and R. C. Osthoff, *J. Am. Chem. Soc.*, **76**, 5190 (1954).
39. T. C. Kendrick, *J. Chem. Soc.*, **1965**, 2027.
40. R. L. Merker, Brit. Pat. 925,433 (Dow Corning Corp., May 8, 1963).
41. Lewis, F. M., Gordon Research Conference on Elastomers, Colby Jr. College, New London, New Hampshire, August 3, 1953.
42. R. L. Merker and M. J. Scott, *J. Polymer Sci.*, **43**, 297 (1960).
43. F. R. Mayo and F. M. Lewis, *J. Am. Chem. Soc.*, **66**, 1954 (1944).
44. O. K. Johannsen, U.S. Pat. 2,868,766 (Jan. 13, 1959); U.S. Pat. 2,994,684 (Aug. 1, 1961); J. C. Saylor, U.S. Pat. 3,032,531 (May 1, 1962).
45. G. M. Omietanski and W. G. Reid, Sixth Joint Army-Navy-Air Force Conference on Elastomer Research and Development, Boston, Oct. 18–20, 1960.
46. K. A. Andrianov, *J. Polymer Sci.*, **52**, 257 (1961).
47. W. J. Bobear, *Rubber Age*, **95**, 31 (1964).
48. G. Egloff, and C. I. Parrish, *Chem. Rev.*, **19**, 145 (1936). D. F. Helm and E. Mack, *J. Am. Chem. Soc.*, **59**, 60 (1937).
49. H. Schroeder, D. G. Schaffling, T. B. Larchar, F. F. Frulla, and T. L. Heying, Division of Rubber Chemistry, Am. Chem. Soc., San Francisco, Cal., May 3–6, 1966.
50. G. A. Russell, *J. Am. Chem. Soc.*, **78**, 1035 (1956).
51. D. C. Atkins, C. M. Murphy, and C. E. Saunders, *Ind. Eng. Chem.*, **39**, 1395 (1947).
52. J. M. Nielsen, U.S. Pat. 3,009,876 (Nov. 21, 1961).
53. J. M. Nielsen, U.S. Pat. 3,009,877 (Nov. 21, 1961).
54. L. C. Scala, *J. Appl. Polymer Sci.*, **2**, 297 (1959).
55. A. S. Kuz'minskii, *Intern. Symp. Organosilicon Chem., Sci. Commun., Prague*, **1965**, 362.
56. C. F. Kohl, Jr., U.S. Pat. 2,571,090 (Oct. 16, 1951); C. F. Kohl, Jr., U.S. Pat. 2,640,063 (May 26, 1953).
57. A. C. Martellock, Division of Polymer Chemistry, American Chemical Society, Boston, April 10, 1959.

58. W. J. Bobear, *Rubber Age,* **84,** 448 (1958).
59. J. H. Hildebrand and R. L. Scott, *The Solubility of Nonelectrolytes,* 3rd ed., Reinhold, New York, 1950.
60. S. I. Reynolds, *Elec. Mfg.* (Feb. 1954).
61. S. W. Kantor, Division of Organic Chemistry, 130th ACS Meeting, Atlantic City, Sept. 1956.
62. L. E. St. Pierre, H. A. Dewhurst, and A. M. Bueche, *J. Polymer Sci.,* **36,** 105 (1959).
63. D. J. Fischer, J. F. Zack, and E. L. Warrick, *Lubrication Eng.,* **15,** 407 (1959).
64. C. E. Weir, W. H. Leser, and L. A. Wood, *Rubber Chem. Technol.,* **24,** 366 (1951).
65. A. M. Bueche, *J. Polymer Sci.,* **15,** 105 (1955).
66. S. W. Kantor, 130th Meeting, Am. Chem. Soc., Sept. 16–20, 1956.
67. G. Alliger and I. J. Sjothun, Eds., *Vulcanization of Elastomers,* Reinhold, New York, 1964, p. 370.
68. M. L. Dunham, D. L. Bailey, and R. Y. Mixer, *Ind. Eng. Chem.,* **49,** 1373 (1957).
69. F. M., Lewis, U.S. Pat. 2,763,609 (Sept. 18, 1956).
70. L. M. Epstein and H. S. Marans, *Rubber Age,* **82,** 825 (1958).
71. C. A. Berridge, U.S. Pat. 2,843,555 (July 15, 1958).
72. S. Nitzsche and M. Wick, *Angew Chem.,* **69,** 515 (1957).
73. Brit. Pat. 835,790 (May 25, 1960) (to Rhone-Poulenc).
74. A. M. Bueche, *J. Polymer Sci.,* **19,** 297 (1956).
75. L. R. G. Treloar, *The Physics of Rubber Elasticity,* Clarendon Press, Oxford, 2nd ed. 1958; P. J. Flory, *Principles of Polymer Chemistry,* Cornell University Press, Ithaca, N.Y., 1953.
76. P. J. Flory, *Ind. Eng. Chem.,* **38,** 417 (1946).
77. W. J. Bobear, *Ind. Eng. Chem. Prod. Res. Develop.,* **3,** 277 (1964).
78. A. L. Klebanskii and V. S. Fikhtengol'ts, *J. Gen. Chem. U.S.S.R.,* **26,** 2795 (1956); P. Trambouze, *Bull. Soc. Chim. France,* **1956,** 1756; R. J. H. Voorhoeve, "The Synthesis of Methylchlorosilanes Processes and Mechanisms, PhD Thesis, Technische Hogesschool, Delft, Jan. 16, 1964.
79. M. Morton, A. A. Rembaum, and E. E. Bostick, *J. Appl Polymer Sci.,* **8,** 2707 (1964).

CHAPTER 8

ELASTOMERS BY CONDENSATION POLYMERIZATION

C. Polysulfide and Monosulfide Elastomers

RIAD H. GOBRAN AND M. B. BERENBAUM

Thiokol Chemical Corporation,
Trenton, New Jersey

Contents

Introduction 806

Polysulfide Elastomers

I. General Method of Preparation of Polysulfide Elastomers 807
II. Characteristics of the Polycondensation Method of Preparing Polysulfide Polymers 808
  A. Stoichiometry of Reactants Is Not Required 808
  B. Ring Formation 809
  C. Polysulfide Segments and "Sulfur Rank" 810
  D. Desulfurization and Thionation 811
  E. Reduction to —SH Terminated Low Molecular Weight Polymers 813
  F. Cure of Mercaptan Terminated Polymers 814
III. Other Methods of Preparation of Polysulfide Elastomers 815
  A. Polycondensation of Organic Dithiosulfates or "Bunte Salts" with Inorganic Polysulfides 815
  B. Polycondensation of Polythiodiglycols 816
  C. Ring Opening of Cyclic Disulfides 817
  D. Oxidation of Monomeric Dimercaptans 818
IV. Physical Properties of Polysulfide Elastomers 819
  A. Polymer Characterization 819
    1. Nature of Terminals 819
    2. Nature of Polysulfide Linkages 820
  B. General Properties 820
  C. Low Temperature Properties 823
  D. High Temperature Properties 826
  E. Viscoelastic Properties 828
  F. Molecular Weight Distribution 831

Monosulfide Elastomers
V. Preparation of Polypropylene Sulfide Elastomers 833
A. Polycondensation 833
B. Ring Opening 833
1. Ionic Catalysis 833
2. Coordinate Anionic Catalysis 835
a. Mechanism of Propylene Sulfide Polymerization by $ZnEt_2$ Systems 836
VI. Properties of Alkyl Monosulfide Elastomers 837
VII. Copolymers of Episulfides with Epoxide and Vinyl Monomers 839
References 840

INTRODUCTION

This chapter will deal with elastomers containing sulfur as part of the repeat unit constituting the polymer backbone. These include both polysulfide and monosulfide polymers which will be discussed separately.

Polysulfide elastomers are polymers containing mainly two or more sulfur atoms per repeat unit and are generally prepared by condensation polymerization. Monosulfide elastomers contain only one sulfur atom for every repeat unit and are best prepared by polymerizations of the ring opening type.

Polysulfide elastomers have been produced in the United States since 1929 after Patrick (1) first discovered the formation of a rubbery product when he reacted ethylene dichloride with sodium polysulfide in 1924. This discovery marked the first man-made rubber in the United States. Since then a large number of polysulfide polymers have been prepared by varying the dihalide and sulfur content of the inorganic polysulfide used.

The unique properties of polysulfide elastomers result from $—S_x—$ sequences in the backbone where $x \geq 2$. The presence of these linkages lead to interchange reactions which make it possible to prepare very high molecular weight polysulfide polymers by using an excess of one of the components, namely, the inorganic polysulfide. This is contrary to other polycondensations where the use of stoichiometric ratios is essential for the preparation of high molecular weight polymers. Also, chemical stress relaxation in these rubber networks takes place by interchange of di-, tri-, or tetrasulfide linkages with each other or with mercaptide linkages. Another unique property of polysulfide polymers is their ease of reduction at the —S—S— bonds to give low molecular weight mercaptan terminated liquid polymers. These liquid polymers can be converted back to the original elastomers by mild oxidizing agents, even at room temperature. It is this property, in addition to their excellent solvent resistance and good aging characteristics, that resulted in the use of polysulfide liquid polymers as sealants in many applications particularly in the construction and automotive industries. It was also the basis for use of these polymers as the first binders for case bonded solid fuel rockets. A number of excellent review articles have recently been written on the preparation (2,3), applications (4), and physical properties of polysulfide polymers (5).

Monosulfide elastomers have only recently been sucessfully prepared from olefin sulfides particularly propylene sulfide. When properly vulcanized, these polymers also have excellent solvent resistance, good aging characteristics, very low permeability, and good low temperature properties. Full commercialization of these elastomers depends on the availability of low cost monomer but they are certain to be useful in special applications in line with their combination of properties.

POLYSULFIDE ELASTOMERS

I. GENERAL METHOD OF PREPARATION OF POLYSULFIDE ELASTOMERS

Polysulfide elastomers are generally prepared in suspension by polycondensation of a dihalide with an aqueous sodium polysulfide solution (1). The reaction proceeds by a nucleophilic displacement of the terminal halide by the polysulfide ion. To point out the unique features of this type of polycondensation, let us take as an example the preparation of poly(diethyl formal disulfide), the most widely used polysulfide elastomer. The reaction can be represented by the following equation:

$$ClCH_2CH_2OCH_2OCH_2CH_2Cl + \text{excess } Na_2S_x \rightarrow \\ -\!\!\!\left[S{-}CH_2CH_2OCH_2OCH_2CH_2{-}S_x\right]\!\!\!-_n + NaCl + \text{excess } Na_2S_x \quad (1)$$

The bis(chloroethylformal) is added slowly to a slight excess of a hot aqueous solution of sodium polysulfide. To facilitate dispersion, a surface active agent of the alkyl aryl sulfonate type, e.g., isobutylnaphthalene sodium sulfonate, is generally used. For practical purposes, it has also been found that a nucleating agent, e.g., freshly precipitated magnesium hydroxide, is effective in producing large polymer particles which are easy to wash and isolate. A typical polymerization procedure is given by Berenbaum on page 66 of Ref. (2).

Polysulfide copolymers or terpolymers can also be readily prepared by this procedure using two or more dihalides in the original feed. It is also possible to introduce branched or crosslinked structures by using small concentrations of trifunctional halides, such as 1,2,3-trichloropropane.

The reactivity of halides used in this condensation polymerization follows the order of reactivities of the simple monofunctional halides in displacement reactions. Thus, allylic and benzyl halides are the most reactive, primary halides are more reactive than secondary or tertiary halides, whereas aromatic halides are very sluggish. As to the halides, bromides are more reactive than chlorides while fluorides are unreactive.

II. CHARACTERISTICS OF THE POLYCONDENSATION METHOD OF PREPARING POLYSULFIDE POLYMERS

A. Stoichiometry of Reactants Is Not Required

Whereas in other polycondensation reactions, such as the preparation of polyamides, it is essential to use equivalent quantities of the reactants to obtain high molecular weight polymers, this is not necessary for the preparation of high molecular weight polysulfides. In practice it is preferred to have an excess of sodium polysulfide which results in polymers terminated by —S_xNa groups. Chains terminated by halogen are converted to —S_xNa terminals by reaction with the excess Na_2S_x, or to —OH terminals by hydrolysis in the alkaline medium of the polymerization.

$$\text{—R—Cl} + Na_2S_x \rightarrow \text{—R—}S_xNa + NaCl \quad (2)$$

$$\text{—R—Cl} + {}^{\ominus}OH \rightarrow \text{—R—OH} + Cl^{\ominus} \quad (3)$$

All these reactions result in the formation of intermediate or low molecular weight polymers depending on the excess Na_2S_x used and the extent of chain termination by hydroxyl groups. The presence of excess Na_2S_x effects interchange reactions, which insures the final conversion of these intermediate or low molecular weight chains into high molecular weight polymers by elimination of chain stoppers. These interchange reactions take place between the sodium polysulfide and di- or polysulfide linkages in the polymer. When this occurs in the middle of a chain, it splits into two fragments according to the following equilibrium:

$$\text{—SRS—SRS—SRS—SRS—} + S_2^{2-} \rightleftharpoons \text{—SRS—SRS—}S^- + {}^-S\text{—SRS—SRS—} \quad (4)$$

However, when the interchange takes place near the end of the chain, particularly those terminated by hydroxyl groups, soluble low molecular weight fragments are formed which are removed by repeated washings after polymerization.

$$\text{—SRS—SRS—SRS—SROH} + S_2^{2-} \rightleftharpoons \text{—SRS—SRS—SRS—}S^- + {}^-\text{S—SROH} \quad (5)$$

As can be seen from these equations, intermediate molecular weight chains with polysulfide anion terminals can be chain extended to high molecular weight polymers by the equilibrium shown in equation (4) which is driven to the high polymer side by removing the excess polysulfide ions i.e., repeated washing of the latex. A deficiency of inorganic polysulfide results in low molecular weight polymer which can be extended by addition of excess polysulfide.

B. Ring Formation

As in other polycondesation reactions, there is a competition between linear polymerization and ring formation during the preparation of polysulfide polymers. The outcome is a function of the structure of both the dihalide and inorganic polysulfide used. Tables I and II show the effect of dihalide and alkali polysulfide structures, respectively, on ring formation.

Table I shows that cyclic sulfides are favored when the dihalide monomer has four or five atoms between the halide terminals. Mostly cyclic monosulfides are formed with no apparent disulfide formation. If any cyclic disulfide is formed, the polysulfide ions present catalyze ring opening resulting in polymer formation.

Table II shows that in the case of pentamethylene dichloride, the lower the sulfur content of the alkali polysulfide used, the higher the

TABLE I
Effect of Dihalide Structure on Cyclization (2)
(2M Na_2S_2 was used)

Cl—R—Cl —R—	Cyclic sulfide (ml/mole of dihalide)
$-(CH_2)_6-$	5
$-(CH_2)_5-$	39
$-(CH_2)_4-$	83
$-(CH_2)_3-$	0
$-(CH_2)_2-$	0
$-C_2H_4OC_2H_4-$	60
$-C_2H_4OCH_2OC_2H_4-$	0

TABLE II
Effect of Sulfur Content in Na_2S_x on Yield of Pentamethylene Sulfide (2)
(2M Na_2S_x was used)

Na_2S_x x	Pentamethylene Sulfide (ml/mole of monomer)
2	39
2.5	32
3.0	25
3.5	20
4.0	14

ratio of the cyclic sulfide formed. In the special case of tetramethylene dichloride, the five-membered ring is favored to such an extent that it is formed in substantial quantity even when Na_2S_4 is used.

C. Polysulfide Segments and "Sulfur Rank"

The polymer derives its sulfide linkages from the inorganic polysulfide used, Na_2S_x, where x varies from 2 to 4 and is known as the "sulfur rank." It should be kept in mind that an aqueous solution of Na_2S_x always contains a distribution of sulfide ions. In practice, sodium polysulfide solutions are prepared by reacting aqueous NaOH solution with sulfur. The ratio of sulfur to NaOH used determines the sulfur rank.

$$6NaOH + (2x + 1)S \rightarrow 2Na_2S_x + Na_2SO_3 + 3H_2O \qquad (6)$$

When excess sulfur is used, it reacts with sodium sulfite to give sodium thiosulfate:

$$S + Na_2SO_3 \rightarrow Na_2S_2O_3 \qquad (7)$$

To retard the latter reaction, Bertozzi (6) found that the sodium sulfite can be crystallized out of solution by using concentrated sodium hydroxide and carrying out the reaction at higher temperatures. Excess NaOH is destroyed by reacting it with sodium hydrosulfide to form sodium sulfide:

$$NaOH + NaSH \rightarrow Na_2S + H_2O \qquad (8)$$

Aqueous solutions of sodium polysulfide Na_2S_x prepared according to the above procedure contain a distribution of sulfide anions ranging from S^{2-} to S_5^{2-} and possibly higher. Since a distribution of all these species always exits, the term "sulfur rank" merely represents the average number of anions present. Thus, when sodium disulfide is used, Na_2S_2, one always obtains a distribution of sulfide linkages, the majority of which are disulfides. This is also reflected in the polysulfide elastomers which have approximately the same sulfur rank as the sodium polysulfide used for their preparation particularly when a slight excess of the alkali sulfide is used. However, with a large excess of sodium polysulfide, the resulting polymer generally has a lower sulfur rank than the corresponding alkali polysulfide. Table III shows the effect of excess alkali polysulfides on the polymer sulfur rank.

The significance of the low sulfur rank of the polymer prepared in presence of a large excess of the corresponding alkali polysulfide leads us to an important characteristic of polysulfide elastomers, namely, "desulfurization."

D. Desulfurization and Thionation

As indicated in the previous section, a polysulfide polymer contains sulfide linkages ranging from monosulfides to high polysulfides depending

TABLE III
Effect of Excess Alkali Sulfide on the Polymer Sulfur Rank (2)

Na_2S_x S Rank	Excess Na_2S_x, %	Polymer S Rank
1.50	10	1.64
	100	1.68
2.00	10	2.09
	100	1.95
2.50	10	2.49
	100	2.16
3.00	10	2.96
	100	2.35
3.50	10	3.54
	100	2.60
4.00	10	3.95
	100	3.25

on the sulfur rank of the inorganic polysulfide used in their preparation. The sulfur in these polymers, even those of high rank, is chemically bound as evidenced by the failure to remove free sulfur by solvent extractions. However, it is possible to remove sulfur from polysulfide linkages by chemical agents in a process called "desulfurization" or "stripping." These agents include alkali hydroxides, hydrosulfides, sulfides, and sulfites. Of these, the use of alkali sulfite (Eq. 9) is the most preferred economically and for its ease of handling.

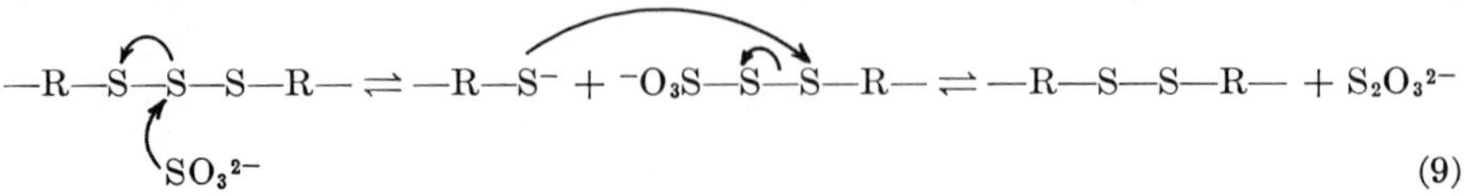

(9)

Desulfurization by aqueous alkali hydroxides was first observed by Patrick (7,8) upon treatment of polyethylene tetrasulfide with aqueous caustic at 80–90°C. This resulted in the reduction of the sulfur rank of the polymer from 4 to 2 with a corresponding change in the state of the polymer from a rubber to a hard plastic. Desulfurization by alkali sulfides depends on the interchange reaction described in Section II-A. and requires an excess alkali sulfide of lower rank than the polymer to be used. As an example, Eq. 10 represents the desulfurization of a polymer of rank 3 to rank 2 by Na_2S_2:

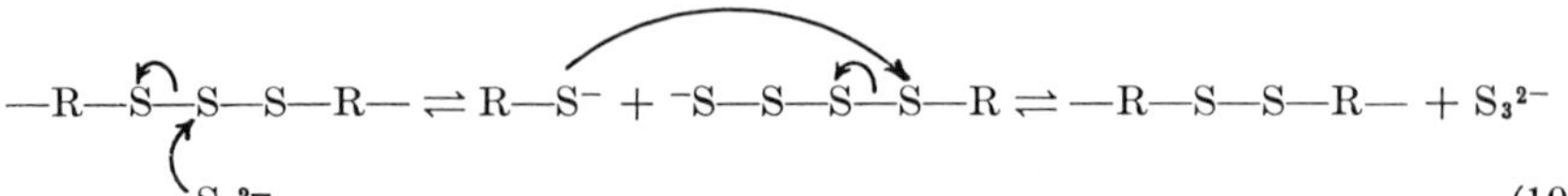

(10)

The reverse of Eq. 10 represents a method for increasing the rank of a polymer using an excess of a higher rank alkali polysulfide. This process is called "thionation" which is another unique feature of these polymers that depends on the ease of distribution of sulfur between polysulfide linkages in the polymer and polysulfide ions. The increase in polymer rank by this technique is limited to a maximum of approximately 4–4.5 due to the instability of aqueous inorganic sulfides of rank higher than 5. Thionation of polysulfide polymers can also be accomplished by milling the polymer with sulfur (7,8) in presence of a base catalyst such as diphenylguanidine. However, the completion of the reaction depends upon the extent of milling and the final product may therefore contain varying amounts of unreacted sulfur.

It is to be noted that the monosulfide linkages in the polymer do not enter into any of the desulfurization or thionation reactions described in this section. Furthermore, polysulfide linkages in a polymer can be "stripped" to no lower than rank 2.

E. Reduction to —SH Terminated Low Molecular Weight Polymers

Disulfide and polysulfide linkages in polysulfide elastomers are susceptible to reduction giving low molecular weight mercaptan terminated polymers. When diethyl formal polysulfide elastomers are reduced, liquid polymers are obtained whose molecular weights vary according to the extent to which the reduction step was undertaken. In practice, liquid polymers of number average molecular weights in the range of 600 to 8000 are preferred and the viscosity of these polymers depends not only on the molecular weight but also upon the extent of branching in the original elastomer. Thus, elastomers prepared from bis(2-chloroethyl) formal as the basic dihalide with varying amounts of trichloropropane (TCP) to provide branching or crosslinking sites are reduced to give a variety of liquid polymers described in Table IV.

The first practical method of reducing polysulfide elastomers was discovered by Patrick and Ferguson (9) and involved treatment of the

TABLE IV
Mercaptan Terminated Liquid Polymers Based on Poly(ethyl Formal Disulfide)

TCP, mole %, initial charge	Viscosity, poises at 23°C	% SH	$\bar{M}_n$, vapor osmometry
0.0	23	6.97	970
0.0	590	1.71	3570
0.5	19	5.36	1050
0.5	399	1.61	3330
0.5	810	1.33	5310
2.0	5	9.99	710
2.0	11	6.83	930
2.0	120	2.88	2030
2.0	386	1.95	3320

polymer latex with sodium hydrosulfide and sodium sulfite followed by acidification to neutralize the sodium mercaptide terminals formed:

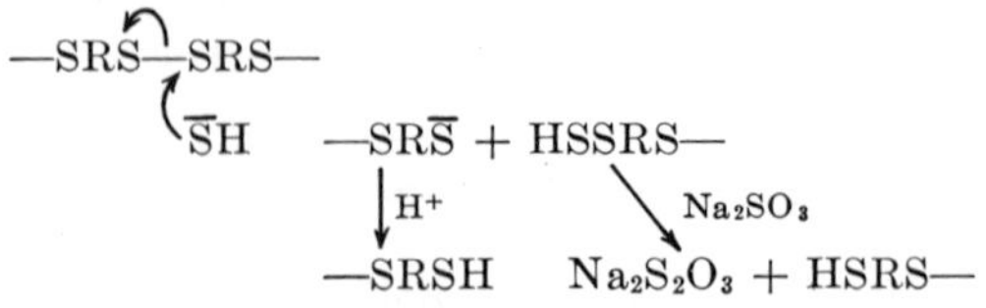

(11)

The sodium sulfite is used to convert the —SSH terminals formed during the reduction step to mercaptan terminals.

F. Cure of Mercaptan Terminated Polymers

The mercaptan terminated liquid polymers can be easily oxidized by a variety of organic and inorganic oxidizing agents (4) to give high molecular weight elastomers. In this respect polysulfide polymers provide a unique elastomeric system which can be used in the high molecular weight liquid form in conjunction with appropriate oxidizing agents.

Oxidizing agents used for these polymers are discussed by Panek (4). Effective agents include lead dioxide, manganese dioxide, tellurium dioxide, zinc peroxide, calcium peroxide, various chromates, and cumene hydroperoxide. Some of these oxidizing agents, such as lead dioxide, cure the polymer at room temperature, particularly in the presence of moisture in weakly alkaline medium. Other oxidizers such as zinc and calcium peroxide in the absence of alkaline activators require heat to effect a cure. The physical properties of the cured products are affected by the type of the oxidizing agent and the effect of the by-products of oxidation on the polymer backbone.

In general liquid polymers in the 4000 to 8000 molecular weight range are easy to oxidize and give good physical properties. Small concentrations of branched sites are necessary to give a three-dimensional network of low compression set. Branching also helps to compensate for unreactive terminals formed during the reduction and subsequent oxidation. Properly cured and reinforced systems show outstanding resistance to water, organic solvents, and fuels and have excellent oxidation, ozone, and weather resistance. They also show very low gas and vapor permeability and good electrical insulating properties. Due to these properties and because of their ease of application, mercaptan terminated liquid polymers are used as sealants, potting compounds, adhesives, coatings, impregnants for leather and other porous materials, and as binders for case bonded solid fuel rockets.

Block copolymers can be made by oxidizing a mixture of two or more mercaptan terminated liquid polymers of different backbone structures. This technique has been used to obtain unique combinations of properties particularly with regard to low temperature performance.

Difunctional reagents capable of reacting with active hydrogen containing compounds can also be used for cocuring mercaptan terminated liquid polymers. These include epoxy resins, diisocyanates and aldehydes. Of these, the cocure with epoxides (10) which requires an acid or base catalyst helps to improve the flexibility, impact strength, and low temperature properties of the epoxy resins. Because of these properties, the system has found applications as adhesives, coatings, potting compounds, and castings.

III. OTHER METHODS OF PREPARATION OF POLYSULFIDE ELASTOMERS

While the polycondensation of dihalides and inorganic polysulfides described in Section I is by far the most widely used technique for the preparation of polysulfide elastomers, other procedures have also been reported in the literature. These include the use of dithiosulfates instead of dihalides, condensation of dithiodiglycols, and ring opening of cyclic disulfides to form high molecular weight polymers. Oxidation of monomeric dimercaptans has also been used to prepare low molecular weight mercaptan terminated polysulfide polymers which can be further oxidized to give the corresponding elastomers.

A. Polycondensation of Organic Dithiosulfates or "Bunte Salts" with Inorganic Polysulfides

Certain dihalides are converted by sodium polysulfide (Section II-B) to cyclic structures in preference over linear polymerization. For example, 1,4-dichlorobutane reacts with sodium polysulfides to give thiacyclopentane exclusively. In such cases, the preparation of polysulfide polymers can be accomplished by first reacting the dihalide with sodium thiosulfate to form the corresponding dithiosulfate (Bunte Salt) followed by reaction with excess sodium polysulfide (11–13). Sodium monosulfide can be used, in which case the reaction can be represented by equations (12) and (13):

$$ClRCl + 2Na_2S_2O_3 \rightarrow NaOSO_2{-}SRS{-}SO_2ONa + 2NaCl \qquad (12)$$

$$nNaOSO_2{-}SRS{-}SO_2ONa + 2nNa_2S \rightarrow$$
$$\lbrack SR{-}S \rbrack_n + nNa_2S_2O_3 + nNa_2SO_3 \qquad (13)$$

Based on model compound studies by Milligan and co-workers (14), the mechanism of reaction between thiosulfate and monosulfide first leads to the formation of trisulfides.

$$S^{2-} + RS{-}SO_3^- \rightleftharpoons RS{-}S^- + SO_3^{2-} \qquad (14)$$

$$R{-}S{-}S^- + RS{-}SO_3^- \rightleftharpoons R{-}S{-}S{-}S{-}R + SO_3^{2-} \qquad (15)$$

The trisulfide is converted to the disulfide by the sulfite formed.

$$SO_3^{2-} + R{-}S{-}S{-}S{-}R \rightleftharpoons R{-}S{-}S{-}SO_3^- + RS^- \qquad (16)$$

$$RS^- + R{-}S{-}S{-}SO_3^- \rightleftharpoons R{-}S{-}S{-}R + S_2O_3^{2-} \qquad (17)$$

It was also shown (15) that the addition of formaldehyde to the reaction mixture minimizes the formation of disulfides by combining with the liberated sulfite.

B. Polycondensation of Polythiodiglycols

Polysulfide polymers can be prepared by conventional polyetherification reactions of polythiodiglycols in the presence of acid catalysts (16). The reactivity of hydroxyl groups was found to be enhanced if present in a beta position to sulfur (17,18). Okita (19) prepared a polysulfide elastomer from bis-2-hydroxyethyl disulfide using an acid catalyst in bulk. Polymerization can also be carried out in organic solvents (20) which help to azeotrope the water of reaction.

$$nHOCH_2CH_2SSCH_2CH_2OH \xrightarrow{H^+}$$
$$HO{-}\lbrack CH_2CH_2SSCH_2CH_2O \rbrack_n{-}H + (n-1)H_2O \qquad (18)$$

The homopolymerization of dithiodiglycol and copolymerization with thiodiglycol has recently been studied by Woodward and co-workers (21,22) who found that P_2O_5 is an effective catalyst. This technique, similar to other polyetherification reactions, suffers from the possibility of dehydration yielding terminal double bonds and limiting the ultimate molecular weight. Thus, although the polymer prepared by polyetherification of dithiodiglycol has the same backbone structure as that prepared from bis-2-chloroethyl ether and Na_2S_2, it could not be vulcanized by conventional reagents.

Polythiodiglycols have also been cocondensed with formaldehyde in the presence of an acid catalyst (23):

$$nHOCH_2CH_2SSCH_2CH_2OH + nCH_2O \xrightarrow{H^+} HO{-}\!\!\left[CH_2CH_2SSCH_2CH_2OCH_2O\right]_n\!{-}H + nH_2O \quad (19)$$

The resulting polymer has the same backbone structure as one prepared by condensing bis-2-chloroethyl formal with sodium disulfide. However, similar to the polyether made from bis-2-hydroxyethyl disulfide, it could not be readily volcanized until treated with sodium polysulfide. This reaction removes unreactive terminals and allows further chain extension as discussed in Section II-A.

Using the polyetherification or acetal techniques, the sulfur rank of the resulting polymer corresponds to that of the glycol used. Thus, if a very pure bis-2-hydroxyethyl disulfide is used, it would be possible to prepare a true disulfide polymer, a polymer which could not be prepared by the conventional dihalide process.

C. Ring Opening of Cyclic Disulfides

Cyclic disulfides can be polymerized to linear high molecular weight polymers using anionic or cationic initiators. As an example, the polymerization of 1-oxa-4,5-dithiacycloheptane is represented by Eq. 20.

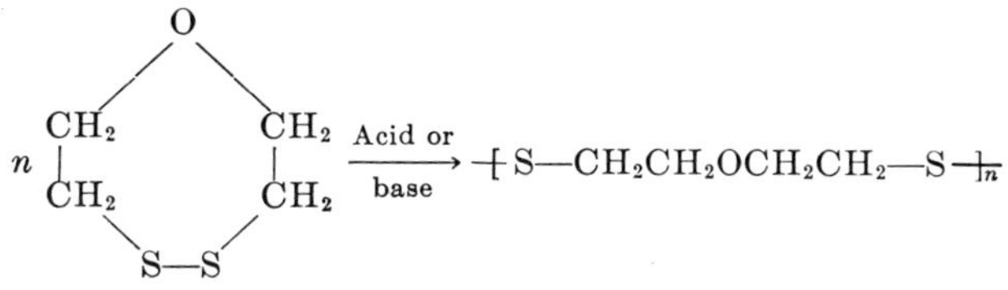

(20)

The anionic polymerization was studied by Davis and Fettes (24) using hydroxides, alcoholates, mercaptides, alkali sulfides, organic amines, as well as other bases as catalysts. All these catalysts are capable of producing high molecular weight polymeric disulfides at room temperature. Tobolsky and co-workers (25) investigated the cationic polymerization of cyclic disulfides using ferric chloride, stannic chloride, boron trifluoride, and other Lewis acids as initiators. Dainton, Davies, Manning, and Zahir (26) studied the polymerization of 1-oxa-4,5-dithiacycloheptane using various mechanisms for initiation including ionic, free radical, UV and β radiation. They investigated the kinetics of polymerization, using iodine as initiator, and determined the heat of polymerization to be -1.90 kcal/mole.

The ability of cyclic disulfides to enter free radical copolymerizations has been demonstrated (27–29) with unsaturated monomers such as styrene, vinyl chloride, acrylates, acrylonitrile, and vinyl acetate.

Ring opening of cyclic disulfides provides an excellent technique of preparing polysulfide elastomers in which the sulfur rank is exactly two. This is in contrast to the condensation type polymerization described in Section I in which a distribution of sulfur ranks always exists. As will be discussed later in this chapter, the viscoelastic properties and interchange reactions in polysulfide polymers depend to a great extent on the sulfur rank. While all the physical studies carried out so far were based on condensation-type polymers, it would be very desirable to study the properties of polymers prepared from cyclic disulfides to elucidate the contributions of pure disulfide linkages.

The polymerization of cyclic disulfides did not receive much attention due to a lack of good monomer preparation methods. Cyclic disulfides have been prepared by the depolymerization of polysulfide polymers (24) made by polycondensation.

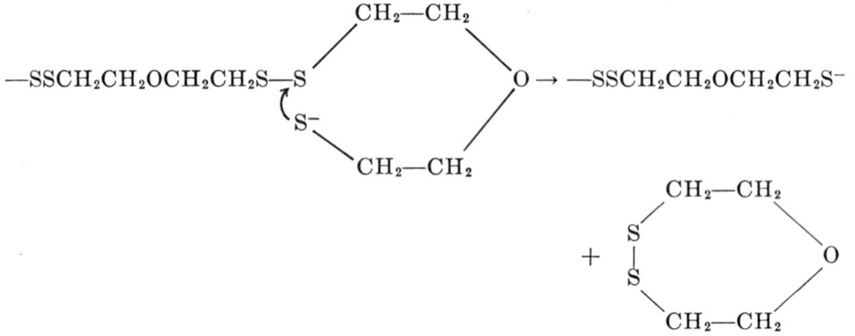

(21)

This unzipping reaction results from the presence of terminal mercaptide groups. Since mercaptide groups can be formed by alkaline cleavage of disulfide bonds, addition of alkali to the polymer dispersion enhances cyclic monomer formation. The cyclic disulfide monomer has to be removed by steam distillation, otherwise it would tend to polymerize by the alkali present or by the mercaptide terminals of the polymer.

D. Oxidation of Monomeric Dimercaptans

Theoretically, pure monomeric dimercaptans can be oxidized to give polymeric disulfides. However, in practice, this approach has not led to the formation of high molecular weight polymers probably because of impurities in the original monomers, deviation from exact difunctionality and possible side reactions during oxidation (13,30). Marvel and Olson (31) studied the oxidation of dithiols to polymeric disulfides and found that air oxidation is better than other oxidizing agents such as bromine or nitric acid. However, the polymers obtained were of low molecular weight. Nummy (32) prepared monomeric dimercaptans by reacting hydrogen sulfide with diolefins and subsequent oxidation with sodium hydroxide and sulfur:

$$CH_2{=}CHOCH_2CH_2OCH_2CH_2OCH{=}CH_2 + 2H_2S \rightarrow$$

$$\underset{(HS{-}R{-}SH)}{HSCH_2CH_2OCH_2CH_2OCH_2CH_2OCH_2CH_2SH} \xrightarrow{\text{oxid.}} H{-}[S{-}R{-}S]_n{-}H \quad (22)$$

IV. PHYSICAL PROPERTIES OF POLYSULFIDE ELASTOMERS

Polysulfide elastomers cover a wide range of properties depending on the structure of the alkyl group in the repeat unit and the sulfur rank. Since all the physical properties studies were carried out on polymers prepared by condensation of alkyl dihalides and alkali polysulfides, this section will only describe these polymers. It should be kept in mind that the term polysulfide elastomers, as used in this Chapter, refers to polymers containing mainly two or more sulfur atoms per repeat unit.

A. Polymer Characterization

1. Nature of Terminals

High molecular weight polysulfide polymers are insoluble in practically all organic solvents. This prevented detailed characterization of the polymers by solution techniques. The nature of the terminals of high molecular weight polysulfides was investigated by Fettes, Jorczak, and Panek (33) who used different vulcanizing agents to differentiate between various possible endgroups. The endgroups resulting from the condensation of organic dihalides with alkali polysulfides could conceivably be: (*1*) halogen that remained unreacted, (*2*) mercaptan or mercaptide resulting from the excess alkali polysulfide used, (*3*) hydroxyl produced by alkaline hydrolysis of the halide terminals, or (*4*) vinyl terminals produced by dehydrohalogenation or dehydration. All evidence pointed to the presence of hydroxyl endgroups. Vulcanization, which in this case represents coupling of available terminals, can be accomplished by metal oxides such as zinc oxide, lead oxide or cadmium oxide or by diisocyanates. This indicates either hydroxyl or mercaptan terminals and excludes the possibility of either halide or vinyl terminals. Since oxidizing agents such as quinone dioxime or cumene hydroperoxide did not cause vulcanization, the possibility of mercaptide or mercaptan terminals was eliminated. To substantiate the postulate of hydroxyl endgroups, Fettes, Jorczak, and Panek (33) deliberately introduced hydroxyl terminals into a polysulfide polymer by redistribution with dithiodiglycol. The resulting polymer when vulcanized by zinc oxide gave properties equivalent to those obtained by vulcanization of the original polymer.

2. Nature of Polysulfide Linkages

As indicated in Section II-D, the sulfur in polysulfide elastomers is chemically bound, even in cases where the sulfur rank is as high as four. However, it was also shown that desulfurization by chemical means can reduce the sulfur rank to close to two. This led Patrick (7) to postulate that polymeric tri- and tetrasulfides are composed of linear disulfides with one or two pendant sulfur atoms:

(23)

Early x-ray diffraction studies (34,35) favored Patrick's postulate. However, recent x-ray and electron diffraction investigations of monomeric trisulfides (36–38) show the sulfur atoms to be arranged in a zigzag or puckered chain configuration. The same conclusions were also derived from x-ray and ultraviolet studies on polymeric polysulfides (39–41). The linear structure of polysulfides is now generally accepted.

B. General Properties

Polysulfide polymers are available in the form of high molecular weight solid elastomers, e.g., ST rubber, or in the form of low molecular weight mercaptan terminated liquid polymers which can be cured to solid elastomers. The commercial liquid polymers have an ethyl formal disulfide repeat unit and are available in a wide range of molecular weights and crosslink densities.

The physical properties of unreinforced polysulfide polymers are relatively poor. However, in the presence of suitable reinforcing pigments adequate tensile and elongation properties can be obtained. Another factor affecting the physical properties is the crosslink density of the polymer (determined by the proportion of trihalide in the initial monomer charge). In the case of mercaptan terminated liquid polymers, their molecular weight before curing also affects the resulting physical properties. However, it is difficult to make a direct comparison of the effect of molecular weight on physical properties since the oxidative cure used is different for the various molecular weights. This arises from the nature of the oxidation reaction in which the high molecular weight elastomer has a relatively low mercaptan content and requires rather active curing agents and elevated temperatures for cure while the intermediate molecular weight polymers (about 4000 mol. wt.) can be cured with a very wide variety of oxidizing agents. The lower molecular weight polymers (mol. wt. about 1000) are highly active because of the high concentration of mercaptan groups and consequently relatively sluggish oxidizing agents are needed. As can be seen from the data in Table V, higher tensile strength is obtained with higher molecular weight materials. This is probably because the reduction of the initial high molecular weight disulfide polymer to the mercaptan terminated product may introduce

TABLE V
Effect of Molecular Weight on Physical Properties

Polymer type[a]	ST	LP-2	LP-3
Polymer	100	100	100
Quinone dioxime	1.5	—	—
PbO_2	—	7.5	—
MnO_2	—	—	3
m-Dinitrobenzene	—	—	1
Zinc oxide	0.5	—	—
Stearic acid	3	—	—
SRF black	60	60	60
Cure conditions	30 min at 287°F	24 hr at R. T.	24 hr at R. T.
Physical Properties of Cured Sheets			
Tensile, psi	1250	900	600
Elongation, %	310	450	450
Hardness, Shore A	70	65	45

[a] All polymers have basic structure $H\text{—}(SCH_2CH_2OCH_2OCH_2CH_2S)_n\text{—}H$ and contain 2 mole % of trichloropropane. They are products of Thiokol Chemical Corporation, Trenton, N.J. ST is a high molecular weight elastomer, LP-2 and LP-3 are mercaptan terminated liquid polymers having number average molecular weights of 4000 and 1000, respectively.

small amounts of inert terminals and the proportion of these would logically be greater the greater the extent of reduction. Further, in the oxidation process, the efficiency of the cure reaction is probably less than 100% and the side reactions would be greater for the low molecular weight materials with highest mercaptan content and therefore the greatest effect would be observed on the properties of these products.

The effect of crosslink density is as expected; the higher the proportion of trifunctional monomer the higher the modulus and the lower the elongation. Table VI lists results obtained with a series of ethyl formal disulfide polymers of approximately 4000 mol wt in which the percent crosslink is varied.

The effect of reinforcing filler is quite significant. Thus, the polymer indicated in column 5 of Table VI cured with the same formulation but omitting the SRF Carbon Black yields a product with tensile strength of 100 psi and elongation of 250%. Increasing the filler content from the 30 parts indicated in Table VI to a 50 part level results in improvement in properties to tensile strength of 700 psi and elongation of 700%. There is a limit to the amount of filler that can be incorporated since the more effective reinforcing agents have a substantial effect on the liquid polymer viscosity and only limited amounts can be added before the system becomes too viscous to handle properly.

TABLE VI
Effect of Crosslinking Agent on the Physical Properties of Polysulfide Liquid Polymers

	1	2	3	4	5	6
Polymer	100	100	100	100	100	100
% Crosslink	4.0	2.0	1.5	1.0	0.5	0.1
SRF black	30	30	30	30	30	30
Stearic acid	1	1	1	1	1	1
C-5 catalyst[a]	15	15	15	15	15	15
	Physical Properties of Molded Sheet					
Tensile, psi	550	500	550	625	575	500
Modulus at 300%, psi	500	375	350	375	250	200
Elongation, %	310	420	700	850	930	1000
Hardness, Shore A	55	53	53	53	45	40

[a] C-5 catalyst consists of 50% PbO_2, 45% dibutyl phthalate and 5% stearic acid. Dibutyl phthalate can be replaced by other plasticizers.

C. Low Temperature Properties

The second order transition temperature is dependent on the nature of the hydrocarbon moiety and the polysulfide rank. The effect of crosslink density is minor since the proportion of crosslinking monomer used is less than a few percent. Table VII lists the glass transition temperatures of the elastomeric polysulfide polymers (42). The greater the hydrocarbon proportion, the lower the glass transition temperature while the higher the polysulfide rank, the higher the glass transition temperature.

The first order transition is more difficult to pinpoint since the crystallization rate of these polymers is usually very slow. Prolonged storage at low temperatures can bring about density and hardness changes corresponding to partial crystallization. The monomer units containing relatively high proportions of hydrocarbon and the most regular structures are the most easily crystallized. For example, pentamethylene and hexamethylene disulfide polymers harden fairly rapidly at −20°C or below. Gobran and Berenbaum (42) reported the crystallization behavior of poly(butyl formal disulfide) and poly(butyl ether disulfide) polymers. At −30°C, the crystallization rate of these polymers appeared to be at an optimum. The changes in specific volume with time were studied for the homopolymers as well as for random and block copolymers of the aforementioned monomers with poly(ethyl formal disulfide).

The random polymers were prepared as described in Eq. 24 by redistributing blends of homopolymer lattices in the desired molar proportions. This procedure is preferred to random copolymerization with the dihalide polymers since differential solubility of the monomer intermediates may

TABLE VII
Glass Transition Temperatures

Polymer	Structure	T_g, °C
Poly(ethylene disulfide)	$\left(SCH_2CH_2S \right)_n$	−27
Poly(ethylene tetrasulfide)	$\left(S_2CH_2CH_2S_2 \right)_n$	−24
Poly(ethyl ether disulfide)	$\left(SCH_2CH_2OCH_2CH_2S \right)_n$	−53
Poly(ethyl ether tetrasulfide)	$\left(S_2CH_2CH_2OCH_2CH_2S_2 \right)_n$	−40
Poly(ethyl formal disulfide)	$\left(SCH_2CH_2OCH_2OCH_2CH_2S \right)_n$	−59
Poly(pentamethylene disulfide)	$\left(SCH_2CH_2CH_2CH_2CH_2S \right)_n$	−72
Poly(hexamethylene disulfide)	$\left(SCH_2CH_2CH_2CH_2CH_2CH_2S \right)_n$	−74
Poly(butyl formal disulfide)	$\left(SCH_2CH_2CH_2CH_2OCH_2OCH_2CH_2CH_2CH_2S \right)_n$	−76
Poly(butyl ether disulfide)	$\left(SCH_2CH_2CH_2CH_2OCH_2CH_2CH_2CH_2S \right)_n$	−76

result in enrichment of a monomer component in the final polymer. The blocked copolymers were prepared by cocuring mercaptan terminated liquid polymers of about 1000 mol. wt. as described in Eq. 25.

$$\text{—S—SRS—SRS—SRS—SRS—S—} + \text{—S—SR'S—SR'S—SR'S—SR'S—S—} \rightarrow \text{—S—SR'S—SRS—SRS—SR'S—S—} \quad (24)$$

$$\text{HSRS}\ [\text{SRS}]_x\ \text{SRSH} + \text{HSR'S}[\text{SR'S}]_y\text{SR'SH} \xrightarrow{[O]} 2\text{—S—SRS}[\text{SRS}]_x\text{SRS—SR'S}[\text{SRS}]_y\text{SR'S—S—} \quad (25)$$

In Fig. 1, the poly(ethyl formal disulfide) does not give any indication of crystallization in 160 hr at -30°C, while both the poly(butyl formal disulfide) and poly(butyl ether disulfide) show fairly rapid changes in specific volume. The more regular poly(butyl ether disulfide) shows a significantly higher crystallization rate than the corresponding butyl formal polymer containing the relatively flexible formal structure.

In Fig. 2, a random copolymer containing a 75/25 mol ratio of the poly(butyl formal disulfide) and poly(ethyl formal disulfide) polymers shows no indication of crystallization in the 160 hr test period. Figure 3 indicates that some crystallization will still occur in a block copolymer of this composition but that this small degree of crystallization can be eliminated by increasing the proportion of the second comonomer to a 64/36 mol ratio.

The crystallization rate of the polymers can be accelerated by main-

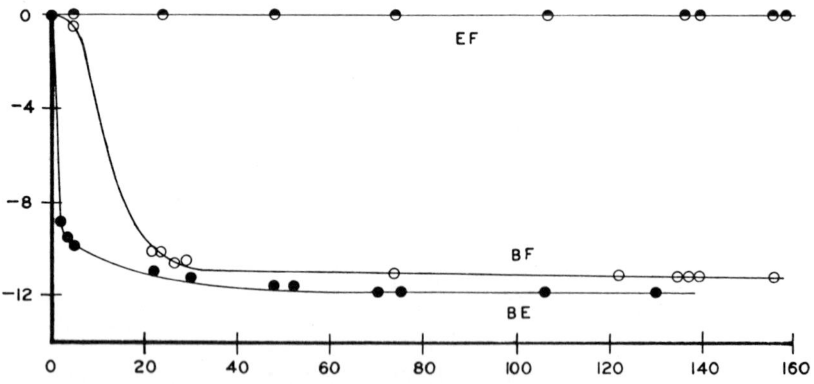

Fig. 1. Crystallization of polysulfide homopolymers at -30°C. x axis, time, hours; y axis, change in volume, $cm^3\ g^{-1} \times 10^3$. (◓) EF; poly(ethyl formal disulfide); (○) BF: poly(butyl formal disulfide); (●) BE: poly(butyl ether disulfide)

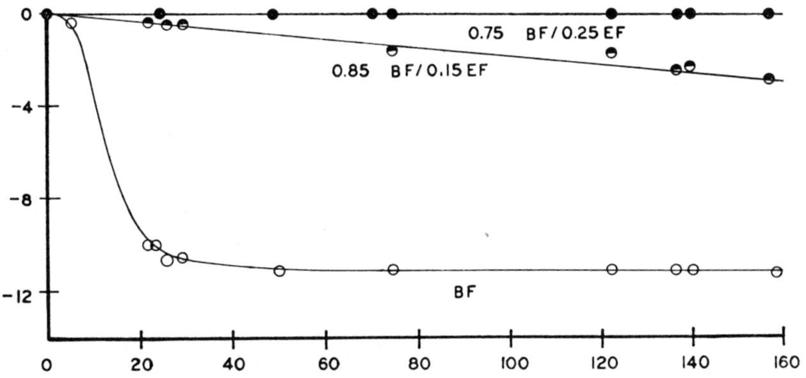

Fig. 2. Crystallization of random copolymers of BE/EF disulfides at $-30°C$. x axis, time, hours; y axis, change in volume, $cm^3\ g^{-1} \times 10^3$.

taining the polymer in a stretched condition at low temperature. The principal effect is on the rate of crystallization although some evidence of crystallization will occur with the poly(ethyl formal disulfide) polymer in a temperature retraction test at $-30°C$. In the compositions normally used in practical formulations containing the residues of the curing agents and other compounding ingredients, there is little evidence of crystalliza-

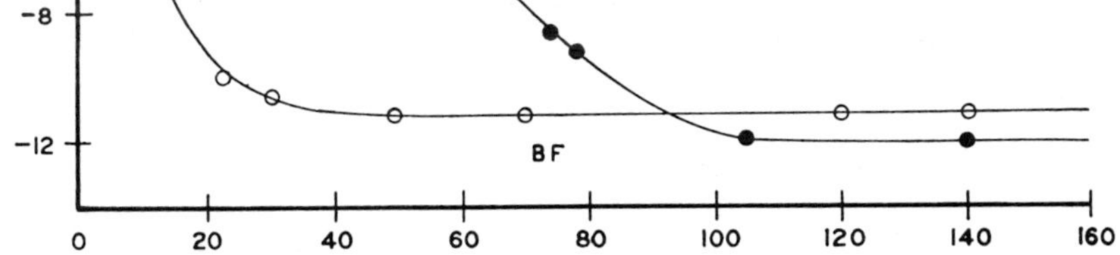

Fig. 3. Crystallization of block copolymers of BF/EF disulfides at $-30°C$. x axis, time, hours; y axis, change in volume, $cm^3\ g^{-1} \times 10^3$.

tion with the poly(ethyl formal disulfide) polymers although the crystallization rate of the polymers containing more hydrocarbon units is still quite substantial.

D. High Temperature Properties

The thermal stability of the polysulfide polymers is a function both of the polymer backbone and of the cure used to convert the polymer to the final vulcanized state. Since the commercially available polymers are based on the poly(ethyl formal disulfide) backbone, the characteristics of the ethyl formal structure govern the upper temperature limits for utility. Rosenthal and Berenbaum (43) have reported that the initial attack on this structure is an acid catalyzed hydrolytic attack on the formal group by trace amounts of water. This reaction releases free formaldehyde which in turn acts as a reducing agent on the polymer disulfide bonds to bring about reduction to thiol with formation of formic acid. Formic acid further catalyzes the hydrolysis at the formal group. The mercaptan terminal in turn can react with the hydroxyl group to yield a monosulfide bond with the evolution of water which is then available for additional hydrolysis. These reactions are described in Eqs. 26, 27, and 28.

$$\text{—SCH}_2\text{CH}_2\text{OCH}_2\text{OCH}_2\text{CH}_2\text{S— } + \text{H}_2\text{O} \xrightarrow{\text{H}^+} \text{—SCH}_2\text{CH}_2\text{OH} + \text{CH}_2\text{O} + \text{HOCH}_2\text{CH}_2\text{S—} \quad (26)$$

$$\text{—CH}_2\text{CH}_2\text{SSCH}_2\text{CH}_2\text{— } + \text{CH}_2\text{O} \xrightarrow{\text{H}^+} 2\text{—CH}_2\text{CH}_2\text{SH} + \text{HCOOH} \quad (27)$$

$$\text{—CH}_2\text{CH}_2\text{SH} + \text{HOCH}_2\text{CH}_2\text{S—} \xrightarrow{\text{H}^+} \text{—CH}_2\text{CH}_2\text{SCH}_2\text{CH}_2\text{S— } + \text{H}_2\text{O} \quad (28)$$

The consequences of these processes is a weight loss together with hardening of the polymer which is a result of the formation of the monosulfide structure and loss of the flexibilizing action available through free rotation at the disulfide and the formal bonds. It was shown that in model compounds addition of calcium oxide would stabilize the liquid polymers at temperatures of 150°C for extended periods of time. The calcium oxide was particularly effective since it was capable of both neutralizing any acid and absorbing any water present in the polymer. This information has not been of practical value since the elimination of water affects the curing systems used with the mercaptan terminated liquid polymers. Practical cure rates cannot be achieved in anhydrous systems with any of the metal dioxide curing agents conventionally used with these polymers.

The acidity required to initiate the polymer hydrolysis reaction is believed to arise from the peroxidation of the formal bond and subsequent breakdown of this intermediate to formic acid and water. This is a free radical process and can be inhibited in model systems by exclusion of air or by addition of conventional antioxidants. Again, in practical systems there has been no significant effect observed by addition of these antioxidants since the effect of oxygen tends to be swamped out by the attack on the polymer backbone of the excess amounts of oxidizing agents that are used in order to bring about commercially useful cure rates. Twice the stoichiometric amount of oxidizing agent may be needed for practical cure systems. Additional study is needed to develop oxidizing agents which will convert the mercaptan to disulfide in the desired cure process without attacking either the formal or the disulfide bonds in the polymer. The substantially improved high temperature performance of polysulfide polymers converted to the high molecular weight state by reaction with diepoxides or diisocyanates is confirmation of this hypothesis. Unfortunately, these materials are not as fully elastomeric as to the disulfide polymer and the addition cures cannot be used in many applications.

Work has been done with hydrocarbon or ether-containing monomers which give somewhat higher temperature operating limits ($\sim$25°C improvement). However, at these higher temperatures, reactions involving the excess oxidizing agent take place and limit further improvement.

One other source of thermal instability arises from incorporation of salt bonds in the polymer backbone from reaction of the mercaptan terminals with metal oxides. The metal oxides arise as a consequence of the redox processes occurring in the cure with metal dioxides. Reactions for lead dioxide, the most commonly used oxidizing agent, are described in Eqs. 29 and 30.

$$2\text{—}CH_2CH_2SH + PbO_2 \longrightarrow \text{—}CH_2CH_2SSCH_2CH_2\text{—} + PbO + H_2O \qquad (29)$$

$$2\text{—}CH_2CH_2SH + PbO \longrightarrow \text{—}CH_2CH_2SPbSCH_2CH_2\text{—} + H_2O \qquad (30)$$

$$\text{—}CH_2CH_2SPbSCH_2CH_2\text{—} \xrightarrow{\text{heat}} \text{—}CH_2CH_2SCH_2CH_2\text{—} + PbS \qquad (31)$$

$$\text{—}CH_2CH_2SPbSCH_2CH_2\text{—} + S \longrightarrow \text{—}CH_2CH_2SSCH_2CH_2\text{—} + PbS \qquad (32)$$

The lead mercaptide structure indicated in Eq. 30 is responsible for a number of the deficiencies of commercial sealants based on this cure. Mercaptide–disulfide interchange, which occurs as a consequence of the presence of these groups, has a profound effect on the compression set characteristics of the product.

Reaction 31, the conversion of the mercaptide bond to a monosulfide linkage, is brought about by heat or light. The principal effect of this phenomenon is loss of adhesion although there is some weight loss as well. Equation 32 indicates one way of minimizing the formation of mercaptide groups by the incorporation of small amounts of molecular sulfur. Larger proportions contribute to thermal instability by the attack of the free sulfur on the hydrocarbon backbone, aggravating the stress relaxation problem and adversely affecting the adhesion properties of the sealant.

Presence of the mercaptide also contributes to weight loss by cyclodepolymerization as in Eq. 33. Since the mercaptide group is regenerated, the interchange can continue until a major part of the polymer is volatilized.

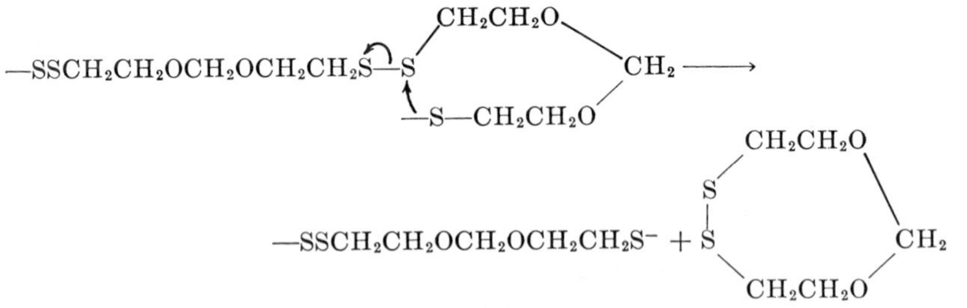

(33)

A good many compounding studies have been carried out to find oxidizing agents with fewer side reactions than lead dioxide. Particularly useful are tellurium dioxide, manganese dioxide and the various chromate salts. Systems formulated with these curing agents will provide continuous service at 250°F and intermittent service at 300°F.

E. Viscoelastic Properties

The viscoelastic properties of polysulfide polymers have been extensively studied by A. V. Tobolsky. In his recent book *Polymeric Sulfur and Related Polymers* (5), Tobolsky devoted two chapters to the review of viscoelastic properties and chemical stress relaxation of polysulfide rubbers. We will therefore not attempt to discuss the subject in detail in this section but rather highlight the important points.

The viscoelastic properties of the polysulfide polymers are governed by the interchange chemistry of the polysulfide linkages in the polymer chain. On rapid application of stress, the crosslinked rubbers behave as conventional elastomers. Under fixed strain, interchange processes set in to relieve the stresses. Disulfide–disulfide exchange is relatively slow at temperatures below 150°C or in the absence of ultraviolet light. Trace amounts of sulfur, mercaptides or alkaline agents capable of generating mercaptides by reaction with the disulfide bonds catalyze the exchange and bring about relaxation of stress at moderate temperatures. The stress decay for a crosslinked rubber sample maintained at constant extension follows the Maxwellian equation:

$$f(t) = f(0) \exp(-t/\tau_{ch}) \tag{34}$$

where $f(0)$ is the initial stress, $f(t)$ is the stress at time t and τ_{ch} is the chemical relaxation time. In practice this results in improperly cured polysulfide polymers showing the solvent resistance of a crosslinked system but behaving as a thermoplastic under load. Since it is very difficult to eliminate the cure accelerator residues which catalyze the exchange process, a well-cured polymer will show only fair resistance to compression set at moderate temperatures up to 70°C. In theory, a full cure yielding a system free of unreacted mercaptan and any traces of ionic salts or other activating impurities should be stable to chemorheologic flow. A study by Colodny and Tobolsky (44) on the effect of curing agents on relaxation times for polysulfide polymer demonstrates very effectively the influence of curing agents.

Cure A is one in which a substantial proportion of mercaptide bonds are present in the initial cured product. Cure B demonstrates the type

TABLE VIII
Chemical Relaxation Time τ_{ch} at 80°C for Polysulfide Liquid Polymers Cured with Different Chemical Agents (44)

Curing agent	Weight of curing agent per 100 parts of polymer	τ_{ch}, hr
A. Lead peroxide	7.3	0.68
B. Lead peroxide plus 5 days of heating at 75°C	7.3	15
C. Manganese dioxide plus morpholine	18.9	32
D. 2,4-Toluene diisocyanate plus *N*-methyl-2-pyrollidone	7.0	200

of effect possible by tightening the cure, the heat process replacing many of the lead mercaptide bonds by the more stable monosulfide linkages as in Eq. 31. More efficient cures that are less likely to result in ionic bonds, such as the manganese dioxide systems, show even greater resistance to chemical flow. Despite the variation in linkage rates, these three cures all show the same activation energy, 24 kcal/mole. This is most probably the value for the mercaptide–disulfide exchange process.

Cure D is different in type since it is an addition reaction involving the condensation of the mercaptan terminals with a diisocyanate. This technique avoids the possible presence of ionic structures or adventitious ionic impurities and should give the relaxation characteristics inherent in the disulfide-disulfide interchange. The very much greater relaxation time, 200 times that of a mercaptan lead dioxide cure, and the higher activation energy observed, 36.6 kcal/mole, shows clearly that relaxation is proceeding by a mechanism different than that in the other three cure examples.

In addition to the effect caused by ionic mechanisms, polymers containing polysulfide bonds of rank higher than two are particularly susceptible to chemical flow. Tobolsky, MacKnight, and Takahashi (45) have studied poly(ethylene tetrasulfide) crosslinked with 10% of trichloropropane prepared directly as the high molecular weight polymers. By avoiding the problems arising from the introduction of curing agents, it was possible to evaluate the effect of rank on the stress relaxation rate. In the 92–104°C range, the tetrasulfide polymers relaxed at fifteen times the rate of the disulfide polymer. However, both the disulfide and tetrasulfide high molecular weight systems showed the same activation energy, 24 kcal/mole, for the relaxation rate. Since the activation energy for a pure disulfide polymer exchange should be closer to the 36.6 kcal value observed in the earlier studies, it was concluded that the relaxation process in the high molecular weight disulfide polymers used probably occurs by the exchange of the tri- and tetrasulfide bonds present. Only 6% of the polysulfide linkages need be present as high rank linkages to explain the observed relaxation times. Work at Thiokol confirms the presence of approximately this proportion of higher rank linkages in polymers with a nominal rank of two.

Tobolsky and co-workers (46) also showed that even polymers prepared with a nominal rank of 1.5 must contain some higher rank linkages. A 10% crosslinked poly(ethylene disulfide) with a sulfur rank of 1.6 showed a τ_{ch} at 100°C of 4300 sec. Treatment of this polymer with sodium sulfite and benzene to eliminate the polysulfide sulfur and free sulfur resulted in a fourfold increase in the relaxation time even though the amount of sulfur removed was so negligible as to not affect the elemental analysis.

Dissolved sulfur also has a substantial effect on the relaxation rate of poly(ethylene disulfide) (45). Addition of 5 wt % of sulfur reduces the τ_{ch} value from 470 to 180 sec at 100°C. No effect was observed on addition of sulfur to poly(ethylene tetrasulfide). The sulfur was not chemically combined on addition to the poly(ethylene disulfide) since carbon disulfide extraction almost completely removed the added molecular sulfur and resulted in return to the initial stress–relaxation rate.

F. Molecular Weight Distribution

The polysulfide linkages in high molecular weight polysulfide polymers are subject to interchange reactions resulting in molecular weight redistribution. Mercaptan terminated polysulfide liquid polymers are capable of mercaptan–polysulfide reactions in addition to polysulfide–polysulfide interchanges. The term polysulfide is used here to refer to sulfur linkages of rank two and higher. Published work on the molecular weight distribution in polysulfide polymers deals mostly with mercaptan terminated liquid polymers.

Using chromatographic fractionation techniques, Genkin, Nasonova, Poddubnyi, and Shlyakhter (47) fractionated mercaptan terminated polysulfide polymers and determined the molecular weight of each fraction. From the distribution curves, polydispersity coefficients ($\bar{M}_w/\bar{M}_n$) of 1.06 to 1.55 were calculated indicating very narrow molecular weight distributions. The polymers studied had original number average molecular weights in the range of 1170 to 2010. Shlyakhter, Apukhtina, and Nasonova (48) reported similar results by fractionating individual polymers as well as mixtures of two polymers having different molecular weights. They showed that the fractional composition of polymers obtained by mixing samples of different viscosities and molecular weights to be similar to that of individual polymers of the same viscosity. It was therefore concluded that mercaptan–disulfide interchange occurs when the polymers are mixed leading to a narrow molecular weight distribution.

Fettes and Mark (49) determined the polydispersity coefficient of mercaptan terminated polysulfide liquid polymers by measuring their number and weight average molecular weights. They obtained $\bar{M}_w/\bar{M}_n$ ratios in the range of 2.8 to 6.2 for polymers having number average molecular weights in the range of 3700 to 6000. The $\bar{M}_w/\bar{M}_n$ ratios did not change by heating under nitrogen at 100°C. Mixtures of low and high molecular weight polymers also gave $\bar{M}_w/\bar{M}_n$ ratios that were not affected by heating under nitrogen with constant ultraviolet irradiation. Heating the mixtures at 100°C under nitrogen and in presence of base, resulted in a decrease in the polydispersity coefficient to about 3 after 94 hr. These results indicate that disulfide–disulfide or mercaptan–disulfide interchanges are slow and that a base catalyst is required for the distribution to take place.

In a recent study, Shlyakhter and co-workers (50), investigated the molecular weight distribution of mercaptan terminated polysulfide liquid polymers using procedures similar to those of Fettes and Mark (49). However, in determining weight average molecular weights by light scattering, Shlyakhter and co-workers observed a considerable depolarization of the scattered light. When the depolarization correction was applied to the light scattering data, the weight average molecular weights dropped to as much as half the uncorrected values in some cases. As a result of this correction, the $\bar{M}_w/\bar{M}_n$ ratios fell to approximately two indicating the expected random molecular weight distribution. It was also found (50) that intense stirring of mixtures of mercaptan terminated liquid polymers of different viscosities resulted in viscosities considerably lower than calculated values for the mixture. The viscosity reduction was very much accelerated on heating the mixture at 100°C under argon. When the mercaptan terminals were converted to thioacetyl groups, the interchange reactions did not take place even at the high temperatures. It was therefore concluded that mercaptan–disulfide interchanges take place very readily during the preparation of mercaptan terminated polymers as well as in bulk. It must be pointed out, however, that no characterization of these polymers was made in terms of the distribution of sulfur linkages. No explanation was offered by the Russian workers for the discrepancies with their earlier work on molecular weight distribution. At Thiokol, the reported rapid drop in viscosity has not been observed. It has been established by Tobolsky that tri- and tetrasulfide linkages behave quite differently from disulfide linkages (45,46). The presence of very few trisulfide bonds or traces of ionic impurities could have major effects on molecular weight distribution. It is therefore essential to know the exact composition of the polymer before attempting to interpret the experimental results. For this purpose it will be necessary to use different techniques of synthesizing specific polysulfide polymers and new analystical techniques will also have to be developed for exact characterization. It is only then that we will establish meaningful correlations between structure and properties.

MONOSULFIDE ELASTOMERS

While considerable interest was focused on polysulfide elastomers, relatively little attention was given to monosulfide polymers. Recently, monosulfide elastomers, particularly those based on polypropylene sulfide, have been under investigation by various research groups in Canada, France, Japan, and the United States.

V. PREPARATION OF POLYPROPYLENE SULFIDE ELASTOMERS

A. Polycondensation

Propylene sulfide polymers can be prepared by polycondensation of 1,2-mercapto propanol using acid catalysts in a manner similar to the polycondensation of mercaptoethanol (17).

$$n\text{HO—CH}_2\text{—}\underset{|}{\overset{\text{CH}_3}{\text{CH}}}\text{—SH} \xrightarrow{\text{H}^+} \text{—[CH}_2\text{—}\overset{\text{CH}_3}{\text{CH}}\text{—S]}_n\text{—} + n\text{H}_2\text{O} \tag{35}$$

However, polymers prepared by this technique are generally of low molecular weight and do not form useful elastomers.

B. Ring Opening

High molecular weight monosulfide polymers can be prepared by ring opening of thiiranes or olefin sulfides. A recent review by Sander (51) describes methods of preparation, physical properties, reactions, and uses of thiiranes. Davis and Fettes also reviewed methods of preparation and polymerization of olefin sulfides (52).

Of the olefin sulfides investigated, propylene sulfide and butylene sulfide give elastomeric products. Other episulfide monomers can be copolymerized with propylene or butylene sulfides to incorporate vulcanization sites or to modify the final properties. Ring opening polymerizations of olefin sulfides have been accomplished by ionic or coordination catalysts. Of these, certain anionic and coordination catalysts give the highest molecular weight polymers.

1. Ionic Catalysis

While ethylene sulfide polymerizes readily by acidic or basic catalysts (51), propylene sulfide and 1,2-butylene sulfide have a lower tendency to polymerization. Delepine and Jaffeux (53) polymerized these monomers cationically using concentrated H_2SO_4 as catalyst, however they obtained no polymers when acetic acid was used. Recently, Boileau and Sigwalt (54) studied the polymerization of propylene sulfide using cationic catalysts such as $TiCl_4$ and $AlCl_3$. They obtained low molecular weight polymers having intrinsic viscosities in benzene well below unity.

Marvel and Weil (55) used sodium ethoxide as an anionic catalyst to polymerize propylene sulfide. The polymerization was carried out at 95–100°C and resulted in low molecular weight viscous polymer soluble in dioxane and chloroform but insoluble in ether and methanol.

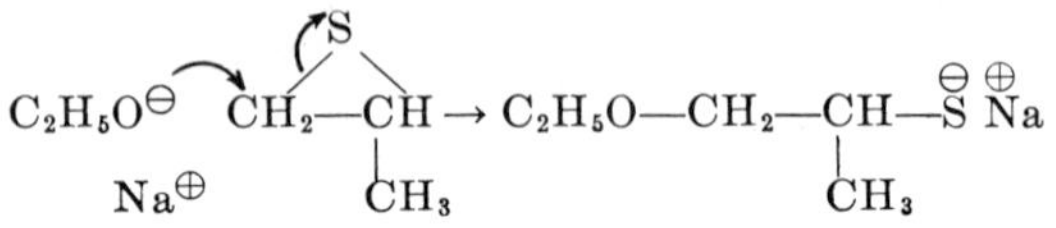

(36)

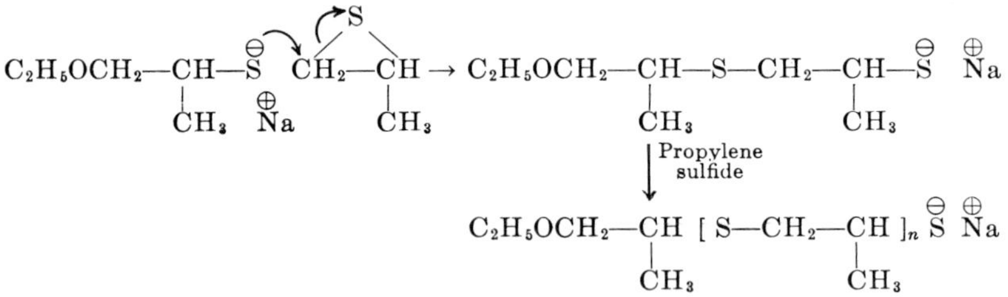

(37)

(38)

Boileau and Sigwalt (54) used anionic catalysts such as $NaNH_2$, KOH, and Na to obtain high molecular weight polymers of propylene sulfide. The polymerizations were carried out at room temperature and the resulting polymers had intrinsic viscosities in the range of 1.20 to 2.65. Other anionic catalysts such as butyllithium and $Al(C_2H_5)_3$ gave at best low molecular weight polymers.

Recently, Sigwalt and co-workers (56) polymerized propylene episulfide with sodium naphthalene in tetrahydrofuran. Initiation at −70°C was accompanied by the disappearance of the green sodium naphthalene color. Propagation did not take place until the temperature was raised to room temperature and was completed in one hour. The resulting polymer was of the "living" type as evidenced by the fact that addition of more propylene sulfide monomer resulted in further polymerization and a corresponding increase in molecular weight.

The resulting polymers have weight average molecular weights ($\bar{M}_w$) as high as 320,000 and heterogeneity indices ($\bar{M}_w/\bar{M}_n$) ranging from 0.93 to 1.22. As in other anionic living polymers, the number average degree of polymerization, $\bar{P}n$, of polypropylene sulfide prepared by this technique is related to the monomer [M], and catalyst [C] concentrations according to

$$\bar{P}n = \frac{[\mathrm{M}]}{\frac{1}{2}[\mathrm{C}]} \qquad (39)$$

Termination by exposing the living polymer to air resulted in a considerable increase in molecular weight. This can be explained by the oxidation of the mercaptide terminals by air to disulfide linkages. Termination by 1-chloromethyl naphthalene or HCl does not lead to a molecular weight increase.

The intrinsic viscosity–molecular weight relationship for polypropylene sulfide prepared by sodium naphthalene as catalyst was determined (57) to be:

$$[\eta] = 0.33 \times 10^{-4} M_w^{0.86} \qquad (40)$$

The polymer used had an intrinsic viscosity of 0.78 dl/g as measured in benzene at 20°C.

2. Coordinate Anionic Catalysis

The dialkyl zinc–water catalysts developed by Furukawa and his co-workers (58) for the polymerization of propylene oxide were found to be particularly effective for the preparation of high molecular weight propylene sulfide polymers (59,60). Ishii, Obara, and Fujita (61) found that binary catalysts consisting of $AlEt_3$ and $(n\text{-BuS})_2Co$ or $(n\text{-BuS})_2Fe$ give high molecular weight polypropylene sulfides and that the molecular weight varied with molar ratios of $AlEt_3$ and the mercaptides. It was also found (60–64) that simple salts of zinc and cadmium, especially the carbonates, are effective catalysts. The catalysts can be used both in organic solvents as well as in aqueous media. Adamek, Wood, and Woodhams (60) found that zinc catalysts produce largely atactic or amorphous polymer whereas cadmium salts tend to give an isotactic or crystalline polymer with a melting range of 40–41°C. They indicated that the melting point of isotactic polypropylene sulfide may vary according to the degree of tacticity and molecular weight. Machon and Sigwalt (65) studied the polymerization of propylene sulfide in different solvents using zinc diethyl plus water as the catalyst system. Most of the work was carried out in benzene as a solvent, varying the $ZnEt_2:H_2O$ ratio from 0 to 3. The resulting polymers were opaque in contrast to the transparent polymers obtained by anionic polymerizations using sodium, KOH or sodium naphthalene as catalysts (54,56). Polypropylene sulfides prepared by the $ZnEt_2$–H_2O catalyst system were shown to be partially crystalline by x-ray diffraction studies. The fraction of the polymer that is stereoregular was found to be insoluble in methyl ethyl ketone at 100°C and reached an optimum of 58% at a mole ratio of $H_2O:ZnEt_2$ of 0.92. On the other hand, the molecular weight reached a maximum at a $H_2O:ZnEt_2$ ratio of 2:1.

a. Mechanism of Propylene Sulfide Polymerization by $ZnEt_2$ Systems

When zinc diethyl is reacted with water the resulting compounds have the structures:

$$\text{EtZnOH}, \quad \text{EtZnOZnEt}, \quad \text{and} \quad \text{Et}\!\left[\text{Zn—O}\right]_n\text{ZnEt}$$

where n depends on the $ZnEt_2:H_2O$ ratio used and reaches a maximum when this ratio is 1. In the presence of oxygen compounds having the structure: $\text{EtO}\!\left[\text{Zn—O}\right]_n\text{ZnEt}$ can be formed. When alcohol is used to activate zinc diethyl, the resulting compounds are RZnOR and ROZnOR.

For the polymerization of propylene oxide using $ZnEt_2$ activated by H_2O or alcohol, Furukawa (66) postulated that the alkoxy or alkyl anion attached to the metallic center of the catalyst initiates the polymerization by acting on the monomer coordinated at another zinc atom of the catalyst. The same mechanism may apply to the polymerization of propylene sulfide in non-aqueous medium as represented by reaction 41. Termination according to this mechanism might take place by disproportionation leading to terminal unsaturation. However, this has not been established.

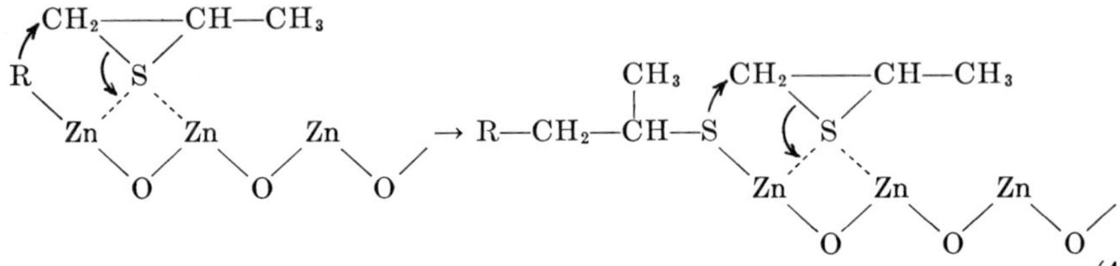

(41)

In aqueous medium, Adamek, Wood, and Woodhams (60) found the polymer produced to have terminal hydroxyl and mercaptan groups with no evidence for any terminal unsaturation. Reactions 42–45 show the mechanism proposed for the polymerization of propylene sulfide in aqueous medium.

Initiation

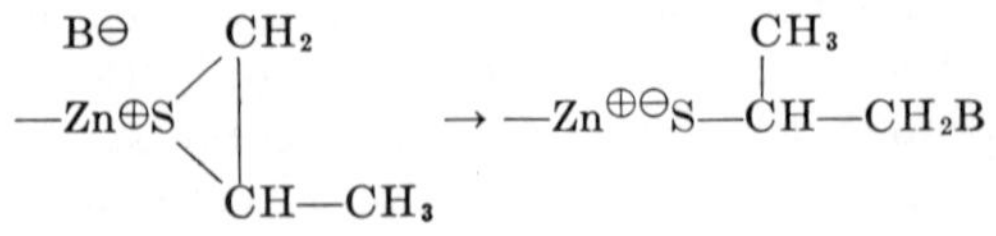

(42)

where $B^{\ominus} = RCOO^{\ominus}, RO^{\ominus}, RS^{\ominus}$

Propagation

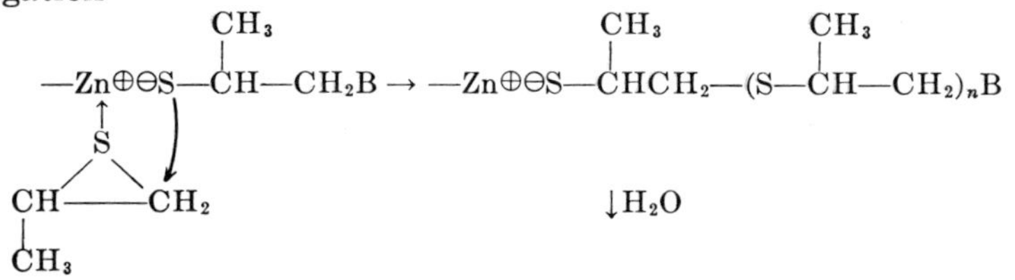

(43)

Termination

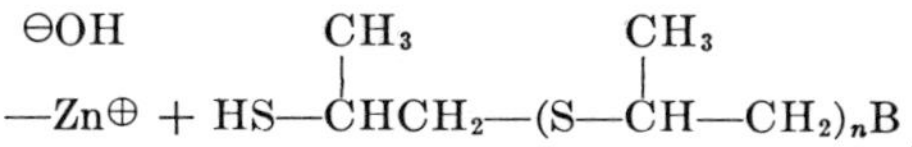

(44)

Reinitiation

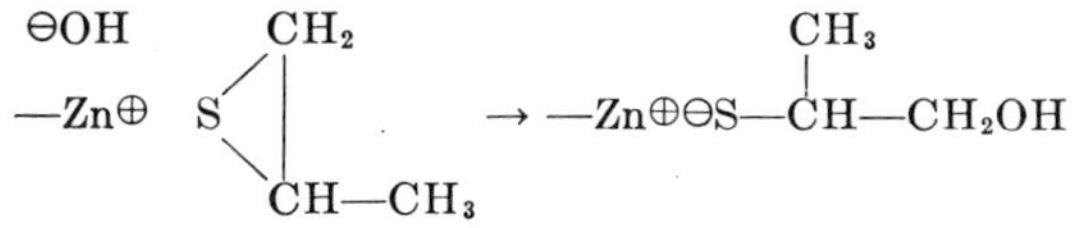

(45)

The chains initiated by —$Zn^{\oplus\ominus}OH$ according to this mechanism, result in polymers with —SH and —OH terminals by action of H_2O. The presence of secondary mercaptan and primary hydroxyl endgroups was demonstrated by proton magnetic resonance studies. The resulting polymers are also capable of being chain extended by diisocyanates.

A great deal of work remains to be done to elucidate the nature of episulfide polymerizations with metal alkyl catalysis. Alkyls of group IIB metals seem to be the best catalysts, but they differ in the degree of tacticity they produce. The molecular weights of the resulting polymers also depend on the group IIB metal used, the nature of the cocatalyst and the ratio of catalyst to cocatalyst. The heterogenous nature of the catalysis makes quantitative studies rather difficult to perform. Several laboratories are presently investigating episulfide polymerizations in a systematic fashion starting with soluble catalyst systems of known composition. It is hoped that in the next few years, more light will be shed on this type of polymerization.

VI. PROPERTIES OF ALKYL MONOSULFIDE ELASTOMERS

In order to vulcanize alkyl monosulfide polymers with conventional sulfur recipes, small concentrations of unsaturated episulfides are generally incorporated as comonomers to provide pendant unsaturation. Unsaturated episulfides that have been successfully used for this purpose include allyl thioglycidyl ether and the monoepisulfides of 1,4-pentadiene, 1,5-hexadiene, and vinyl cyclohexene (59,60).

Table IX gives the properties of a typical composition of propylene sulfide-allyl thioglycidyl ether copolymer cured with a sulfur recipe (67). The glass transition temperature of polypropylene sulfide is reported (60) to be −52.5°C. However, carbon black reinforced and vulcanized copolymers of propylene sulfide-allyl thioglycidyl ether give T_g values of about −40°C (67).

To improve the physical properties of propylene sulfide elastomers, copolymerization with ethylene sulfide was found to be effective (60,67). The best balance of elastomeric properties are obtained when the ethylene sulfide content is in the range of 30–40 mole %.

Physical properties of terpolymers of propylene sulfide-ethylene sulfide-allyl thioglycidyl ether (PS-ES-ATGE) are given in Table X showing the effect of ethylene sulfide content on properties (67). The vulcanization recipe used was the same as that given in Table IX. Due to the

TABLE IX
Physical Properties of a Typical Propylene Sulfide–Allyl Thioglycidyl Ether Copolymer Cured with a Sulfur Recipe

Polymer Composition (mole %, initial charge)	
Propylene sulfide	90
Allyl thioglycidyl ether	10
Vulcanization Recipe (parts by wt)	
Copolymer	100
Stearic acid	1
Philblack O	50
ZnO	5
Sulfur	1
Ethyl Selenac	2
Cure Cycle	
Time, min	20
Temp., °C	150
Vulcanizate Properties	
Tensile strength, psi	1550
Elongation, %	225
Hardness, Shore A	80
Tear strength, pi	125
Solvent Resistance (% volume swell, 7 days at room temperature)	
Ethyl acetate	75
MEK	101
Hexane	10
Toluene	173

TABLE X
Effect of Varying Ethylene Sulfide Content on Elastomer Properties

Polymer composition, mole %, initial charge						
PS	ES	ATGE	Tensile, psi	Elongation, %	Hardness, Shore A	Tear, pi
80	10	10	1550	368	72	240
70	20	10	1835	380	75	255
60	30	10	2020	350	81	365
55	35	10	2230	390	87	435
50	40	10	2380	300	95	520

differences in reactivities between the episulfide monomers used, it is not unlikely that block rather than random copolymers are obtained. This is indicated by the fact that T_g for the carbon black reinforced vulcanizates of the terpolymers described in Table X is about -40°C which is approximately the same as that for vulcanized PS-ATGE copolymer. The solvent resistance of monosulfide elastomers based on propylene sulfide is further enhanced by increasing their ethylene sulfide content. The aging characteristics of the vulcanized monosulfide elastomers studied appear to be good. Slight changes in physical properties have been reported (60) after heat aging in air for 3 days at 120°C in the presence of 2% phenyl-β-naphthylamine.

VII. COPOLYMERS OF EPISULFIDES WITH EPOXIDE AND VINYL MONOMERS

An early attempt to copolymerize propylene sulfide and ethylene oxide was carried out by Dermer (68) using triethylamine as catalyst. The product obtained was of low molecular weight and analyzed for practically a homopolymer of propylene sulfide. Gurgiolo (69) reported the preparation of copolymers of 1,2-butylene sulfide or propylene sulfide and propylene oxide using ferric chloride-propylene oxide complex catalyst. However, the products were not characterized. Due to the differences in reactivities between the two types of monomer, it is unlikely that true copolymers were obtained. Using anionic catalysts, block copolymers of propylene sulfide with styrene (70–72), butadiene (70), α-methyl styrene and methylmethacrylate (71) have been prepared. Generally, the vinyl or diene monomer is first allowed to polymerize to a living polymer to which propylene sulfide is added to give A-B or A-B-A type block copolymers. Terpolymers of styrene-acrylonitrile and propylene sulfide have also been reported (70). The properties of these block copolymers have not been studied.

References

1. J. C. Patrick and N. M. Mnookin, Brit. Pat. 302,270 (1927).
2. M. B. Berenbaum, in *Polyethers,* Part III, N. G. Gaylord, Ed., Interscience, New York, 1962, Ch. 13.
3. E. M. Fettes, in *Organic Sulfur Compounds,* N. Kharasch, Ed., Pergamon Press, New York, 1961, Vol. 1, Ch. 24.
4. J. R. Panek, in *Polyethers,* Part III, N. G. Gaylord, Ed., Interscience, New York, 1962, Ch. 14.
5. A. V. Tobolsky and W. J. MacKnight, *Polymeric Sulfur and Related Polymers,* Interscience, New York, 1965.
6. E. R. Bertozzi, U.S. Pat. 2,796,325, (June 18, 1957) (to Thiokol Chem. Corp.).
7. J. C. Patrick, *Trans. Faraday Soc.,* **32,** 347 (1936).
8. J. C. Patrick, *Rubber Chem. Technol.,* **9,** 373 (1936).
9. J. C. Patrick and H. R. Ferguson, U.S. Pat. 2,466,963 (April 12, 1949) (to Thiokol Corp.).
10. E. M. Fettes and J. A. Gannon, U.S. Pat. 2,789,958 (April 23, 1957) (to Thiokol Chem. Corp.).
11. I. G. Farbenindustrie A. G., Ger. Pat. 612,665 (April 16, 1935).
12. D. F. Twiss and A. E. T. Neale, U.S. Pat. 2,056,026 (Sept. 29, 1936) (to Dunlop Tire & Rubber Co.).
13. J. C. Patrick, U.S. Pat. 2,363,614 (Nov. 28, 1944) (to Thiokol Corp.).
14. B. Milligan, B. Saville, and J. M. Swan, *J. Chem. Soc.,* **1961,** 4850.
15. B. Milligan, B. Saville, and J. M. Swan, *J. Chem. Soc.,* **1963,** 3608.
16. K. K. Sumitomo Densen Seizosho, Brit. Pat. 485,554 (May 16, 1938) and 491,309 (Aug. 29, 1938).
17. G. M. Bennett, *J. Chem. Soc.,* **121,** 2139 (1922).
18. G. M. Bennett and A. L. Hock, *J. Chem. Soc.,* **477** (1927).
19. T. Okita, *J. Soc. Rubber Ind., Japan,* **21,** 35 (1948); *Chem. Abstr.,* **42,** 9229e (1948); *ibid.,* **21,** 77 (1948); *ibid.,* **43,** 4043b (1949).
20. S. A. Ballard, R. C. Morris, and J. L. Van Winkle, U.S. Pat. 2,484,369 (October 11, 1949) (to Shell Development Co.).
21. J. T. Abrams, K. J. M. Andrews, and F. N. Woodward, *J. Polymer Sci.,* **41,** 225 (1959).
22. K. J. M. Andrews, R. J. Rosser, and F. N. Woodward, *J. Polymer Sci.,* **41,** 231 (1959).
23. J. C. Patrick, U.S. Pat. 2,469,404 (May 10, 1949) (to Thiokol Corp.).
24. F. O. Davis and E. M. Fettes, *J. Am. Chem. Soc.,* **70,** 2611 (1948).
25. A. V. Tobolsky, F. Leonard, and G. P. Roeser, *J. Polymer Sci.,* **3,** 604 (1948).
26. F. S. Dainton, J. A. Davies, P. O. Manning, and S. A. Zahir, *Trans. Faraday Soc.,* **53,** 813 (1957).
27. A. V. Tobolsky and T. H. Meltzer, U.S. Pat. 2,728,750 (Dec. 27, 1955) (to Thiokol Chem. Corp.).

28. A. V. Tobolsky and B. Baysal, *J. Am. Chem. Soc.*, **75**, 1757 (1953).
29. W. H. Stockmayer, R. O. Howard, and J. T. Clarke, *J. Am. Chem. Soc.*, **75**, 1756 (1953).
30. J. C. Patrick, U.S. Pat. 2,142,145 (Jan. 3, 1939) (to Thiokol Corp.).
31. C. S. Marvel and L. E. Olson, *J. Am. Chem. Soc.*, **79**, 3089 (1957).
32. W. R. Nummy, U.S. Pat. 2,866,776 (Dec. 30, 1958) (to Dow Chem. Co.).
33. E. M. Fettes, J. S. Jorczak, and J. R. Panek, *Ind. Eng. Chem.*, **46**, 1539 (1954).
34. J. J. Trillat and R. Tertian, *Compt. Rend.*, **219**, 395 (1944).
35. R. Tertian, *Rev. Gen. Caoutchonc*, **23**, 245 (1946), *Chem. Abstr.*, **41**, 6760 (1947).
36. I. M. Dawson, A. M. Mathieson, and J. M. Robertson, *J. Chem. Soc.*, **1948**, 322.
37. I. M. Dawson and J. M. Robertson, *J. Chem. Soc.*, **1948**, 1256.
38. J. Donohue and V. Schomaker, *J. Chem. Phys.*, **16**, 92 (1948).
39. O. Foss, *Acta Chem. Scand.*, **4**, 404 (1950).
40. H. P. Koch, *J. Chem. Soc.*, **1948**, 394.
41. J. E. Baer and M. Carmack, *J. Am. Chem. Soc.*, **71**, 1215 (1949).
42. R. H. Gobran and M. B. Berenbaum, Paper presented at the 133rd Meeting of the American Chemical Society, San Francisco, Calif., (April 13–18, 1958).
43. N. A. Rosenthal and M. B. Berenbaum, Paper presented at the 131st Meeting of the American Chemical Society, Miami, Florida, (April 7–12, 1957).
44. P. C. Colodny and A. V. Tobolsky, *J. Appl. Polymer Sci.*, **2**, 39 (1959).
45. A. V. Tobolsky, W. J. MacKnight, and M. Takahashi, *J. Phys. Chem.*, **68**, 787 (1964).
46. A. V. Tobolsky, W. J. MacKnight, and N. Canter, ONR Tech. Rep. RLT 84, Princeton University, December 1964.
47. A. N. Genkin, T. P. Nasonova, I. Ya. Poddubnyi, and R. A. Shlyakhter, *Vysokomolekul. Soedin;* **4**, 1088, (1962), through *Resins, Rubbers, Plastics,* P10: 489 2607.
48. R. A. Shlyakhter, N. P. Apukhtina, and T. P. Nasonova, *Dokl. Akad. Nauk SSSR,* **149**, 345 (1963).
49. E. M. Fettes and H. F. Mark, *J. Appl. Polymer Sci.*, **7**, 2239 (1963).
50. R. A. Shlyakhter, E. G. Ehrenburgh, T. P. Nasonova, and E. P. Piskarewa, Paper presented at the IUPAC International Symposium on Macromolecular Chemistry, Prague (1965), *Preprint No. P 412.*
51. M. Sander, *Chem. Rev.*, **66** (3), 297 (1966).
52. F. O. Davis and E. M. Fettes, in *Polyethers,* Part III, N. Gaylord, Ed., Interscience, New York, 1962.
53. M. Delepine and P. Jaffeux, *Compt. Rend.*, **172**, 158 (1921).
54. S. Boileau and P. Sigwalt, *Compt. Rend.*, **252**, 882 (1961).
55. C. S. Marvel and E. D. Weil, *J. Am. Chem. Soc.*, **76**, 61 (1954).
56. S. Boileau, G. Champetier, and P. Sigwalt, *Makromol. Chem.*, **69**, 180 (1963).
57. V. E. Eskin and A. E. Nesterov, *Vysokomolekul. Soedin.*, **8** (1), 141 (1966), through *Chem. Abstr.*, **64**, 12817g (1966).
58. J. Furukawa and T. Saegusa, *Polymerization of Aldehydes and Oxides,* Interscience, New York, 1964.
59. Thiokol Chemical Corp., Brit. Pat. 1,036,091 (July 1966).
60. S. Adamek, B. B. J. Wood, and R. T. Woodhams, *Rubber Age,* **96**, 581 (1965).
61. Y. Ishii, M. Obara, and Y. Fujita, Paper presented at the 11th Annual Meeting, Society of High Polymers (Japan), Paper No. E09 (1962).

62. R. Kobayashi and Y. Moriwaki, Paper presented at the 11th Annual Meeting, Society of High Polymers (Japan), Paper No. E10 (1962); also 15th Annual Chemical Society Meeting (Japan), Paper No. 8311 (1962).
63. S. W. Osborn, Can. Pat. 698,781 (Nov. 24, 1964) (to Thiokol Chem. Corp.).
64. S. W. Osborn, T. F. Wells, III, and E. L. Kutch, Can. Pat. 698,782 (Nov. 24, 1964) (to Thiokol Chem. Corp.).
65. Jean-Pierre Machon and Pierre Sigwalt, *Compt. Rend.*, **260** (2), 549 (1965).
66. J. Furukawa, *Polymer*, **3**, 487 (1962).
67. R. H. Gobran, S. W. Osborn, T. F. Wells, III, and A. J. Yu, unpublished work.
68. O. C. Dermer, WADC Tech. Report No. 55.447, ASTIA Document No. AD 110.496 (June 1956).
69. A. E. Gurgiolo, U.S. Pat. 3,000,865 (Sept. 19, 1961) (to Dow Chem. Co.).
70. French Pat. 1,357,934 (March 2, 1964) (to duPont); and Brit. Pat. 997,498 (July 7, 1965) (to duPont).
71. R. S. Nevin and E. M. Pearce, *J. Polymer Sci. B*, **3**, 487 (1965).
72. S. Boileau and P. Sigwalt, *Compt. Rend.*, **261**, 132 (1965).

CHAPTER 9

ELASTOMERS BY MISCELLANEOUS OR UNKNOWN MECHANISMS

A. Liquid Rubbers

J. FURUKAWA AND S. YAMASHITA

Kyoto University, Kyoto, Japan

AND

S. IDO

Japan Synthetic Rubber Co., Ltd.,
Tokyo, Japan

Contents

I. Definition and Scope of Liquid Rubber 843
II. Liquid Rubbers by Radical Polymerization 845
A. Liquid Polybutadiene 846
B. Liquid Polychloroprene 848
III. Liquid Rubbers by Anionic Polymerization 848
IV. Liquid Rubbers by Cationic Polymerization 856
V. Liquid Rubbers by Coordination Polymerization 861
VI. Depolymerized Rubbers 862
VII. Liquid Rubbers by Condensation and Addition Polymerization 862
References 864

I. DEFINITION AND SCOPE OF LIQUID RUBBER

Conventional industrial rubbers are vulcanizable high polymers which convert to rubber goods by mastication, compounding, building, and curing. These procedures require considerable manpower and consume large amounts of electricity. Moreover, careful process control is necessary to avoid scorching. A liquid rubber would not need mastication, and would render compounding easy. Also, it would enable casting, potting, or injecting. With liquid rubbers the rubber industry could be streamlined similarly to the plastics industry. This explains the rapid industrial expansion of polyurethane rubbers. Silicone rubbers and polysulfide rubbers (cf. chapters by Lewis, p. 767, and Gobran, and Berenbaum, p. 805) are also available in liquid form for special industrial applications. This paper concerns mainly the preparation of liquid rubbers from inexpensive hydrocarbons.

According to the theory of rubber elasticity, useful vulcanized rubbers are high molecular weight polymers with a moderate amount of crosslinking. This theory suggests that liquid rubbers could be obtained from the following substances.

Type 1: Liquid polymers having flexible backbones and containing reactive terminal and internal groups. The terminal groups provide sites for chain extension and the internal groups for crosslinking:

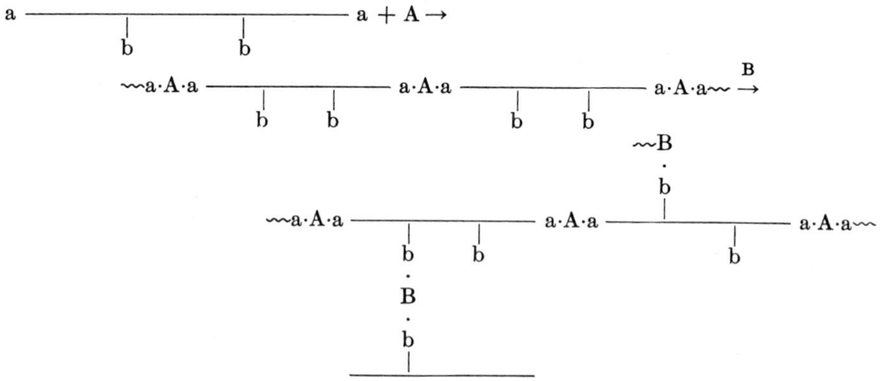

Type 2: Liquid polymers containing reactive internal functional groups exclusively. In this case, crosslinking is obtained by the reaction of internal groups. Undesirable chain branching may be inevitable in this case.

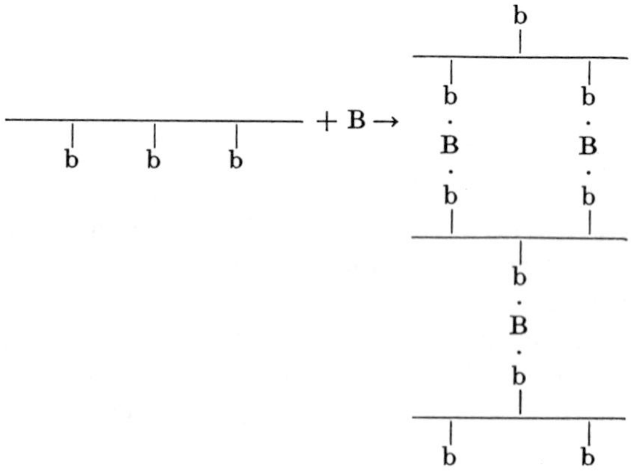

Type 3: Liquid polymers containing reactive terminal functional groups exclusively. In this case, crosslinked polymers can be prepared with tri- or polyfunctional chain extending agents.

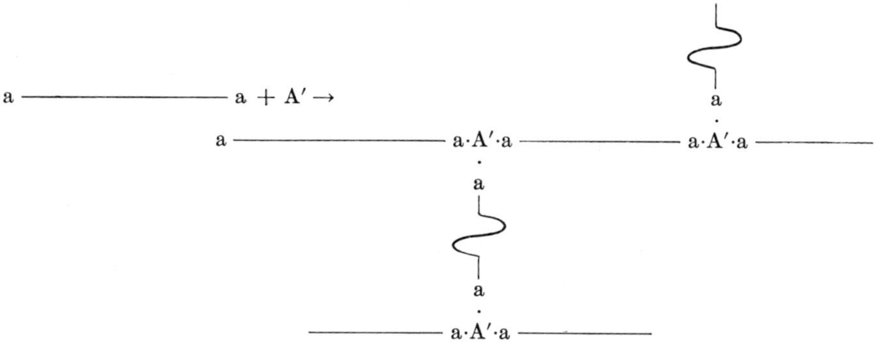

In these formulas a and b are terminal and internal reactive groups, and A, A′, and B are bifunctional chain extenders, polyfunctional chain extenders, and crosslinking agents, respectively.

Polyurethanes, polysulfides, or silicon rubbers are examples for the above principles:

	Backbone	a	b	A, A′	B
Polyether-urethane rubber	—O—$(CH_2)_n$—	—OH,—NH_2	—	OCNRNCO	—
Polysulfide rubber	—S_x—$(CH_2)_n$—	—SH	—	Oxidizing agent	—
Silicone rubber	—O—Si(R)(R)—	—O—Si(R)(R)—OH	—OR	Dehydration agent	$RSi(OC(=O)—R)_3$

Liquid hydrocarbon rubbers have also been explored. Low polymers and copolymers of butadiene, isoprene, chloroprene belong to type 2, which can be vulcanized with suitable agents such as sulfur, amines, or metal oxides. Low polymers of type 3 can also be prepared by "living" polymerization in which functional terminal groups are obtained.

Low molecular weight polymers in general can be obtained in radical, anionic, and cationic reactions. Among these, anionic polymerization seems to be the most favorable from the point of view of molecular weight control and introduction of terminal functional groups.

II. LIQUID RUBBERS BY RADICAL POLYMERIZATION

Low molecular weight polymers are generally prepared in the presence of fairly large amounts of initiator, transfer agent, and terminating agent.

With suitable initiators terminal functional groups can be introduced into the macromolecule.

A. Liquid Polybutadiene

Liquid polybutadienes can be prepared by emulsion polymerization in the presence of a chain transfer agent such as dodecylmercaptan (1,60). The polymer can be vulcanized with sulfur–accelerator systems (2) or with peroxide systems (3). The product can be converted to hydroxyl polybutadiene with formic acid and hydrogen peroxide (4).

Liquid polymers possessing two terminal carboxyl groups can be prepared by solution polymerization with azodicarboxylic acid as functional initiator (5). For example, butadiene dissolved in tetrahydrofuran is polymerized with 4,4′-azobis(4-cyanopentanoic acid) (**1**) in tetrahydrofuran solution for 9 hr at 90°C. Dicarboxylic polybutadiene of viscosity of 174 poises at 25°C is obtained which can be vulcanized by polyepoxides.

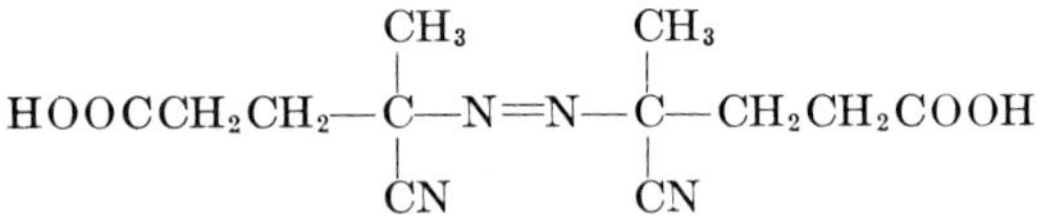

(**1**)

Diazothioethers (6,7) (**2**) are not only initiators but also modifiers, since these molecules contain two functional groups, i.e., a phenyl group as initiator and a thiyl group as chain transfer agent. This type of catalyst

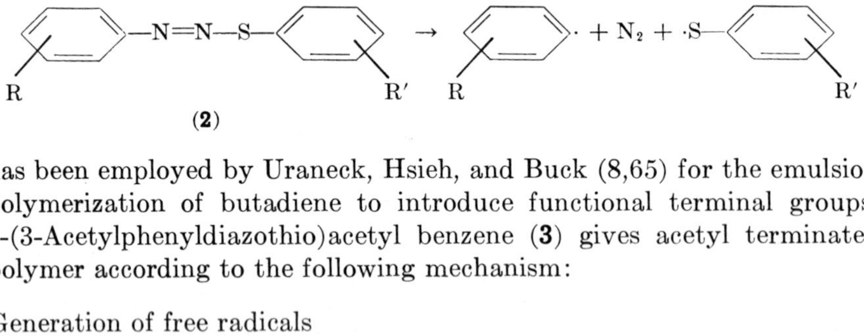

(**2**)

has been employed by Uraneck, Hsieh, and Buck (8,65) for the emulsion polymerization of butadiene to introduce functional terminal groups. 3-(3-Acetylphenyldiazothio)acetyl benzene (**3**) gives acetyl terminated polymer according to the following mechanism:

Generation of free radicals

$$\underset{(\mathbf{3})}{CH_3COC_6H_4N{=}NSC_6H_4COCH_3} \rightarrow CH_3COC_6H_4\cdot + N_2 + \cdot SC_6H_4COCH_3$$

Initiation and propagation

$$CH_3COC_6H_4\cdot + n\mathrm{M} \rightarrow CH_3COC_6H_4(\mathrm{M})_n\cdot$$

Chain transfer

$$CH_3COC_6H_4(M)_n\cdot + CH_3COC_6H_4N{=}NSC_6H_4COCH_3 \rightarrow CH_3COC_6H_4(M)_nSC_6H_4COCH_3 + CH_3COC_6H_4\cdot + N_2$$

Termination

$$CH_3COC_6H_4(M)_n\cdot + CH_3COC_6H_4S\cdot \rightarrow CH_3COC_6H_4(M)_nSC_6H_4COCH_3$$

Table I shows viscosities of acetyl-terminated polybutadienes obtained with various amounts of acetyldiazothioether.

The fact that the polymer contained acetophenone groups was demonstrated by infrared spectroscopy and by reaction with hydroxylamine, semicarbazide, hydrazides, *n*-butyllithium and thiosemicarbazide. Sulfur, oxygen, and hydroxyl contents of a reduced polymer with an inherent viscosity of 0.79 were 0.2, 0.4, and 0.26%, respectively. An acetyl-terminated butadiene-styrene copolymer of 47 Mooney viscosity was compounded in a tread formulation with three parts of a mixture of 9- and 10-mercaptostearohydrazide. The vulcanizate showed improved heat buildup and resilience in comparison to a SBR 1000 control. The authors (8) suggest reactions between the acetyl group and the hydrazide, and between the mercapto group and the polymer chain.

Liquid or readily fusible curable polybutadienes with terminal carboxyl groups were also prepared by a combination of a bifunctional initiator and a bifunctional chain transfer agent, both of which are easily decomposed into two fragments with carboxyl groups (9,61).

YSSY-type chain transfer agent:

HOOCRSSRCOOH
Dithioalkyl dicarboxylic acid

TABLE I
Viscosities of Acetyl-Terminated Polybutadiene (8)

Acetyldiazothioether, part	Polym. time, hr	Polym. conv., %	Inherent visc.	Gel content, %	Mooney visc., ML-4
0.4	20	80	1.82	15	141
0.8	20	69	2.45	0	57
1.2	21	67	1.39	0	22
4.0	40	73	0.96	0	Too soft
4.0	32	42	0.46	0	Too soft

XN=NX-type initiator:

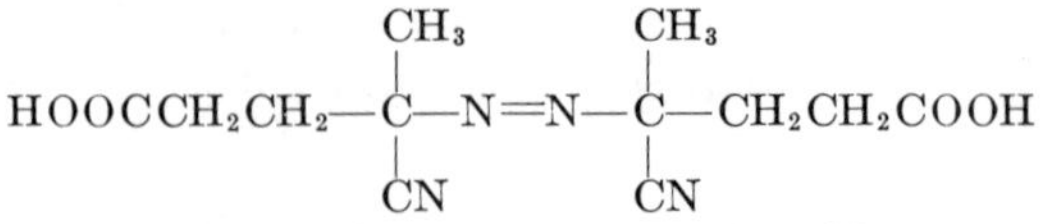

4,4′-Azobis(4-cyanopentanoic acid)

The polymerization proceeds as follows:

$$XN{=}NX \rightarrow 2X\cdot + N_2$$
$$X\cdot + nM \rightarrow XM_n\cdot$$
$$XM_n\cdot + YSSY \rightarrow XM_nSY + \cdot SY$$
$$\cdot SY + mM \rightarrow YSM_m\cdot$$

Liquid polybutadienes with pendant carboxylic groups on the backbone were prepared by copolymerizing butadiene and acrylic or methacrylic acid (11). A large amount of modifier (mercaptans or bisxanthogens) was needed to control the molecular weight of the polymer (10). Table II shows the viscosity–molecular weight relation of the copolymers.

A butadiene copolymer with 12.6% methacrylic acid having a molecular weight of the order of 7000 was reported by Cooper (11). Zinc salts of this copolymer were soluble thermoplastics whose rheological properties were similar to a silicone "bouncing putty" (12). Lead and calcium salts were harder at room temperature than the zinc salts. Evidence was presented to show that the zinc salts were basic: polymer-$(COOZnOH)_n$ (11).

B. Liquid Polychloroprene

Liquid polychloroprene is prepared by emulsion polymerization with relatively large amounts of dialkyl xanthogen disulfide modifier (14,64). "Neoprene FC" is a tan colored soft crystalline solid which melts at 60°C. It gives a viscous amber liquid, whose viscosities at 50 and 90°C are 550 and 75 poises, respectively (13). The product can be vulcanized at room temperature with piperazine or hexamethylenediamine and metal oxides (13,14). This polymer can be used as a plasticizer, and for sealants, coatings, adhesives, and binders.

III. LIQUID RUBBERS BY ANIONIC POLYMERIZATION

Anionic "living" polymerization (15–17) seems to be one of the most promising ways to prepare liquid rubbers. Molecular weight control is easy and functional groups can be introduced.

Living polymerizations have recently been investigated with lithium

TABLE II
Liquid Carboxylic Copolymers (10)[a]
B = butadiene, MA = methacrylic acid, S = styrene, V = acrylonitrile

Polymer type	Monomer ratio	Conv., %	Carboxyl, ephr[b]	Mol wt cryo-scopic[c]	Viscosity, Brookfield[d]
B/MA	96/3	58	0.04	910	210
B/MA	95/5	60	0.068	1100	600
B/MA	90/10	60	0.13	1080	1,950
B/MA	89/11	93	0.11	2000	40,000
B/S/MA	85.5/4.5/10	21	0.166	680	2,000
B/S/MA	85.5/4.5/10	41	0.156	950	2,200
B/S/MA	85.5/4.5/10	53	0.140	1340	4,900
B/S/MA	85.5/4.5/10	76	0.122	1630	8,800
B/V/MA	67/24.4/8.6	90	0.094	2064	44,300
B/V/MA	55/42.14/2.86	90	0.027	2140	68,600
B/V/MA	55/42.14/2.86	91	0.030	—[g]	>100,000[e]
B/V/MA	55/42.14/2.86	82	0.032	—[g]	ML-4′-RT-21[f]
B/V/MA	55/42.14/2.86	90	0.030	—[g]	ML-4′-RT-51[f]
B/V/MA	55/25/20	89	0.190	1360	40,000
B/V/MA	55/25/20	80	0.192	1420	>100,000[e]
B/V/MA	55/25/20	89	0.190	1700	>100,000[e]

[a] Prepared with tertiary mercaptan modifier.
[b] Analytically determined equivalents per 100 g of polymer.
[c] Sulfur analyses indicate essentially one thioalkyl (—SR) radical per molecule thus contributing about 200 units of molecular weight per molecule.
[d] Brookfield viscosity at 50°C expressed in centipoises.
[e] Could be measured at higher temperatures.
[f] Room temperature Mooney viscosity, large rotor. A soft near-solid copolymer.
[g] Too high to measure cryoscopically.

or alkyllithium catalyst. Liquid polybutadienes have been prepared earlier with sodium catalyst (2,18,67). The anionic polymerization of liquid polybutadiene goes back to the old German technique used in the manufacture of Buna. Liquid polybutadiene prepared by sodium dispersion (19) has been in semicommercial production in the United States and was marketed under the trade name of Butarez liquid polybutadiene. A similar German product, Plastikator 32, was manufactured during World War II (34).

Liquid polybutadienes without functional terminal groups were reported in detail by Crouch and Shotton (2). To obtain low polymers these authors recommended the use of large amounts of extremely finely dispersed sodium, elevated temperatures, and suitable hydrocarbon solvents. In this way, polymer of molecular weight of 1300 and of viscosity of 2500 cp at 100°F was obtained (2).

Butarez liquid polybutadiene is a mixture of 1,2,1,4 linkages and some cyclized structures (2). Its unsaturation is 0.8 mole/mole of 4 carbon unit and its specific refraction is 0.333, which is lower than that for an open chain polyolefin. The hydrogen content is in the range of compounds containing naphthene rings. The presence of about 60% vinyl side chains was suggested (2,20).

Lithium is a more suitable initiator than sodium for liquid polybutadienes or polyisoprenes having functional terminal groups. Ziegler and co-workers (21,22) postulate that the polymerization of conjugated dienes with lithium proceeds by the formation of dilithiodiene adducts. Propagation is believed to be a series of addition reactions. In support of this theory, the authors (21,22) isolated and identified low molecular weight compounds from the reaction of 2,3-dimethyl-1,3-butadiene with

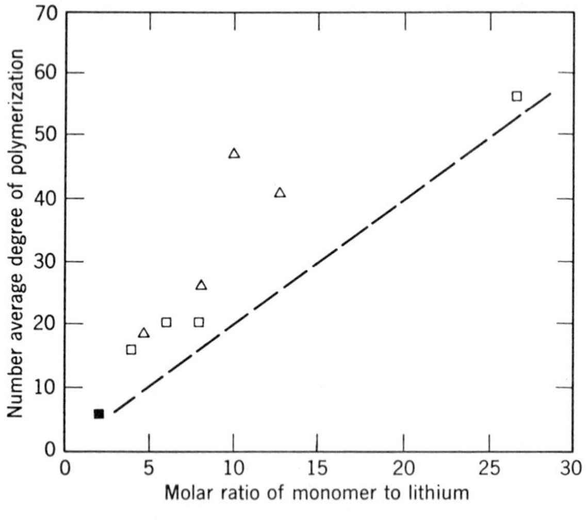

Fig. 1. Number-average degree of polymerization of polydienes as a function of the molar ratio of monomer to lithium in THF solvent at −20 to −40°C (23). □, Polyisoprenes; △, polybutadienes; ■, polyisoprene prepared in DME at −40°C; ----, calculated for $\overline{DP}$ = [monomer]/½[Li].

lithium in diethyl ether. However, only a small fraction of the employed lithium was bonded to carbon, and only unidentified high molecular weight species were formed.

Schoenberg (23) improved the synthesis of low molecular weight dilithiopolyisoprene and -polybutadiene by the use of tetrahydrofuran (THF) and 1,2-dimethoxyethane (DME), i.e., ethers with great solvating power toward alkali metal cations (24). Thus, in THF and DME 50–80% lithium was bonded to carbon, in contrast to 13–15% in diethyl ether, and the molecular weight of the polybutadiene was one and a half or two times higher than predicted. Polyisoprenes and polybutadienes of increasing molecular weights were obtained with increasing molar ratios of monomer to lithium charged. Figure 1 shows the number average degree of polymerization ($\overline{DP}$) as a function of the monomer/lithium ratio. The theoretical line (dashed) was obtained from $\overline{DP}$ = monomer/0.5 Li, which is implicit in the mechanism proposed by Ziegler. The experimental $\overline{DP}$'s were obtained from hydroxyl equivalents of isolated polymers, assuming that the polymers were diols. Experimental conditions and polymer properties are summarized in Tables III and IV. The microstructure of the polyisoprene prepared in THF was predominantly that from 3,4 and 1,2 addition and that of polybutadienes largely (75–92%) that from 1,2 addition.

Bis(alkalimetalorgano) initiators were used by Uraneck et al. (8,63,68) in the polymerization of butadiene to obtain alkalimetal-telechelic and

TABLE III
Preparation of Polydienes (23)

No.	Monomer, g		Li, g	Solvent, ml		Temp., °C	Terminator
1	Dimethyl butadiene	41	3.5	Ether	500	30	CO_2
2	Dimethyl butadiene	41	3.5	Ether	500	30	EO[c]
3	Isoprene	34	3.5	Ether	500	30	CO_2
4	Isoprene	204	10.5	DME[a]	700	−40	EO[c]
5	Butadiene	271	3.5	THF[b]	1500	−40	EO[c]

[a] Dimethyl ether.
[b] Tetrahydrofuran.
[c] Ethylene oxide.

TABLE IV
Properties of Polydienes in Table III (23)

No.	Polymer, g	Mol wt	η_{inh}	Neutralization equiv. Calc.	Neutralization equiv. Found	OH value Calc.	OH value Found
1	Waxy 40	338[c]	—	—	195	—	—
2	Viscous oil	371[c]	—	—	—	168	195
3	17 (acid)[a]	625[d]	—	283	291	—	—
	13 (acid)[b]	1940[d]	—	—	1230	—	—
4	Viscous oil 216	—	0.026	—	—	—	216
5	Viscous oil 237	—	0.11	—	—	—	1330

[a] From aqueous fraction.
[b] From ether fraction.
[c] Cryoscopic molecular weight.
[d] Ebullioscopic molecular weight.

carboxyl-telechelic polymers. The term "telechelic" is proposed by these authors to describe polymers with two functional terminal groups. The reaction sequence is as follows:

Initiation and propagation

$$Me_2R + 2nA \rightarrow MeA_nRA_nMe$$
(alkali metal-telechelic polymer)

Carbonation

$$MeA_nRA_nMe + 2CO_2 \rightarrow MeO_2CA_nRA_nCO_2Me$$
(metal carboxylate-telechelic polymer)

Acidification

$$MeO_2CA_nRA_nCO_2Me + 2H^+ \rightarrow 2Me^+ + HOOCA_nRA_nCOOH$$
(carboxyl-telechelic polymer)

where Me is an alkali metal and A is a monomer.

Liquid polymers were found to be over 90% telechelic. These products were mixed with pigments and cured (Tables V and VI). The physical properties of cured carboxyl-telechelic polybutadienes are far superior to cured nontelechelic polybutadienes.

Chain extenders containing tri- or multifunctional groups, i.e., epoxidized compounds (**4**) or compounds with ethylene imine groups (**5–7**) were used for carboxyl terminated rubber (25).

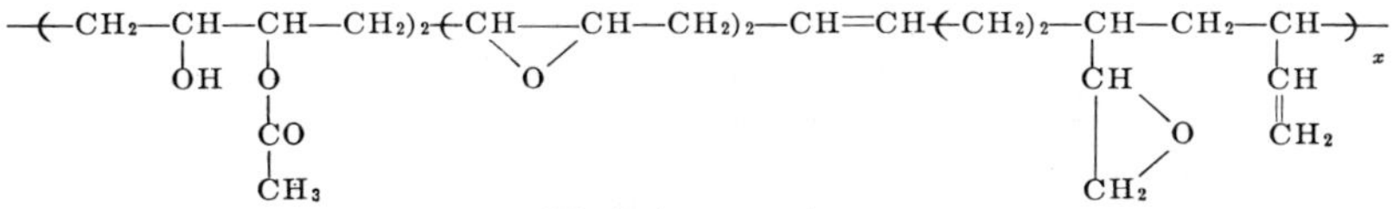

(4) Oxirane resins

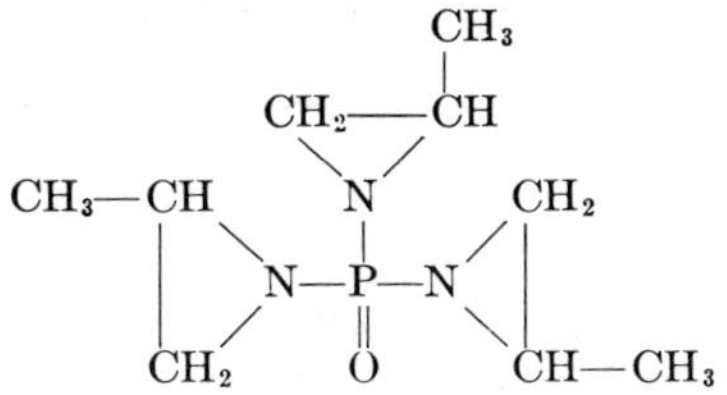

(5) Tris[1-(2-methyl)aziridinyl]phosphine oxide

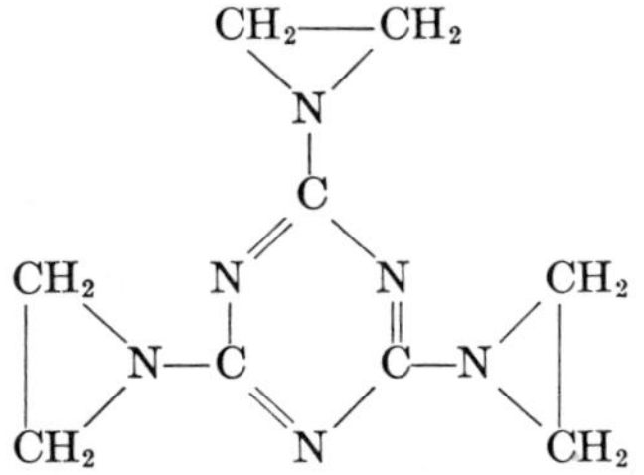

(6) Tris-2,4,6-(1-aziridinyl)-1,3,5-triazine

(7) Hexa[1-(2-methyl)aziridinyl]triphosphatriazine

TABLE V

Cure of a Liquid Carboxyl-Telechelic Polybutadiene Pigmented Formulation (8)

Recipe	Parts
Carboxyl-telechelic polybutadiene[a]	100
HAF carbon black	50
Polyaziridinyl curing agent[b]	Variable
Precure, time and temperature	30 min, 110°C
Final cure, time and temperature	60 min, 113°C

[a] Carboxyl content, 1.14–1.03%, inherent viscosity 0.35.

[b] Hexa[1-(2-methyl)aziridinyl]triphosphatriazine obtained from Interchemical Corporation.

TABLE VI
Physical Properties (8)

Polyaziridinyl curing agent, % of stoichiometric[a]	V_r[b]	Tensile, psi	Elongation, %	ΔT,[c] °F	Resilience, %	Shore hardness
150	0.364	1300	160	80	52	68
160	0.377	1350	160	71	60	75
200	0.373	1400	170	76	60	67

[a] Aziridinyl units equivalent to carboxyl units.
[b] Volume fraction of cured polymer in *n*-heptane swollen gel.
[c] Temperature rise.

The preparation of liquid polymers of butadiene with butyllithium has also been reported. In these cases, the viscosities of polymers obtained depended upon the amount of catalyst and the time of polymerization. For example, 40–65 mole % of butyllithium after 6 hr polymerization gave liquid polybutadiene with 96.2–53.1 cp at 50°C. The products contained 1,2, *trans*-1,4, and *cis*-1,4 structures in the amounts of 22–27, 37–24, and 38–53%, respectively (26). Butyllithium initiated polybutadiene contains only monofunctional terminal groups which limits further chain extension. Coupling only doubles the molecular weight.

1,2-Dithiacyclohexane reacts readily with alkali terminated polymer in the range −100 to +100°C and gives a liquid or semisolid polymer. This product possesses thiol terminal groups and is capable of crosslinking without any curing agents (27).

Terminal hydroxyl groups can be introduced in liquid polymers by reacting an alkali metal terminated polymer with alkylene oxide. This polymer undergoes further coupling with diisocyanate which gives rise to an elastomer (28,29). For instance, pale yellow low viscosity oily polymers with hydroxyl endgroups having the molecular weights of 650–9900 were prepared by polymerizing butadiene, isoprene, or 2-ethyl-1,3-butadiene with lithionaphthalene in tetrahydrofuran solvent under argon atmosphere at −30°C, followed by subsequent treatments with ethylene oxide at −55°C and water. Oily polyisoprene and poly-2-ethyl-1,3-butadiene with hydroxyl endgroup were also prepared with a similar method. These products can further react with diisocyanate to form valuable high molecular weight elastomers (28).

Hayashi and Marvel (30) obtained α,ω bifunctional derivatives of polybutadiene, polyisoprene, and polystyrene by the use of the living polymer technique developed by Szwarc (15–17). The glycol derived from polybutadiene was hydrogenated to give saturated glycol. The glycol from polyisoprene was partially hydrogenated. The macroglycol was treated with an excess of diisocyanate to give prepolymer with terminal isocyanate groups. A chain extender such as water or hydrazine was added to the prepolymer solution. Chain extension proceeded slowly with water, but rapidly with hydrazine. The inherent viscosities of the products ranged from 0.2 to 0.8.

The same authors (30) also studied the block copolymer formed from the macroglycol and polystyrene dicarboxylic acid. The polycondensation was carried out by refluxing a toluene solution in the presence of *p*-toluenesulfonic acid under inert atmosphere. The degree of block polymerization, which was calculated by dividing the molecular weight of the product by the sum of the molecular weights of the corresponding two starting materials, ranged from 0.8 to 2.0 for the polybutadiene glycol series, and from 2.0 to 4.4 for the hydrogenated polybutadine glycol series. Block copolymers were further subjected to melt polycondensation under high vacuum at 200–210°C. This treatment increased the degree of block polymerization to 3 to 6.

Dihaloalkane was used as a coupling agent for lithium terminated polymers (31,32,66). These interesting (nonliquid) products can be molded to give elastomers without vulcanization (31,32). For example (32), styrene was at first polymerized with lithium or with alkyllithium, that is, *sec*-butyl-, isobutyl-, isoamyl-, or *sec*-amyllithium, to give a polystyryl lithium. Subsequently, isoprene was added to continue polymerization. In this way a block copolymer of type R-(styrene)$_m$-(isoprene)$_n$Li was obtained, in which the molecular weights of the styrene block and the isoprene block were 2000–100,000 and 5000–500,000, respectively. This block copolymer was still living and could be coupled with a dihaloalkane, e.g., CH_2Br_2, $C_2H_4Br_2$, $C_3H_6Br_2$, or $C_4H_8Br_2$ to form a block polymer of type R-(styrene)$_m$-(isoprene)$_n$-C-(isoprene)$_n$-(styrene)$_m$-R, where C is the hydrocarbon radical of the dihalogenohydrocarbon. Butadiene can also be employed as a comonomer instead of isoprene. Such styrene-isoprene block polymers with block molecular weights of 24,000 and 84,000, respectively, show, after coupling with stoichiometric amounts of methylene dibromide at 50°C for 16 hr, excellent tensile properties. Table VII summarizes some of the properties of styrene-isoprene block copolymers.

TABLE VII
Styrene-Isoprene Block Copolymer Properties (32)

Properties	Before coupling	After coupling
Intrinsic viscosity	0.74	1.03
Tensile strength at break, psi	115	2750
Elongation at break, %	1290	1180
Permanent set, %	25	20

IV. LIQUID RUBBERS BY CATIONIC POLYMERIZATION

Cationic polymerization is not a suitable method for the preparation of liquid rubbers since the reaction is accompanied by termination or isomerization, by hydride transfer and the lifetime of the propagating species is very short. These circumstances are unfavorable for molecular weight control and for the introduction of terminal functional groups. Liquid polyisobutenes are being manufactured and sold under the names Vistanex in the U.S.A. and Oppanol in Germany. However, these products cannot be vulcanized and therefore have only limited applicability (see the Kennedy chapter, p. 291, this volume). Low molecular weight polybutadienes or copolymers of butadiene and α-methylstyrene prepared with boron trifluoride etherate catalyst (33) can be used as drying oils but not as liquid rubbers.

Liquid polymers with functional terminal groups can be prepared by polymerizing olefins in the presence of formaldehyde and acetic acid. Under these conditions formaldehyde is the initiator and acetic acid the terminator. The product is a 1,3-glycol (35). Using styrene the α, ω-glycol diacetate of styrene telomer with the following structure was obtained: $AcOCH_2(CH_2CH\text{-}C_6H_5)_nOAc$ (36). The product was a mixture of oligomeric diacetates with $n = 1, 2$, and 5. Moreover, the glycol diacetates obtained in this synthesis were contaminated with various quantities of the simple styrene-acetic acid adduct together with an unsaturated product. The latter may arise by the elimination of acetic acid from glycol diacetate.

Furukawa et al. (37) investigated this reaction in some detail. The possibility to extend the chains of the telomeric glycols to liquid rubbers

TABLE VIII
Properties of Fractionated Diacetate of Polystyrene (37)

Sample no.	Bp, °C/7 mm Hg	Solubility to CH_3OH	n_D^{25}	Yield, %	MW[a]	MW[b]	Appearance
S-1	80–120	—	1.4958	3.3	—	—	Colorless liquid
S-2	120–143	—	1.4979	15.1	264	229	Colorless liquid
S-3	143–147	—	1.5038	5.0	—	—	Colorless liquid
S-4	147–151	—	1.5166	5.3	—	—	Colorless liquid
S-5	—	Soluble at −70°C	1.5487	20.8	—	—	Light yellow liquid
S-6	—	Insoluble at −70°C	1.5549	32.7	612	437	Light yellow liquid
S-7	—	Insoluble at 0°C	1.5680	17.8	778	680	Light yellow semisolid

[a] Molecular weight by the Rast method.
[b] Molecular weight from saponification equivalent.

has been studied. The reaction product of styrene, formaldehyde, and acetic acid was analyzed by infrared spectroscopy. Molecular weight measurements indicated styrene diacetate telomers having one to five styrene units. Table VIII shows some of the properties of fractionated polystyrene diacetates. These diacetates were then saponified with

TABLE IX
Properties of Glycol of Polystyrene (37)

Sample no.	Diacetate used	MW[a]	Number of styrene units	Appearance
S-2′	S-2	171	1.1	Colorless, viscous liquid
S-6′	S-6	390	3.1	Light yellow, viscous liquid
S-7′	S-7	596	5.1	Light yellow, semisolid

[a] Molecular weight from hydroxyl equivalent.

TABLE X
Preparation and Characterization of Polyurethane (37)

Sample no.	Glycol used	Diiso-cyanate	Reaction temp., °C	Reaction time, min	$[\eta]$[a]
PS-1	S-2′	TDI[b]	100	20	0.04
PS-2	S-6′	TDI	100	60	0.06
PS-3	S-7′	TDI	100	25	0.07
PS-4	S-2′	HDI[c]	120	150	0.09
PS-5	S-6′	HDI	120	150	0.11
PS-6	S-7′	HDI	120 + 150	60 + 60	0.13

[a] Determined in toluene at 30°C.
[b] Toluene-2,4-diisocyanate.
[c] Hexamethylene diisocyanate.

alcoholic potassium hydroxide to glycols. Subsequently, chain extension with toluene diisocyanate or hexamethylene diisocyanate was tried. The product was a brittle resinous polyurethane. Results are shown in Tables IX and X.

The telomerization of isoprene was investigated in a similar manner

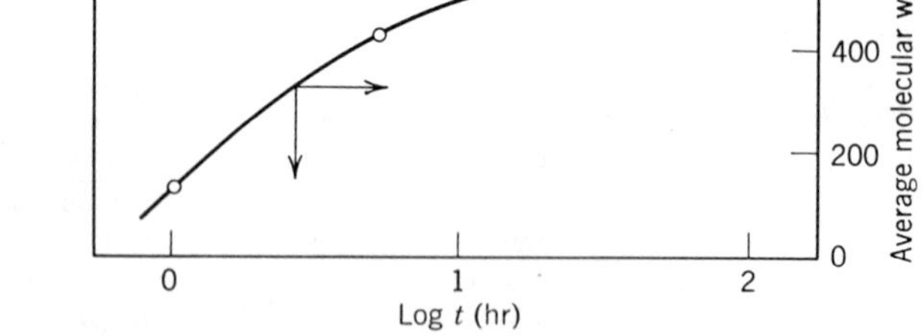

Fig. 2. The effect of reaction time on the functionality and average molecular weight of the acetate of isoprene telomer (38).

(38). For example, 0.25 mole of boron trifluoride etherate in acetic acid was added slowly at 0–10°C to a mixture of acetic acid, paraformaldehyde and isoprene (2.0, 1.5, and 2.0 moles, respectively) and the mixture was allowed to stand at the same temperature. After 24 hr, conversion was 80–90%. After about 100 hr the remaining acetic acid was removed by diluting with toluene, distilling, washing with aqueous sodium chloride solution and with water and vacuum distillation. The remaining product was a viscous liquid or a light yellow or brown semisolid, whose molecular weight by the Rast method was 449 to 1340. These values together with the saponification equivalents suggested that the number of acetate groups in the telomer was 1–3.7. Infrared spectra indicated that the telomer contained acetate and hydroxyl groups and vinyl-, *trans*-, and *cis*-type structures. Molecular weights and the number of acetyl groups increased with increasing amounts of catalyst and reaction time as shown in Fig. 2. The acetate content in the polymer increased when a part of the acetic acid was replaced with acetic anhydride. This observation suggests that telomerization was initiated not only by the protonated formaldehyde but also by direct protonation:

Initiation by protonated formaldehyde

$$H^+ + HCHO \rightarrow HOCH_2^+$$

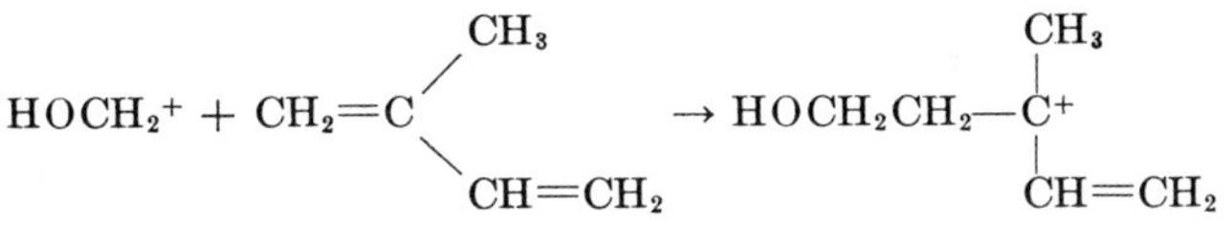

Initiation by proton

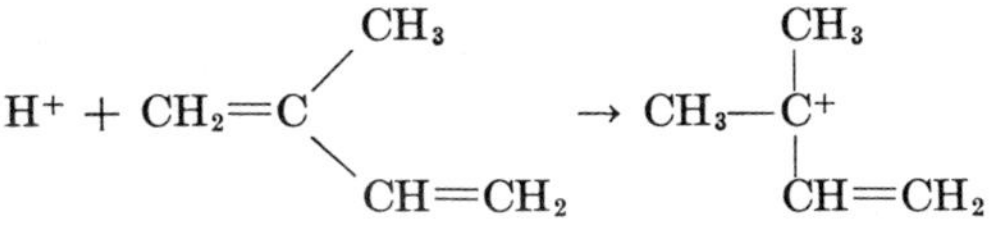

Initiation by the combination of proton, aldehyde, and acetic acid

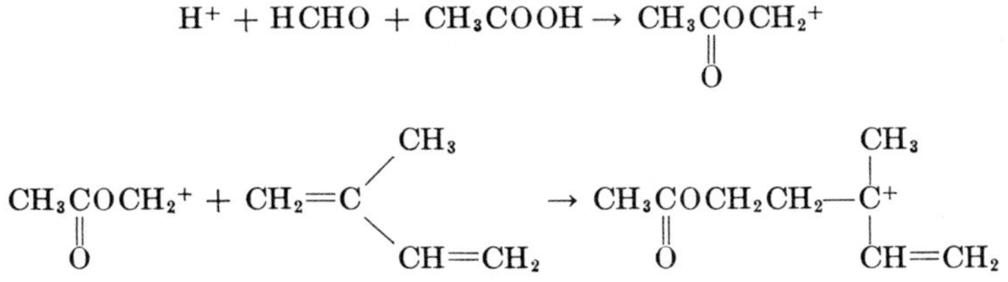

Due to the bifunctional nature of isoprene, acetate groups may be introduced not only as terminal units but also as in-chain groups. Moreover isomerizations may also proceed. Termination may occur by combination with hydroxyl ions, acetate anions, or polymeric hydroxyl groups giving terminal hydroxyl, acetate, or ether groups. Glycols of

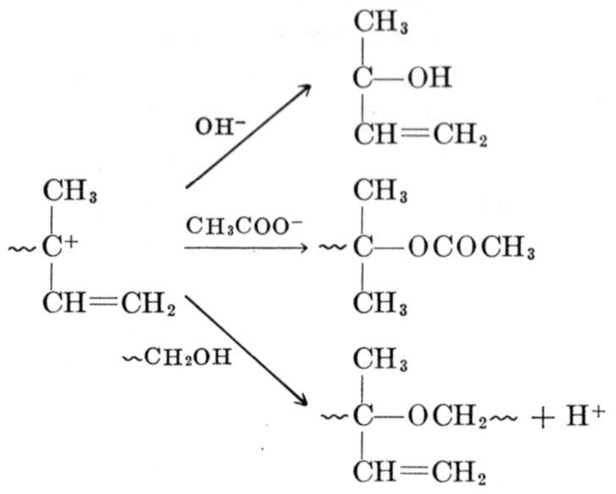

polyisoprene obtained in this manner were reacted with diisocyanates

TABLE XI
Physical Properties of Polyurethane Vulcanizates (38)

Polyurethane[a]		Vulcanizate[b]				
Telomer added (mole/1 mole of PTMG)	[η]	Cure time, min	Shore hardness	Tensile strength at break, kg/cm²	300% modulus, kg/cm²	Elongation at break, %
0.1	0.56	60	50	66	8.6	862
0.3	0.19[c]	60	52	101	8.5	1059
0.4	0.26[c]	30	40	90	16.3	1138
0	0.58	30	45	32	19.9	428

[a] Reaction product of polytetramethylene glycol (PTMG) of a mol wt of 1296 with an equivalent amount of tolylene diisocyanate heated for 2 hr at 80°C and then 3 hr at 120°C in the presence or absence of telomer glycol of a mol wt of 820.

[b] Polyurethanes with telomer additive compounded with 5 phr zinc oxide, 1 phr stearic acid, 2 phr sulfur and 2 phr tetramethylthiuram disulfide, and cured at 130°C. Homopolyurethane cured with 0.5 phr dicumyl peroxide and 3.0 phr *N,N'*-*p*-phenylene bismaleimide at 160°C.

[c] Gel fraction was removed.

to give resinous polyurethanes. Such nonrubbery products may arise from complicated structures of polyisoprene glycols with 1,2, and 3,4 addition and *cis* and *trans* unsaturation. The products seemed to be useful additives for conventional liquid urethane rubbers, since the unsaturation in the additive could be vulcanized. Table XI shows the improvement in the tensile strength of a sulfur vulcanized polymer containing additives in comparison with peroxide cured conventional polymers without additives.

V. LIQUID RUBBERS BY COORDINATION POLYMERIZATION

The coordination polymerization of olefins or diolefins with Ziegler-type catalysts may proceed by anionic or cationic mechanisms. These polymerizations are not of the "living" type since product molecular weight distributions are rather broad as compared with those of typical anionic polymerizations. Little work has been reported concerning liquid rubbers prepared by coordination polymerization.

Polybutadienes of 1000–10,000 molecular weight have been prepared with certain nickel catalyst, e.g., combinations of nickel(II)-acetylacetonate, -benzoyl acetonate, or -bis(cyclopentadienyl) with alkylaluminum sesquihalides of the type $R_{1.5}AlX_{1.5}$, where X is halogen and R is alkyl (39). The polymer was a liquid with predominantly *cis*-1,4 structure. Its viscosity was between 80 and 350 cp at 50°C. In contrast to monoethylaluminum dichloride, diethylaluminum chloride yielded somewhat higher molecular weight (38,000) polymer.

Oily to rubbery products with almost entirely 1,4 structures can also be prepared by polymerizing 1,3 dienes with a catalyst containing boron trifluoride and complex nickel compounds, e.g., triphenyl phosphine–nickel carbonyl complex (40). A colorless oily polybutadiene with a viscosity of 1900 cp at 20°C and a mol wt of 2130 was obtained. Approximately 73% of the polymer was of the *cis*-1,4 configuration while about 26% showed *trans*-1,4 configuration (40).

In this context the molecular weight jump reaction proposed by Engel (41,42) is of interest, although at the present it is only applied to solid rubbers. In this process the polymerization is initiated by a cobalt compound–alkyl aluminum halide catalyst system and during the final stage of the polymerization *tert*-butyl chloride is added. Under these conditions a sudden increase in the molecular weight of polybutadiene or polyisoprene occurs in a very short time. Carbon black or oil extension can be effected easily in this process, because handling of the high molecular weight polymer in solution can be eliminated.

VI. DEPOLYMERIZED RUBBERS

The thermal degradation of natural rubber in the presence of a suitable peptizer, i.e., *o,o′*-dibenzamidodiphenyl disulfide yields viscous liquid polymers with viscosities ranging between 5000–25,000 poises at 20°C (43). These rubbers are used as softeners, tackifiers, and binders for rubbers and facilitate potting and casting (43,44,62). Sulfur and non-sulfur vulcanizations were suggested by several patents (43,45–47).

Polymers with hydroxyl functionality can be prepared by ozone depolymerization of natural rubber, balata, gutta-percha or *cis*-1,4 poly-butadiene (48). For example, 5 g of *cis*-1,4 polybutadiene with an intrinsic viscosity of 1.4 was ozonized in chloroform for 75 min. A total of 1.87 g of ozone was consumed. Subsequently, 27 g of ozonized polymer from four samples was treated with lithiumaluminum hydride in ether at −5 to −10°C for 1.5 hr, and then refluxed for 6.5 hr. In this manner, 5.8 g of yellow liquid was obtained, whose mol wt was 300 and it contained 2.18 hydroxyl group equivalents per molecule. The method was also applied to the ozonization of butyl rubber containing about 2 mole % of isoprene (49).

VII. LIQUID RUBBERS BY CONDENSATION AND ADDITION POLYMERIZATION

Polyurethane rubbers, silicon rubbers, and polysulfide rubbers (cf. appropriate chapters in this book) are also available in liquid form. These materials are prepared similarly to conventional solid rubbers except that molecular weight regulators are used and the intermediate liquid polymers are stabilized.

Polydimethylsiloxanes with a degree of polymerization of 100–1000 are available in liquid form. These liquids can be vulcanized with poly-(alkoxysilane) in the presence of fillers (50).

$$\mathrm{HO{-}\underset{CH_3}{\overset{CH_3}{Si}}}\left(\mathrm{{-}O{-}\underset{CH_3}{\overset{CH_3}{Si}}}\right)_x\mathrm{{-}O{-}\underset{CH_3}{\overset{CH_3}{Si}}{-}OH} + \mathrm{C_2H_5O{-}\underset{OC_2H_5}{\overset{OC_2H_5}{Si}}{-}O}\left(\mathrm{{-}\underset{OC_2H_5}{\overset{OC_2H_5}{Si}}{-}O{-}}\right)_y\mathrm{\underset{OC_2H_5}{\overset{OC_2H_5}{Si}}{-}OC_2H_5}$$

$$+\ \text{Filler} \xrightarrow{\text{Catalyst}} \text{Room temperature} - \text{vulcanizable silicone rubber}$$

According to the patents (51,52) metal soaps, chelates, oxides, salts of thiols, organometallic compounds, organic bases, and basic fillers can be used as room temperature vulcanization catalysts. The above two-component method was simplified by the use of triacetoxysilane in conjunction with polysiloxane (53):

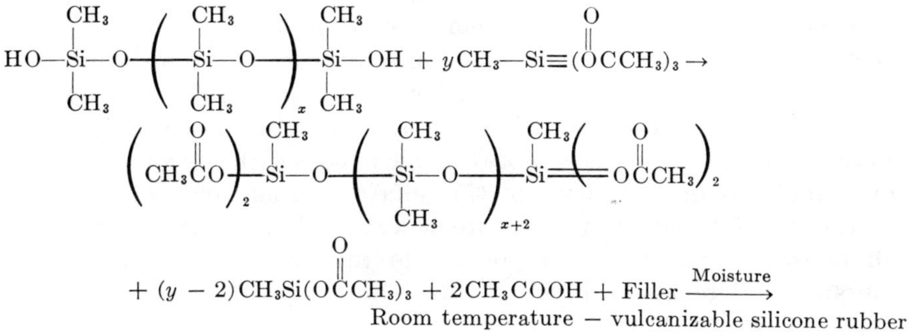

The modified liquid polymer is stable but can be crosslinked readily at room temperature with moisture. Other trisilanol and oxime derivatives were used in a similar method (54–56). (For more on silicone rubbers see the chapter by Lewis, p. 767.)

Liquid polysulfide polymers have been prepared by a complicated procedure involving polycondensation, sulfur elimination and degradation as follows (57,58,69):

Synthesis of bis(2-chloroethyl) formal

$$ClCH_2CH_2OH + (CH_2O)_x \xrightarrow[CaCl_2]{95\text{–}100°C} \underset{\textbf{(8)}}{ClCH_2CH_2OCH_2OCH_2CH_2Cl}$$

Polycondensation

$$\textbf{8} + Na_2S_4 \xrightarrow[\text{alk. emulsion}]{90\text{–}95°C} \underset{\textbf{(9)}}{\text{Tetrasulfide thiokol}}$$

Sulfur elimination

$$\textbf{9} \xrightarrow[NaOH]{90\text{–}95°C} \underset{\textbf{(10)}}{\text{Disulfide thiokol}}$$

Reductive cleavage

$$\underset{\textbf{(10)}}{\sim RSSR \sim} + NaSH + Na_2SO_3 \rightarrow \underset{\textbf{(11)}}{\sim RSNa + HSR \sim} + Na_2S_2O_3$$

$$\textbf{11} \xrightarrow{HCl} \text{Coagulation} \rightarrow \text{Liquid thiokol}$$

The structure of the repeating chain segment can be varied to produce liquid polymers of different chemical structures. Thiokol LP-2, LP-3, and LP-8 are composed of 98 mole % dichloroethyl formal and 2 mole % trichloropropane (58). The vulcanized rubber thus consists of linear polymer chains which are held together by a small amount of trifunctionality introduced into the polymer by the trichloropropane (58).

To achieve better yields, a low level of undesirable by-products, and improved molecular weight control, polysulfide polymers are produced by first reacting one or more organic halides with aqueous inorganic thiosulfate to form an organic thiosulfate solution and subsequently treating this solution with a mixture of water soluble hydrosulfide and a sulfide (59). (For more on polysulfide rubbers see the chapter by Gobran and Berenbaum, p. 805.)

References

1. T. W. Boyer, R. O. Stucker, and E. L. Ries, U.S. Pat. 3,099,650 (July 30, 1963); *Chem. Abstr.*, **59,** 10328 (1963).
2. W. W. Crouch and J. A. Shotton, *Ind. Eng. Chem.*, **47,** 2091 (1955).
3. M. Pike, Brit. Pat. 875,424 (Appl. Mar. 28, 1957); *Chem. Abstr.*, **56,** 2547 (1962).
4. Phillips Petroleum Co., Brit. Pat. 711,512 (July 7, 1954); *Chem. Abstr.*, **49,** 9326 (1955).
5. J. Blaise, A. M. Geyer, and E. Grimaud, Fr. Pat. 1,332,622 (July 19, 1963); *Chem. Abstr.*, **59,** 10329 (1963).
6. W. B. Reynolds and E. W. Cotten, *Ind. Eng. Chem.*, **42,** 1905 (1950).
7. J. M. Willis, G. Alliger, B. L. Johnson, and W. M. Otto, *Ind. Eng. Chem.*, **45,** 1316 (1953).
8. C. A. Uraneck, H. L. Hsieh, and O. G. Buck, *J. Polymer Sci.*, **46,** 535 (1960).
9. Thiokol Chemical Corp., Brit. Pat. 945,713 (Appl. U.S.A., Nov. 13, 1959); *Rubber Abstr.*, **42,** 226 (1964).
10. H. P. Brown, *Rubber Chem. Technol.*, **30,** 1347 (1957).
11. W. Cooper, *Chem. Ind. (London)*, **74,** 1741 (1955).
12. W. Cooper, Brit. Pat. 831,061 (Mar. 23, 1960).
13. J. W. Graham, "Neoprene FC," BL-374 (Jan., 1963) (to du Pont).
14. E. I. du Pont de Nemours & Co. Ind., Brit. Pat. 963,075 (July 8, 1964); *Rubber Abstr.*, **42,** 512 (1964).
15. M. Szwarc, *Nature,* **178,** 1168 (1956).
16. M. Szwarc, M. Levy, and R. Milkovich, *J. Am. Chem. Soc.*, **78,** 2656 (1956).
17. H. Brody, M. Ladacki, R. Milkovich, and M. Szwarc, *J. Polymer Sci.*, **25,** 221 (1957).
18. W. A. Schulze, W. W. Crouch, and C. S. Lynch, *Ind. Eng. Chem.*, **41,** 414 (1949).
19. W. W. Crouch, U.S. Pat. 2,631,175 (March 10, 1953).
20. A. W. Meyer, R. R. Hampton, and J. A. Davison, *J. Am. Chem. Soc.*, **74,** 2294 (1952).
21. K. Ziegler, L. Jakob, H. Wollthan, and A. Wenz, *Ann. Chem.*, **511,** 64 (1934).
22. K. Ziegler, E. Eimers, W. Hechelhammer, and H. Wilms, *Ann. Chem.*, **567,** 43 (1950).
23. E. Schoenberg, *J. Polymer Sci.*, **49,** S-9 (1961).

24. J. L. Down, Y. Lewis, B. Moore, and G. Wilkinson, *Proc. Chem. Soc.*, **1957,** 209.
25. J. T. Gruver, private communication.
26. Chemische Werke Huels A.-G., Fr. Pat. 1,366,699 (July 10, 1964); *Chem. Abstr.*, **62,** 6658 (1965).
27. J. W. Cleary, U.S. Pat. 3,048,568 (Aug. 7, 1962); *Rubber Abstr.*, **41,** 210 (1963); *Chem. Abstr.*, **58,** 14139 (1963).
28. E. J. Goldberg, U.S. Pat. 3,055,952 (Sept. 25, 1962); *Chem. Abstr.*, **58,** 645 (1963).
29. J. C. Park, Brit. Pat. 964,259 (July 22, 1964); *Chem. Abstr.* **61,** 13509 (1964).
30. K. Hayashi and C. S. Marvel, *J. Polymer Sci.*, **A2,** 2571 (1964).
31. Shell Internationale Research Maatschappij N.V., Belg. Pat. 627,652 (Jan. 28, 1963); U.S. Pat. 169,674 (Jan. 29, 1962); Belg. Pat. 646,835 (April 21, 1964); U.S. Pat. 274,864 (April 22, 1963); *Chem. Abstr.*, **62,** 6657 (1965).
32. Shell Internationale Research Maatschappij N.V., Belg. Pat. 647,860 (May 13, 1964); *Chem. Abstr.*, **62,** 10648 (1965).
33. H. C. Miller, U.S. Pat. 2,708,639 (May 17, 1955); *Chem. Abstr.*, **49,** 13666 (1955).
34. J. W. Livingston, Office Tech. Services Rept., PB-517 (1945), through ref. 2.
35. E. Arundale and L. A. Mikeska, *Chem. Rev.*, **51,** 505 (1952).
36. D. D. Coffman and E. L. Jenner, *J. Am. Chem. Soc.*, **76,** 2685 (1954).
37. J. Furukawa, S. Yamashita, and T. Sato, *Kobunshi Kagaku,* **22,** 363 (1964).
38. J. Furukawa, S. Yamashita, and T. Sato, *Kobunshi Kagaku,* **22,** 366 (1965).
39. Chemische Werke Huels A.-G., Belg. Pat. 630,428 (Aug. 1, 1963); *Chem. Abstr.*, **61,** 808 (1964).
40. Badische Anilin- & Soda-Fabrik A.-G., Neth. Appl. 6,410,331 (March 8, 1965); *Chem. Abstr.*, **63,** 4494 (1965).
41. E. F. Engel, J. Schaefer, and K. M. Kiepert, *Rubber Age (NY)*, **96,** 410 (1964).
42. E. F. Engel, J. Schaefer, and K. M. Kiepert, *Kautschuk Gummi,* **17,** 702 (1964).
43. C. Speight, *Rubber Develop.*, **8,** No. 1, 18 (1955).
44. R. A. Moncrieff, *Rubber Age Synthetics,* **34,** 241 (1953).
45. R. J. Reid and O. D. Cole, U.S. Pat. 2,983,699 (May 9, 1961); *Chem. Abstr.*, **55,** 20478 (1961).
46. K. V. Hardman and J. Lang, U.S. Pat. 3,160,595 (Dec. 8, 1964).
47. K. V. Hardman and J. Lang, *Rubber Age (NY)*, **90,** 431 (1961).
48. C. R. McIntosh, J. A. Farr, and W. D. Stephens, Belg. Pat. 636,565 (Dec. 16, 1963).
49. E. B. Jones and C. S. Marvel, *J. Polymer Sci.* **A2,** 5313 (1964).
50. M. J. Hunter, *Kautschuk Gummi,* **17,** 498 (1964).
51. S. Nitzsche and M. Wick, U.S. Pat. 3,127,363 (Mar. 31, 1964); *Chem. Abstr.*, **61,** 3285 (1964).
52. F. A. Smith, Brit. Pat. 975,708 (Nov. 18, 1964).
53. L. B. Bruner, U.S. Pat. 3,077,465 (Feb. 12, 1963).
54. D. R. Weyenberg, Fr. Pat. 1,359,396 (April 24, 1964); *Chem. Abstr.*, **62,** 4197 (1965).
55. P. L. Brown and J. F. Hyde, U.S. Pat. 3,122,522 (Feb. 25, 1964); *Chem. Abstr.*, **61,** 3284 (1964).
56. E. Sweet, Fr. Pat. 1,370,885 (Aug. 28, 1964); *Chem. Abstr.*, **62,** 6660 (1965).
57. N. P. Apukhtina, R. A. Shlyakhter, and F. B. Novoselov, *Kauchuk i Rezina,* **16,** No. 6, 7 (1957); *Chem. Abstr.*, **52,** 15111 (1958).
58. J. S. Jorczak and E. M. Fettes, *Ind. Eng. Chem.*, **43,** 324 (1951).

59. E. M. Fettes and E. R. Bertozzi, U.S. Pat. 2,875,182 (Feb. 24, 1959); *Chem. Abstr.*, **53,** 9726 (1959).
60. W. A. Schulze and W. W. Crouch, U.S. Pat. 2,469,132 (May 3, 1949).
61. Thiokol Chemical Corp., Brit. Pat. 957,652 (May 6, 1964); *Chem. Abstr.*, **61,** 7210 (1964).
62. H. Pande, *India Rubber World*, **130,** 211 (1954).
63. Phillips Petroleum Co., Brit. Pat. 921,803 (Mar. 27, 1963); *Chem. Abstr.*, **58,** 14149 (1963).
64. E. I. du Pont de Nemours & Co. Inc., Brit. Pat. 952,156 (Mar. 11, 1964).
65. Phillips Petroleum Co., Brit. Pat. 878,841 (Appl. Feb. 8, 1960); *Chem. Abstr.*, **56,** 6141 (1962).
66. G. Finaz, Y. Gallot, J. Parrod and P. Rempp, *J. Polymer Sci.*, **58,** 1363 (1962).
67. W. A. Schulze and W. W. Crouch, U.S. Pat. 2,721,185 (Oct. 18, 1955); *Chem. Abstr.*, **52,** 780 (1958).
68. Phillips Petroleum Co., U.S. Pat. 3,108,994 (Oct. 29, 1963); *Rubber Abstr.*, **42,** 280 (1964).
69. G. Göbel, *Kunststoffe*, **49,** No. 2, 56 (1959).

CHAPTER 9

ELASTOMERS BY MISCELLANEOUS OR UNKNOWN MECHANISMS

B. Catalysis by Transition Metal Salts in Water and Other Polar Solvents

R. E. RINEHART

Uniroyal–U.S. Rubber Co., Research Center, Wayne, New Jersey

Contents

I. Introduction 867
II. Effects of Metal Compounds in Free Radical Polymerizations 868
A. Salts 868
B. Chelates 871
C. Carbonyls 872
D. Peroxides 873
E. Summary 873
III. Coordination Catalysis 873
A. General 873
B. Competitive Olefin Reactions 875
C. Polymerization of Butadiene 877
1. Rhodium 877
2. Palladium 879
3. Ruthenium, Iridium, Cobalt, and Nickel 879
D. Polymerization of Bicyclo[2.2.1]-hept-2-ene and Derivatives 880
E. Polymerization of Cyclobutene 882
IV. Mechanism of Rhodium Catalyzed Butadiene Polymerization 883
A. π-Allyl Mechanism 884
B. Metal–Hydride Mechanism 886
References 889

I. INTRODUCTION

Even before the discovery of water stable coordination catalysts, it had been recognized that there is no theoretically sound basis for assuming that Ziegler-Natta catalysts can operate only under anhydrous conditions. Ziegler-Natta catalysts are, of course, very reactive toward water and oxygen, and are rapidly destroyed by trace amounts of either. However, many compounds containing metal–carbon bonds, or metal–hydride bonds—the types of structures which are considered important in polymerization—are very stable toward polar reagents, even to the extent that some of these compounds are prepared most conveniently in water or alcohol.

The platinum group noble metals are remarkable for the great variety of air and water stable organometallic compounds which they form, and for the diversity of methods of preparation of such compounds. It is not surprising that, with few exceptions, catalysts for coordination polymerization in water and alcohol are based on the platinum metals.

There had been very little systematic research on the effects of noble metals on emulsion polymerization until a few years ago. The effects of certain transition metals other than platinum metals had, however, been known for a long time. Transition metal compounds were used early in the development of redox free radical formulations. Many of the older observations could not be explained solely on the basis of free radical chemistry. Specific effects of metal upon polymerization had often been observed in free radical reactions in polar and nonpolar media.

The effects of metal upon polymerization appear to fall into two distinct categories. There are the typical free radical polymerizations in which metal species play a role either by influencing the overall rate of polymerization, or by exerting a structural modification upon the polymer. Additionally, there are those reactions in which metal species clearly act as catalyst in the initiation and propagation of polymerization, and in which free radicals are considered to play no important part in the mechanism. Although the distinction between these two types of behavior may be somewhat arbitrary, and several examples cannot be clearly assigned to one as opposed to the other, it is convenient to establish two categories for a discussion of the effect of metals on polymerization in protonic solvents.

II. EFFECTS OF METAL COMPOUNDS IN FREE RADICAL POLYMERIZATIONS

A. Salts

Catalytic amounts of metal compounds have long been used in emulsion recipes to aid in the decomposition of peroxides for the initiation of vinyl polymerization. Many early recipes contained compounds of metals which have since been shown to form stable olefin–metal coordination complexes. For example, standard emulsion redox recipes for the polymerization of butadiene included salts or complexes of iron, cobalt (1–4), and other metals (2,5,6).

Rainard (6) reported that silver nitrate even in the absence of peroxide accelerated the rate of styrene-butadiene copolymerization. The general effect of silver nitrate in an emulsion recipe containing butadiene with hydrogen peroxide initiator was to decrease the overall rate of conversion.

Kolthoff et al. (7) examined a series of free-radically initiated butadiene-styrene copolymers using perbenzoic acid to determine possible changes in butadiene microstructure. Three samples prepared at 30° (one sample prepared by a redox recipe) gave analyses for external double bonds of 19.5, 19.0, and 20%. A sample prepared by a redox recipe containing ferrous sulfate contained 24% external double bonds. Although this last analysis (as compared to the other three) was somewhat higher than could be accounted for by experimental errors in the method, at the time no particular significance was attached to the slight change in microstructure.

The effect of a variety of metal salts and complexes on solution free radical polymerization of butadiene was more recently investigated by Yamashita et al. (8). Some of the results are summarized in Table I.

Salts of all metals, with the exception of silver nitrate which increased conversion rates, retarded the rate of free radical solution polymerization of butadiene. The salts of silver and palladium had a particularly large influence on the polymer microstructure, increasing the vinyl structure and, at least in the case of palladium, suppressing *cis*-1,4 structure.

TABLE I
Effect of Metal Salts on Solution Free Radical Polymerization of Butadiene (8)

Additive, mole %	Conversion (% conversion, no additive)	Microstructure: Vinyl	*trans*	*cis*
None	100	25	62	13
CuCl, 20	50	17	66	17
$AgNO_3$, 10	500	Vinyl/*trans* ratio = 0.70		
$PdCl_2$, 2	22	45	53	2
$CoCl_2$, 10	40	20	66	14

In emulsion polymerization, all metal salts retarded the conversion rates.

Some interesting observations on the use of transition metal salts which by reaction with olefins generate radicals capable of initiating polymerization have been reported recently by Berger and Youngman (9). The results are particularly enlightening because some of the metals used to initiate radical polymerization of certain monomers are active catalysts for the coordination (non-free radical) polymerization of other monomers under identical reaction conditions. Rhodium chloride, the outstanding example of a catalyst active for coordination polymerization of butadiene in emulsion, is inactive for the initiation of styrene. Rhodium chloride will, however, initiate polymerization of methyl methacrylate (but only in the absence of butadiene) by a radical mechanism, and will initiate methyl methacrylate in the presence of styrene to give a copolymer whose composition is that expected from free radical initiation (10). These results are summarized in Table II.

In free radical polymerizations, it is reported that formation of a metal–olefin π complex is a necessary but not sufficient condition to be met in order to generate the radical (9). This concept is a reasonable one, which, in addition, explains the inhibition of free radical polymerization by olefins which do not generate radicals in combination with the metal, but which successfully compete for coordination sites on the metal atom (as, for example, inhibition of methyl methacrylate by butadiene). Presumably, other olefins or diolefins which would not be polymerized by coordination or free radical mechanisms could inhibit

TABLE II
Initiation of Polymerization and Copolymerization by Rhodium Chloride (9)

	Comonomer		
Monomer	None	Styrene	Methyl methacrylate
Butadiene (mechanism)	*trans*-1,4-PBD (coordination)	*trans*-1,4-PBD (coordination)	*trans*-1,4-PBD (coordination)
Methyl methacrylate (mechanism)	Free radical PMMA (radical)	Copolymer (radical)	—
Styrene	No polymer	—	—

the free radical polymerization of suitable monomers by forming strong but unreactive complexes with the metal.

B. Chelates

Kastning et al. (11) obtained polyethylene by treating solutions of ethylene with transition metal acetylacetonates. This work was extended to include polymerization of a variety of vinyl monomers and monomer pairs.

Polymerization of butadiene was initiated in emulsion as well as in solution, particularly by acetylacetonates of Mn(II), Co(III) and Cu(II). With these three catalysts, the relative amount of *cis*-1,4 microstructure is higher than that obtained by peroxide initiation (about 13–18%) (see Table III). In a recent patent, a similar enhancement of *cis*-1,4 polybutadiene microstructure is reported using Co(II) acetylacetonate in free radical emulsion polymerization (11a).

The polybutadiene obtained in solution and in emulsion by metal chelate initiation is high molecular weight and is virtually free from gel. The mechanical properties are reported to be similar to commercial 75:25 butadiene-styrene copolymer at ordinary temperatures, but to be far superior at lower temperatures, because of a low glass transition temperature for the homopolymer (11).

An interesting feature of the polymerizations initiated by metal chelates, is the variety of copolymers which can be prepared from monomer pairs which do not readily form copolymers by peroxide initiation. Among the pairs which have formed copolymers are ethylene-vinyl ethers, ethylene-styrene, and styrene-vinyl acetate.

The radical nature of the polymerization initiated by chelates is

TABLE III
Butadiene Polymerization Initiated by Metal Acetylacetonates (11)

	cis-1,4 Mictostructure, %	
Catalyst	Soln, 80–100°	Emulsion, 50°
$Mn(C_5H_7O_2)_3$	60	55
$Co(C_5H_7O_2)_3$	~50	45
$Cu(C_5H_7O_2)_2$	~30	32

indicated by the copolymer obtained from styrene-methyl methacrylate, which has the same composition as the monomer feed. Halocarbons are effective cocatalysts, increasing the reactivity of the metal chelates. This also implies a free radical nature in the initiation, and is similar to the rate enhancement produced by halocarbons in polymerizations initiated by metal carbonyls (Section II-C).

Despite the fundamental free radical nature of these chelate initiated polymerizations, the specific metal atom influences the structure of the polymer produced, as is shown, for example, by the steric control exerted on polybutadiene. It would appear that propagation takes place within the coordination sphere of the metal, and consequently the overall mechanism may not be exclusively free radical in nature. It is necessary to consider either that the metal atom imposes a modification upon the nature of the growing end of the polymer chain, or that a mechanism for polymerization—one of undetermined nature controlled by the metal—is operative, either in addition to, or instead of, free radical propagation. Problems of this nature will be answered fully only on the basis of future investigations.

C. Carbonyls

Carbonyl derivatives of zerovalent metals have been used by Bamford et al. to initiate polymerization in solution or in bulk (12–15). The free radical nature of these polymerizations is emphasized by the cocatalytic effect of polyhalocarbons, such as CCl_4 and CBr_4, on the polymerization rates. The metal carbonyls are either inactive or else much less active initiators in the absence of halocarbons.

The radical which initiates polymerization arises from homolytic scission of a halide–carbon bond, involving a one-electron oxidation of the metal atom (14,15). Polymerization is initiated 100% by the halocarbon radical.

$$M^0 + CX_4 \rightarrow M^+ + X^- + \cdot CX_3 \qquad (1)$$

The metal exerts a measurable influence upon the structure of the polymer. Thus with methyl methacrylate, the monomer which has been investigated in greatest detail, in every case where polymerization was initiated by metal carbonyl in combination with halocarbon, the polymers obtained had tacticities unlike those obtained by free radical catalysis. Using halocarbons in combination with carbonyls of Ni, Cr, Mo, W, Fe, and Mn, isotactic microstructure accounted for 12–31% of the total, in contrast to the 7–9% isotactic content in free radical polymethyl methacrylate (13). Similar changes in tacticity were produced in polymer initiated by free iron or cobalt metal in combination with CCl_4.

D. Peroxides

Metal peroxides prepared as insoluble fine powders have been used as polymerization initiators by Imoto et al. (16). Nickel peroxide was especially active for the bulk polymerization of styrene. Below about 10° the polymer contained a fraction which was insoluble in MEK, and possessed properties, including x-ray diffraction pattern, characteristic of isotactic polystyrene. A free radical initiation mechanism was indicated both by the analysis of methyl methacrylate-styrene copolymer, and by the inhibiting effect of hydroquinone upon vinyl acetate polymerization.

E. Summary

Metal compounds have been shown to influence the structure of polymers, and to influence the rate of polymerization under a variety of free radical conditions. For every polymerization considered in this section, a free radical mechanism seems more plausible than does ionic or coordination initiation. Even in those polymerizations in which large structural modifications have been imposed upon the polymer, sizable portions of the total polymer have shown structures which can be accounted for by assuming normal free radical propagation. None of the results from these investigations of free radical polymerizations would have led to a prediction of the dramatic results which have been obtained from a proper combination of metal catalysts with monomers in water or alcohol, leading to formation of highly stereospecific polymers by coordination–polymerization mechanisms.

III. COORDINATION CATALYSIS

A. General

Examples of polymerizations catalyzed by transition metals in protonic solvents yielding polymers which differ from those obtained from free radical initiation belong to a selective group, all of which have been reported only within the last few years. For polymerization to occur, it is necessary to bring together a proper combination of monomer, soluble metal catalyst with proper ligands, and a properly chosen solvent system. Other conditions often must be carefully defined. For example,

TABLE IV
Transition Metal Catalyzed Polymerizations

Monomer	Catalyst	Solvent	Polymer	Ref.
Ethylene	$RhCl_3$	Ethanol	*n*-Butenes (other dimers and mixed dimers from other monomers and monomer pairs)	17–19
Butadiene	$RhCl_3$	Aqueous emulsion	Cryst. *trans*-1,4 polybutadiene	20–32
	$RhCl_3$	Ethanol	Low mol wt products	17, 17a, 22
	$(C_8H_{12}RhCl)_2$	Aqueous emulsion	Cryst. *trans*-1,4 polybutadiene	21
	$Rh(NO_3)_3$	Aqueous emulsion; water; ethanol; DMF	Cryst. *trans*-1,4 polybutadiene	20, 22, 26
	Pd(II)	Aqueous emulsion	High vinyl polybutadiene	21, 33
	$Co(SiF_4)_2$	Aqueous emulsion	High *cis*-1,4 polybutadiene. (See, however, Ref. 34)	21
	$(C_3H_5NiBr)_2$	Ethanol	*trans*-1,4 polybutadiene	35
Cyclobutene	$RhCl_3{\cdot}3H_2O$	Aqueous emulsion	Polycyclobutene	36
	$RuCl_3$	Ethanol	*trans*-1,4-polybutadiene	37
	$RuCl_3$	Aqueous emulsion	50% *cis*-1,4 polybutadiene 50% *trans*-1,4 polybutadiene	37
	$(C_3H_5NiBr)_2$	Ethanol	Polycyclobutene	35
Norbornene and derivatives	Ir(III) Ru(III) Os(III)	Ethanol	Amorphous ring opened polynorbornene and derivatives	38
	Ir(III)	Ethanol in benzene	Amorphous ring opened polynorbornene and derivatives	39
	Ir(III) Ir(IV) Ru(III) (plus reducing agent)	Aqueous emulsion	Amorphous ring opened polynorbornenes and derivatives	40

an effective reducing agent, control of pH, an emulsifier chosen from a very limited group, are factors which can determine whether or not polymerization will take place. The reported examples of polymerization by coordination mechanisms in protonic solvents are shown in Table IV.

None of the polymerizations (with the exception of the polymerization of norbornenes containing polar functional groups) has led to a novel product. All the polymers have been prepared independently by Ziegler-Natta catalyst systems. This observation strengthens the conviction of a close mechanistic relationship between the catalyst systems which are stable in water, as compared with the Ziegler-Natta catalysts which are not.

B. Competitive Olefin Reactions

Most olefins, if treated with the catalyst systems described in Table IV, do not form polymers. Several types of olefin reaction other than polymerization have been observed. Treatment of ethylene or other olefins with palladium chloride in water leads to oxygenated products (acetaldehyde) and a concomitant reduction of the palladium salt to free metal, the basis of the well-known Wacker process (41).

An important potential side reaction to polymerization is olefin isomerization which, in the presence of catalytic amounts of noble metal salts, can be very rapid (22, 42–48). The mechanism of olefin isomerization is currently a topic of controversy. Possibly no one mechanism can be used to explain all the experimental observations made under various conditions. One attractive mechanistic approach might be called the hydrido π-allyl concept (44,47,48). Migration of an allylic hydride of an olefin metal π complex leads to formation of the hydrido π-allyl–metal complex **1**.

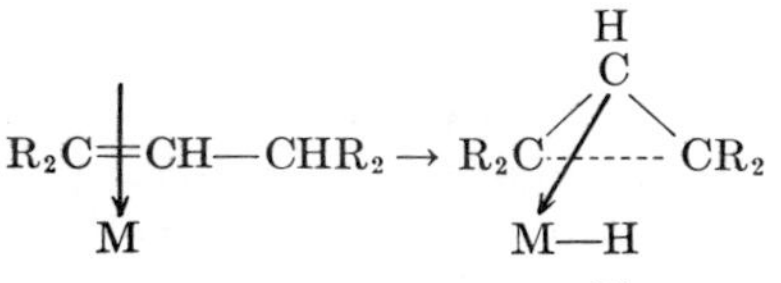

(2)

(1)

Among the monomers in Table IV, few have structures which would permit ready formation of a π-allyl complex (49) by the path shown in Eq. 2. Thus, ethylene lacks the necessary 3-carbon structure; butadiene has no allylic hydrogens (removal of hydrogen would result not in a π-

allyl complex, but in an allenic complex); a π-allyl complex from norbornene would be highly strained even to the point where it might be considered a violation of Bredt's rule. Polymerization may be a mechanistic consequence of the inability of an olefin to form a π-allyl complex and hence to undergo reactions such as isomerization instead of polymerization.

This interpretation of olefin isomerization accounts well for the high reactivity of ethylene in rhodium catalyzed dimerization, as compared to the reactivity of other α-olefins, including even propylene (Table V). Propylene, upon isomerization, would form propylene indistinguishable from the starting material except by tagging. But on a competitive basis, isomerization predominates over propylene dimerization, judging from the much smaller yields of this dimer compared with the production of butene from ethylene. Butene-1, which upon isomerization forms the internal olefins *cis*- and *trans*- butene-2, has not been observed to dimerize (19,22), nor have the higher α-olefins (42,44). The isomerization of butene-1 is so rapid, that butene formed from ethylene dimerization shows no tendency to add additional ethylene to form hexene (19).

Olefin isomerization is suppressed by use of a monomer which forms a stronger complex with the metal than does the isomerizable olefin. This concept is important in rhodium catalyzed butadiene polymerization, where the reaction product is 99% pure *trans*-1,4 polybutadiene. Monomeric butadiene forms a tight complex with the catalyst, preventing formation of a complex between polybutadiene and the rhodium. If it were not for this inhibition by the monomer, it would be expected that the polybutadiene would be no more than about 75–85% *trans*-1,4 structure. The balance would be *cis*-1,4 microstructure produced by rapid isomerization (22). Thus, butadiene suppresses isomerization of poly-

TABLE V
Dimerization vs. Isomerization
(Catalyst: $RhCl_3$ in Ethanol)

Olefin	Temp.	Amt. dimer (comparable scale)	Isomerization	Ref.
Ethylene	45°	178 g	Not possible	17a
Propylene	50°	6 g	Not determined	17a
Butene-1	50°	0	Complete to equilibrium	19, 22

butadiene and of other olefins including butene; ethylene does not suppress the isomerization of butene.

C. Polymerization of Butadiene

1. Rhodium

Rhodium is the outstanding coordination catalyst for the polymerization of butadiene in aqueous media and compared to other metal catalysts has received the greatest attention in the literature. Much of this interest is centered on the hope that conclusions drawn from observations on rhodium may have direct bearing upon the mechanism of polymerization by catalyst systems which are experimentally more difficult to study. At present, this hope appears to be justifiable, although the mechanism for rhodium catalysis has proven complicated (Section IV).

All the common soluble salts of trivalent rhodium have shown catalytic activity in emulsion. There is, however, wide variation in polymerization rates depending upon the anions associated with the rhodium.

No success has been reported using soluble rhodium catalysts for polymerization of butadiene in nonpolar solvents or in bulk. Polymerization in bulk has been effected, however, using an insoluble rhodium catalyst. Commercial aqueous solution of rhodium nitrate, which is very complex, forms a tarry solid upon evaporation to dryness, only part of which will redissolve in water. When butadiene (bulk) is treated with this crude tarry solid, *trans*-1,4 polybutadiene forms on the surface of the inorganic tar and grows out from this surface as a monomer insoluble polymer phase (50).

Rhodium nitrate in aqueous solution is unusual among rhodium catalysts in that polymerization of butadiene can be effected in water without emulsifier, or in polar solvents such as ethanol and dimethylformamide (22). The other common rhodium salts, such as rhodium chloride, require the use of carefully chosen emulsifiers. The emulsifier must be either an alkyl sulfate or an alkaryl sulfonate (22,31). The observation of specific structure requirements has induced the study of emulsifier chain length, which in some cases is a critical factor (26). The only successful alkyl sulfate emulsifier for polymerizations catalyzed by rhodium chloride is sodium lauryl sulfate. Longer or shorter alkyl chains lead to no polymer. Sodium alkyl sulfonates are inactive emulsifiers. Sodium alkylbenzene sulfonates lead to polymers, the length of the alkyl chain not being critical.

The reasons for such selective behavior of emulsifiers, which vary but little in structure, are obscure. (It has been suggested that the emulsifier serves as a ligand, but that alkyl chains of certain lengths may tend to block the active catalyst site.) The one inescapable conclusion is that these polymerizations differ in many ways from normal free radically catalyzed emulsion polymerizations. One unusual difference is the morphology of the latex particles produced by rhodium catalysis as compared with the spherical particles from free radical catalysis. Evidence by electronmicroscopy shows that in the colloidal state at least some, if not most, of the latex particles from rhodium catalysis are not spheres, but are instead oblate spheroids (51).

Neither free radical initiators nor inhibitors have much effect upon the rate of rhodium catalyzed butadiene polymerization (20–22,26). Again, a nonradical mechanism is indicated. Polymerization rates can be drastically altered, however, by a number of reactants. The rate can be slowed or stopped by ligands which successfully compete with the monomer for active catalyst sites. Rate enhancement is observed for selected reagents which either may aid in the formation of a more active catalyst, or may convert more metal atoms into active catalyst. Specific examples of rate effects are listed below:

(*1*) Catalysis by rhodium chloride is sensitive to the pH of the aqueous phase. The maximum rate is observed at pH 2–4, being much slower either above or below this range (21).

(*2*) Formic acid enhances the rate in a specific manner which is not imparted by other common carboxylic acids (32).

(*3*) 1,3-Cyclohexadiene at a cyclohexadiene to rhodium molar ratio of about 20:1 enhances the polymerization rate by a factor greater than 20, activation being less at higher or lower molar ratios (24).

(*4*) 1,5-Cyclooctadiene is a powerful inhibitor for rhodium chloride even when present in less than molar ratio (24,52). This inhibition is somewhat surprising in view of the excellent catalytic properties of the rhodium(I) chloride–cyclooctadiene complex $(1,5\text{-}C_8H_{12}RhCl)_2$ (21). In the complexed form, 1,5-cyclooctadiene apparently does not compete for polymerization sites, but it does compete when added as free diolefin. (1,5-Cyclooctadiene at every concentration inhibits polymerization initiated by $(1,5\text{-}C_8H_{12}RhCl)_2$ (52).)

(*5*) Nitrogeneous ligands, such as pyridine and ethylene diamine tetraacetic acid, are powerful inhibitors at any molar ratio. Chelating oxygen compounds, e.g., acetylacetone, have very little effect upon the reaction rate (23).

2. Palladium

Palladium compounds influence the microstructure of polybutadiene either in solution (Section II-A) or in emulsion (21,33). To obtain large effects in emulsion it is necessary to use relatively large ratios of palladium to monomer and relatively long reaction times. The polymers usually exhibit high ratios of 1,2-polybutadiene to *trans*-1,4 structure, but this ratio is dependent upon the anion associated with the palladium. As high as 98:2 ratio of vinyl to *trans* structure is obtained using K_2PdCl_6. By use of difficultly soluble PdI_2 and $Pd(CN)_2$, low yields of polybutadiene containing high *trans*-1,4 content were obtained (33). Enhanced *trans*-1,4 structure (73% *trans*, 9% vinyl, 18% *cis*) can be obtained efficiently by use of diamine oxalato palladium(II) in aqueous emulsion with a free radical initiator (50).

An oddity of the palladium catalyzed systems is the lack of sensitivity to the type of emulsifier. Nonionic, cationic, and anionic emulsifiers, or even no emulsifier, gave satisfactory conversions and reasonably consistent steric control using palladium chloride as catalyst (33).

The amount of information on the influence of palladium in aqueous systems is not complete enough to permit a conclusion as to the relative importance of a free radical mechanism. There are, however, at least some indications that a radical mechanism may be more important for palladium than for other polymerizations discussed in this section.

3. Ruthenium, Iridium, Cobalt, and Nickel

Most of the soluble salts and complexes of rhodium and palladium are active catalysts for the polymerization of butadiene. There are, however, some transition metals which exhibit catalytic activity only in the form of certain of their complexes.

"Ruthenium trichloride trihydrate" is inactive as a catalyst for butadiene. Polymerization can be effected if a phosphine is added to the polymerization recipe (21,53). Addition of triphenyl phosphine leads to polymer with enhanced *cis*-1,4 structure; tributyl phosphine enhances vinyl addition. With ruthenium, butadiene apparently is not able to serve as a satisfactory stabilizing ligand for the active catalyst; stronger ligands such as the phosphines are required.

Hypophosphorous acid is an interesting activator for the ruthenium chloride–phosphine–butadiene system (53). This accelerating effect could imply that polymerization is initiated by a ruthenium complex in a low oxidation state, stabilized by the phosphine ligands, with hypophosphorous acid serving the function of an efficient reducing agent. Or, it is possible that hypophosphorous acid, like other strong reducing agents, can serve as a source of hydride ligand for the active complex. A change in oxidation number does not always accompany substitution by hydride (54). Whether the active ruthenium catalyst is a metal hydride, or whether it is a nonhydridic complex of the metal in low oxidation state, cannot be decided on the basis of available evidence. (A discussion of the possibility of metal–hydride structures in connection with polymerization mechanisms is presented in Section IV-B).

Ruthenium is unusual among the noble metals, being the only catalyst which appears to have activity both for ring opening polymerizations (cyclobutene, norbornene) and for vinyl addition polymerizations (butadiene, ethylene). Iridium might also appear to fit into this class. Iridium is an excellent catalyst for the ring opening polymerization of norbornene (Section III-D) and has also been reported as a catalyst for the preparation of *trans*-1,4 polybutadiene (21). For butadiene, however, iridium is at best a sluggish catalyst which does not always yield polymer (26).

High *cis*-1,4 polybutadiene was reported using $CoSiF_6$ as the catalyst in emulsion (21). It has been questioned whether this polymer is *cis* polybutadiene, or whether it is butadiene with free radical microstructure, but heavily contaminated by catalyst residues (34). The original report of high *cis* polymer has been defended in a footnote in a recent publication from Shell Development (55). A fuller evaluation of the cobalt catalyst must await the publication of complete experimental details of a reliable procedure.

π-Allyl nickel bromide $(\pi\text{-}C_3H_5NiBr)_2$ (56), stable toward alcohol but not to air, is an active catalyst for the polymerization of butadiene in ethanol or benzene (35). In each solvent the product is *trans*-1,4 polybutadiene of rather low molecular weight. This polymerization represents the only example in which an identical product is obtained from butadiene by the same catalyst either in a polar solvent, or under typical Ziegler polymerization conditions.

D. Polymerization of Bicyclo[2.2.1]-hept-2-ene and Derivatives

Norbornene is resistant to polymerization by free radicals or ions. The first successful polymerization of norbornene was accomplished by a coordination catalyst based on titanium tetrachloride and lithium aluminum tetraheptyl (57). More recently, norbornene has been polymerized in alcohol using salts of iridium, ruthenium, and osmium (38). Catalysis by alcoholic solutions of metal salts leads to polymers of somewhat low intrinsic viscosities. The low molecular weights are possibly caused by low solubility of the polymers in the reaction medium. Refinements of the original method include homogeneous polymerization in benzene containing 10% ethanol which is added to dissolve and activate the iridium catalyst (39), and polymerization in emulsion using reducing agents in conjunction with an iridium or ruthenium catalyst (40). Both these newer methods lead to soluble polymers of high molecular weight ([η] greater than 2). A comparison of catalytic conditions for the polymerization of norbornene is shown in Table VI.

Polymerization in polar solvents leads to polymers containing cyclopentane rings and unsaturation (predominantly *trans* configuration) along the polymer chain (Eq. 4). Such a structure corresponds most closely to the "type B" polynorbornene prepared by the du Pont catalyst (57). However, in contrast to the crystalline polymers prepared by the titanium catalyst, the polymers prepared by noble metals in alcohol and water are amorphous. Polynorbornene prepared by catalysts such as iridium melts lower than does crystalline polynorbornene.

An outstanding advantage of the use of noble metals for norbornene polymerization is the ability of these catalysts to polymerize polar monomers. Many of these polar polymers have attractive physical properties, as a result of their functional groups. Norbornenes are conveniently prepared by the Diels-Alder addition of cyclopentadiene to olefins. Any olefin which can undergo addition to cyclopentadiene can

TABLE VI
Catalysts for Polymerization of Norbornene

Catalyst system	Solvent	Reaction temp., °C	Conversion, g/hr-mole cat.	[η], Benzene	Ref.
$TiCl_4 + LiAl(C_7H_{16})_4$ .03 .015	Hydrocarbon	Room	9	Partly insol.	57
$TiCl_4 + LiAl(C_7H_{16})_4$ .01 .02	Hydrocarbon	Room	60	Partly insol.	57
$IrCl_3{\cdot}4H_2O$ + EtOH	Ethanol	24	2.0×10^2	—	38
$IrCl_3{\cdot}4H_2O$ + EtOH	Ethanol	80	1.1×10^5	0.57	38
$RuCl_3{\cdot}3H_2O$ + EtOH	Ethanol	80	1.24×10^3	0.69	38
$OsCl_3{\cdot}$ + EtOH	Ethanol	80	2×10^3	0.15	38
$IrCl_3{\cdot}4H_2O$ + EtOH	Benzene	Room	—	2.9	39
$(NH_4)_2IrCl_6$ + EtOH	Aqueous emulsion	50	2.4×10^3	2.4	40
$RuCl_3{\cdot}3H_2O + H_2CO$	Aqueous emulsion	50	5.2	—	40

be considered a potential monomer for polymerization. Custom synthesis of new monomers is very straightforward, and a variety of polymers have been prepared. With certain monomers, however, one or more functional groups may behave as a chelating ligand leading to inactive catalyst by reaction with iridium (38,39).

Monomer preparation:

(3)

Polymerization:

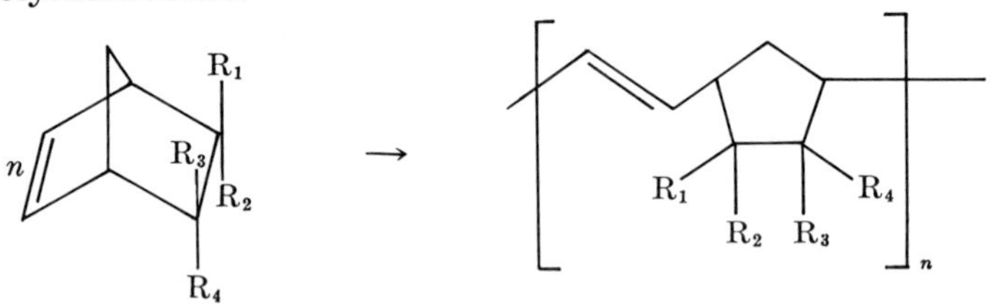

(4)

E. Polymerization of Cyclobutene

Ruthenium chloride catalyzes the ring opening polymerization of cyclobutene in alcohol and in aqueous emulsion (37). In alcohol, the product is crystalline *trans*-1,4 polybutadiene; in water, the polymer contains 50% *trans* and 50% *cis*-1,4 microstructure. 3-Methyl cyclobutene gives a product with a polypiperylene structure (Eq. 6) (cf. pp. 715 and 720ff.) Rhodium chloride with cyclobutene in emulsion leads to polymer with no polybutadiene units.

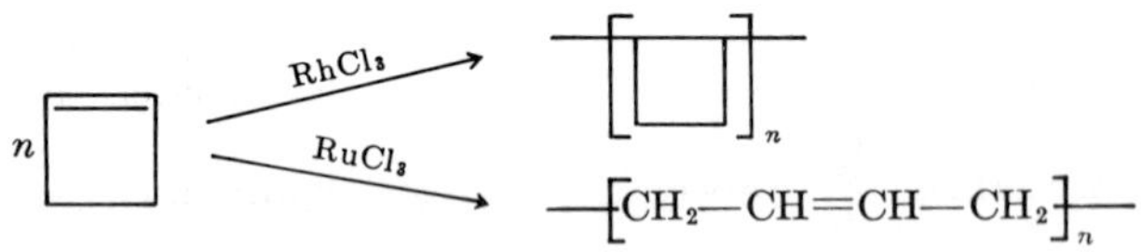

(5)

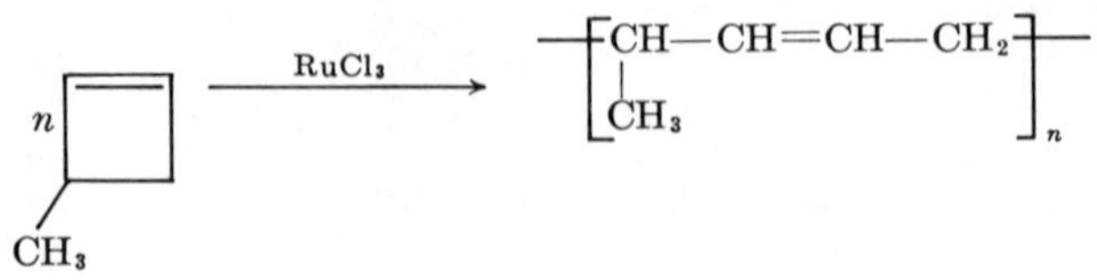

(6)

It is interesting that ruthenium chloride, which is not a good catalyst for the polymerization of butadiene in the absence of stabilizing ligands (Section III-C-3), forms polybutadiene from cyclobutene by the ring opening mechanism in the absence of such ligands. The lack of need for added stabilizers corresponds more closely to the behavior of ruthenium chloride as a catalyst for norbornene polymerization, which also proceeds by a ring opening route (Section III-D). It has not been reported that ring opening of cyclobutene is effected by iridium chloride, although it might well be that iridium (possibly in conjunction with a reducing agent) would be superior to ruthenium for the preparation of polybutadiene.

Rhodium chloride, which shows no ability to polymerize norbornene by the ring opening mechanism, also shows no ability to open the cyclobutene ring, leading instead to saturated polymers.

The observations on the polymerization of cyclobutene thus agree well with the results observed with other monomers. Some of the noble metal catalysts are effective only for ring opening polymerization, while others catalyze polymerization by addition. This same behavior is shown by Ziegler catalysts. Titanium catalysts polymerize norbornene and cyclobutene to ring opened products; vanadium catalysts on the other hand, form saturated polymers from cyclobutene (58,59).

The study of the polymerization of cyclobutene by noble metal halides has done much to relate the behavior of these catalysts to the behavior of the more unstable, but more widely used, Ziegler-Natta catalysts.

IV. MECHANISM OF RHODIUM CATALYZED BUTADIENE POLYMERIZATION

Much speculation on the mechanism of butadiene polymerization catalyzed by aqueous rhodium chloride has appeared in the literature. Available data do not, however, justify proposing a detailed step-by-step mechanism. Part of the difficulty is the lack of information about the structures of complexes between rhodium and butadiene. The important features of every proposed mechanism receive their strongest support from work reported on metals other than rhodium. The relative instability of rhodium–butadiene complexes is probably the very reason for the high catalytic activity.

Two possible mechanisms for the polymerization of butadiene by rhodium chloride will be sketched, together with the strongest supporting evidence for each. It is premature to choose one mechanism as favored over the other, or to exclude other possibilities. It is hoped that this discussion will serve to emphasize the types of problems which must be considered in reaching a fuller understanding of this novel method of polymerization.

A. π-Allyl Mechanism

Butadiene forms π-allyl complexes with metals by addition of cations (proton) (Eq. 7) or anions (chloride, for example) (Eq. 8), to the organic moiety of a butadiene–metal π complex

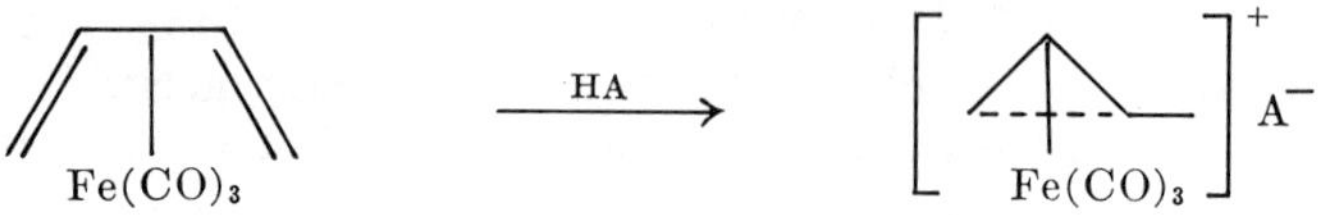

(7)

Ref. 60

$2C_4H_6 + 2PdCl_2 \rightarrow$ 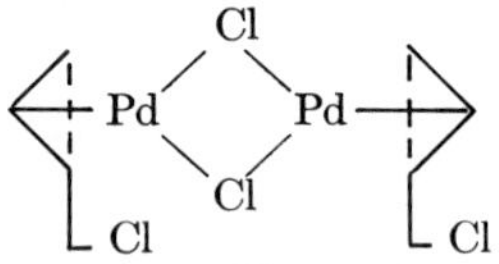

(8)

Ref. 61

(**2**)

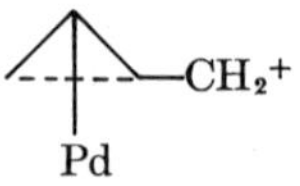

(**3**)

Proposed mechanisms for catalysis by π-allyl complexes tend to favor structures such as **2** (with Rh substituted for Pd) as being important for the initiation of butadiene polymerization catalyzed by rhodium. One compelling argument is the proven stability of cation **3**, formed by loss of Cl^- from **2** (61). Cation **3** is comparable in stability to the ferrocenyl carbinyl cation, which in turn is as stable as the trityl cation (62). A cation from butadiene and rhodium having a structure similar to **3**, might be stable even in water.

There is good evidence that complexes such as **3** are able to add to butadiene, forming structures in which butadiene molecules are linked together. A complex from rhodium chloride $Rh_2Cl_4C_{12}H_{18}$ has been mentioned, which may be structurally related to a well-defined ruthenium complex, $RuCl_2C_{12}H_{18}$ **4** (63). The structure of **4** has been demonstrated by single crystal x-ray diffraction. Two of the three molecules of butadiene retain a π-allyl configuration, the third contains a π complexed

trans double bond

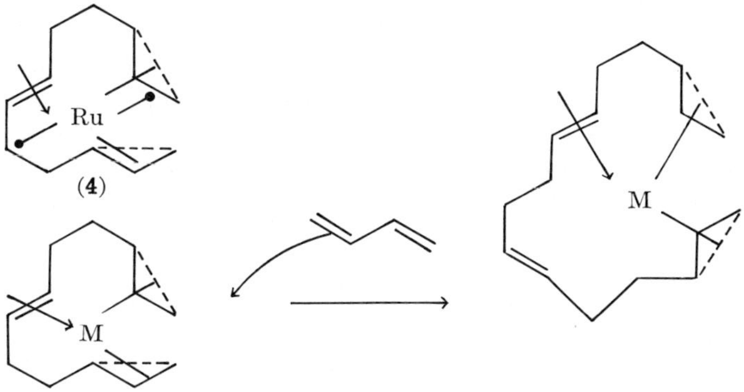

(9)

By the proposed π-allyl mechanism for rhodium catalyzed polymerization, propagation could be effected by reaction of butadiene with complex **5** (ligands other than hydrocarbon not specified) (Eq. 9). The entering butadiene displaces one of the π-allylic hydrocarbon ends, forming a new π-allyl complex, a new π bonded *trans* double bond, and an uncomplexed *trans* double bond, as shown in the hypothetical complex **6**. That no transfers of hydrogen are required in the initiation step is an interesting feature of this mechanism.

In this incomplete mechanism, no definite statements can be made about the termination step. Possibly, the two π-allyl structures combine, giving a macroring polymer. Such a termination mechanism has been proposed for the formation of *trans, trans, trans*-cyclododeca-1,5,9-triene by Ni^0 catalysts (64). Alternative termination mechanisms for rhodium catalyzed butadiene polymerization are plausible. Experimentally, the cyclic termination mechanism would receive needed support, if it were shown that the polybutadiene chains are macrorings. This has neither been proved nor disproved (cf. p. 722).

If termination were effected by ring closure, vinyl unsaturation theoretically could be missing altogether. In point of fact, the polybutadiene shows very little (sometimes barely detectable or not noticeable by the method of analysis) vinyl unsaturation, even though the molecular weight of the polymer may be quite low. The π-allyl mechanism for rhodium catalyzed butadiene polymerization thus is an attractive one, which accounts well for the production of pure *trans* polymer, with only traces of *cis* or vinyl structure.

In support of the π-allyl mechanism, it may be pointed out that piperylene is a more reactive monomer than is isoprene, and will form homopolymer, or copolymer with butadiene (25). Both butadiene and piperylene have structures which can give rise to monosubstituted π-allyl cationic complexes (**7a** and **7b**, respectively), whereas isoprene has a structure which could give rise only to disubstituted complexes **8** or **9**. Disubstituted π-allyl complexes are demonstrably less stable than are the monosubstituted complexes (60). The failure of isoprene to polymerize well could be ascribed to the lessened stability of the π-allyl complexes **8** or **9**.

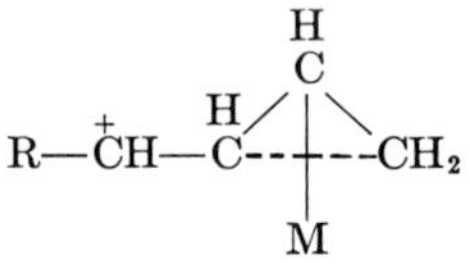

(**7a**) R = H
(**7b**) R = CH_3

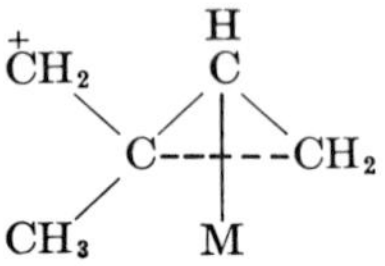

(**8**)

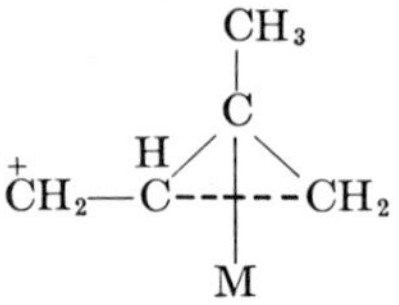

(**9**)

The complex from rhodium chloride and butadiene, $Rh_2Cl_4C_{12}H_{18}$ (63), despite being sparingly soluble, is an effective catalyst for the polymerization of butadiene. On an equivalent basis and without cocatalysts, the complex is about twice as active as is $RhCl_3{\cdot}3H_2O$ without cocatalysts (52). Assuming that the $Rh_2Cl_4C_{12}H_{18}$ is structurally related to **4**, the good catalytic properties may be the consequence of π-allylic nature of the complex. It might be expected, however, that the ideal catalyst for butadiene polymerization would be a rhodium complex containing only one metal atom per molecule, thus being more soluble in the reaction medium.

B. Metal–Hydride Mechanism

The mechanism of rhodium catalyzed dimerization of ethylene has been described in detail by Cramer (19). By Cramer's mechanism, the active catalyst for initiation is a π-ethylene hydridorhodium complex. Initiation is effected by insertion of complexed ethylene into the rhodium–hydride bond. It may reasonably be expected that a similar mechanism may be operative in the polymerization of butadiene in emulsion. It must be cautioned, however, that under the conditions of ethylene dimerization, butadiene does not form high polymers; instead, dimer and other low molecular products are produced (17a,22).

A metal hydride mechanism can be formulated, if it is assumed that hydridorhodium complexes undergo reactions similar to other transition metal hydrides. Known reactions include insertion of butadiene between the hydride and the metal:

$$HFe(CO)_2(C_5H_5) + CH_2{=}CH{-}CH{=}CH_2 \rightarrow HCH_2{-}CH{=}CH{-}CH_2{-}Fe(CO)_2(C_5H_5) \quad (10)$$

Ref. 65

$$HMn(CO)_5 + CH_2{=}CH{-}CH{=}CH_2 \rightarrow HCH_2{-}CH{=}CH{-}CH_2{-}Mn(CO)_5 \quad (11)$$

Ref. 66

Initiation of polymerization would be dependent upon the ability of complexed butadiene to insert into a water stable rhodium hydride bond, giving rise to a butenyl rhodium complex. All *trans* structure of the polymer may be imparted by steric requirements brought about by the presence of the metal atom. Or, the addition may be reversible, in which case *trans* structure would tend to accumulate, being the less displaceable ligand.

$$HRh + C_4H_6 \rightarrow HCH_2{-}CH{=}CH{-}CH_2{-}Rh \quad (12)$$

Propagation would occur by insertion of more butadiene between the rhodium–carbon σ bond. It can be emphasized that insertion between rhodium–carbon σ bonds is a known reaction (67) as shown in Eq. 13.

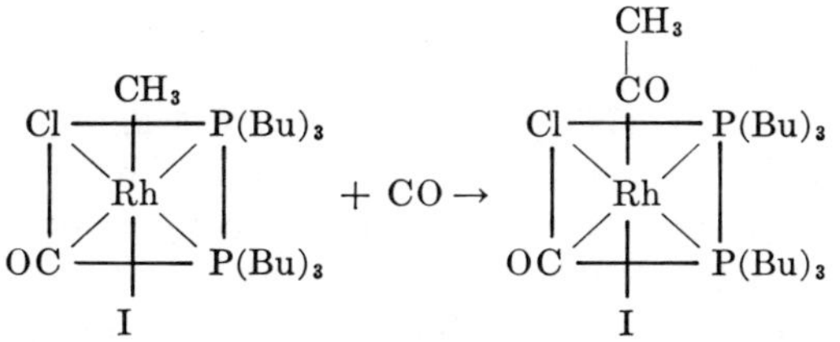

(13)

Experimental evidence can be cited which tends to favor the metal–hydride mechanism over the π-allyl mechanism. Teyssié has shown that 1,3-cyclohexadiene enhances the rate of butadiene polymerization catalyzed by $RhCl_3$ (Section III-C-1). He attributes this rate enhancement to a stabilization by 1,3-cyclohexadiene ligand of a lower oxidation state of rhodium. However, 1,3-cyclohexadiene is not considered to be a very effective stabilizing ligand for rhodium. A complex which has been prepared from rhodium chloride and 1,3-cyclohexadiene is, in fact, relatively unstable, especially above room temperature (52). 1,3-Cyclohexadiene enhances the polymerization of butadiene catalyzed by rhodium chloride–1,5-cyclooctadiene complex. No added stabilization of Rh^{1+} is necessary in this remarkably stable complex. Nor is the cyclohexadiene serving the function of a reducing agent in the case of the cyclooctadiene complex. The only lower oxidation state is Rh^0, of which no stable well-defined olefin complexes are known. It would be assumed that strong reducing agents would produce catalytically inactive rhodium metal. This assumption has been experimentally verified. In the absence of butadiene necessary to stabilize the lower oxidation state, 1,3-cyclohexadiene does indeed reduce rhodium chloride to catalytically inactive free metal (25). It would appear that the primary function of cyclohexadiene is to contribute a hydride ion to the rhodium, forming benzene and giving a complex with enhanced catalytic activity.

Ability to form a hydride may be an explanation for the experimental observation that formic acid is a very effective cocatalyst for polymerization (32). Formic acid increases the rate of polymerization of butadiene to about 100 times the rate by the same complex containing no cocatalyst (Table VII).

Formic acid reacts with certain metal halides to produce hydrogen and carbon dioxide. One mechanism which has been proposed (68) for this decomposition is shown below:

$$HCOO^- + M^{n+} \rightarrow CO_2 + HM^{(n-1)+} \tag{14}$$

It is reasonable to expect that formic acid may be a source of hydride forming an active catalyst by a route such as that shown in Eq. 14.

For additional support of the metal–hydride mechanism the investigations by Babitskii et al. (14) using radioactive tagging techniques could be cited. (Babitskii et al., however, favor a π-allyl mechanism.) Several examples were reported in which polymerizations were conducted in tritiated water. Using $RhCl_3$, it was found that tritium is introduced into the polymer chain, some of which is reversibly displaceable by H_2O, and therefore is considered to consist of alcohol groups.

$$\gt COT + H_2O \rightarrow HTO + \gt COH \tag{15}$$

Alkyl tritium is not displaceable.

In polymerizations catalyzed by rhodium chloride, or by rhodium chloride–olefin complexes, there are complicating factors such as the

TABLE VII
Polymerization of Butadiene by $[RhCl(1,5\text{-}C_8H_{12})]_2$ (24, 32)

Cocatalyst	Rate, g/hr-g catalyst (52)
None	2.3
1,3-Cyclohexadiene	86
Formic acid	268

appearance of radioactivity in the polymer chain, when Cl^{36} tagging is used. This allylic chloride represents a potential site for the introduction of hydroxyl groups into the polymer chain, by a process not connected with the polymerization mechanism. When, however, $[1,5\text{-}C_8H_{12}RhCH_3CO_2]_2$ is used as catalyst in tritiated water, the complications arising from the presence of chloride are avoided. Using this catalyst one finds that none of the tritium in the polymer chain is displaceable by water. All the tritium which is present is attached to carbon.

The π-allyl mechanism proposes structures such as **7a** which offer no good explanation for the introduction of alkyl hydrogen in initiation. (Babitskii proposes that tritium is introduced in the termination step.) The metal–hydride mechanism assumes a rhodium hydride complex in the initiation step. Such rhodium hydrides are labile, and can undergo solvent exchange before the insertion reaction takes place (19). Thus, it might be expected from the metal–hydride mechanism that alkyl hydrogens are introduced by solvent in the initiation step. The finding of alkyl substituted tritium, but not hydroxyl substitution can be considered evidence for favoring the metal–hydride mechanism.

References

1. C. F. Fryling, in *Synthetic Rubber,* G. S. Whitby, Ed., Wiley, New York, 1954 pp. 261–272, 277.
2. C. S. Marvel, R. Deanin, B. M. Kuhn, and G. B. Landes, *J. Polymer Sci.,* **3,** 433 (1948).
3. C. S. Marvel, G. E. Inskeep, R. J. Dearborn, J. H. Saunders, H. W. Johnston, D. A. Shepherd, A. J. Deutschman, J. A. Damman, and L. A. Oppegard, *J. Polymer Sci.,* **3,** 181 (1948).
4. R. Deanin, R. D. Lindsay, and S. E. Leventer, *J. Polymer Sci.,* **3,** 421 (1948).
5. E. Tschunkur and W. Bock, U.S. Pat. 1,935,733 to I. G. Farbenindustrie (Nov. 21, 1933).
6. L. W. Rainard, *J. Polymer Sci.,* **2,** 16 (1947).
7. I. M. Kolthoff, T. S. Lee, and M. A. Mairs, *J. Polymer Sci.,* **2,** 220 (1947).
8. I. Yamashita, J. Furukawa, T. Saegusa, and A. Kawasaki, *Kogyo Kagaku Zasshi,* **65,** 239 (1962).
9. R. S. Berger and E. A. Youngman, *J. Polymer Sci.,* **A2,** 357 (1964).
10. C. Walling, E. R. Briggs, W. Cummings, and F. R. Mayo, *J. Am. Chem. Soc.,* **72,** 48 (1950).
11. E.-G. Kastning, H. Naarmann, H. Reis, and C. Berding, *Angew. Chem. Intern. Ed.,* **4,** 322 (1965).

11a. H. P. Smith, U.S. Pat. 3,226,376 to U.S. Rubber Company (Dec. 28, 1965).

12. C. H. Bamford and C. A. Finch, *Proc. Roy. Soc.,* **A268,** 553 (1962).
13. C. H. Bamford, M. S. Blackie, and C. A. Finch, *Chem. Ind. (London),* **1962,** 1763.
14. C. H. Bamford, G. C. Eastmond, and V. J. Robinson, *Trans. Faraday Soc.,* **60,** 751 (1964).

15. C. H. Bamford, G. C. Eastmond, and W. R. Maltman, *Trans. Faraday Soc.*, **60,** 1432 (1964).
16. M. Imoto, T. Otsu, T. Nakata, and Y. Kinoshita, *J. Polymer Sci.*, **B2,** 227 (1964).
16a. T. Nakata, T. Otsu, and M. Imoto, *J. Polymer Sci.*, **A3,** 3383 (1965).
16b. T. Nakata, Y. Kinoshita, T. Otsu, and M. Imoto, *Kogyo Kagaku Zasshi,* **68,** 858 (1965); through *Resins, Rubbers, Plastics,* **1965,** 2591.
16c. T. Nakata, Y. Kinoshita, T. Otsu, and M. Imoto, *Kogyo Kagaku Zasshi,* **68,** 864 (1965); through *Resins, Rubbers, Plastics,* **1965,** p. 2615.
17. T. Alderson, U.S. Pat. 3,013,066 to du Pont (Dec. 12, 1961).
17a. T. Alderson, E. L. Jenner, and R. V. Lindsey, Jr., *J. Am. Chem. Soc.*, **87,** 5638 (1965).
18. J. J. Verbanc, U.S. Pat. 3,152,195 to du Pont (Oct. 6, 1964).
19. R. Cramer, *J. Am. Chem. Soc.*, **87,** 4717 (1965).
20. R. E. Rinehart, H. P. Smith, H. S. Witt, and H. Romeyn, Jr., *J. Am. Chem. Soc.* **83,** 4864 (1961).
21. A. J. Canale, W. A. Hewett, T. M. Shryne, and E. A. Youngman, *Chem. Ind. (London),* **1962,** 1054.
22. R. E. Rinehart, H. P. Smith, H. S. Witt, and H. Romeyn, Jr., *J. Am. Chem. Soc.*, **84,** 4145 (1962).
23. Ph. Teyssié, *Compt. Rend.*, **256,** 2846 (1963).
24. Ph. Teyssié and R. Dauby, *J. Polymer Sci.*, **B2,** 413 (1964).
25. Ph. Teyssié and R. Dauby, *Bull. Soc. Chim. France,* **1965,** 2842.
26. M. Morton, I. Piirma, and B. Das, *Rubber Plastics Age,* **46,** 404 (1965).
27. B. D. Babitskii, V. A. Kormer, I. Ya. Poddubnyi, V. N. Sokolov, and N. N. Chesnokova, *Dokl. Akad. Nauk SSSR,* **162,** 1060 (1965).
28. J. Kálal, S. Doszlop, and F. Švec, *Abstr., IUPAC Symp. Macromol. Chem., Prague,* **1965,** P 52.
29. V. N. Sokolov, B. D. Babitskii, I. P. Bezhan, V. A. Kormer, I. Ya. Poddubnyi, and N. N. Chesnokova, *J. Polymer Sci.*, **C16** (8) (1969).
30. R. Dauby, F. Dawans, and Ph. Teyssié, *J. Polymer Sci.*, **C16** (4), 1989 (1967).
31. R. E. Rinehart and H. P. Smith in *Macromolecular Synthesis,* Vol. II, J. R. Elliott, Ed., Wiley, New York, 1966, p. 39.
32. T. M. Shryne, U.S. Pat. 3,168,507 to Shell Oil (Feb. 2, 1965).
33. A. J. Canale and W. A. Hewett, *J. Polymer Sci.*, **B2,** 1041 (1964).
34. U. Giannini, E. Ciampelli, and G. Bruckner, *Makromol. Chem.*, **66,** 209 (1963).
35. L. Porri, G. Natta, and M. C. Gallazzi, *Chim. Ind. (Milan)*, **46,** 428 (1964).
36. G. Natta, G. Dall'Asta, and G. Motroni, *J. Polymer Sci.*, **B2,** 349 (1964).
37. G. Natta, G. Dall'Asta, and L. Porri, *Makromol. Chem.*, **81,** 253 (1965).
38. F. W. Michelotti and W. P. Keaveney, *J. Polymer Sci.*, **A3,** 895 (1965).
39. F. W. Michelotti and J. H. Carter, *A.C.S. Polymer Preprints,* **6** (No. 1), 224 (1965).
40. R. E. Rinehart and H. P. Smith, *J. Polymer Sci.*, **B3,** 1049 (1965).
41. J. Smidt, W. Hafner, R. Jira, R. Sieber, J. Sedlmeier, and A. Sabel, *Angew. Chem., Intern. Ed.* **1,** 80 (1962).
42. J. F. Harrod and A. J. Chalk, *J. Am. Chem. Soc.*, **86,** 1776 (1964).
43. J. F. Harrod and A. J. Chalk, *Nature,* **205,** 280 (1965).
44. G. C. Bond and M. Heillier, *J. Catalysis,* **4,** 1 (1965).
45. N. R. Davies, *Nature,* **201,** 490 (1964).
46. N. R. Davies, *Nature,* **205,** 281 (1965).

47. R. E. Rinehart and J. S. Lasky, *J. Am. Chem. Soc.*, **86,** 2516 (1964).
48. J. K. Nicholson and B. L. Shaw, *Tetrahedron Letters*, **1965,** 3533.
49. M. L. H. Green and P. L. I. Nagy, in *Advances in Organometallic Chemistry*, Vol. 2, F. G. A. Stone and R. West, Eds., Academic Press, New York, 1964, pp. 325–363.
50. F. C. Cesare, private communication.
51. E. B. Bradford and J. W. Vanderhoff, J. *Polymer Sci.*, **C3,** 41 (1963).
52. R. E. Rinehart, unpublished observations.
53. A. J. Canale, U.S. Pat. 3,168,508 to Shell Oil (Feb. 2, 1965).
54. B. N. Figgis, R. D. Gillard, R. S. Nyholm, and G. Wilkinson, *J. Chem. Soc.*, **1964,** 5189.
55. J. G. Balas, H. E. De La Mare, and D. O. Schissler, *J. Polymer Sci.*, **A3,** 2243 (1965).
56. E. O. Fischer and G. Bürger, *Z. Naturforsch.*, **16b,** 77 (1961).
57. W. L. Truett, D. R. Johnson, I. M. Robinson, and B. A. Montague, *J. Am. Chem. Soc.*, **82,** 2337 (1960).
58. G. Dall'Asta, G. Mazzanti, G. Natta, and L. Porri, *Makromol. Chem.*, **56,** 224 (1962).
59. G. Natta, G. Dall'Asta, G. Mazzanti, and G. Motroni, *Makromol. Chem.*, **69,** 163 (1963).
60. G. F. Emerson and R. Pettit, *J. Am. Chem. Soc.*, **84,** 4591 (1962).
61. S. D. Robinson and B. L. Shaw, *J. Chem. Soc.*, **1963,** 4806.
62. E. A. Hill and J. H. Richards, *J. Am. Chem. Soc.*, **83,** 4216 (1961).
63. J. E. Lydon, J. K. Nicholson, B. L. Shaw, and M. R. Truter, *Proc. Chem. Soc.* **1964,** 421.
64. G. Wilke, *Angew. Chem. Intern. Ed.*, **2,** 105 (1963).
65. M. L. H. Green and P. L. I. Nagy, *J. Chem. Soc.*, **1963,** 189.
66. W. R. McClellan, H. H. Hoehn, H. N. Cripps, E. L. Muetterties, and B. W. Howk, *J. Am. Chem. Soc.*, **83,** 1601 (1961).
67. R. F. Heck, *J. Am. Chem. Soc.*, **86,** 2796 (1964).
68. J. Halpern and S. M. Taylor, *Discussions Faraday Soc.*, **29,** 174 (1960).

CHAPTER 9

ELASTOMERS BY MISCELLANEOUS OR UNKNOWN MECHANISMS

C. Poly(Thiocarbonyl Fluoride) and Related Elastomers

W. H. SHARKEY

Central Research Department,
E. I. du Pont de Nemours and Company,
Wilmington, Delaware

Contents

I. Poly(Thiocarbonyl Fluoride) 894
II. Poly(Fluorothioacyl Halides) and Polyfluorothioketones 898
III. Free Radical Polymerization 900
IV. Copolymerization of Thiocarbonyl Fluoride with Unsaturated Compounds. 901
V. Thiocarbonyl Chlorofluoride Polymers and Copolymers 902
References 903

In recent years, the synthesis and chemistry of a number of fluorothiocarbonyl compounds have been reported (1,3). These materials undergo an exceptionally large number of chemical transformations because of the apparent enhancement of the reactivity of the C═S group by fluorine or by fluoroalkyl. One of their important reactions is polymerization, which has led to a new family of elastomeric polymers (2). Included in this class are poly(thiocarbonyl fluoride) (**1**), poly(thioacyl fluorides) (**2**), and poly(hexafluorothioacetone) (**3**). Of these, poly(thiocarbonyl fluoride) (**1**) has received the most attention. It is a highly resilient elastomer that has surprising chemical stability considering the fact that it is a poly(thioacetal).

$$-(CF_2-S)_n-$$

(1)

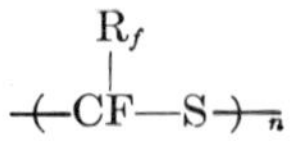

(2)

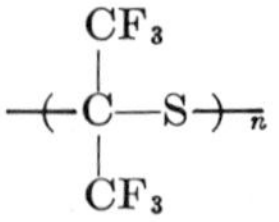

(3)

R_f = perfluoroalkyl, C_nF_{2n+1}

I. POLY(THIOCARBONYL FLUORIDE)

When thiocarbonyl fluoride (**4**) is exposed to an anionic initiator at low temperatures, it rapidly polymerizes to a high molecular weight polymer.

$$n\,CF_2{=}S \rightarrow -(CF_2-S)_n-$$

(**4**)

The polymerization proceeds best at about −80°C. The best solvent of the considerable number that have been tried (2), appears to be diethyl ether. In this solvent at −80°C, the polymerization is essentially complete in about 2 hr. The polymer separates as a white, spongy mass insoluble in the solvent. Anionic initiators capable of bringing about polymerization of $CF_2{=}S$ include amides, amines, phosphines, quaternary ammonium salts, tetraalkyl titanates, and trialkyl aluminates. The two initiators that have been studied most (2) are dimethylformamide and tetraisopropyl titanate.

The key to formation of high molecular weight polymer is the use of very pure monomer. Because $CF_2{=}S$ is so very reactive, it is difficult to purify. Therefore, it is best to choose the cleanest synthesis available for making the monomer and to take all possible precaution against contamination through hydrolysis. Of the several routes to $CF_2{=}S$ (3) that have been reported, the most convenient for laboratory-scale production of very pure monomer is one based on thiophosgene dimer (**5**). Fluorination of this compound with antimony trifluoride (1) gives 2,2,4,4-tetrafluoro-1,3-dithietane (**6**), which undergoes cleavage to $CF_2{=}S$ when pyrolyzed at 475–500°C. Material prepared in this way, after redistilla-

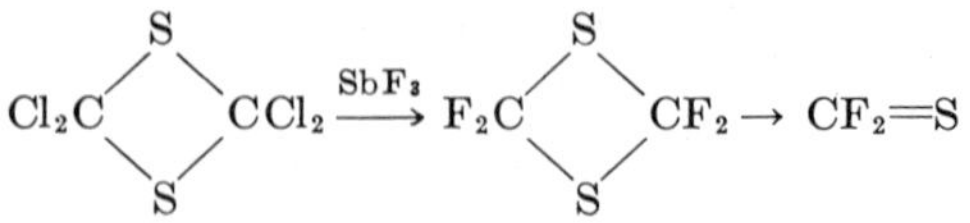

(**5**) (**6**)

tion in a low temperature column, is free of all measurable impurities other than about 15–25 ppm of carbonyl sulfide.

Poly(thiocarbonyl fluoride) formed by dimethylformamide initiation in ether at −80°C typically has $\bar{M}_n$ of 300,000–500,000 as determined by osmometry on chloroform solutions. Inherent viscosities of 0.1% solutions of these polymers in chloroform vary from 2 to 6. This polymer is a tough, highly resilient elastomer. Measurement by the Yerzley method gives a resilience of 95%, a very high value. Films of poly(thiocarbonyl fluoride) that are stretched beyond the elastic limit undergo cold drawing with simultaneous crystallization and orientation. Films of drawn, crystalline polymer have tensile strengths of approximately 11,000 psi and elongations of about 90%. The polymer, which has a freezing point of 35°C, crystallizes on long standing at room temperature whether it is oriented or not. Crystalline polymer is easily remelted to regenerate the highly resilient, elastomeric form. As would be expected, oriented film, when heated, retracts as it melts to give back the shape it had before it was drawn. Measurement of internal friction of undrawn polymer by use of a torsion pendulum showed it to have the unusually low glass transition point of −118°C.

As mentioned earlier, poly(thiocarbonyl fluoride) is surprisingly resistant to chemical attack. It shows no appreciable change in inherent viscosity when boiled 21 hr in 10% NaOH. This treatment does lead, however, to a weight loss of about 9%. Boiling for brief periods in fuming nitric acid causes no apparent damage, but continuation of this treatment for long periods results in serious loss of molecular weight. On the other hand, poly(thiocarbonyl fluoride) is rapidly attacked by bases that wet the surface of the polymer. For example, the polymer is rapidly degraded by triethylamine. Products are thiocarbonyl fluoride monomer and a small amount of a black solid. The polymer is also degraded when it is heated above 175°C, in which case thiocarbonyl fluoride monomer is regenerated almost quantitatively.

Some measure of molecular weight control of poly(thiocarbonyl fluoride) can be exercised by variation in temperature of polymerization, by choice of initiator, and by use of isopropyl alcohol as a chain transfer agent. At −80°C, thiocarbonyl fluoride initiated with tetraisopropyl titanate leads to polymers with inherent viscosities of 2–4.5. Addition of 0.35–0.7% of isopropyl alcohol to the polymerization mixture leads to polymer of inherent viscosity a little over 1. At −25°C in chloroform and in the presence of a relatively large amount of tetraisopropyl titanate, thiocarbonyl fluoride forms low molecular weight oils.

It has been suggested (2) that poly(thiocarbonyl fluoride) formed by dimethylformamide initiation is mainly, if not entirely

$$CF_3S\left(CF_2{-}S\right)_n CF{=}S$$

This structure was arrived at as a result of a number of chemical and spectral studies. Firstly, the polymer contains a group that reacts with methanol. Reaction of methanol-C^{14} with a polymer of $\bar{M}_n$ 335,000 gave a modified polymer, the radioactivity of which was consistent for the presence of one methanol reactive group per chain. High molecular weight polymer was not suitable for infrared study aimed at identification of this reactive endgroup because its absorption is masked by a broad band near 9 μ for C—F and a strong band at 12.25 μ for C—S. However, the infrared spectrum of low molecular weight polymer prepared by dimethylformamide initiation in methylene chloride at −25°C has bands at 5.4, 8.2, 10.1, and 13.1 μ. Analysis of this spectrum backed up by fluorine NMR has provided the basis for the structure proposed.

The 5.4 μ band has been assigned to —SCF=O because of its similarity to absorption of COF_2 (5.25 μ) and $R_fCF{=}O$ (5.3 μ). Polymer that has been reacted with methanol does not have the 5.4 μ band. The —SCF=O endgroup content of the polymer is quite small as it is not detectable by fluorine NMR. This endgroup is completely missing in low molecular weight polymer formed by tetraisopropyl titanate initiation. Its genesis may be by transformation of —SCF=S or by removal of an initiator fragment from one end of the chain.

The 8.2 μ band has been assigned to CF absorption in —SCF=S. It is present in all low molecular weight polymers and is removed by reaction with methanol. This is also the case for the model compound, $CF_3SCF{=}S$. Comparison of the fluorine NMR of the model compound and the low molecular weight polymer indicates that F in —SCF=S has a peak at 71.5 ppm lower field than that of CCl_3F used as an external standard. The polymer has a small resonance peak at this point that is eliminated by reaction with methanol.

Though it is associated with a reactive group, an exact assignment for the 10.1 μ infrared band has not been made.

The CF_3S— group is responsible for infrared absorption at 13.1 μ. Such model compounds as $CF_3SCF{=}S$ and $CF_3SC(OCH_3){=}S$ have a characteristic absorption at about 13 μ. The 13.1 μ band varies in intensity with molecular weight, but it is not affected by reaction with methanol. The intensity of this band is increased by reaction of the polymer with SF_4, which is known to convert —SCF=O and —SCF=S to $—SCF_3$. Oils in which short chains are capped with $CF_3S—$ have been prepared by reaction of high molecular weight polymer with antimony pentafluoride.

$$-\!(CF_2—S)_n- \rightarrow CF_3S(CF_2—S)_{<25}—CF_3$$

The infrared spectrum of these oils contains a relatively strong 13.1 μ band. Fluorine NMR of the oils has a peak at 37.6 ppm higher field than that of CCl_3F used as an external standard, which compares well for the resonance of $CF_3S—$ in $CF_3SCF{=}S$.

All attempts to find initiator fragments in poly(thiocarbonyl fluoride) prepared by dimethylformamide initiation have failed. However, polymer prepared by tetraisopropyl titanate initiation has been shown to contain isopropyl groups. The infrared spectrum of low molecular weight polymers so prepared contains a double peak at 7.24 μ characteristic of *gem*-dimethyl groups. This and other absorptions of the isopropyl group are not noticeably changed by reaction of the polymer with methanol. On the other hand, they are destroyed by reaction with thionyl chloride and replaced with a 5.4 μ band, which indicates conversion to $—SCF{=}O$.

A resume of the data supporting the structures proposed can be shown as follows:

Dimethylformamide Initiated Polymer

NMR: 37.6 ppm higher field (CF_3S); 43.5 ppm higher field (CF_2); 71.5 ppm lower field ($CF{=}S$)

$$CF_3S—(CF_2—S)_n—CF{=}S$$

IR: 13.1 μ (CF_3S); 8.2 μ ($CF{=}S$)

Tetraisopropyl Titanate Initiated Polymer

$$(CH_3)_2CHOCF_2S(CF_2—S)_n—CF{=}S$$

IR: 7.24 μ; 8.2 μ

↓ $SOCl_2$

$$O{=}CFS—(CF_2—S)_n—CF{=}S$$

IR: 5.4 μ; 8.2 μ

With the elucidation of the endgroup, it becomes possible to propose reasonable propagating and terminating reactions. Initiation remains more obscure. It has been suggested that the first step in dimethylformamide initiation is reaction with an impurity or monomer to form a base.

$$DMF + HB \rightarrow DMFH^{\oplus} + B^{\ominus}$$
$$B^{\ominus} + CF_2{=}S \rightarrow BCF_2—S^{\ominus}$$

If $B^{\ominus}$ is $F^{\ominus}$, then propagation and termination would be

$$CF_3\text{—}S^{\ominus} + CF_2\text{=}S \rightarrow CF_3\text{—}S\sim\sim\sim CF_2\text{—}S^{\ominus}$$
$$CF_3\text{—}S\sim\sim\sim CF_2\text{—}S^{\ominus} \rightarrow CF_3\text{—}S\sim\sim\sim CF\text{=}S + F^{\ominus}$$

In the case of tetraisopropyl titanate initiation, the first step is postulated to be

$$(RO)_4Ti + CF_2\text{=}S \rightarrow ROCF_2S^{\ominus} + (RO)_3Ti^{\oplus}$$

Propagation and termination would be as before and as soon as $F^{\ominus}$ is formed, it would become the primary initiator.

A consequence of the presence of reactive —SCF=S ends is the sensitivity of poly(thiocarbonyl fluoride) to high temperatures and to amines. The acid fluoride groups slowly hydrolyze in the presence of occluded moisture. Glass containers used for storage of the polymer gradually become etched. A possible degradation mechanism is

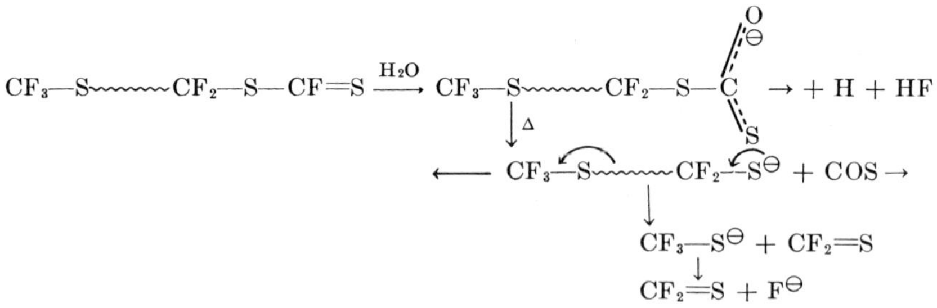

Amine degradation is visualized as proceeding similarly.

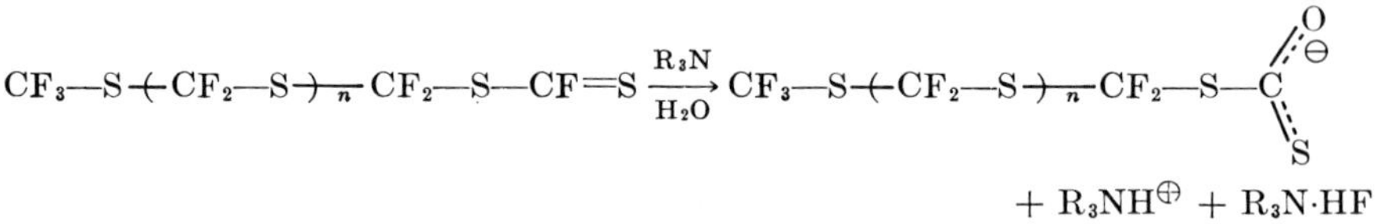

II. POLY(FLUOROTHIOACYL HALIDES) AND POLYFLUOROTHIOKETONES

In the past several years, a number of fluorothioacyl halides and fluorothioketones have been reported. Harris and Stacey (4) have prepared $HCF_2CF\text{=}S$ and $HCFClCF\text{=}S$ by addition of H_2S to tetrafluoroethylene and chlorotrifluoroethylene, respectively, followed by removal of HF. Both of these compounds polymerize at low temperatures when initiated by dimethylformamide under conditions similar to those used for polymerizing thiocarbonyl fluoride (2). The products are elastic polymers somewhat less resilient than poly(thiocarbonyl fluoride). Other fluorothioacyl fluorides that have been polymerized include $CF_3CF{=}S$ (2), which forms a rubbery polymer, $ClCF_2CF{=}S$ (1), which gives a crystalline polymer, and $CF_3CF_2CF{=}S$ (2), which polymerizes to a tacky solid.

Fluorothioacyl fluorides copolymerize with thiocarbonyl fluoride in anionic systems. Copolymers containing about 3% of chlorofluorothioacetyl fluoride have crystallization temperatures below 0°C. Copolymers containing 13–40% of trifluorothioacetyl fluoride are much less elastic than poly(thiocarbonyl fluoride) and have melting temperatures almost as high.

Fluorothioacyl chlorides (5) also polymerize. The first member of this series, thiocarbonyl chlorofluoride, $CFCl{=}S$, will be discussed later. Poly(chlorodifluorothioacetyl chloride) is readily formed by dimethylformamide initiation of $ClCF_2CCl{=}S$ at low temperatures (2). This polymer is not elastomeric.

Several fluorothioketones have been described (1). These compounds rapidly dimerize to 1,3-dithietanes under conditions normally used for anionic polymerization of fluorothiocarbonyls. Study of hexafluorothioacetone (2) has indicated that the ceiling temperature for polymerization of this compound is very low. At −80°C, dimethylformamide catalyzes rapid and quantitative conversion of the thioketone to 2,2,4,4-tetrakis-(trifluoromethyl)-1,3-dithietane (**7**). This reaction does not take place at −110°C; instead, the ketone polymerizes to give (**3**). Polyhexafluoro-

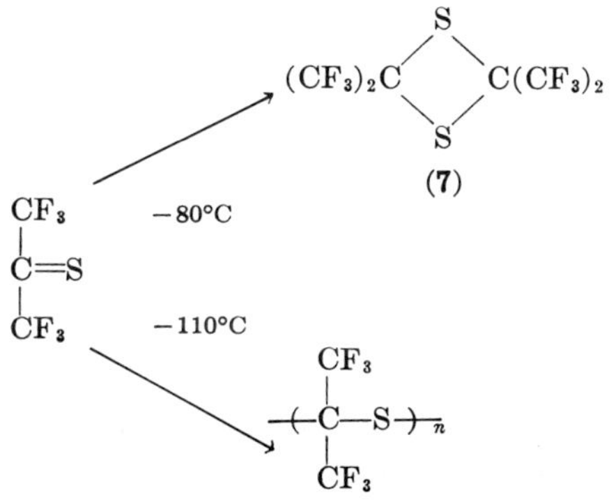

(**7**)

(**3**)

thioacetone is white, elastomeric, and insoluble in most common organic solvents. It slowly depolymerizes at room temperature to regenerate monomer, which immediately dimerizes to form the dithietane.

III. FREE RADICAL POLYMERIZATION

A most remarkable property of the thiocarbonyl group in fluorothiocarbonyl compounds is susceptibility to initiation of polymerization by free radicals (6). Inasmuch as formation of polymer in these systems is favored at low temperatures, a key development in free radical initiation was the discovery of a method for supplying radicals at very low temperatures. This method is reaction of a trialkylborane with oxygen, which is capable of giving free radicals at temperatures as low as $-100°C$. The trialkylborane–oxygen couple had been used earlier (7) for other polymerizations that are carried out at more normal temperatures. Polymerization of thiocarbonyl fluoride at $-80°C$ with hexafluoropropylene as the solvent, and with triethylborane and oxygen as the initiator gives polymer equivalent in toughness to that formed by anionic initiation (6).

The trialkylborane–oxygen reaction occurs in two steps, and these stages can be separated. The first is a mole-for-mole reaction that yields a dialkyl(alkylperoxy)borane (**8**). At $-80°C$, the reaction stops after

$$R_3B + O_2 \rightarrow \underset{(\mathbf{8})}{R_2BOOR}.$$

1 mole of oxygen is consumed even though excess oxygen is present. The second stage is reaction of the peroxyborane with excess trialkyl-

$$R_2BOOR + 2R'_3B \rightarrow R_2BOBR'_2 + R'_2BOR + 2R'\cdot$$

borane. That free radicals arise as a result of the second reaction was indicated by examination of gases formed. For example, when R′ was ethyl and R was butyl, the principal C_2-C_4 gases obtained from the reaction were ethylene, ethane, and *n*-butane, which undoubtedly were formed by disproportionation and combination of ethyl radicals.

There are two important consequences of this initiator mechanism. One is that it is important to use less oxygen than trialkylborane in order to preserve enough of the borane for the second reaction. R_3B/O_2 of 0.5 appears to be satisfactory in most cases. A second consequence is that preformed dialkyl(alkylperoxy)boranes can be used with trialkylboranes. This combination is more convenient in many cases because standard solutions can be made up ahead of time. The half-life of peroxyboranes in heptane at $-80°C$ is well in excess of one week. Also, use of two liquids in place of a liquid and a gas is advantageous because of greater homogeneity at the start of the polymerization.

IV. COPOLYMERIZATION OF THIOCARBONYL FLUORIDE WITH UNSATURATED COMPOUNDS

The trialkylborane–oxygen couple not only promotes the homopolymerization of thiocarbonyl fluoride, but also its copolymerization with a wide variety of unsaturated compounds (6). A partial list of such compounds is as follows:

Ethylene	Vinyl chloride	Vinyl acetate
Propylene	Vinyl fluoride	Ethyl acrylate
Isobutylene	2-Chloropropene	Allyl acetate
2-Butene	Allyl chloride	Ethyl vinyl ether
Cyclohexene	Allylchloroform	Allyl vinyl ether
2,4-Dimethyl-2-butene	Allyltrichlorosilane	Allyl chloroformate
	Vinyltrichlorosilane	

Copolymerization of thiocarbonyl fluoride with propylene is one of the most unusual examples. This copolymerization proceeds even more rapidly than homopolymerization of thiocarbonyl fluoride. Moreover, the copolymerization tends to give a 2:1 $CF_2{=}S$/propylene copolymer. The best copolymers have been prepared in dichlorodifluoromethane solutions, had compositions of 2.3–2.1 $CF_2{=}S$/propylene, and had $\bar{M}_n \sim$ 820,000. These products are soft, pliable elastomers that retain flexibility at very low temperatures. Their crystalline melting points are about -55 to -60°C.

Other comonomers behave differently. For example, *tert*-butylethylene copolymerizes well with thiocarbonyl fluoride, but the products, which are of high molecular weight, have compositions that closely approximate the monomer mixtures used. Much the same can be said for vinyl acetate copolymers.

Vinyl acetate copolymers are unusual, however, in another respect. When they are subjected to methanolysis, acetate groups are removed and the polymers suffer extensive degradation. This is thought to indicate that acetate and sulfur are on the same carbon atom as in (**9**).

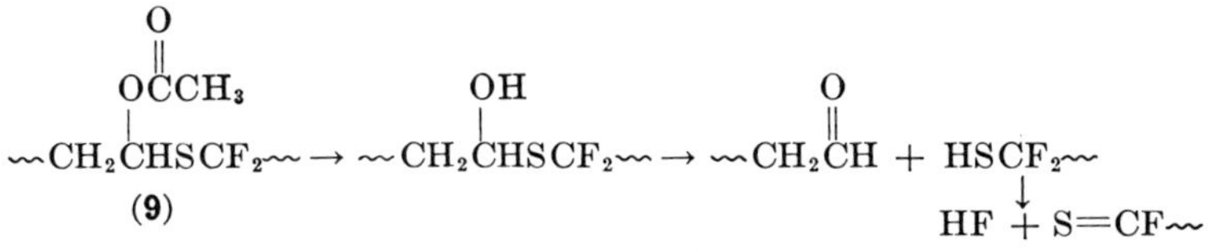

(**9**)

Such a structure is unexpected because it appears to be the result of addition of a free radical to the sulfur atom to form (**10**). A more reasona-

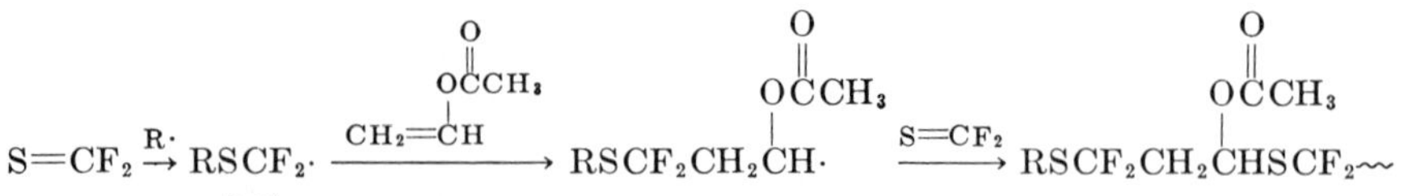

(10)

ble product from the first step is (**11**), which would be expected to add to the terminal carbon of vinyl acetate. It has been suggested (6) that (**11**)

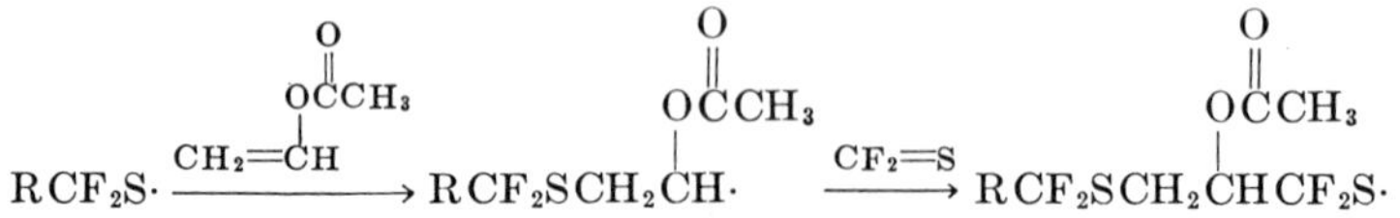

(11)

is formed first and that it then adds abnormally to vinyl acetate to give (**12**).

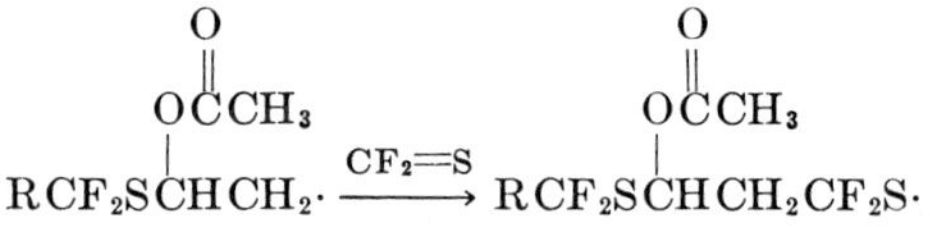

(12)

To find out if the acetate group per se is responsible for the hydrolytic instability of vinyl acetate copolymers, monomers have been used which would result in the insulation of the acetate groups from the chain. Use of allyl acetate as the comonomer in an attempt to interpose one methylene group between the acetate and the chain led to insoluble copolymers. 3-Butenyl acetate and thiocarbonyl fluoride copolymerize readily to give soluble products of $\bar{M}_n \sim 800{,}000$. Methanolysis of such copolymers proceeded without degradation to give tough elastomers that can be readily crosslinked by reaction with diisocyanates.

Some attention has been given to other crosslinkable copolymers because curability is an important property of any elastomer. Allyl chloroformate, $CH_2{=}CHCH_2OCOCl$, copolymerizes readily with thiocarbonyl fluoride to give products of high molecular weight. Copolymers containing as little as 2–3 mole % of the chloroformate have crystalline melting points below 0°C. Furthermore, these copolymers can be crosslinked by incorporating 3–5% of zinc oxide and heating the mixture under pressure in a mold.

V. THIOCARBONYL CHLOROFLUORIDE POLYMERS AND COPOLYMERS

Earlier in this section, mention was made of thiocarbonyl chlorofluoride, $CFCl{=}S$, as the simplest of the fluorothioacyl chlorides. This compound polymerizes even more rapidly in free radical systems (6) than does thiocarbonyl fluoride. Initiation of this carbonyl chlorofluoride with the tributylborane–oxygen combination at either 0 or −80°C leads to the formation of a tough, high molecular weight elastomer. This polymer has a lower freezing point than polythiocarbonyl fluoride. It does not crystallize when stretched at 0°C.

Copolymerization of thiocarbonyl chlorofluoride with unsaturated compounds in free radical systems is in many respects similar to that of thiocarbonyl fluoride. For example, copolymers have been obtained with ethyl acrylate, methyl acrylate, vinyl acetate, styrene, acrylonitrile, allyl chloride, and chlorotrifluoroethylene. In all of these cases, the chlorofluoride is the major component because it polymerizes so rapidly. A monomer that polymerizes just about as rapidly as thiocarbonyl chlorofluoride, is 2,3-dichloro-1,3-butadiene. Mixtures of the dichlorobutadiene and the chlorofluoride copolymerize to products having compositions approximating those of the original monomer mixture. Copolymers containing 60% or more of the chlorofluoride are elastomeric; those containing mostly diene are plastics.

References

1. W. J. Middleton, E. G. Howard, and W. H. Sharkey, *J. Org. Chem.*, **30,** 1375 (1965).
2. W. J. Middleton, H. W. Jacobson, R. E. Putnam, H. C. Walter, D. G. Pye, and W. H. Sharkey, *J. Polymer Sci.*, A, **3,** 4115–4129 (1965).
3. W. Sundermeyer and W. Meise, *Z. Anorg. Allgem. Chem.*, **317,** 334 (1962).
4. J. F. Harris and F. W. Stacey, *J. Am. Chem. Soc.*, **85,** 749 (1963).
5. W. J. Middleton, U.S. Pat. 3,113,936 (Dec. 10, 1963).
6. A. L. Barney, J. M. Bruce, Jr., J. N. Coker, H. W. Jacobson, and W. H. Sharkey, *J. Polymer Sci.*, A-1, **4,** 2617–2636 (1966).
7. J. Furukawa and T. Tsuruta, *J. Polymer Sci.*, **28,** 227 (1958).

CHAPTER 10

ELASTOMERS BY POSTPOLYMERIZATION TECHNIQUES

A. Halogenation

HENRY S. MAKOWSKI

Esso Research and Engineering Co., Linden, New Jersey

Contents

I. Diolefin Elastomers 906
A. Halogenation 907
1. Natural Rubber and Synthetic Polyisoprenes 907
2. Butadiene Rubbers 911
B. Hydrohalogenation 912
II. Chlorinated Polyethylene Elastomer 914
A. Curable Chlorinated Polyethylene 916
1. Chlorosulfonation 917
2. Dehydrohalogenation to Unsaturation 920
3. Chlorophosphonation 920
III. Butyl Rubber 921
A. Bromination 921
B. Chlorination 923
C. Iodination 925
D. Fluorination 928
E. Curing of Halogenated Butyl Rubber 928
IV. Poly-α-Olefins and Ethylene-α-Olefin Copolymers 929
A. Chlorosulfonation and Chlorophosphonation 930
B. Halogenation 931
References 933

Halogenation of elastomers is normally effected to modify the physical or chemical properties of the elastomer. In some instances, for example, chlorosulfonated polyethylene, both are deliberately effected. Halogenation of elastomers may be broadly defined as any reaction which results in the introduction of chemically combined halogen. Normally, however, halogenation refers to a reaction involving direct interaction of a halogen free radical or ion which results in the introduction of halogen into the elastomer.

Most often the halogenation of elastomers represents the least desirable method of elastomer modification. The incorporation of the desired functional groups during elastomer preparation, i.e., during the course of polymerization, is the preferred mode of elastomer modification. However, the lack of availability of a suitable functional monomer or its adverse effect on the course of polymerization requires postpolymerization chemical modification. Thus halogenation is a secondary elastomer process normally designed to improve on a weak characteristic of the primary elastomer. Only chlorosulfonated polyethylene elastomer is the exception which in fact requires chlorination to produce an elastomeric product from polyethylene.

Ideally, halogenation should result only in the incorporation of the desired halogeno group and be free from scission or crosslinking reactions occurring via ionic or radical processes. However, the halogenation of polymers is rarely free from these side reactions, and the avoidance or mitigation of these processes is required to produce useful products.

Polymers of major interest for halogenation are the polyhydrocarbons which are either saturated or contain unsaturation as the sole functionality. Further, of primary concern are those polymers which are *elastomeric* after halogenation, specifically chlorinated polyethylene, butyl rubber, and ethylene-α-olefin copolymers. Halogenated polydiolefin elastomers are most useful when fully halogenated; however, at this point they are no longer elastomeric but hard, rigid resins. The largest part of the chemistry of polymer halogenation has been elucidated with these elastomers.

I. DIOLEFIN ELASTOMERS

Polydiolefin elastomers contain far more functionality for vulcanization than necessary. At the same time, the unsaturated nature of the polymer chain largely determines the elastomeric characteristics of polydiolefin rubbers (1). Indeed where a regularity of structure exists without any tendency toward crystallization (cf. Chapter 6) as with *cis*-1,4-polyisoprene and *cis*-1,4 polybutadiene, the polymer possesses outstanding elastomeric qualities (2–5). The disruption of this regularity by the reaction and removal of unsaturation coupled with the introduction of polar groups via halogenation results in a loss in the stability and the elastomeric characteristics of the rubber.

Polydiolefin rubbers are of little or no use in the preparation of halogenated *elastomers* with properties modified from the original. Indeed, chlorinated polydiolefins at low levels of halogen are generally rather unstable.

Halogenation of polydiolefin elastomers was initially of interest as a diagnostic tool for natural and synthetic rubbers. In addition, halogenation has provided a method for the conversion of readily available rubbers to hard, rigid resins which find utility because of their solvent and chemical resistance and nonflammable characteristics.

A. Halogenation

1. *Natural Rubber and Synthetic Polyisoprenes*

The chlorination of natural rubber (*cis*-1,4 polyisoprene) with elemental chlorine has been the subject of extensive investigation (6–15). The chemical and physical properties of chlorinated polyisoprenes vary with the chlorine content, which may be as high as 70% by weight. At chlorine levels up to 50–55% the chlorinated polyisoprenes are unstable particularly at the lower levels where, within a period of several days after chlorination, highly crosslinked, brittle products result (15). More highly chlorinated products (65% chlorine) are much more stable but dehydrochlorinate at elevated temperatures.

In the first stages of chlorination a combination of allylic substitution and cyclization reactions predominate. These reactions have been thoroughly substantiated through determination of evolved HCl (7,8), infrared measurements (15), chemical unsaturation determination (12), ozonization (13), rheological characterization of polymer solutions (8,11,15), kinetic identification of chloride groups (11,15) and studies on model compounds (7,9).

It is well known that liquid phase chlorination of linear olefins gives predominantly addition products, while chlorination of olefins with branching at the double bond gives predominantly allylic substitution (16–19). Thus, two allylic chlorides are formed from the chlorination of 2-methyl-2-butene (16).

$$CH_3{-}\overset{\overset{\displaystyle CH_3}{|}}{C}{=}CH{-}CH_3 \xrightarrow[-HCl]{Cl_2} CH_2{=}\overset{\overset{\displaystyle CH_3}{|}}{C}{-}\underset{\underset{\displaystyle Cl}{|}}{CH}{-}CH_3 + Cl{-}CH_2{-}\overset{\overset{\displaystyle CH_3}{|}}{C}{=}CH{-}CH_3$$

Methallyl chloride produced by chlorination of 1-C^{14} isobutene contains essentially all the label at the chlorine-bearing carbon atom and none at the terminal olefinic carbon atom (19).

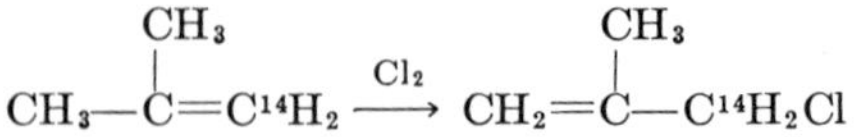

This rules out any symmetrical intermediate such as an allylic radical. Taft (18) has proposed that, in a number of systems, the addition: substitution ratios are best correlated with olefin structure on the basis of an ionic mechanism. Initial attack produces a chlorocarbonium ion which

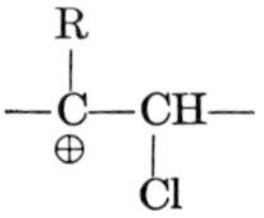

can either react with chloride ion to produce the addition product or lose a proton to form the allylic chloride. That branched olefins favor substitution is consistent with the greater number of available α-hydrogens (20) and with the tendency of tertiary carbonium ions to give larger E_1:S_N1 ratios during solvolysis than secondary carbonium ions (21). It is generally accepted that ionic mechanisms are operative when the chlorination of olefins is effected in polar solvents (22). In nonpolar solvents, however, two competing reactions are involved, one radical and one polar (20,23). The balance between these reaction mechanisms is determined primarily by olefin structure but also by olefin concentration and conditions of chlorination. Thus Poutsma (23) found that the pathway involved in the chlorination of 1-butene, 2-butene, and allyl chloride could be changed from largely ionic to predominantly free radical. In contrast, isobutene and other branched olefins (24) gave no change in ionic behavior regardless of conditions.

The work of Fahey (25,26) has established that the bridged chloronium ion rather than the open ion is the immediate precursor of both the addition product and the substitution product. The stability derived from

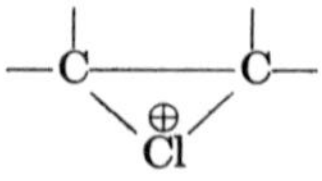

this bridging of the intermediate ion was estimated at about 9 kcal.

Thus the first reactions occurring in polyisoprenes, i.e., substitution and cyclization, can be written as follows:

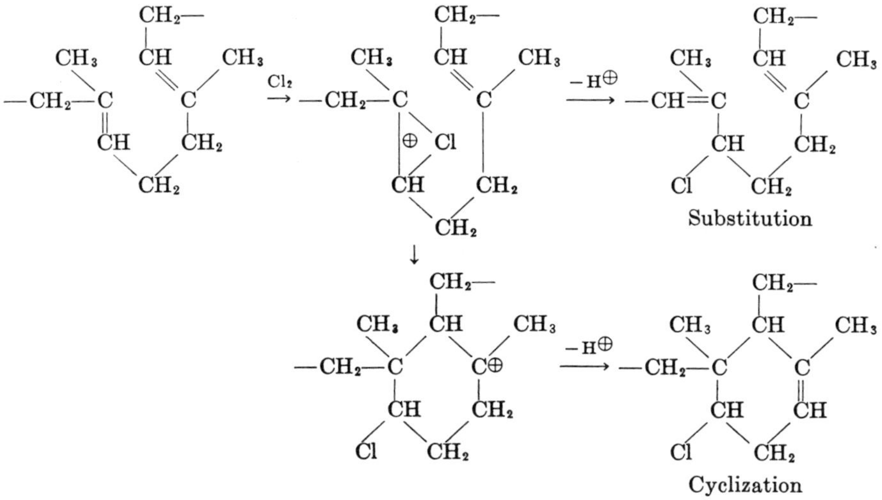

This mechanism is essentially that first proposed by Bloomfield (7). This combination of allylic substitution and cyclization accounts for the high reactivity of the chloride (11,15), the loss in unsaturation (12,13,15), and the rheological characteristics of solutions of chlorinated polyisoprenes containing 35–50% chlorine. Troussier (15) has suggested, on the basis of infrared studies, that cyclization does not occur up to 35% chlorine. To account for the lower solution viscosities of the chlorinated polyisoprenes he suggests the formation of pseudocyclic structures due to intramolecular polar interactions. He further suggests that such pseudocyclic structures subsequently cyclize via the addition of an α-methylenic C—H to a neighboring double bond.

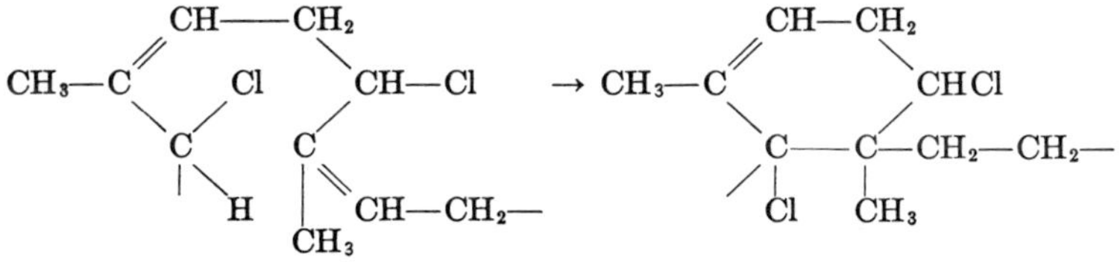

It is difficult to accept these explanations on the basis of the wealth of other evidence and the well-known mechanisms of reaction of olefins with chlorine.

The amount of allylic chloride in chlorinated polyisoprene decreases with increasing chlorine content (11). At 30% chlorine, approximately

80% is allylic whereas, at 65% chlorine, apparently only 15% is allylic (or reactive). With 50% chlorine, which is equivalent to two chlorine atoms per isoprene unit, half of the isoprene units contain only one, loosely bound chlorine, and the other half of the units contain three atoms more firmly attached.

Thus it is presumed that the initial cyclized and allylic substitution products undergo further allylic substitution, and finally addition to a fully chlorinated, saturated system.

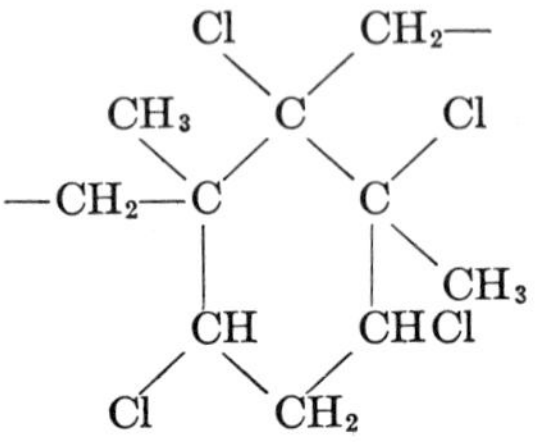

Properly and fully chlorinated polyisoprenes are reputed to contain little residual unsaturation (10).

The work of Ramakrishman et al. (13) suggests that addition of HCl liberated during chlorination also occurs. Thus, the full nature of the chlorination and the structures resulting therefrom are extremely complicated.

The chlorination of synthetic polyisoprenes has been studied only briefly (10,12). Emulsion polyisoprene, which contains some 1,2 and 3,4 addition, behaves similarly to Hevea (*cis*-1,4 polyisoprene) and gutta percha (*trans*-1,4 polyisoprene) except that less cyclization occurs due to the presence of the pendant vinyl groups resulting from 1,2 addition (12).

The peroxide catalyzed (free radical) chlorination of natural rubber with sulfuryl chloride is essentially additive in nature although some substitution occurs (9). Similarly, the thermal decomposition of phenyl iododichloride produces an essentially additive chlorination of natural rubber (9,14).

The reaction of bromine with polyisoprenes is very old (27,28). Staudinger and Staudinger (8) brominated Balata (*trans*-1,4 polyisoprene) at 0° in the absence of light and oxygen but still some HBr was evolved, and the bromine content was lower than theoretical. They postulated that cyclization reactions occur as in the chlorination of polyisoprene. On the other hand, Bloomfield (9) found that in the bromination of natural rubber in chloroform solution at 0 to −40°, no HBr was formed, and the brominated polymer underwent no decomposition or rearrangement upon mild heat treatment. The reaction of bromine with natural rubber under analytical conditions is essentially additive, but some substitution apparently cannot be easily avoided (29).

The bromination of natural rubber with *N*-bromosuccinimide proceeds via free radical intermediates to products substituted in the allylic position (9,30). Bloomfield (9) claimed that a considerable degree of cyclization occurred during bromine substitution. Pinazzi and Gueniffey (30) showed that besides the primary formation of three isomeric allyl bromides, the major side reactions were dibromide formation and coupling of polymeric radicals to produce crosslinks. These workers treated the resultant brominated polymers with LiBr-dimethylformamide to effect dehydrobromination and thereby produce sequences of conjugated double bonds.

Kemp and Mueller (29) made a detailed study on the use of halogens as analytical reagents in the determination of unsaturation in natural rubber and gutta-percha. The order of reactivity of halogens was $Cl_2 > Br_2 > ICl > IBr > I_2$. The additive reaction of ICl was found to be essentially theoretical whereas the other halogens were either too reactive or unreactive. Since this early work, the use of ICl with several modifications has been widely accepted as an analytical method of unsaturation determination. Lee, Kolthoff, and Mairs (31) showed that with natural rubber a small amount of substitution and "splitting out" occurs.

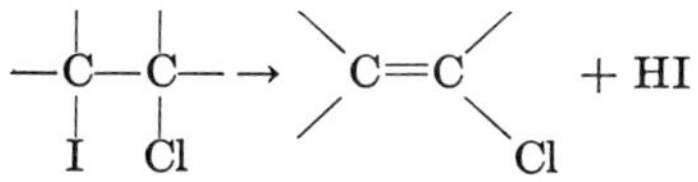

With emulsion and sodium polyisoprenes this "splitting out" is appreciable.

2. Butadiene Rubbers

The chemistry of the halogenation of synthetic rubbers other than polyisoprenes has not been studied in any detail. On the other hand, halogenation of butadiene rubbers has been the subject of rather extensive patent literature.

Endres (32) described the properties of some of the early chlorination products of butadiene-styrene and butadiene-acrylonitrile copolymers. The properties of highly chlorinated butadiene-styrene copolymers compared favorably with those of chlorinated natural rubber.

The addition of ICl and other halogens to butadiene polymers and copolymers under analytical conditions has been studied extensively to establish a method of unsaturation determination in these polymers (31,33). The earlier work showed no difference in reactivities between the isoprene rubbers and the butadiene rubbers. However, Lee, Kolthoff, and Mairs (31) showed that isoprene rubbers indeed react more rapidly but that butadiene rubbers exhibited less substitution and HI "splitting out" than the corresponding isoprene rubbers.

Unless adequate precautions are taken, chlorination of butadiene polymers under conditions used for chlorinating natural rubber results in crosslinked products (8). Canterino (34) has examined the chlorination products of emulsion polybutadienes and butadiene-styrene copolymers and the vulcanization behavior of lower chlorine content polymers. Soluble products were obtained by the proper choice of chlorination solvent and the use of such additives as phosphorus halides and iodine. Contrary to the results with natural rubber, little cyclization occurs during the chlorination of butadiene rubbers. At chlorine levels below 35%, the butadiene polymers are still rubbery and relatively thermally stable. Elastomeric vulcanizates were obtained from chlorinated (15–20%) polymers by using metal oxides or conventional sulfur curing systems. No HCl evolution was noted during vulcanization.

The bromination of *cis*-1,4 polybutadiene with elemental bromine in dilute chloroform solution and at relatively low temperatures results in essentially quantitative addition and no cyclization (35). Similar results are obtained with phenyltrimethylammoniumtribromide as the brominating agent (36). With *N*-bromosuccinimide primarily allylic substitution is obtained, although additive and crosslinking reactions occur to some extent (30).

B. Hydrohalogenation

In 1900 Weber (28) reacted natural rubber with hydrogen chloride and obtained a product of composition $(C_5H_9Cl)_n$. Subsequently, Harries and Fonrobert (37) were successful in hydrohalogenating natural rubber, gutta-percha, synthetic polyisoprene, and poly(dimethylbutadiene). Whereas natural and synthetic polyisoprenes react readily with hydrogen halide, butadiene polymers and copolymers are relatively inert (10). This order of reactivity is not surprising in view of the well-established facility of branched olefins to undergo electrophilic attack (38).

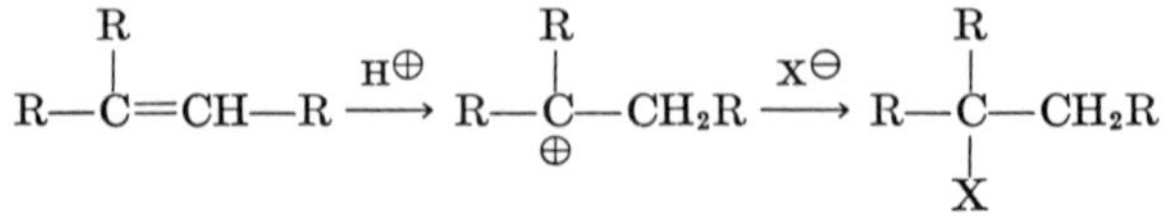

Thus, the branched olefinic structures in 1,4 and 3,4 polyisoprenes and

1,4 poly(dimethylbutadiene):

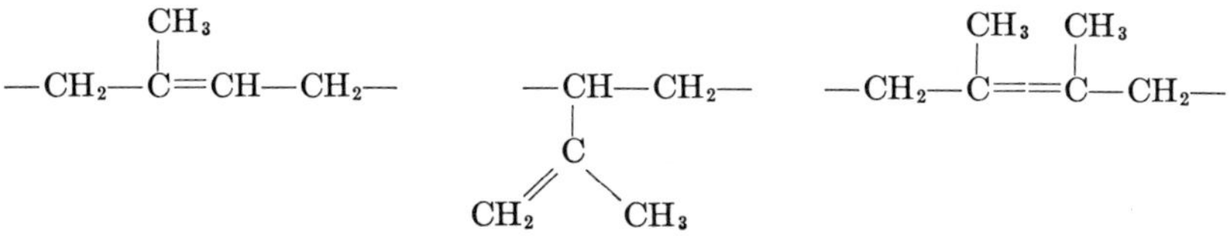

add hydrogen halide with ease. On the other hand, 1,2-polyisoprene

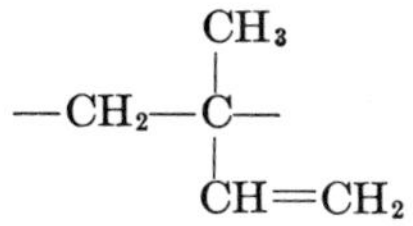

is as unreactive to hydrogen halide as are 1,2 and 1,4 polybutadienes.

The hydrochlorination of natural rubber has been studied extensively (39). Fully hydrochlorinated natural rubber is a solid, crystallizable product (10) but does not contain the theoretical amount of chlorine (8). On this basis and the physical characteristics of the hydrochlorinated products, it was early concluded that some cyclization occurs during hydrochlorination. Until recently there was disagreement about the existence of and the mechanism of cyclization in hydrochlorinated natural rubber. It has now been established on the basis of NMR studies that a small amount of cyclization does occur (40).

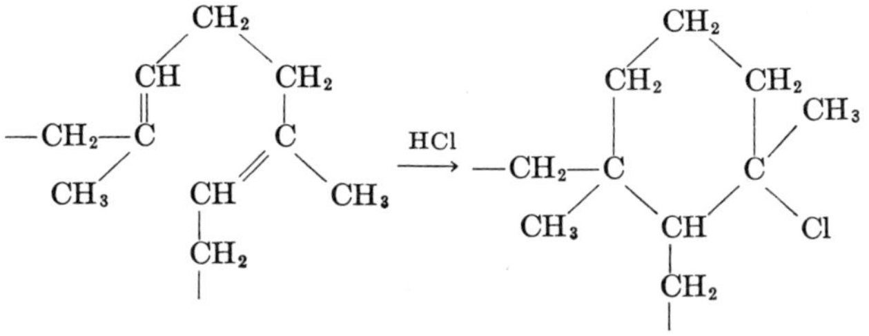

Golub and Heller (41) have shown that 3,4 polyisoprene undergoes simultaneous hydrochlorination and cyclization to a product with predominantly monocyclic structure containing very nearly one chlorine per two double bonds.

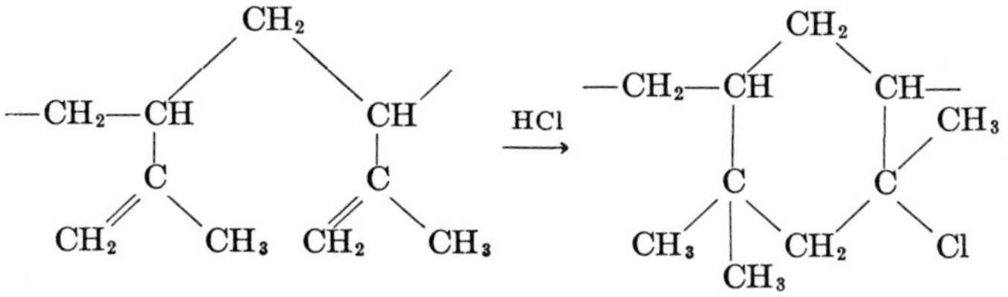

Under the same conditions 1,2 polybutadiene does not react; however, under forcing conditions hydrochlorination can be made to occur. Apparently, cyclization to monocyclic structures also occurs with this polymer.

Salomon and Koningsberger (42) have prepared the hydrochloride of butadiene-styrene rubber by reaction under pressure. Since hydrochlorination of butadiene polymers results in the formation of secondary chlorides the products thus obtained are more stable than the corresponding isoprene rubbers.

The addition of HBr to natural rubber and gutta-percha occurs with great facility (42). The hydrodromides are physically similar to the hydrochlorides but chemically much more reactive. However, the hydrobromides apparently contain about 20% stable bromide. The nature of these stable bromides has not been elucidated.

II. CHLORINATED POLYETHYLENE ELASTOMER

Elastomeric products can be obtained via chlorination of polyethylene, a crystalline plastic. The nature of the starting polyethylene, the final chlorine content, and the chlorination process used are determinants in the nature of the final chlorinated polyethylene.

In the solution chlorination of polyethylene a continuous series of products is obtained as chlorine content increases up to about 70 wt %. The effect of chlorine content on the physical properties of solution-chlorinated low density polyethylene is illustrated in Table I (43).

TABLE I
Physical Properties of Chlorinated Polyethylenes

Chlorine content (wt %)	Structure at room temp.	Physical form at room temp.	Brittleness temp. (°C)	Softening point (°C)
2	Mainly crystalline	Flexible, similar to polyethylene	—	82
8	Crystalline	More flexible	< −70	69
25	Mainly Amorphous	Rubbery	< −70	<20
40	Amorphous	Soft and flexible	< −70	20
45	Amorphous	Flexible, leathery	−20	30
54	Amorphous	Rigid	+20	52
60	Amorphous	Rigid, brittle	+40	67

Polymer flexibility is a function of a number of molecular factors. The presence of polar groups on the polymer chain per se increases stiffness through inter- and intrachain dipole interactions. At low chlorine levels, the ability of the polyethylene structure to crystallize is reduced (45) which results in a reduction in softening point and crystal melting point; however, the flexibility of the polymer is not markedly affected. At chlorine levels between 25 and 40 wt %, chlorinated polyethylene is essentially elastomeric; however, polyethylene crystallinity disappears completely only at a chlorine content of around 35%. In this region the substantially flexible nature of the polyethylene backbone predominates over chlorine dipole interactions. As the chlorine content is increased from 40 wt % the products become increasingly stiffer and more brittle, even though they remain amorphous.

The distribution of the chlorine in the polymer is an important factor in determining the physical properties of chlorinated polyethylene. Infrared analyses (46,47) of solution chlorinated polyethylene show the presence of —CHCl— and —CCl_2— groups as chlorination proceeds. At a chlorine level of 50 wt % the band at 722 cm^{-1}, characteristic of four or more adjacent CH_2 groups in paraffins, disappears. At chlorine levels of about 30 wt % the —CCl_2— and —CHCl—CHCl— contents are very low as might be expected due to deactivation of carbon–hydrogen bonds of the carbon containing the chlorine atom and those of the next three carbons (48). Thus solution chlorination can be considered to be reasonably random and uniform. At higher chlorine levels chlorinated polyethylene can be described as a terpolymer of ethylene, vinyl chloride and 1,2-dichloroethylene. Such a description accurately predicts glass transition temperatures of chlorinated polyethylene (47).

Polyethylenes have been chlorinated in gel form, i.e., swollen by solvent (43,49) and in slurry form (40). Even in the swollen condition polyethylene is partly crystalline (51) so that in gel chlorination attack is concentrated in the amorphous phase. Slurry chlorination produces a more uneven distribution since the surface of the particle is highly chlorinated relative to the polyethylene at the core. Such a difference in chlorine distribution affects the physical properties of the polymer except possibly at the highest chlorine levels. In gel-chlorinated low density polyethylene the polyethylene x-ray diffraction pattern is still present up to chlorine contents of about 55% compared to 35% for solution chlorinated products (43). The polyethylene segments increase the hardness and the softening point whereas the highly chlorinated segments reduce flexibility by dipole interaction. Thus suitable elastomeric chlorinated polyethylenes are not preparable via the gel or slurry technique.

The physical properties of chlorinated polyethylene are a function of the molecular weight and linearity (as measured by crystallinity or density) of the starting polyethylene. Low density polyethylene has about the same crystallinity as high density polyethylene containing 15 wt % chlorine (49). High density polyethylene is less soluble in solvents suitable for halogenation and therefore, requires higher chlorination temperatures in order to yield uniform polymers (47,49,52). Tensile properties of chlorinated polyethylene vary in a complex manner depending on polyethylene density and molecular weight (49). The flexibility characteristics of chlorinated polyethylenes at lower chlorine levels are dependent on the starting polyethylene; however, above 30 wt % chlorine little difference in flexibility is noted (49).

Chlorinated polyethylene elastomer is relatively unreactive, and therefore difficult to cure (53), and thermally stable (47). Chlorinated polyethylene is more stable to dehydrochlorination than poly(vinyl chloride). This stability is due to the virtual absence of unsaturation, fewer branches (less of the more reactive tertiary chloride) and random placement of chlorine along the polymer chain (which decreases the dehydrochlorination propagation reaction). Druesdow and Gibbs have shown that secondary chlorides found in poly(vinyl chloride) are thermally stable compared to tertiary or allylic chlorides (54). In addition Baum and Wartman have found that allylic chlorides dehydrochlorinate much more readily than tertiary chlorides (55).

Recently, a high molecular weight chlorinated polyethylene elastomer containing 40% chlorine has been reported (56). The elastomer is fully saturated so that conventional sulfur cures are ineffective; however, the elastomer is readily curable with amines or peroxides. The resultant vulcanizates possess excellent ozone, heat, solvent and flame resistance.

Elastomeric chlorinated polyethylene has been used as an impact modifier for poly(vinyl chloride) (57). Blends of these materials have substantially the same rigidity and solvent resistance as poly(vinyl chloride) but better impact strength and low temperature brittleness characteristics.

A. Curable Chlorinated Polyethylene

Chlorinated polyethylenes prepared in solution and at moderate temperatures cannot be cured easily because of the absence of functionality other than the relatively unreactive secondary chlorides. For a readily curable elastomer it is necessary that other more reactive functional groups be introduced into the polymer chain.

1. Chlorosulfonation

The best known method of introducing a reactive functional group into chlorinated polyethylene is the Reed-Horn process (58) for chlorosulfonation. This process involves the coreaction of SO_2 and Cl_2 in the presence of light according the following sequence (59):

$$Cl_2 \rightarrow 2Cl\cdot$$
$$RH + Cl\cdot \rightarrow R\cdot + HCl$$
$$R\cdot + SO_2 \rightleftharpoons RSO_2\cdot$$
$$RSO_2\cdot + Cl_2 \rightarrow RSO_2Cl + Cl\cdot$$

An appropriately small amount of sulfonyl chloride can be introduced simultaneous with the introduction of chlorine by controlling concentrations and reaction conditions.

Chlorosulfonated polyethylene has been a commercial product since about 1952 under the name Hypalon, a trademark of E. I. du Pont de Nemours and Co., Inc. (60). This product contains about 27% chlorine and 1.5% sulfur as sulfonyl chloride. The chlorine content of 27% was considered to be a good compromise of all elastomer characteristics for a multipurpose elastomer (61).

Chlorosulfonated polyethylene can be crosslinked with a variety of agents, all of which are designed to proceed through the sulfonyl chloride group or its derivatives.

a. Metal Oxide Systems. The most generally useful formulations for curing chlorosulfonated polyethylene are those comprised of a metal oxide, a weak organic acid, and a sulfur-type accelerator. In these systems crosslinking is effected via hydrolysis of the sulfonyl chloride to sulfonic acid followed by formation of a metal sulfonate (62,63).

The organic acid functions as a source of H_2O for the cure and as a solubilizer for the metal salt.

$$MO + 2RCOOH \rightarrow (RCOO)_2M + H_2O$$

The metal oxide functions not only as the crosslinking agent but also catalyzes the hydrolysis of the sulfonyl chloride and acts as an HCl acceptor (63).

$$RSO_2Cl + H_2O \rightarrow RSO_3H + HCl$$
$$MO + 2HCl \rightarrow MCl_2 + H_2O$$

The final crosslinking reaction is effected via metal oxide or metal–organic acid salt.

$$2RSO_3H + (RCOO)_2M \text{ (or MO)} \rightarrow (RSO_3)_2M + 2RCOOH \text{ (or } H_2O)$$

In the absence of a sulfur accelerator, poor cures and severe blowing due to the evolution of acid gases are obtained. The primary function of a sulfur accelerator is to prevent radical-initiated decomposition of the sulfonyl chloride group thereby allowing the metal oxide system to function efficiently in sulfonate crosslinking. Sulfur accelerators per se have shown curing activity in chlorosulfonated polyethylene probably by reaction with unsaturation produced by decomposition of the sulfonyl chloride (63) or by interaction with radicals generated during sulfonyl chloride decomposition (64,65).

$$\text{—}CH_2\text{—}\underset{\displaystyle SO_2Cl}{\underset{|}{CH}}\text{—} \rightarrow \text{—}CH{=}CH\text{—} + HCl + SO_2$$

$$RSO_2Cl + X\cdot \rightarrow RSO_2\cdot + XCl$$

$$RSO_2\cdot \rightleftharpoons R\cdot + SO_2$$

The free radical nature of alkane sulfonyl chlorides has been well established (66). Maynard and Johnson (64) have shown that a wide variety of free radical scavengers function as well as sulfur accelerators in metal oxide curing systems.

b. Polyfunctional Alcohols. Polyfunctional alcohols in the presence of strong base rapidly crosslink chlorosulfonated polyethylene through esterification to the bis-sulfonate (63,65,67).

$$2RSO_2Cl + HO\text{—}R'\text{—}OH \rightarrow RSO_2O\text{—}R'\text{—}OSO_2R + 2HCl$$

Less reactive inorganic bases, such as CaO and MgO, give more controllable crosslinking, and sulfur accelerators are required, again presumably to prevent radical decomposition of the sulfonyl chloride.

Polyols containing primary hydroxyl are highly active compared to those containing secondary hydroxyl. Chlorosulfonated polyethylene which has been reacted with monofunctional alcohols can be crosslinked with metal oxides. Thus polyol cures in the presence of metal oxides can be considered to proceed via the following steps (65).

$$2RSO_2Cl + 2R'OH + MO \rightarrow 2RSO_2OR' + MCl_2 + H_2O$$

$$2RSO_2OR' + MCl_2 \rightarrow (RSO_2O)_2M + 2R'Cl$$

Most primary polyols react too rapidly, thereby affecting processing safety ("scorch") and processing behavior of the elastomer. A balance of processing behavior and vulcanizate properties has been achieved by using pentaerythritol (68).

c. Amines, Imines, Aziridines. Basic organic nitrogen compounds react rapidly with sulfonyl chlorides to form sulfonamide crosslinks and also serve as acid acceptors (63,65,67,69).

$$RSO_2Cl + 2R'NH_2 \rightarrow RSO_2NHR' + R'NH_2{\cdot}HCl$$

$$RSO_2Cl + R'CH{=}NH \rightarrow RSO_2NH{-}\underset{\displaystyle Cl}{\underset{|}{CH}}{-}R'$$

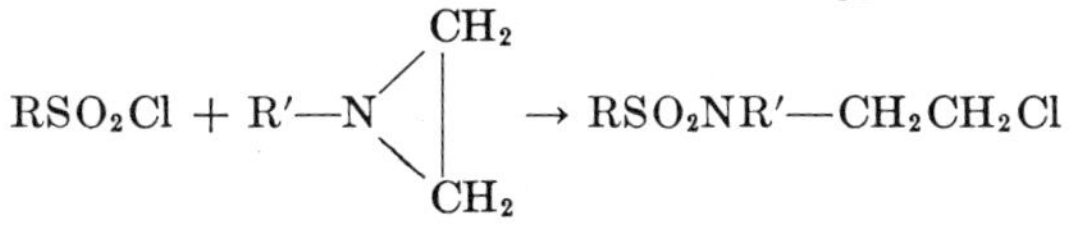

At higher temperatures these nitrogen compounds can also react with the chlorine atoms along the chain and act as HCl acceptors to aid in the formation of unsaturation through dehydrochlorination.

Simple diamines react too rapidly to be useful. Hindered diamines are more easily handled but yield poor cures and poor vulcanizate properties. Benzaldimines, and cyclohexyl ketimines, derived from aliphatic and aromatic amines, and polyaziridines suffer the same disadvantages as the diamines (65).

Interesting, if impractical, curing agents for chlorosulfonated polyethylene are the 2,3-dialkyl substituted quinoxalines. Since it is necessary that the quinoxaline be substituted in the 2- and 3- positions with nonbulky alkyl groups, Nersasian, King, and Johnson (65) have proposed a mechanism involving amidation of the sulfonyl chloride group with the enamine form of the quinoxaline, the resultant bissulfonamide possibly rearranging to the more stable bissulfone.

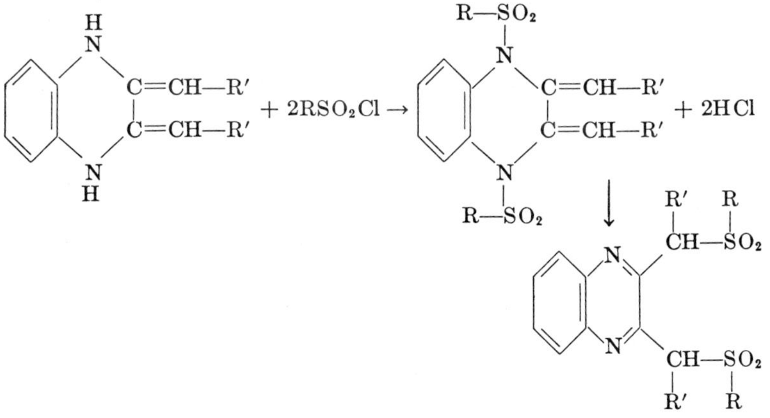

2. Dehydrohalogenation to Unsaturation

At high temperatures chlorinated polyethylene will suffer the loss of HCl with consequent formation of unsaturation. Such a treatment also results in extensive polymer degradation and gel formation. Thus dehydrohalogenation is not a preferred method for the introduction of unsaturation in chlorinated polyethylene.

Canterino and DeVault (70) have dehydrochlorinated chlorinated polyethylene by extensive heating at 250°C. The resultant polymer, although low in chlorine and not elastomeric was curable with conventional sulfur formulations.

3. Chlorophosphonation

The reaction of alkanes with PCl_3 and oxygen to produce phosphonyl chlorides

$$RH + 2PCl_3 + O_2 \rightarrow RPOCl_2 + POCl_3 + HCl$$

was discovered independently by Clayton and Jensen (71), Saborovsky, Zinovyev, and Englin (72) and Graf (73). Product yields are sensitive to impurities, somewhat sensitive to the molar ratios of reactants, and relatively independent of reaction temperature (74). Reaction proceeds via a free radical mechanism in which PCl_3 rather unexpectedly, successfully competes with oxygen for the generated free radicals (75,76,77).

$$R\cdot + PCl_3 \rightleftharpoons R\dot{P}Cl_3 \xrightarrow[PCl_3]{O_2} RPOCl_2 + POCl_3 + Cl\cdot$$

Using this reaction on polyethylene, Schroeder and Sopchak (78) prepared a series of phosphonic acid and phosphonate ester derivatives containing as much as 14.7% phosphorus. The modified resins were not crosslinked and varied in nature from tough plastics to soft, tacky resins. A polyethylene containing 1.3% phosphorus was curable with litharge to a stiff leathery vulcanizate.

Canterino and Edmonds (79) applied the chlorophosphonation reaction to chlorinated polyethylene elastomer to produce a curable elastomer. The phosphonyl chlorides were converted to phosphonate esters during isolation, and the modified products so produced were readily curable with metal oxide formulations similar to those described for chlorosulfonated polyethylene. By analogy crosslinking most likely occurs through formation of a metal diphosphonate either by direct reaction of the phosphonate ester with the metal-organic acid salt

$$2R{-}P(OR')_2 + (R''COO)_2M \rightarrow R{-}\overset{OR'}{\overset{|}{P}}{-}OMO{-}\overset{OR'}{\overset{|}{P}}{-}R + 2R''COOR'$$

or by reaction of metal salts with hydrolyzed phosphonate.

$$RP(OR')_2 + H_2O \rightarrow RP\begin{matrix}\diagup OR' \\ \diagdown OH\end{matrix} + R'OH$$

$$2RP\begin{matrix}\diagup OR' \\ \diagdown OH\end{matrix} + MO \rightarrow R{-}\overset{OR'}{\overset{|}{P}}{-}OMO{-}\overset{OR'}{\overset{|}{P}}{-}R + H_2O$$

III. BUTYL RUBBER

Originated and developed by Thomas and co-workers at the Standard Oil Development Co., butyl rubbers are copolymers of isobutylene and small amounts of isoprene prepared at about −150°F with a Friedel-Crafts catalyst (80–83). Polyisobutylene itself is a rubber but contains no functionality for crosslinking; hence, copolymerization with a difunctional monomer is required. Butyl rubber has many desirable characteristics, among them good ozone resistance (84,85) and air impermeability (86). However, two major shortcomings of butyl rubber have been incompatibility of cure with other elastomers and poor adhesive properties to other elastomers and metals (87). These shortcomings are directly related to low cure rate and to lack of polar functional groups. In these regards the performance of butyl rubber is improved by halogenation.

A. Bromination

Crawford and Morrissey (88) found that the "incomplete" bromination of butyl rubber increased its cure rate, improved adhesion and quality of vulcanizates, and imparted compatibility with high unsaturation rubbers, such as natural rubber and styrene-butadiene rubbers. The reaction of bromine with butyl rubber was considered to be predominantly additive to the isoprene moiety which is incorporated into the polymer in a

$${-}CH_2{-}\overset{CH_3}{\overset{|}{C}}{=}C{-}CH_2{-} + Br_2 \rightarrow {-}CH_2{-}\underset{Br}{\underset{|}{\overset{CH_3}{\overset{|}{C}}}}{-}\underset{Br}{\underset{|}{CH}}{-}CH_2{-}$$

1,4 fashion with lesser amounts of substitution (89).

Baldwin and Kuntz (90) have claimed that bromination of butyl rubber is primarily substitutive rather than additive. They noted that bromination of butyl with elemental bromine was accompanied by the formation of large amounts of HBr. Further, bromine can be incorporated in the polymer to levels between 2 and 3 bromine atoms per double bond with relatively little molecular weight breakdown. When the unsaturation in brominated butyl rubber was measured by the iodine-mercuric acetate method (91), a regular decrease in unsaturation with increasing bromine content was noted. However, this method, relying as it does on halogen addition to an already halogenated system, was found to be inapplicable. Indeed, when unsaturation was measured by the ozonolysis method of Rehner and Gray (92) the unsaturation in brominated butyl was found to be essentially retained. All of these findings strongly suggest that the bromination of butyl rubber is predominantly a substitutive reaction resulting in the introduction of allylic bromides of the type

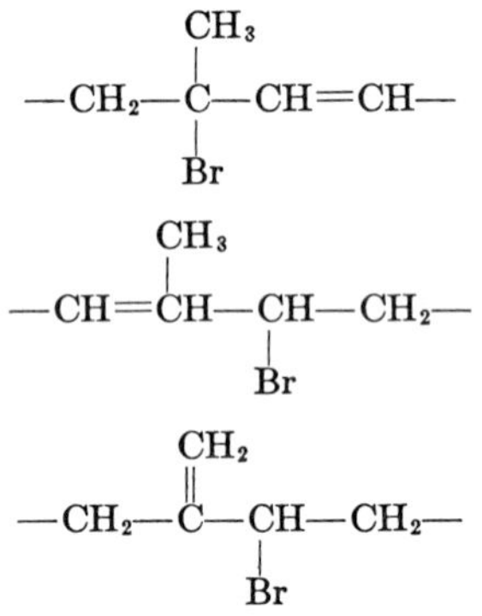

In the discussion on polydiene elastomers it was noted that the reaction of 1,4 polyisoprenes with elemental bromine and phenyl trimethyl ammonium tribromide was essentially additive. On the other hand, reaction of bromine radicals via *N*-bromosuccinimide resulted in primarily substitution. On the basis of these results it would appear that, under the conditions of bromination of butyl rubber, ionic substitution involving deprotonation of an intermediate bromonium ion complex

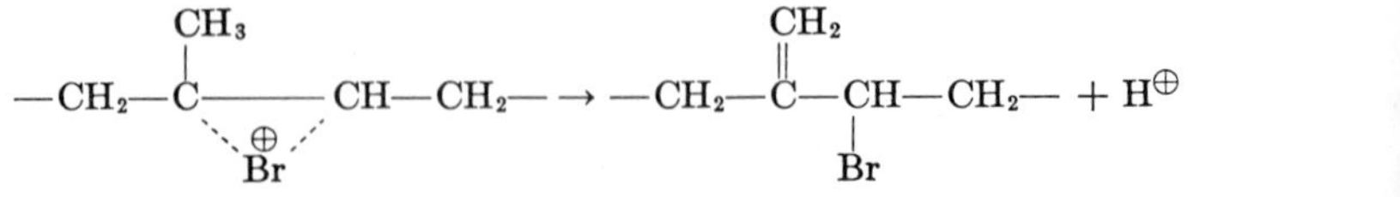

is less likely than radical allylic substitution

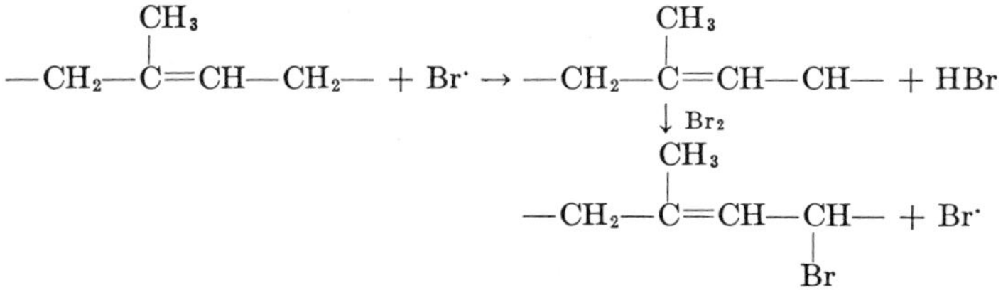

The relatively low, but regular, decrease in molecular weight with increasing bromine content is best explained by the radical attack on the polyisobutylene main chain. Chain cleavage via the resultant polyisobutylene radical is facile and has been elucidated by Charlesby, et al. (93). The low rate of molecular weight degradation during bromination can be attributed to the relatively low reactivity of a bromine free radical in the abstraction of primary hydrogen atoms from a polyisobutylene chain (94).

B. Chlorination

The chlorination of butyl rubber at 25°C with excess chlorine is accompanied by HCl evolution and results in marked molecular weight breakdown (90,95). This contrasts with the bromination of butyl rubber where molecular weight breakdown is less severe. When chlorination is effected at −20°C little degradation occurs and, apparently, addition to the double bond occurs (96). With incremental addition of chlorine at 25°C, the molecular weight is essentially unchanged up to the introduction of one chlorine per double bond (90,95). The polymer unsaturation is essentially retained up to this point.

The initial introduction of chlorine is very rapid. Reaction proceeds readily in the dark, and the presence of oxygen or an antioxidant has little or no effect. Baldwin et al. (90,95) conclude that the reaction is so rapid and specific that the mechanism of chlorination is probably ionic in nature. Their proposed mechanism involves initial attack of a chloronium ion on the double bond to form the cyclic carbonium ion intermediate

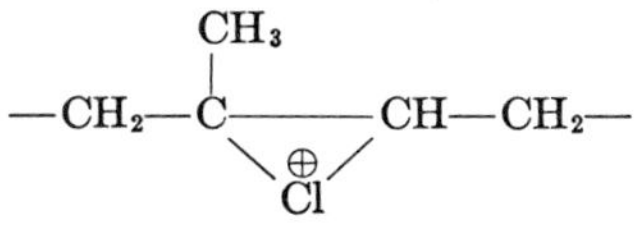

followed by deprotonation from originally allylic carbon atoms, thereby resulting in three allylic chloride structures.

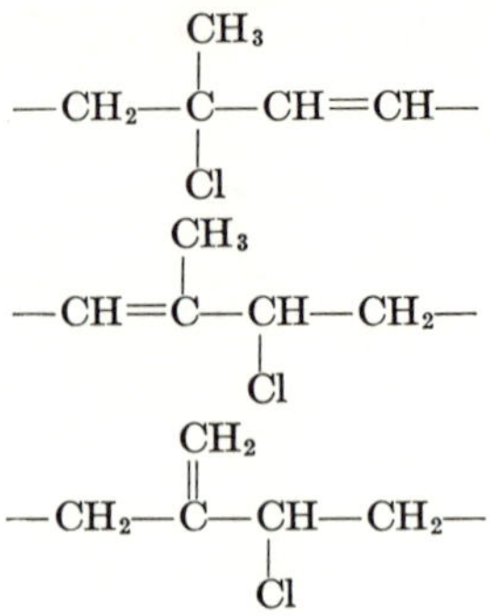

Once this first step is achieved further introduction of chlorine results in marked chain cleavage indicating that ionic substitution of the allylic chloride is considerably less facile than the unsubstituted double bond and that reaction is occurring by a substantially free radical mechanism. This mechanism is essentially identical to that discussed in the chlorination of 1,4 polyisoprenes.

McNeill (97) has investigated the reaction of butyl rubber with radiochlorine. He finds that two chlorine atoms are introduced per double bond, the first being rapidly incorporated while, the second, less so. In agreement with the results obtained previously by Baldwin et al. (90,95), chlorination was found to be substitutive rather than additive, and McNeill concludes that a free radical reaction is unlikely.

Based on these findings McNeill concludes that reaction proceeds analogously to the isobutylene-chlorine reaction (98) via a concerted ionic substitution at the methyl group of the isoprenoid moiety of butyl rubber

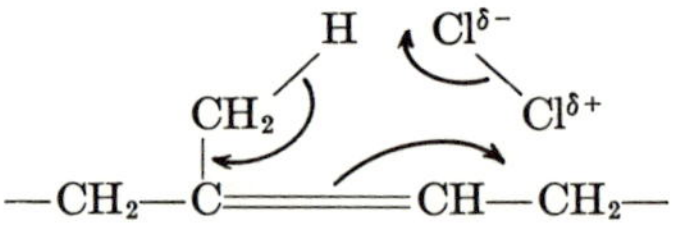

and

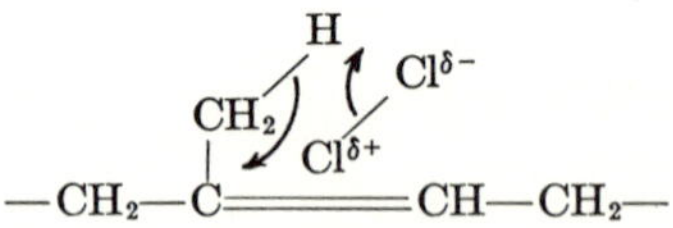

to produce

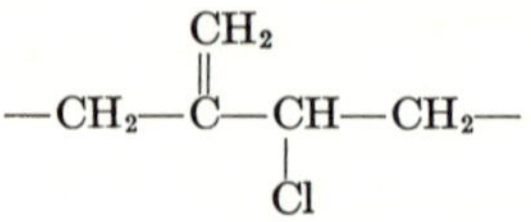

(Minor)

and

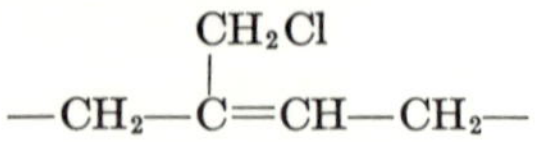

(Major)

The second, slower substitution then results in a disubstituted methyl group.

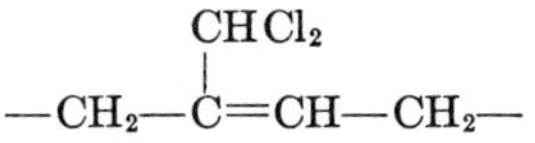

Baldwin et al. (95) have concluded on the basis of thermal decomposition data that 20% of the combined chlorine is of a more active form than the remainder and thereby suggest that these activity differences are due to differences in reactivity of secondary and tertiary allylic chlorides that might be present. The mechanism proposed by McNeill necessarily produces only primary and secondary allylic chlorides; however, the differences in reactivities of these species could account for the chloride activity differences in chlorinated butyl rubber demonstrated by Baldwin et al. McNeill maintains the major portion of substitution results in the formation of primary allylic chloride relative to secondary allylic chloride. This predicts that the more reactive chloride should be present in smaller amounts. Indeed, this is found to be the case.

C. Iodination

Even in the presence of a catalyst and excess iodine only a small amount of iodine can be introduced into butyl rubber (87). The slightly iodinated polymers show no improvement over butyl rubber itself. Treatment of butyl rubber in CCl_4 solution with iodine at reflux temperature results in HI evolution and gelled polymer (90).

An analytical method for the determination of unsaturation in butyl rubber, developed by Gallo, Wiese, and Nelson (91), involves treatment of a solution of the polymer with iodine in the presence of mercuric acetate and trichloroacetic acid. The method is highly reproducible and results in the *consumption* of three atoms of iodine per double bond. Although this treatment results in the introduction of some iodine (99) it has never been determined whether the unsaturation is consumed, or to what extent iodine enters the polymer.

The mechanism which best explains the stoichiometry, but nevertheless is least likely, involves addition of iodine across the double bond followed by elimination to equal portions of allylic and vinylic iodide. The allylic

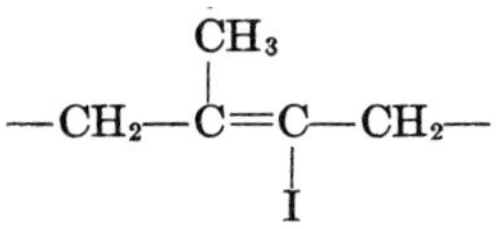

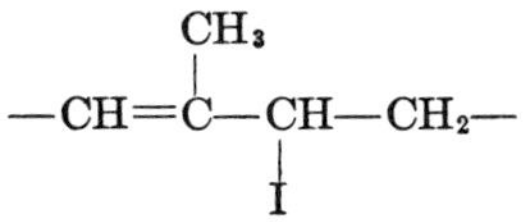

iodide is considered to react with a second mole of iodine to produce triiodide, while the vinylic iodide is inert (91).

Mechanisms involving reagents other than iodine appear more reasonable, but unfortunately, do not account for stoichiometry. Iodine and acetic acid react in the presence of mercuric acetate to produce some iodoacetate, CH_3COOI, and mercuric iodide (99). The iodoacetate can then be considered to react with unsaturation either via an additive process or a concerted ionic substitutive process.

Another possibility that has not been ruled out is the intermediate formation of mercurial compounds. It is well established that aromatic compounds can be mercurated with mercuric acetate in nonpolar solvents at high temperatures (100,101) although peculiar orientation effects are noted. However, in strongly acid aqueous solution mercuration is facile and orientation on the aromatic ring normal at 25°C (102). The addition of basic mercuric salts to olefins has been demonstrated (103). Indeed, furan is mercurated almost instantaneously at room temperature with mercuric acetate (104). Finally, it is known that halogens, and particu-

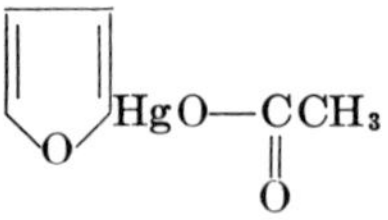

larly iodine, react smoothly with organomercurials (105). In view of

$$RHgX + I_2 \rightarrow RI + HgIX$$

these known reactions part of the mechanism for the reaction of butyl rubber with iodine in the presence of mercuric acetate can be written as follows:

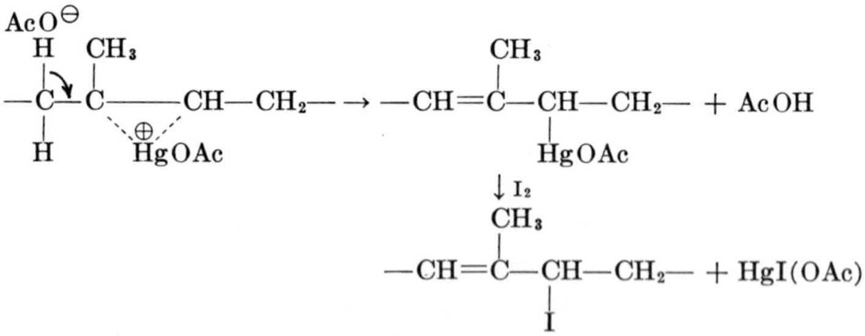

Iodine has been introduced into butyl rubber via reaction with ICl and IBr by Morrissey (87). Halogen analysis of the resultant polymer showed that the amount of iodine introduced is considerably less than that of either chlorine or bromine. Reaction with these reagents are very rapid. In the case of ICl Morrissey finds that initial iodine content relative to chlorine content is low and that an increase in reaction time has no effect on chlorine content or residual unsaturation but results in decreased iodine content. Morrissey considers these data substantiate the theory that iodine–halide adds across a double bond,

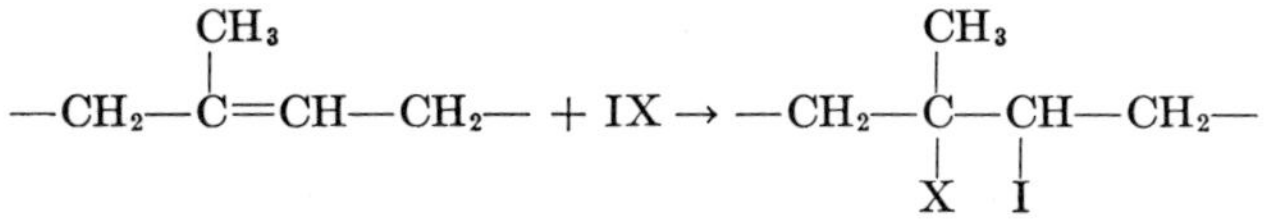

followed by dehydroiodination to a less reactive allylic halide

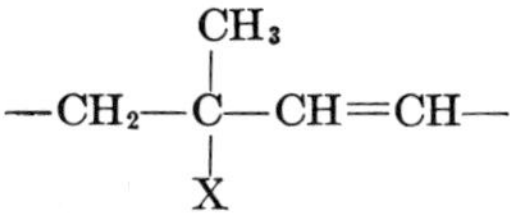

The work of Lee, Kolthoff, and Mairs (31) on the treatment of unsaturated polymers with ICl leaves little doubt that the reaction is ionic in nature. Rehner (106) has shown that butyl rubber will continue to react slowly with an excess of ICl in acetic acid after the theoretical amount of ICl had been rapidly absorbed.

In view of these results it is considered probable that the reaction of iodine halides with butyl rubber proceeds as follows:

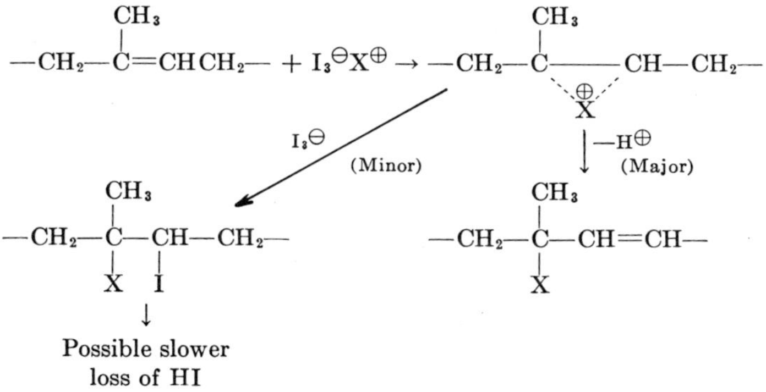

This mechanism is consistent with the fact that less iodine is incorporated with IBr than ICl (due to steric factors) (87) and that IX continues to be consumed even after the theoretical amount of IX has been absorbed.

D. Fluorination

Little work has been done on the fluorination of butyl rubber because of the accompanying extensive molecular weight degradation (87). This phenomenon is not unexpected since reactions of fluorine are invariably homolytic in nature, and the fluorine radicals are highly reactive. The free radical attack on the polyisobutylene chain, followed by facile chain scission, is the major reaction path. This extensive polymer degradation precludes any improvement of a fluorinated butyl rubber over butyl rubber itself.

E. Curing of Halogenated Butyl Rubber

The presence of allylic halides in halogenated butyl rubber allows for crosslinking reactions through reactive halogen in addition to conventional curing through unsaturation (87,89,90,95). Halogenation of butyl rubber results in increased cure rate, improved adhesion and quality of vulcanizates, and compatibility with high unsaturation rubbers, such as natural rubber and styrene-butadiene rubber.

The ability to effect crosslinking via reactive allylic halides has been demonstrated and elucidated by Kovacic (107) in studies on neoprene, which polymer contains some tertiary allylic chloride.

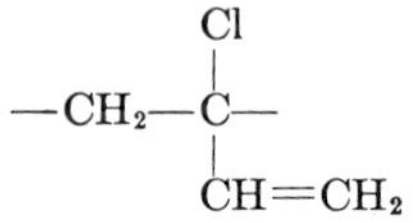

Piperidine or aniline react with neoprene with the elimination of chloride

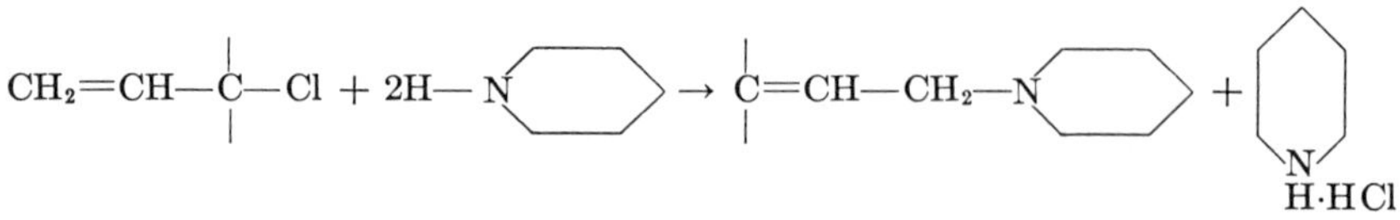

Thus, halogenated butyl rubber can be cured via bisalkylations by utilizing diamines, dihydric phenols, aminophenols, dimercaptans, thioureas, and thioamides (90,95,107).

Metal oxides, specifically zinc oxide, exhibit cure activity in halogenated butyl rubber which can be attributed to the formation of ether

crosslinks

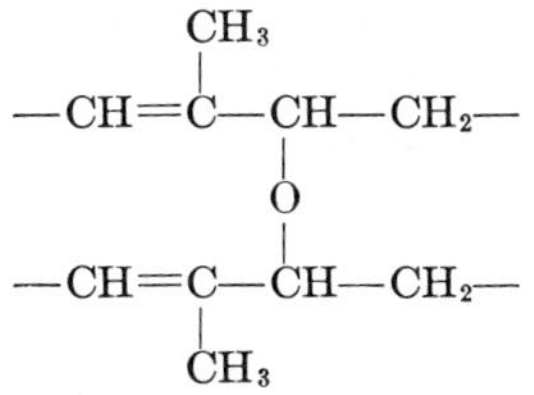

and to crosslinking via polymerization catalyzed by ZnX_2 formed *in situ.*

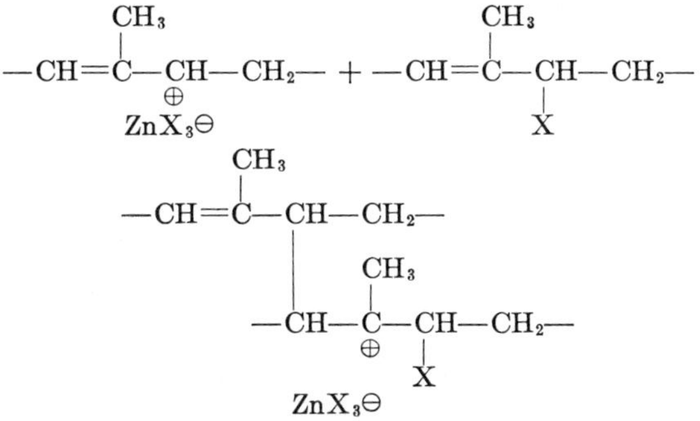

Baldwin et al. (90,95) have demonstrated that with ZnO most of the chlorine present in chlorinated butyl rubber can be extracted out as $ZnCl_2$, and that $ZnCl_2$ is as effective as ZnO in effecting cure.

Brominated butyl rubber cures faster than chlorinated butyl rubber. The cure rates of butyl rubber and its brominated and chlorinated derivatives have been related to the bond dissociation energies of allylic hydrogen and allylic halides (95). Iodobrominated butyl rubber cures better than iodochlorinated butyl rubber which in turn is better than chlorinated butyl rubber (87).

IV. POLY-α-OLEFINS AND ETHYLENE-α-OLEFIN COPOLYMERS

Considerable effort has been expended in the area of elastomeric ethylene-α-olefin copolymers. Early studies on ethylene-propylene copolymers showed them to be exceptionally resistant to oxidation and ozone attack and to possess very good dynamic characteristics (108–110). Just as with polyisobutylene these elastomers contain no functionality for the traditional methods of vulcanization. Specialized procedures have been developed for direct curing which utilize primarily peroxidic agents (110–115) but also a variety of halogen-containing agents (116–120). These direct curing methods in the past have imposed some limitations on the choice of compounding ingredients, processing methods, and end use characteristics.

The problems associated with the direct curing of ethylene-α-olefin copolymers are largely overcome by the introduction of a third difunctional monomer during polymerization. Extensive efforts have been expended on the production of ethylene-propylene terpolymers wherein the third monomer is a diolefin (121–127). The result, of course, is a sulfur-curable elastomer.

The other approach to the synthesis of curable polyolefin elastomers is by postpolymerization chemical modification, notably halogenation and sulfochlorination.

In the chemical modification of polyolefin elastomers the primary, if not the sole, purpose is the introduction of sufficient functionality to effect the subsequent vulcanization of the elastomer. Since these elastomers are essentially saturated hydrocarbons, substitution of functional groups into the polymer chain can be effected only via a free radical mechanism. As the content of the functional groups increases the elastomeric properties of the modified polyolefin elastomer are adversely affected due to the polar interactions of the functional groups (128).

Amorphous linear poly-α-olefins, from polypropylene to poly-l-hexene, are elastomeric and can be chemically modified to permit vulcanization. However, poly-α-olefins per se possess poor elastomeric properties (110). In addition, high molecular weight, amorphous poly-α-olefins are not readily prepared. On the other hand, elastomeric ethylene-α-olefin copolymers, specifically ethylene-propylene copolymers, are readily prepared and possess good elastomeric porperties (110).

A. Chlorosulfonation and Chlorophosphonation

Sulfonyl chloride groups have been introduced into poly-α-olefins and ethylene-α-olefin copolymers by utilizing sulfuryl chloride or combinations of SO_2 and Cl_2 (129–132). The chlorosulphonated polyolefins are readily vulcanized according to all the procedures developed for chlorosulfonated polyethylene.

During the course of chlorosulfonation substantial amounts of chlorine are introduced into the polymer chain. With polyolefin elastomers this additional introduction of chlorine serves no useful purpose for vulcanization but has a deleterious effect upon the elastomeric properties of the modified polymer. Thus chlorination during chlorosulfonation must at least be minimized. By operating at high SO_2/Cl_2 ratios (1/3) and at temperatures below 70°C, it is possible to reduce the chlorine substitution to a level of about two chloro groups per chlorosulfonyl group (132).

Ethylene-propylene copolymers have been chlorophosphonated (133) in the same manner as chlorinated polyethylene (79). These modified copolymers were vulcanized with lead oxide.

B. Halogenation

In order to obtain a curable elastomeric polyolefin via halogenation, it is necessary for at least some of the introduced halogen to undergo facile displacement reactions under normal conditions of vulcanization. The practical modification of reactivity by variation of the halogeno group is limited to bromo and chloro derivatives. Fluoro derivatives are too inert, iodo derivatives are too labile, and both are extremely difficult to prepare.

Another method of improving the reactivity of the halogeno group is via structural variations of the organic moiety. Under conventional vulcanization conditions the order of reactivity of aliphatic halides is allyl $\gg$ tertiary $>$ secondary $>$ primary (134). With chlorinated derivatives, it is clear from the inability of chlorinated polyethylene to cure (53) that secondary chlorides are highly inert. Druesdow and Gibbs (54) have shown that in poly(vinyl chloride) the secondary chlorides are thermally stable compared to tertiary or allylic chlorides. Thus with halogenated polyolefinic elastomers only the tertiary halides are useful in effecting vulcanization.

In the free radical chlorination of aliphatics frequently the intermediate free radicals are so highly reactive that hydrogen substitution occurs rather indiscriminately. For example, in the photochlorination of isobutane at -15°C the tertiary hydrogen is still only 4.5 times as reactive as the primary hydrogen (135). Bruzzone and Crespi have calculated that, in the photochlorination of a 50 mole % ethylene-propylene copolymer at 50°C, approximately 20% of the substituted chlorines are tertiary (136). Since chlorinations were effected in CCl_4 solvent the calculated value of tertiary chloride may be high (135,137). Nevertheless, it does illustrate that under the usual conditions of halogenation a substantial amount of halogen must be incorporated to achieve a reasonable level of tertiary substitution.

The chlorination of isotactic polypropylene powder suspended in a nonsolvent is rapid but, over the range of 5–35% chlorine, does not produce elastomers (138). On the other hand, the chlorination of partly crystalline, but essentially elastomeric, polypropylene in CCl_4 solution resulted in elastomeric products up to a chlorine content of 17% (139). Products containing 30% and more chlorine were very hard and had softening points greater than 100°C. The elastomeric chlorinated polypropylenes were claimed to be partly vulcanizable.

The photochlorination of ethylene-propylene copolymers in CCl_4 solution and the vulcanization of the resultant polymers has been described in some detail (136,138,140,141). Chlorinated polymers containing less than 10% chlorine did not cure sufficiently well whereas those containing above 20% chlorine were overly stiff. Best properties were obtained with 17% chlorine. Vulcanization did not occur in the absence of a metal oxide nor in the absence of sulfur. These results clearly suggest that the mechanism of vulcanization involves the prior formation of unsaturation via dehydrohalogenation. The high chlorine contents required for adequate vulcanization result in extensive molecular weight degradation during chlorination and in relatively poor elastomeric properties due to dipole–dipole interactions (141).

Makowski, Cain, and Wei (142) utilized aromatic solvents in the preparation of chlorinated polypropylenes and ethylene-propylene copolymers. The chlorinated polymers were far more active in vulcanization than those prepared in CCl_4 solvent. Copolymers containing as little as 2–3% chlorine were readily cured with conventional rubber vulcanizing formulations. When chlorinations were effected at 110°C in chlorobenzene chlorinated copolymers containing 5–10% chlorine could be cured with diamines and metal oxides. In addition, curing could be effected with sulfur and organic accelerators in the absence of metal oxides. On the other hand, when chlorinations were effected at 70°C to low chlorine levels (2–3%) adequate vulcanization did not occur; however, treatment of the chlorinated copolymer with 1% zinc oxide for 1 min at 300°F resulted in a substantial loss in chlorine and a consequently large increase in iodine number (unsaturation). The treated polymers then cured rapidly with conventional rubber formulations.

The results obtained with chlorinated copolymers prepared in aromatic solvents were explained on the basis of (*1*) the effect of solvents on the selectivity of chlorine substitution, and (*2*) the relative ease of dehydrochlorination of primary, secondary, and tertiary chlorides.

The effect of solvents on the selectivity of chlorination of aliphatics has been studied in detail by Russell (137,143,144). In the presence of certain aromatic solvents, the reactivity of a chlorine atom can be modified so that it attacks a tertiary hydrogen 50–300 times as readily as a primary hydrogen. This selectivity arises from association of the chlorine atom with the π-electron of the aromatic nucleus.

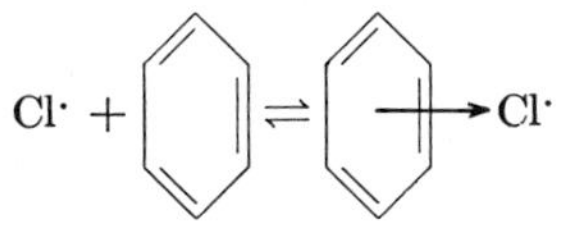

These complexes are less reactive and, therefore, more selective than a free chlorine atom. The selectivity of chlorine is a function of solvent basicity, solvent concentration, and chlorination temperature.

The facility of tertiary and allylic chlorides to dehydrochlorinate has been well established (55,145). Thus, chlorination in aromatic solvents provides conditions favoring tertiary substitution, and the resultant tertiary chlorides are relatively easily dehydrochlorinated either during high temperature chlorination or during subsequent vulcanization. The net result is a system containing unsaturation and both allylic and tertiary chlorides. Since conventional vulcanization formulations contain metal oxides in addition to sulfur and organic accelerators, vulcanization proceeds through both the unsaturation and the reactive chlorides.

Since the chlorine levels required for facile and efficient vulcanization are low (2–3%) the two major drawbacks of chlorinated polyolefins are avoided, i.e., (*1*) extensive molecular weight degradation during chlorination, and (*2*) adverse dynamic characteristics of the vulcanizates due to polar interactions of chlorine atoms.

Brominated polyolefin elastomers have been studied only briefly (128,146). In contrast to the chlorinated derivatives brominated polymers containing low molar percentages of bromine are readily cured with metal oxides in the absence of sulfur and with diamines. This enhanced reactivity is directly attributable to the lower bond energy of the C—Br bond (147).

References

1. F. W. Billmeyer, Jr., *Textbook of Polymer Chemistry,* Interscience, New York, 1957, Part VI.
2. G. Kraus, J. N. Short, and V. Thornton, *Rubber Plastics Age,* **38,** 880 (1957).
3. K. W. Scott, G. S. Trick, R. H. Mayer, W. M. Saltman, and R. M. Pierson, *Rubber Plastics Age,* **42,** 175 (1961).
4. J. D. D'Ianni, *Rubber Chem. Technol.,* **34,** 361 (1961).
5. H. Blümel, *Kautschuk Gummi,* **16,** 571 (1963); *Rubber Chem. Technol.,* **37,** 408 (1964).

6. J. P. Baxter and J. G. Moore, *J. Soc. Chem. Ind.*, **57,** 327 (1938); *Rubber Chem. Technol.*, **12,** 82 (1939).
7. G. F. Bloomfield, *J. Chem. Soc.*, **1943,** 289; *Rubber Chem. Technol*, **17,** 1, (1944).
8. H. Staudinger and H. Staudinger, *J. Prakt. Chem.*, **162,** 148 (1943); *Rubber Chem. Technol.*, **17,** 15 (1944).
9. G. F. Bloomfield, *J. Chem. Soc.*, **1944,** 114.
10. J. D. D'Ianni, F. J. Naples, J. W. Marsh, and J. L. Zarney, *Ind. Eng. Chem.*, **38,** 1171 (1946).
11. G. J. Van Amerongen, C. Koningsberger, and G. Salomon, *J. Polymer Sci.*, **5,** 639 (1950).
12. G. Kraus and W. B. Reynolds, *J. Am. Chem. Soc.*, **72,** 5621 (1950).
13. C. S. Ramakrishnan, D. Raghunath, and J. B. Pande, *Trans. Inst. Rubber Ind.*, **29,** 190 (1953); *Rubber Chem. Technol.*, **26,** 902 (1953).
14. C. S. Ramakrishnan, D. Raghunath, and J. B. Pande, *Trans. Inst. Rubber Ind.*, **30,** 129 (1954); *Rubber Chem. Technol.*, **28,** 598, (1955).
15. M. Troussier, *Rev. Gen. Caoutchouc*, **32,** 229 (1955); *Rubber Chem. Technol.*, **29,** 302 (1956).
16. J. Burgin, W. Engs, H. P. A. Groll, and G. Hearne, *Ind. Eng. Chem.*, **31,** 1413 (1939).
17. H. P. A. Groll, G. Hearne, F. F. Rust, and W. E. Vaughan, *Ind. Eng. Chem.*, **31,** 1239 (1939).
18. R. W. Taft, Jr., *J. Am. Chem. Soc.*, **70,** 3364 (1948).
19. W. Reeve, D. H. Chambers, and C. S. Prickett, *J. Am. Chem. Soc.*, **74,** 5369 (1952).
20. M. L. Poutsma, *J. Am. Chem. Soc.*, **87,** 2161 (1965).
21. E. D. Hughes, C. K. Ingold, S. Masterman, and B. J. McNulty, *J. Chem. Soc.*, **1940,** 899.
22. P. B. D. de la Mare, *Quart. Rev. (London)*, **3,** 126 (1949).
23. M. L. Poutsma, *J. Am. Chem. Soc.*, **87,** 2172 (1965).
24. M. L. Poutsma, *J. Am. Chem. Soc.*, **87,** 4285 (1965).
25. R. C. Fahey and C. Schubert, *J. Am. Chem. Soc.*, **87,** 5172 (1965).
26. R. C. Fahey, *J. Am. Chem. Soc.*, **88,** 4681 (1966).
27. J. H. Gladstone and W. Hibbert, *J. Chem. Soc.*, **53,** 679 (1888).
28. C. O. Weber, *Ber.*, **33,** 779 (1900).
29. A. R. Kemp and G. S. Mueller, *Ind. Eng. Chem., Anal. Ed.*, **6,** 52 (1934).
30. P. Pinazzi, and H. Gueniffey, *Makromol. Chem.*, **93,** 109 (1966).
31. T. S. Lee, I. M. Kolthoff, and M. A. Mairs, *J. Polymer Sci.*, **3,** 66 (1948).
32. H. A. Endres, *Rubber Age*, **55,** 361 (1944).
33. A. R. Kemp and H. Peters, *Ind. Eng. Chem., Anal. Ed.*, **15,** 453, (1943).
34. P. J. Canterino, *Ind. Eng. Chem.*, **49,** 712 (1957).
35. C. Pinazzi, H. Gueniffey, and J. Brossas, *Compt. Rend.*, **258,** 4982 (1964).
36. C. Pinazzi and H. Gueniffey, *Compt. Rend.*, **C263,** 915 (1966).
37. C. Harries and E. Fonrobert, *Ber.*, **46,** 773 (1913).
38. E. S. Gould, *Mechanism and Structure in Organic Chemistry*, Henry Holt, New York, 1959.
39. J. B. Pande, D. Raghunath, and C. S. Ramakrishnan, *Makromol. Chem.*, **20,** 181 (1956).
40. M. A. Golub and J. Heller, *J. Polymer Sci.*, **B2,** 733 (1964).
41. M. A. Golub and J. Heller, *J. Polymer Sci.*, **B2,** 523 (1964).

42. G. Salomon and C. Koningsberger, *Rec. Trav. Chem.*, **69**, 711 (1958).
43. W. G. Oakes and R. B. Richards, *Trans. Faraday Soc.*, **42A**, 197 (1946).
44. V. L. Simril, *J. Polymer Sci.*, **2**, 142 (1947).
45. (*a*) C. W. Bunn, *Trans. Faraday Soc.*, **35**, 482 (1939); (*b*) C. W. Bunn and T. C. Alcock, *ibid.*, **41**, 317 (1945).
46. H. W. Thompson and P. Torkington, *Trans. Faraday Soc.*, **41**, 246 (1945).
47. H. J. Oswald and E. T. Kubu, *SPE Transactions*, **3**, 168 (1963).
48. D. J. Hurley, R. W. Rosenthal, and R. C. Williamson, *J. Org. Chem.*, **30**, 4314 (1965).
49. P. J. Canterino and G. R. Kahle, *J. Appl. Polymer Sci.*, **6**, 20 (1962).
50. Brit. Pat. 815,086 (June 17, 1959) (to Petrochemicals Limited).
51. R. B. Richards, *Trans. Faraday Soc.*, **42**, 10 (1946).
52. Brit. Pat. 815,088 (June 17, 1959) (to Phillips Petroleum Co.).
53. R. E. Brooks, D. E. Strain, and A. McAlevy, *India Rubber World*, **127**, 79 (1953).
54. D. Druesdow and C. F. Gibbs, *Natl. Bur. Std. Circ.*, **525**, 69 (1951).
55. B. Baum and L. H. Wartman, *J. Polymer Sci.*, **38**, 537 (1958).
56. F. C. Csaszar and J. A. Shannon, A.C.S. Division of Rubber Chemistry, San Francisco, Calif., May, 1966.
57. F. Hans-Helmut, U.S. Pat. 3,006,889 (Oct. 31, 1961) (to Farbwerke Hoechst).
58. C. F. Reed and C. L. Horn, U.S. Pat. 2,046,090 (June 30, 1936) (to du Pont).
59. M. S. Kharasch, T. H. Chao, and H. C. Brown, *J. Am. Chem. Soc.*, **62**, 2393 (1940).
60. R. R. Warner, *Rubber Age*, **71**, 205 (1952).
61. R. E. Brooks, D. E. Strain, and A. McAlevy, *India Rubber World*, **127**, 791 (1953).
62. M. A. Smook, I. D. Roche, W. B. Clark, and O. G. Youngquist, *India Rubber World*, **128**, 54 (1953).
63. M. A. Smook, E. T. Pieski, and C. F. Hammer, *Ind. Eng. Chem.*, **45**, 2731 (1953).
64. J. T. Maynard and R. R. Johnson, *J. Appl. Polymer Sci.*, **7**, 1943 (1963).
65. A. Nersasian, K. F. King, and P. R. Johnson, *J. Appl. Polymer Sci.*, **8**, 337 (1964).
66. H. F. Herbrandson, W. S. Kelly, and J. Versnel, *J. Am. Chem. Soc.*, **80**, 3301 (1958).
67. W. F. Busse and M. A. Smook, *India Rubber World*, **128**, 348 (1953).
68. K. F. King, U.S. Pat. 2,994, 688 (Aug. 1, 1961) (to du Pont).
69. W. F. Busse and F. W. Billmeyer, Jr., *J. Polymer Sci.*, **12**, 599 (1954).
70. P. J. Canterino and A. N. DeVault, U.S. Pat. 2,850,490 (Sept. 2, 1958) (to Phillips Petroleum Co.).
71. J. O. Clayton and W. L. Jensen, *J. Am. Chem. Soc.*, **70**, 3880 (1948).
72. L. Z. Soborovsky, Y. M. Zinovyev, and M. A. Englin, *Dokl. Akad. Nauk SSSR*, **67**, 293 (1949).
73. R. Graf, *Chem. Ber.*, **85**, 9 (1952).
74. A. F. Isbell and F. T. Wadsworth, *J. Am. Chem. Soc.*, **78**, 6042 (1956).
75. F. R. Mayo, Abstracts of Papers, 134th A.C.S. Meeting, Chicago, Sept., 1958, p. 6P.
76. F. R. Mayo and L. J. Durham, Abstracts of Papers, 140th A.C.S. Meeting, Chicago, Sept., 1961, p. 41Q.
77. R. L. Flurry, Jr. and C. E. Boozer, *J. Org. Chem.*, **31**, 2076 (1966).
78. J. P. Schroeder and W. P. Sopchak, *J. Polymer Sci.*, **47**, 417 (1960).
79. P. J. Canterino and J. T. Edmonds, Jr., U.S. Pat. 3,023,180 (Feb. 27, 1962) (to Phillips Petroleum Co.).

80. R. M. Thomas and W. J. Sparks, U.S. Pat. 2,356,128 (Aug. 22, 1944) (to Standard Oil Development Co.).
81. R. M. Thomas and W. J. Sparks, U.S. Pat. 2,356,130 (Aug. 22, 1944) (to Standard Oil Development Co.).
82. R. M. Thomas and O. C. Slotterbeck, U.S. Pat. 2,243,658 (May 27, 1941) (to Standard Oil Development Co.).
83. L. M. Welch, J. F. Nelson, and H. L. Wilson, *Ind. Eng. Chem.*, **41,** 2834 (1949).
84. C. D. Edwards and E. B. Storey, *Trans. Inst. Rubber Ind.*, **31,** 45 (1955).
85. E. W. Ford and L. V. Cooper, *India Rubber World,* **125,** 55 (1951).
86. I. E. Lightbown, *Rubber Age N.Y.*, **51,** 377 (1942).
87. R. T. Morrissey, *Rubber World,* **138,** 725 (1955).
88. R. A. Crawford and R. T. Morrissey, U.S. Pat. 2,631,984 (March 17, 1953) (to B. F. Goodrich Co.).
89. R. T. Morrissey, *Ind. Eng. Chem.*, **47,** 1562 (1955).
90. F. P. Baldwin and I. Kuntz, in *Encyclopedia of Chemical Technology,* Second Supplement, The Interscience Encyclopedia, Inc., New York, N.Y. (1960).
91. S. G. Gallo, H. K. Wiese, and J. F. Nelson, *Ind. Eng. Chem.*, **40,** 1277 (1948).
92. J. Rehner, Jr. and P. Gray, *Ind. Eng. Chem., Anal. Ed.*, **17,** 367 (1945).
93. P. Alexander, R. M. Black, and A. Charlesby, *Proc. Roy. Soc. (London),* **31A,** 232 (1955).
94. C. Walling, *Free Radicals in Solution,* Wiley, New York, 1957.
95. F. P. Baldwin, D. J. Buckley, I. Kuntz, and S. B. Robison, *Rubber Plastics Age,* **42,** 500 (1961).
96. R. T. Morrissey and M. R. Frederick, U.S. Pat. 2,732,354 (Jan. 24, 1956) (to B. F. Goodrich Co.).
97. I. C. McNeill, *Polymer,* **4,** 15 (1963).
98. G. Mayeur, J. C. Kuriacose, F. Eschard, and G. E. Limido, *Bull. Soc. Chem. Fr.*, **1961,** 625.
99. H. K. Wiese, Private Communication.
100. S. Coffey, *J. Chem. Soc.*, **1925,** 1029.
101. S. Coffey, *J. Chem. Soc.*, **1926,** 3215.
102. W. J. Klapproth and F. H. Westheimer, *J. Am. Chem. Soc.*, **72,** 4461 (1950).
103. G. F. Wright, *J. Am. Chem. Soc.*, **57,** 1993 (1935).
104. H. Gilman, Ed., *Organic Chemistry,* Vol. I, 2nd ed., Wiley, New York, 1943.
105. F. C. Whitmore and M. A. Thorpe, *J. Am. Chem. Soc.*, **55,** 782 (1933).
106. J. Rehner, Jr., *Ind. Eng. Chem.*, **36,** 118 (1944).
107. P. Kovacic, *Ind. Eng. Chem.*, **47,** 1090 (1955).
108. L. O. Amberg and A. E. Robinson, *Ind. Eng. Chem.*, **53,** 368 (1961).
109. G. Natta, *Rubber Plastics Age,* **38,** 495 (1957).
110. G. Natta and G. Crespi, *Chim. Ind. (Milan),* **41,** 123 (1959).
111. G. Crespi and M. Bruzzone, *Chim. Ind. (Milan),* **41,** 741 (1959).
112. Goldberg, E. J., U.S. Pat. 2,958,672 (Nov. 1, 1960) (to du Pont).
113. R. J. Kelly, H. K. Garner, H. E. Haxo, and W. R. Bingham, *Ind. Eng. Chem., Prod. Res. Develop.*, **1,** 210 (1962).
114. A. E. Robinson, J. V. Marra, and L. O. Amberg, *Ind. Eng. Chem., Prod. Res. Develop.*, **1,** 78 (1962).
115. G. G. Wanless, P. E. Wei, and J. Rehner, Jr., *Rubber Chem. Technol.*, **35,** 118 (1962).

116. H. S. Makowski and J. V. Fusco, U.S. Pat. 2,997,452 (Aug. 22, 1961) (to Esso Research & Engineering Co.).
117. P. E. Wei and J. Rehner, Jr., *Rubber Chem. Technol.*, **35,** 118 (1962).
118. P. E. Wei and J. Rehner, Jr., *Rubber Chem. Technol.*, **35,** 1091 (1962).
119. P. E. Wei, G. E. Serniuk, and J. Rehner, Jr., *Rubber Chem. Technol.*, **39,** 1094 (1966).
120. G. E. Serniuk, P. E. Wei, and J. Rehner, Jr., *Rubber Chem. Technol.*, **39,** 1105 (1966).
121. Austral. Pat. 29,477 (July 8, 1957) (to Montecatini Societa Generale per L' Industria Mineraria e Chimica).
122. W. F. Gresham and M. Hunt, U.S. Pat. 2,933,480 (April 19, 1960) (to du Pont).
123. E. K. Gladding, B. S. Fischer, and J. W. Collette, *Ind. Eng. Chem., Prod. Res. Develop.*, **1,** 65 (1962).
124. J. J. Verbanc, M. S. Fawcett, and E. J. Goldberg, *Ind. Eng. Chem., Prod. Res. Develop.*, **1,** 70 (1962).
125. G. Natta and G. Crespi, *J. Polymer Sci.*, **61,** 83 (1962).
126. Hank, R., *Kautschuk Gummi,* **18,** 295 (1965).
127. G. Natta, G. Crespi, A. Valvassori, G. Sartori, N. Cameli, and V. Turba, *Rubber Plastics Age,* **46,** 683 (1965).
128. G. Crespi and M. Bruzzone, *Chim. Ind. (Milan)*, **43,** 137 (1961).
129. Brit. Pat. 811,848 (April 15, 1959) (to Montecatini Societa Generale per L'Industria Mineraria e Chimica).
130. G. Natta, M. Bruzzone, and C. Borsini, Belg. Pat. 556,846 (April 19, 1957) (to Montecatini Societa Generale per L'Industria Mineraria e Chimica).
131. P. R. Johnson and M. A. Smook, U.S. Pat. 2,879,261 (March 24, 1959) (to du Pont).
132. G. Natta, G. Crespi, and M. Bruzzone, *Chim. Ind. (Milan)*, **42,** 463 (1960).
133. E. C. Leonard, Jr., W. E. Loeb, J. H. Mason, and J. A. Stenstrom, *J. Polymer Sci.*, **55,** 799 (1961).
134. A. Renfrew and P. Morgan, *Polythene,* Illiffe and Sons, London, 1957, p. 268.
135. G. A. Russell, *J. Am. Chem. Soc.*, **80,** 4987 (1958).
136. M. Bruzzone and G. Crespi, *Chim. Ind. (Milan)*, **42,** 1226 (1960).
137. G. A. Russell, *J. Am. Chem. Soc.*, **80,** 4997 (1958).
138. T. W. Campbell and D. J. Lyman, *J. Polymer Sci.*, **55,** 169 (1961).
139. Belg. Pat. 540,362 (April 5, 1955) (to Montecatini Societa Generale per L'Industria Mineraria e Chimica).
140. J. E. Hodgkins and G. Thompson, Fr. Pat. 1,174,512 (March 12, 1959) (to du Pont).
141. G. Crespi and M. Bruzzone, *Preprints, ACS Division of Petroleum Chemistry,* **6** (4-A), (A-105) (1961).
142. H. S. Makowski, W. P. Cain, and P. E. Wei, *Ind. Eng. Chem., Prod. Res. Develop.*, **3,** 282 (1964).
143. G. A. Russell, *J. Am. Chem. Soc.*, **80,** 4997 (1958).
144. G. A. Russell, A. Ito, and D. G. Hendry, *J. Am. Chem. Soc.*, **85,** 2976 (1963).
145. M. Asahina and M. Onozuka, *J. Polymer Sci.*, **2A,** 3505, 3515 (1964).
146. H. S. Makowski and C. W. Seelbach, U.S. Pat. 3,084,145 (April 2, 1963) (to Esso Research & Engineering Co.).
147. J. D. Cox, *Tetrahedron,* **18,** 1337 (1962).

CHAPTER 10

ELASTOMERS BY POSTPOLYMERIZATION TECHNIQUES

B. Cyclized and Isomerized Rubber

M. A. GOLUB

Stanford Research Institute,
Menlo Park, California

Contents

I. Introduction 939
II. Cyclized Rubber 940
A. From 1,4 Polyisoprene 940
B. From Butadiene Polymers and Copolymers with 1,4 Units 955
C. From 3,4 Polyisoprene 956
D. Cyclopolymerization of 1,3 Diene Monomers 963
E. Ladder Polymers 967
III. Isomerized Rubber 969
A. From 1,4 Polybutadiene 970
B. From 1,4 Polyisoprene 978
References 987

I. INTRODUCTION

Prior to the discovery of *cis-trans* isomerization of polybutadiene in 1957 (1), the only known isomerization of a high polymer was the cyclization of certain diene polymers—polyisoprene (either natural or synthetic), polybutadiene, and various isoprene or butadiene copolymers—to yield hard resinous products of commercial importance. That no other polymer isomerization of consequence was observed for many years subsequent to the first preparation of cyclized rubber in 1910 (2,3) accounts for the fact that this material often has been called "isomerized rubber," this term and the terms "cyclized rubber" or "cyclorubber" being used interchangeably. Indeed, as recently as 1962 the patent literature referred to isomerized rubbers or polymers which were actually cyclized modifications of the starting polymers (4). To add to the confusion, the term "isorubber" has been used to refer to the rubbery substances which are obtained in the dehydrochlorination of rubber hydrochloride (2) and which have the same amount of unsaturation as rubber itself but different double bonds.

Since another important isomerization of a high polymer is now known, viz., *cis-trans* isomerization of diene polymers (5), it is desirable to refer to the polymeric products resulting from cyclization as cyclized polymers and those obtained from *cis-trans* isomerization as isomerized polymers. Inasmuch as the diene polymers which have been made to undergo these two isomerization reactions are elastomers, it is now customary to designate the respective products as cyclized and isomerized rubbers, even though the resulting materials may not be rubbery at all. In this chapter the topics of cyclized and isomerized rubber are considered together since, apart from the fact that they are both examples of "isomerized" rubber, they have much chemistry in common. Under the heading, "Cyclized Rubber," (Section II), we shall discuss also the cyclization of other diene polymers (1,2 polybutadiene, 1,2 polyisoprene, and 3,4 polyisoprene), the cyclohydrochlorination of 3,4 polyisoprene and the cyclopolymerization of diene monomers to give "ladder" or double chain polymers, and briefly other ladder polymers, because of the close relationship of these topics to the cyclization of the 1,4 diene polymers. Similarly, under the heading, "Isomerized Rubber," (Section III) we shall consider the various chemical routes for achieving *cis-trans* isomerization of polyisoprene and polybutadiene and their microstructural characterization, as well as comment on other double bond alterations which may or may not be encountered in diene polymers or copolymers.

II. CYCLIZED RUBBER

A. From 1,4 Polyisoprene

Natural rubber (*cis*-1,4 polyisoprene), balata (*trans*-1,4 polyisoprene), or a synthetic polyisoprene of predominantly 1,4 configuration, when treated at somewhat elevated temperatures with strong acids (e.g., H_2SO_4), with organic acids and their derivatives (e.g., *p*-toluenesulfonic acid and its chloride), with Lewis acids (e.g., $SnCl_4$, $TiCl_4$, BF_3, $FeCl_3$), or with other catalysts of an acidic character, undergoes a progressive resinification with the formation of so-called cyclized rubber. Cycliza-

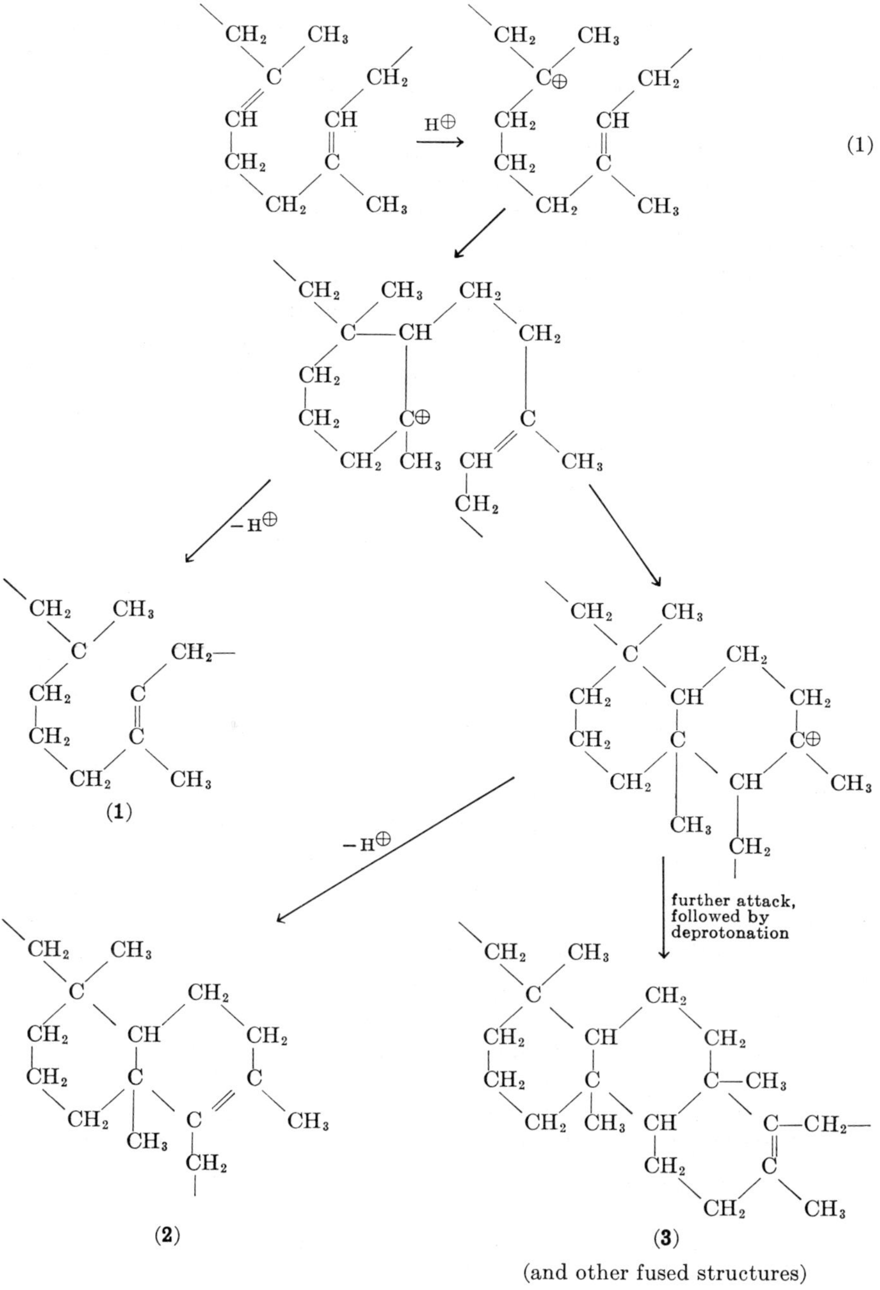
H⊕
(1)
−H⊕
(1)
−H⊕
further attack, followed by deprotonation
(2)
(3)
(and other fused structures)

Scheme I

tion of natural rubber can be carried out on the solid rubber, in solution, or even on the latex. Since the products formed in this reaction have the same empirical composition as the initial polyisoprene, $(C_5H_8)_n$, although of markedly reduced unsaturation, the process is a true isomerization. In this process a long linear macromolecule is converted into a greatly shortened polymer chain consisting of an assortment of mono-, bi-, tri-, tetra-, and other polycyclic groups distributed at random throughout the polymer backbone, interrupted occasionally by unreacted monomer units.

The cyclization of the polyisoprenes, which is considered to have a carbonium ion mechanism (6), can be depicted by the reaction steps shown in Scheme I. This mechanism is essentially the same as that proposed by Bloomfield (7) for the cyclization of dihydromyrcene in sulfuric acid–acetic acid (reaction 2). The carbonium ion which is

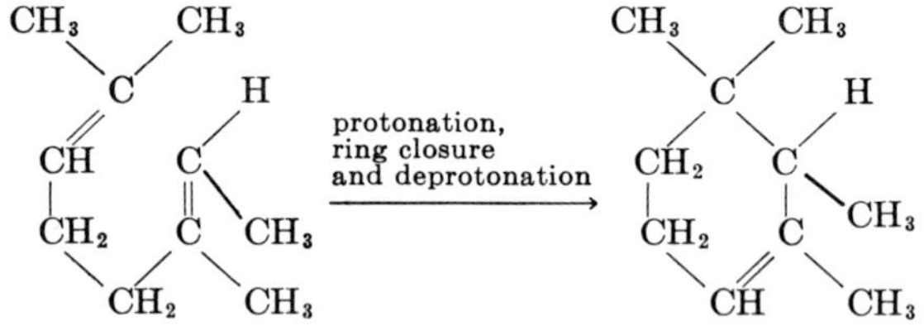

(2)

formed on protonation of a double bond in polyisoprene attacks the double bond in an adjacent isoprene unit to produce a cyclic carbonium ion which either deprotonates (to give the monocyclic group **1**) or attacks the next adjacent double bond to form a bicyclic carbonium ion; the latter can likewise deprotonate (to give **2**) or go on to produce more highly fused ring structures (as in **3**). Evidently a competition exists between deprotonation and further attack on neighboring double bonds, since the final product has neither a strictly monocyclic nor polycyclic structure; depending somewhat on the reaction conditions, the structure of the typical resin has, on the average, about three six-membered rings in each fused segment, with an unsaturation of the order of one residual double bond for every four C_5H_8 units compared to an initial unsaturation of one double bond per C_5H_8 unit (8). As a result of these structural changes, cyclized rubber has higher density, refractive index, and softening point, but a lower intrinsic viscosity than the original rubber. The microstructure of cyclized rubber shows additional minor heterogeneity because the final deprotonation step can give rise to three different double bonds: di- and trisubstituted double bonds (exemplified by structures **4** and **5**, respectively), in addition to the tetrasubstituted double bonds illustrated in structures **1**, **2**, and **3**. As discussed below, the relative amounts of these different double bonds are seen to be in the order, tetra- > tri- > disubstituted.

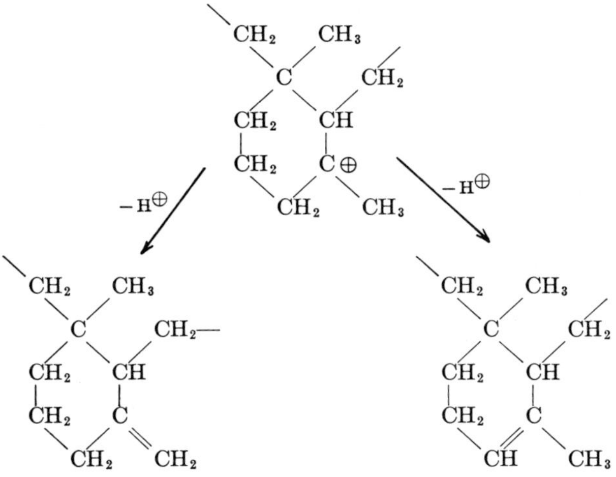

(**4**) (**5**)

Where the cyclization is catalyzed by a Lewis acid such as $TiCl_4$ rather than a strong Brönsted acid like H_2SO_4, the initial carbonium ion may be regarded as having either structure **6**, or the analogous structure

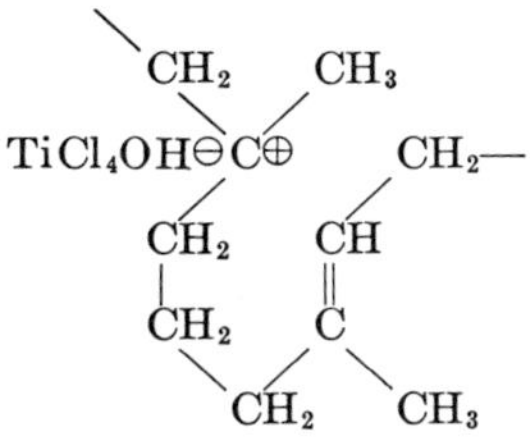

(**6**)

(without attached $TiCl_4$) formed in reaction 1 above. The $TiCl_4$ is generally considered to react with adventitious moisture in the system according to the process,

$$H_2O + TiCl_4 \rightarrow H^{\oplus} + TiCl_4OH^{\ominus}$$

which is then followed by protonation of an isoprenic double bond, with consequent cyclization of the polymer (9).

Cyclized rubber can also be prepared by reductive dehydrohalogenation of rubber hydrochloride or hydrobromide with zinc dust and acid, the product having one double bond for every four isoprene units (10). The reaction conditions are much more severe than those encountered in the simple dehydrochlorination of rubber hydrochloride with alkaline reagents to yield rubber and "isorubber" structures (2); the isoprene double bonds, as soon as they are formed in the zinc reaction, are induced to cyclize. Cyclized rubbers are also obtained by subjecting rubber and synthetic polyisoprenes to a silent electric discharge (11). The reaction mechanism in this last case is probably very similar to the cyclization mechanism suggested to account for the pronounced loss of unsaturation in polyisoprene on electron or γ-irradiation (12). It is well known that the preparation of rubber derivatives is often attended by some cyclization as an undesired side reaction; an example is the hydrochlorination of 1,4 polyisoprene (13). Interest in the cyclization of polyisoprene thus extends beyond merely that associated with the preparation of cyclized rubber itself.

The detailed structure of the cyclized rubber molecule has been the subject of considerable controversy over the years. D'Ianni et al. (14), Gordon (15–17), and various other workers (18,19) concluded on the basis of a loss of about one-half the unsaturation, and of the apparent complete disappearance of the 12 μ absorption band (associated with the —$C(CH_3)$=CH— units, whether *cis* or *trans*), that cyclized rubber has structure **1**. Flory (20) calculated that if monocyclic rings are formed, a definite proportion (13.5%) of the isoprene units should end up as "widows," i.e., not cyclized by virtue of their neighbors having already reacted, so that the final unsaturation of the completely cyclized rubber should be about 57% of that of the original rubber instead of the 50% unsaturation indicated by structure **1** alone. This view accounted for the early unsaturation determinations on cyclized rubber by Fisher and McColm (21). On the other hand, van Veersen (22), who held that previous unsaturation measurements on cyclized rubber involving iodine monochloride were not reliable because of complications due to substitution reactions, claimed that cyclized rubber consists of condensed polycyclohexyl groups connected by shorter or longer polyisoprene chains, i.e., structures like **3** and even more highly fused forms. His analysis, which involved the measurement of residual unsaturation in cyclized rubber by means of hydrogen chloride addition, gave values as low as 17% of the original unsaturation. This would correspond to an average number of rings per fused segment ("cyclicity") of about four to five. Wallenberger (23) concluded, from an analysis of the aromatization products from cyclized rubber, that this material is mostly polycyclic but has some monocyclic segments as well. More recently, Lee, Scanlan, and

Watson (24) have also argued in favor of a polycyclic structure, obtaining some $SnCl_4$ cyclized rubber samples with unsaturations of less than 20% of the original value. They claimed that the cyclicity was markedly dependent on reaction temperature, varying from as low as 1.5 at 110°C to 6 at 60°C, and even as high as 10 at reaction temperatures below 30°C. These results are at some variance with those obtained by van Veersen, who, although also affirming a polycyclic structure for cyclized rubber, found that the reaction temperature does not affect the ultimate cyclicity but only the rate of cyclization. Support for this latter view is the observation that the NMR spectra of $TiCl_4$ cyclized rubbers obtained over the temperature range 40–80°C do not differ significantly (25).

Some of the most decisive evidence in favor of a polycyclic over a monocyclic structure for cyclized rubber was obtained by Golub and Heller (8,9), who made an infrared and NMR study of the cyclization products obtained from *cis* and *trans* polyisoprenes, squalene (a hexaisoprene model compound), and several deuterated forms of polyisoprene. On the basis of a detailed comparison of the NMR spectra of cyclized *cis* polyisoprene and cyclized *cis* poly(2-methyl-d_3-1,3-butadiene-1,1-d_2), and an examination of the infrared spectrum of cyclized *cis* polyisoprene-3-*d*, they concluded at first that cyclized rubber is predominantly bicyclic (9). Although a predominantly monocyclic structure was definitely eliminated, it was not possible to rule out a structure having a cyclicity in excess of 2. These authors subsequently showed, by means of a superposition of the NMR spectrum of tetracyclosqualene on that of cyclized rubber, that the earlier estimate of cyclicity was low and had to be revised to a value around 3 (8). This same value has recently been obtained by Tutorskii and co-workers (26–29) in the cyclization of natural rubber and synthetic *cis* polyisoprene catalyzed by a phenol–phosphoric anhydride complex. In addition to studying the course of cyclization by means of wide line NMR spectroscopy of the reaction products, they determined the average molecular weight of the cyclized segments using a cryoscopic method for segmental molecular weights (30), and also by ozonization of the cyclorubber and decomposition of the ozonides. Their cryoscopic measurements indicated 2–3 cyclohexyl rings in each cyclized segment, while their ozonization results indicated an average tricyclic structure for cyclized rubber. From the various studies made to date, it can be concluded that cyclized rubber does not have a unique structure but consists of an assortment of mono- and polycyclic groups such that the average size of the condensed ring system is not very large, of the order of 2–4. Scanlan (31), in a recent survey of the kinetics of rubber cyclization and of cyclized rubber structure, reached this same conclusion; residual unsaturations obtained for latex cyclized rubber and $SnCl_4$ cyclized rubber samples were consistent with structures having 1.5–4 condensed rings per cyclized segment.

Cyclized 1,4 polyisoprenes have also been examined recently by Gaylord, Kössler, and co-workers (32–35) in connection with the ladder-like polymers formed in the cyclopolymerization of various diene monomers. This work is discussed in Section II-D.

Typical infrared spectra of cyclized rubbers obtained in the $TiCl_4$ catalyzed cyclization of synthetic *cis* and natural *trans* polyisoprenes are shown in Figs. 1 and 2, along with the spectra of the original polymers (9). The most important spectroscopic changes resulting from cyclization are the disappearance of the 12 μ band (C—H out-of-plane deformation of the *cis* and *trans* —$C(CH_3)$=CH— units), the decrease in the 6.0 μ band (C=C stretching vibration of an internal double bond), and the alteration in shape and reduction in intensity of various bands in the 7.5–10.0 μ region, bands which are characteristic of the particular double bonds in the isomeric polyisoprenes. These changes all signify that the *cis* or *trans* —$C(CH_3)$=CH— units originally present in these polymers are almost completely consumed in the cyclization reaction. Significantly, the spectra of the cyclized products from both *cis* and *trans* polyisoprenes are virtually identical, indicating that the same polymeric

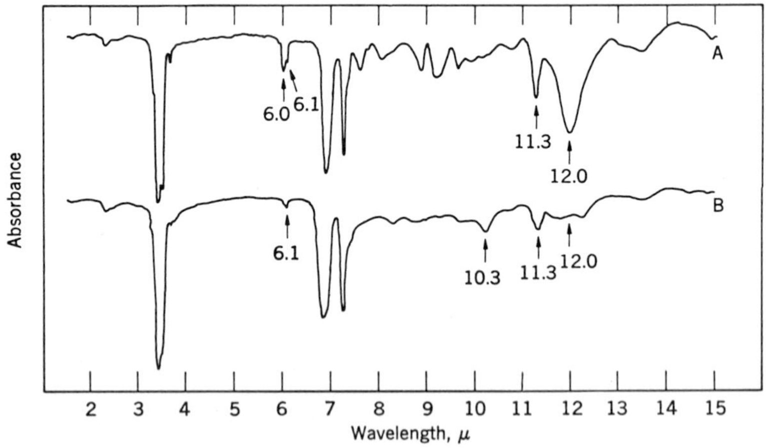

Fig. 1. Infrared spectra of synthetic *cis* polyisoprene before (A) and after (B) cyclization. (Taken from Ref. 9.)

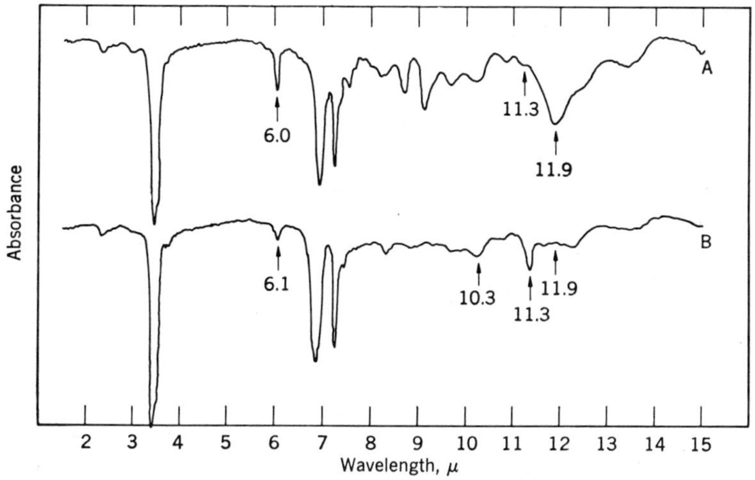

Fig. 2. Infrared spectra of natural *trans* polyisoprene before (A) and after (B) cyclization. (Taken from Ref. 9.)

structures are produced. This is in accord with the experience of Ferri (36) who obtained very similar products on treating hevea and balata (natural *cis* and *trans* polyisoprenes, respectively) with $TiCl_4$.

Another feature of interest in the infrared spectra of the cyclized rubbers is the band at 11.3 μ which is seen to grow in the case of the natural *trans* polyisoprene and to decrease somewhat in the case of the synthetic *cis* polyisoprene. This band and that at 6.1 μ (C═C stretching vibration of an external double bond) correspond to exomethylene groups, >C═CH_2, which reach an equilibrium content during cyclization of about 2.5% of the *original* double bonds in polyisoprene. These exomethylene units are present in the unreacted synthetic *cis* polyisoprene, in the form of 3,4 polymerization units

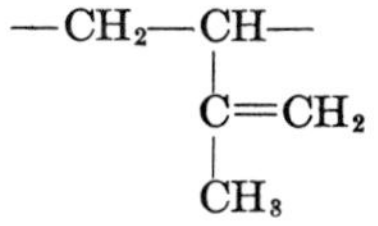

to the extent of about 4.4% of the total unsaturation, but are absent in the unreacted natural *trans* (or natural *cis*) polyisoprene (37). The spectrum of cyclized hevea likewise shows an 11.3 μ band which is comparable in intensity to this same band in the spectra of the cyclized rubbers shown in Figs. 1 and 2. Since the cyclized hevea spectrum is very similar to that of cyclized synthetic *cis* polyisoprene, there is no need to present it here. The advantage of discussing the latter spectrum (instead of the former) in conjunction with the spectrum of cyclized balata is that these two spectra illustrate very well the relative changes that can occur in the $\rangle C{=}CH_2$ content in polyisoprene in the course of cyclization. It is not known to what extent these changes are due to an isomerization of the type

$$\begin{array}{c} CH_3 \\ | \\ -C{=}CH- \end{array} \rightleftharpoons \begin{array}{c} CH_2 \\ \| \\ -C-CH_2- \end{array} \qquad (3)$$

and to a competition between the formation of exomethylene double bonds, and their consumption in cyclization.

A better insight into the structure of cyclized rubber and its infrared spectrum is obtained with the aid of the spectra of polyisoprene-3-*d* before and after cyclization (Fig. 3). Corresponding to the nearly complete disappearance of the 12 μ band in the perprotio polymers is the complete elimination of the 14.7 μ band in the cyclized polyisoprene-3-*d*, representing the loss of the original $—C(CH_3){=}CD—$ double bonds in this

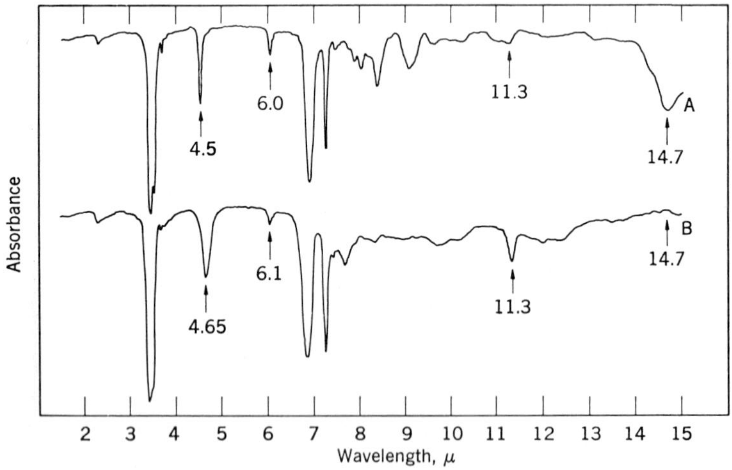

Fig. 3. Infrared spectra of *cis* polyisoprene-3-*d* before (A) and after (B) cyclization. (Taken from Ref. 9.)

polymer. Inspection of another spectrum extending to 25 μ confirmed this disappearance of the 14.7 μ band. As seen in Fig. 3b, the sharp band at 4.5 μ (C—D stretching vibration for an olefinic carbon atom) is replaced by the broader band at 4.65 μ (C—D stretching vibration for a saturated carbon atom). This spectral change not only verifies the loss of the original —$C(CH_3)$=CD— units in polyisoprene-3-*d* through cyclization but also indicates that these double bonds have become saturated to give mostly $>C(CH_3)—CDH—$ and/or $>C(CH_3)—CD<$ units, with relatively little $>C(CH_3)—CD_2—$ units. These last units, if present in large amount, would give rise to a prominent pair of bands at 4.5 and 4.75 μ (38), but Fig. 3b shows only a fairly symmetrical singlet at 4.65 μ, which may, however, overlap a weak doublet due to some CD_2 groups. As demonstrated elsewhere (9), these results definitely rule out the monocyclic ring **1** as an important structural element in cyclized rubber, and instead point to a moderately fused structure. Such a structure, in the case of polyisoprene-3-*d*, would have the form:

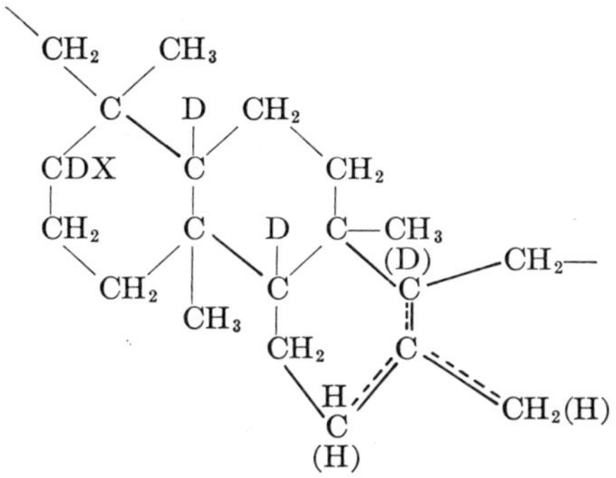

where X is H or D. Since there is nearly complete retention of deuterium in cyclized polyisoprene-3-*d*, the relative amounts of X as H or D will be in strict accordance with the relative amounts of (H) or (D) released (on the average) in the deprotonation steps of the cyclization process.

Since the 11.5 to 13 μ regions in the spectra of the three cyclized polymers shown in Figs. 1–3 are very similar in shape and in relative intensity, it is reasonable to assume that deprotonation to yield trisubstituted double bond (as in **5**) occurs to about the same extent in all these polymers. Moreover, cyclized polyisoprene-3-*d*, in common with the cyclized *cis* and *trans* perprotiopolyisoprenes, also shows a band at 11.3 μ, indicating the presence of exomethylene groups which probably arise in the deprotonation to yield disubstituted double bonds (as in **4**). The other important double bonds in the cyclic structures, viz., tetrasubstituted double bonds (as in **3**), are essentially infrared invisible. The completeness with which the 14.7 μ band has disappeared in Fig. 3, in contrast to the residual absorption at 12 μ in Figs. 1b and 2b, suggests that most of the —C(CH_3)═CD— units which are "widowed" in the cyclization are replaced by —C(CH_3)═CH— units through a double bond shift (reaction 4).

$$\mathrm{-CH_2-\overset{\overset{\displaystyle CH_3}{|}}{C}{=}CD-CH_2-} \xrightarrow{+H^{\oplus}} \mathrm{-CH_2-\underset{\oplus}{\overset{\overset{\displaystyle CH_3}{|}}{C}}-CDH-CH_2-} \xrightarrow{-H^{\oplus}} \mathrm{-CH{=}\overset{\overset{\displaystyle CH_3}{|}}{C}-CDH-CH_2-} \qquad (4)$$

The 10.3 μ band present in Figs. 1b and 2b, but not in 3b, has been attributed to CH_2 deformation vibrations associated with the ring structure, and not to —CH═CH— units as might be thought at first glance. If vinylene double bonds were formed in cyclized polyisoprene through a double bond shift,

$$\mathrm{-CH_2-\overset{\overset{\displaystyle CH_3}{|}}{C}{=}CH-CH_2-} \rightarrow \mathrm{-CH_2-\overset{\overset{\displaystyle CH_3}{|}}{C}H-CH{=}CH-} \qquad (5)$$

a similar shift should take place in polyisoprene-3-*d* to form —CD═CH— double bonds, but this is not observed (9).

Before leaving the discussion of the infrared spectra of cyclized rubbers, it should be mentioned that Dolgoplosk and co-workers (39–41) reported several years ago that natural rubber in benzene undergoes extensive *cis-trans* isomerization when treated at 80 to 90°C with $TiCl_4$, anhydrous HCl, or various organometallic compounds. Such a reaction could be expected to take place during the $TiCl_4$ catalyzed cyclization if the protonation step (reaction 1) is reversible. However, close examination of the infrared spectra of both *cis* and *trans* polyisoprenes at different stages in their reaction with $TiCl_4$ (9) failed to disclose any spectroscopic evidence (such as changes in characteristic absorption at around 7.5 μ and in the 8.5–10.0 μ region (42–44)) to support the *cis-trans* isomerization claim. What changes have occurred in these regions, and at 12 μ, can be accounted for entirely by the disappearance of the original isoprenic double bonds in cyclization. It is worth noting that the pseudo-first order rate constants for the diminution of the 12 μ band in the infrared spectra of balata were found to be approximately the same as those for the disappearance of this band in the spectra of hevea at comparable $TiCl_4$ concentrations. Since *cis* and *trans* —$C(CH_3)$=CH— units have different extinction coefficients at 12 μ, the kinetic data also indicate that *cis-trans* isomerization makes little or no contribution to the overall reaction of polyisoprene with $TiCl_4$. Evidently, the carbonium ion **7**, as soon as it is formed, undergoes ring closure with an

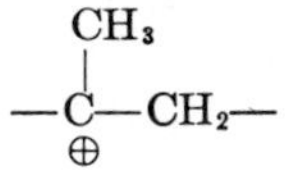

(7)

adjacent isoprenic double bond, if available for cyclization, before deprotonation can take place. On the other hand, in the case of a widowed double bond, where the opportunity for cyclization no longer exists, deprotonation with consequent *cis-trans* isomerization could conceivably take place, but this effect would be of minor importance.

Very recently, Dolgoplosk and co-workers (45) reported that natural rubber in dilute benzene solution, when treated at 60°C with ethylaluminum dichloride at quite low concentrations, undergoes *cis-trans* isomerization without cyclization, while at higher catalyst concentrations the rubber undergoes extensive cyclization. They also reported that 3-methylpentene-2, a model compound for polyisoprene, when treated with ethylaluminum dichloride or $TiCl_4$ undergoes both *cis-trans* isomerization and dimerization. The dimerization reaction represents in the small molecule the counterpart to cyclization in the macromolecule. The latest work on the $AlC_2H_5Cl_2$ catalyzed isomerization of polyisoprene, and the implications from the methylpentene work, stand in contrast to the conclusion reached above that the $TiCl_4$–polyisoprene reaction involves cyclization almost exclusively with little or no isomerization. These conflicting results might be reconciled on the grounds that the dominance of isomerization over cyclization, and vice versa, depends in a subtle way on the specific reaction conditions employed, so that different catalysts and different catalyst concentrations could make one reaction take precedence over the other. Further work on this topic would be of definite interest.

A final comment regarding the infrared spectra of cyclized rubber is in order. It has been demonstrated (46) that, because of solvent retention by films of cyclized hevea or balata, spurious bands may appear in the spectra unless deliberate steps are taken to remove occluded solvent. The unsaturation of the cyclized products must be lower than 65% of that of the original material for solvent retention to occur. This effect has, in one instance at least, led to a band (at ~13 μ, due to occluded carbon tetrachloride) being improperly assigned to cyclized rubber itself. In another instance (28), definite bands due to bound phenol appeared in the infrared spectra of cyclorubber but were recognized as such.

Further insight into the structure of cyclized rubber is afforded by an examination of its NMR spectrum, which is compared in Fig. 4 with that of tetracyclosqualene. These spectra are evidently quite similar, both showing peaks at around 8.4 and 9.1 τ (corresponding to protons on methyl groups attached to olefinic and saturated carbon atoms, respectively). The broadness and extensive overlapping of resonance peaks (in each spectrum) throughout the 7–10 τ region is due to the cyclic structure of the two products which contain a variety of nonequivalent methylene groups with different chemical shifts. Inasmuch as tetracyclosqualene has a structure consisting of two bicyclic segments (**8**)

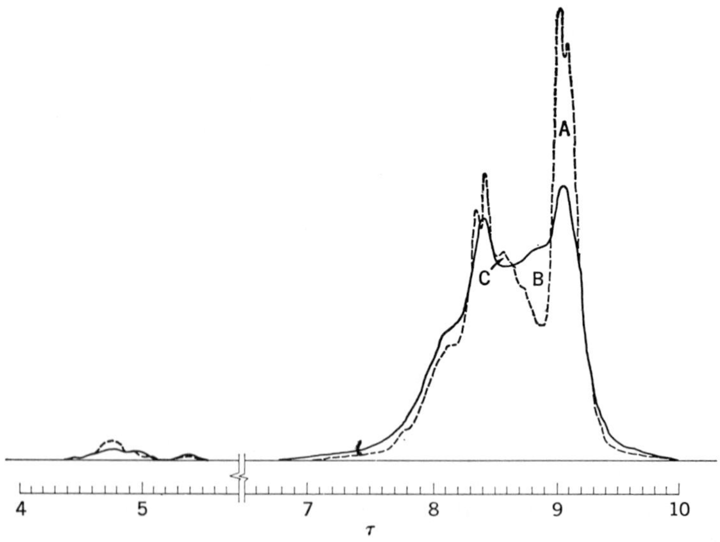

Fig. 4. NMR spectra of cyclized rubber (solid line) and of tetracyclosqualene (dotted line) adjusted to the same total area (or proton content). (Taken from Ref. 8.)

connected through the methylene groups, if cyclized rubber were also to have a (predominantly) bicyclic structure (**2**), then area (a) in Fig. 4 could be identified with the encircled CH_3 in **8** and area (b) identified

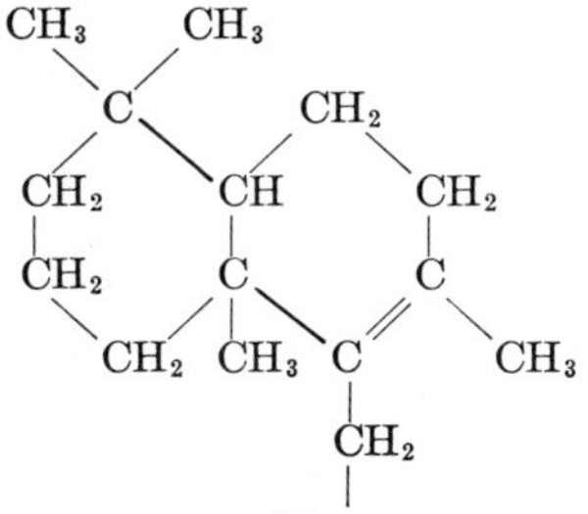

(**8**)

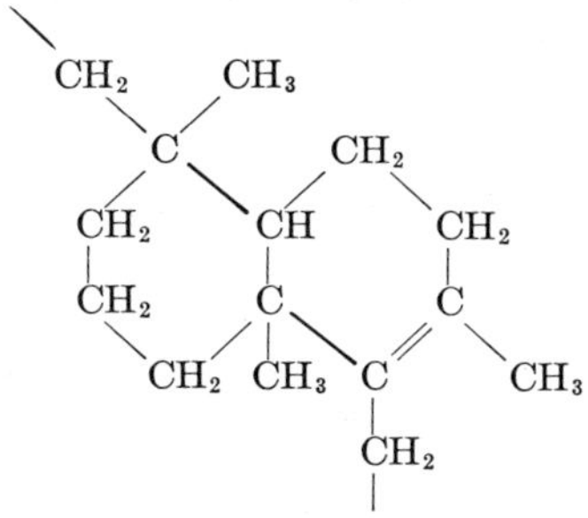

(**2**)

with the encircled CH_2 in **2**. On this basis, the areas of (a) and (b) should be in the ratio of 1.45:1 (i.e., $3/25 \div 2/24$), but the actual ratio is ~1.65:1. This is not a serious discrepancy, since the spectra do not superimpose too well in the region of (b) and (c). More serious, however, is the fact that (a) comprises only 9% of the total area of the tetracyclosqualene spectrum, whereas a value of 11% is calculated on the basis of the difference in saturated methyl content of **8** and **2** (i.e., $9/25$ or 36% in **8** minus $6/24$ or 25% in **2**). Because the NMR spectra show satisfactory superposition in the saturated methyl region, area (a) can nevertheless be taken as a measure of the difference in percent saturated methyl protons of tetracyclosqualene and cyclized rubber, irrespective of the cyclicity of the latter compound. For the tricyclic structure **3**, in which the saturated CH_3 protons comprise $9/32$ or 28.1% of all the protons,

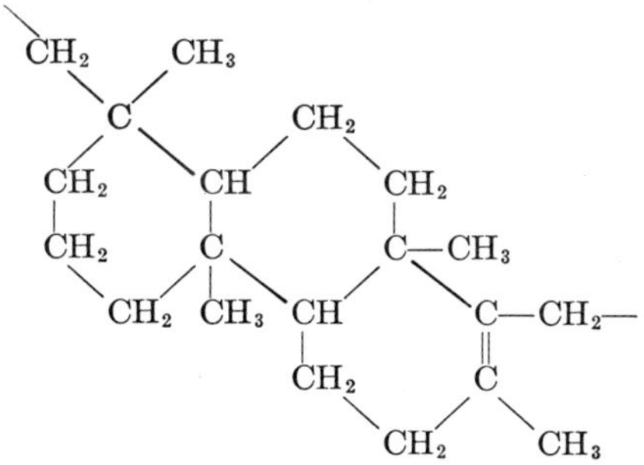

(**3**)

the difference between this value and the corresponding value in tetracyclosqualene (36%) is about 8%, or somewhat less than the proton content (9%) of area (a). Although this analysis of the NMR spectra of cyclized rubber and tetracyclosqualene is not rigorous, it is nevertheless reliable enough to indicate that the former compound has indeed a nearly tricyclic structure, or more exactly, a "cyclicity" of around 3.

Other features to be noted in the NMR spectra shown in Fig. 4 are the olefinic proton peaks at 4.75 and 4.95 τ (—C(CH_3)=CH— units in cyclized and uncyclized segments, respectively) and at 5.4 τ ($\diagdown$C=CH_2 $\diagup$ units). Because of the revision in estimated cyclicity of cyclized rubber from 2 to 3 (8), the previous assessment of the distribution of olefinic protons in this compound (9) required revision also. Accordingly, from Fig. 4 it is estimated that 1.1% of all protons in cyclized rubber are in cyclized =CH— units, 0.7% in uncyclized =CH— units, and 0.6% in $\diagdown$C=CH_2 $\diagup$ units; for an average tricyclic structure, these numbers give 49, 35, and 10% of the isoprene (monomer) units in cyclized segments (such as **3**) having tetra-, tri-, and disubstituted double bonds, respectively, with an additional 6% isoprene units being widowed. These numbers are similar to those estimated for "bicyclic" tetracyclosqualene: 54, 36, and 5% of the isoprene units in cyclized segments (such as **8**) having tetra-, tri-, and disubstituted double bonds, with an additional 5% isoprene units being left uncyclized. These latter numbers are based on 1.5% protons in cyclized =CH— units, 0.6% in uncyclized =CH— units, and 0.4% in $\diagdown$C=CH_2 $\diagup$ units. Thus, cyclized rubber and tetracyclosqualene show comparable order for the different double bonds formed in the deprotonation step: tetra- > tri- > disubstituted. It should be noted that the present analysis for tetracyclosqualene represents a revision of an earlier estimate (8) which disregarded the "widow" content.

The physical properties of cyclized rubber, and hence also the uses to which it has been put, have depended in large measure on the methods by which the resins have been prepared. Commercially manufactured under the trade names Marbon, Plioform, Pliolite, and Thermoprene, these resins are white or cream colored powdery materials, and are soluble in a wide range of solvents such as benzene, chloroform, carbon tetrachloride, carbon disulfide, gasoline, and turpentine. The density (d_4, 0.992) and refractive index (n_D^{25}, 1.545) of cyclized rubber are higher than for natural rubber (0.920 and 1.520, respectively), while the intrinsic viscosity

(0.49–0.36) is lower than that of rubbers from which it has been prepared (4.5, natural rubber; 1.5, synthetic polyisoprene). The cyclized rubbers have found application in the formulation of adhesives, paints, printing inks, and acid and alkali resistant coatings; as a rubber reinforcing agent; and also in the preparation of lacquers and molding compositions.

B. From Butadiene Polymers and Copolymers with 1,4 Units

Just as in the case of the 1,4 polyisoprenes, polymers and copolymers which contain butadiene largely in the form of 1,4 polymerization units can be made to cyclize, but the required conditions are more severe. Thus, Buizov and Kusov (47) in 1935 heated a sodium polybutadiene (~40% 1,4 and 60% 1,2 polymerization units) to 230–270°C and obtained 33–67% yields of cyclized product. Natural rubber underwent the same reaction but at a much lower temperature (160°C). Moreover, addition of sulfuric acid, sulfonic acids, or other catalysts lowered the cyclization temperature to 100–140°C in the case of natural rubber but had little effect on polybutadiene. The difference in ease of cyclization of these polymers is attributed to the methyl group which confers on the isoprenic double bond, —C(CH_3)=CH—, a greater tendency to form the requisite carbonium ion than is the case with the butadiene double bond, —CH=CH—. Gordon (15,16) calculated the energy of activation for natural rubber cyclization to be 32.7 kcal/mole. The presence of a methyl group in place of a hydrogen atom has been calculated to increase the proton affinity of a C=C group by 13.5 kcal/mole, so that the activation energy for cyclization of polybutadiene should be higher than for natural rubber by this amount. The effect of chemical structure on the relative ease of the cyclization reaction is further emphasized in work on GR-S (butadiene-styrene rubber) reported by Endres (48). This rubber is cyclized by heating in a solution in phenol, cresol, or naphthalene at 160–180°C with chlorostannic acid, stannic chloride, or boron trifluoride. Again, by way of contrast, polyisoprene is cyclized with $SnCl_4$ at only 70–75°C. Although cyclized GR-S has properties similar to those of cyclized rubber, production of that material has never gone beyond the pilot plant stage. A recent patent (49) has described the cyclization of butadiene-styrene copolymer membranes with Friedel-Crafts catalysts, followed by sulfonation to produce special cation exchange membranes.

Shelton and Lee (50) studied the structure of cyclized polybutadiene obtained by treating polybutadiene (having about 80% 1,4 and 20% 1,2 polymerization units) in xylene with concentrated sulfuric acid at 140°C for 18 hr. They concluded, from unsaturation measurements and examination of the oxidative degradation products, that cyclized polybutadiene had a predominantly tricyclic structure (**9**). Considerable crosslinking occurred as a side reaction in the cyclization of polybutadiene,

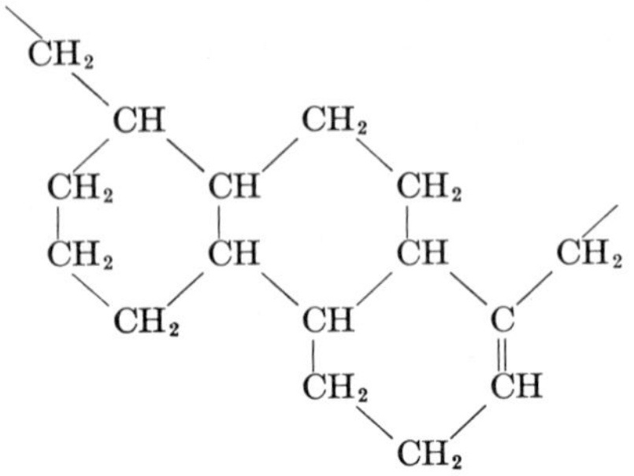

(**9**)

due probably to the vinyl groups in the 1,2 polymerization units. However, these groups are mostly involved in the cyclization process inasmuch as the infrared spectra showed marked decrease of the characteristic 11.0 and 10.15 μ bands (—CH=CH_2 units) even where crosslinking was minimal. The overall structure of cyclized polybutadiene, like that of cyclized rubber, must involve different mono- and polycyclic groups along with uncyclized monomer segments.

Kössler et al. (51) have very recently examined the cyclization of *cis*- and *trans*-1,4 polybutadienes as well as that of poly-2,3-dimethylbutadiene in connection with an extensive study of cyclo and cyclized diene polymers (see Section II-D). The infrared spectra of the highly cyclized *cis*- and *trans*-1,4 polybutadienes were identical, and showed virtually complete elimination of all bands indicative of the original unsaturation in these polymers.

C. From 3,4 Polyisoprene

Cyclization of a predominantly 3,4 polyisoprene is of considerable interest from the standpoint of attempts to prepare ladder or double chain polymers. Such polymers, because of a connected, double backbone structure of greatly reduced unsaturation, are more stable at high temperatures than the corresponding single chain polymers from which they are prepared. Reaction 6 represents the application to 3,4 polyisoprene of the carbonium ion mechanism for the cyclization of 1,4 polyisoprene (reaction 1).

Tocker (52) first mentioned reaction 6 in connection with the cycliza-

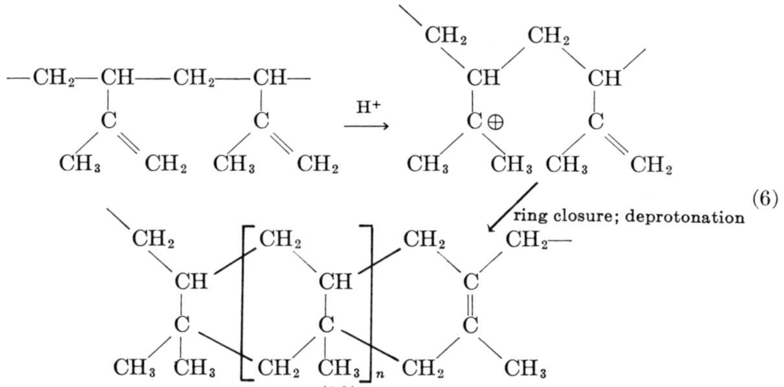

(10)

tion, by means of the Lewis acid catalysts BF_3 or $POCl_3$, of a novel ethylene-isoprene block copolymer (25:1 mole ratio) in which the isoprene is present almost completely in the form of 3,4 polymerization units. The resulting cyclized product was depicted as having blocks of linearly fused cyclohexane units separated by blocks of methylene groups; on the basis of nitrogen dioxide addition to the terminal double bond in each fused segment (typified by structure **10**), it was concluded that the average isoprene block length in the 25:1 cyclized copolymer was 12 fused cyclohexane rings (or 13 isoprene units). This high cyclicity stands in contrast to the low values obtained with cyclized rubber.

Angelo (53) subsequently extended this work to the cyclization of a high 3,4 polyisoprene (about 90% 3,4 and 10% 1,4 polymerization units), obtaining a completely soluble, white to cream colored powdery product which approached more closely the structure of a ladder polymer. Its structure has been considered to have the form of **10** where n = 2–6, although n = 1–3 may be a better assignment. The cyclized 3,4 polyisoprene, like cyclized rubber, showed higher density, refractive index, and softening point and lower inherent viscosity than the original elastomer. For optimum properties in the product, and the avoidance of crosslinking, the cyclization was carried out with $POCl_3$ at 80°C on a very dilute benzene solution of polymer (0.25%). Osmotic molecular weight determinations on the cyclized material showed that chain scission accompanied the cationic cyclization. From a comparison of the molecular weight changes sustained by various polyisoprenes during cyclization, such as hevea, balata, and an approximately equimolar 3,4/1,4 polyisoprene, Angelo postulated that the junctions between the 3,4 and 1,4 structural units were the polymer links most susceptible to chain scission during the cationic treatment of the polyisoprene. He suggested mechanism 7 to account for this effect.

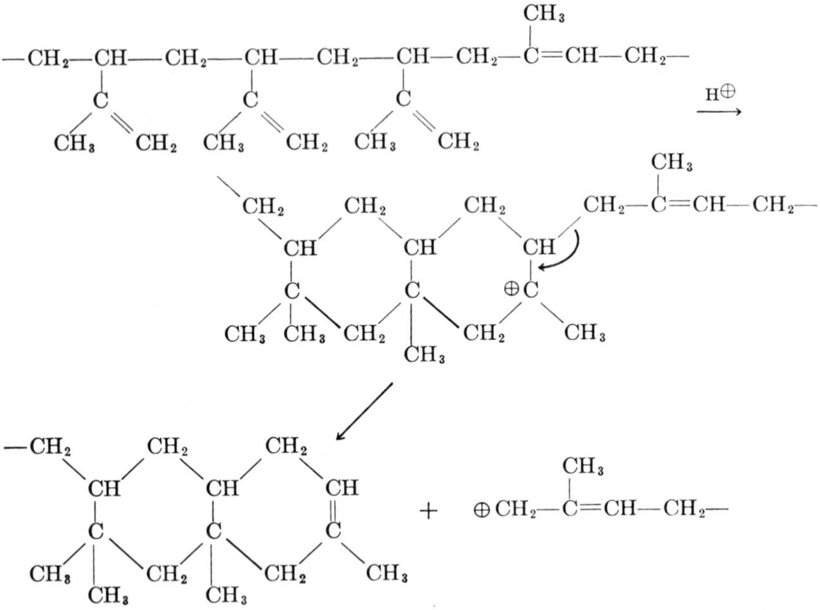

(7)

As with cyclized rubber, the structure of cyclized 3,4 polyisoprene was elucidated with the aid of infrared and NMR spectroscopy, but reinforced with aromatization experiments using Wallenberger's technique (23). Thus, examination of the ultraviolet spectra of the aromatization products provided some evidence of the existence of derivatives of naphthalene, anthracene, naphthacene, and possibly pentacene, and hence indicated a polycyclic structure for cyclized 3,4 polyisoprene. These results correspond to a cyclicity in the range of 2 to 5. The pronounced decrease in infrared bands at 11.3 and 6.1 μ (Fig. 5) points to the extensive consumption of the isopropenyl double bonds ($-\overset{CH_3}{\overset{|}{C}}=CH_2$) in 3,4 polyisoprene during cyclization. The infrared spectrum of the completely cyclized 3,4 polyisoprene is remarkably similar to the spectra of cyclized rubber (Figs. 1 and 2), even to the point of showing a band at 10.3 μ which was previously assigned to vibrations in ring structures. In line with the expected formation of *gem*-dimethyls (at one end of the fused segment, as in **10**), Fig. 5b also shows splitting of the 7.25 μ band, with broadening

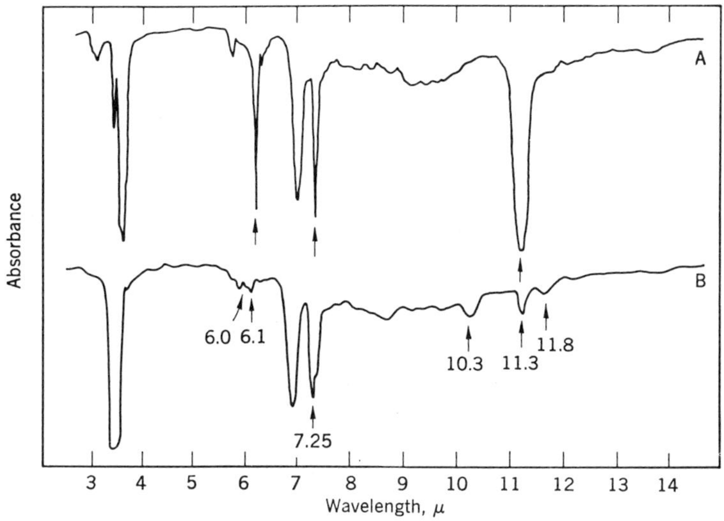

Fig. 5. Infrared spectra of 3,4-polyisoprene before (A) and after (B) cyclization. (Taken from Ref. 53.)

of the whole absorption at this wavelength. In addition, weak peaks at around 11.8 and 6.0 μ suggest trisubstituted double bonds which can result from an alternative deprotonation to yield **11** as the endgroup in a fused segment. Unfortunately, it is not possible to determine the cyclic-

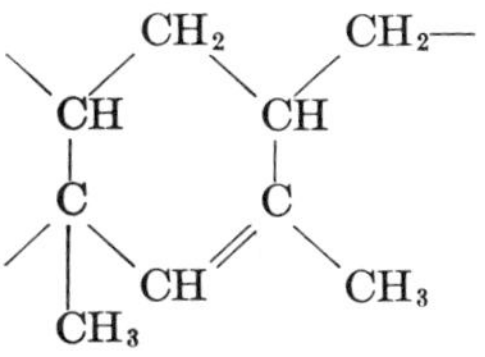

(**11**)

ity from the appearance of the shoulder to the 7.25 μ methyl band, but it seems too intense to be compatible with a highly fused structure and not intense enough to indicate a monocyclic structure; a reasonable estimate might be 2–5 fused rings per cyclized segment (33).

A more definite indication of cyclicity is afforded by a consideration of Fig. 6, which shows the NMR spectra of uncyclized and cyclized 3,4

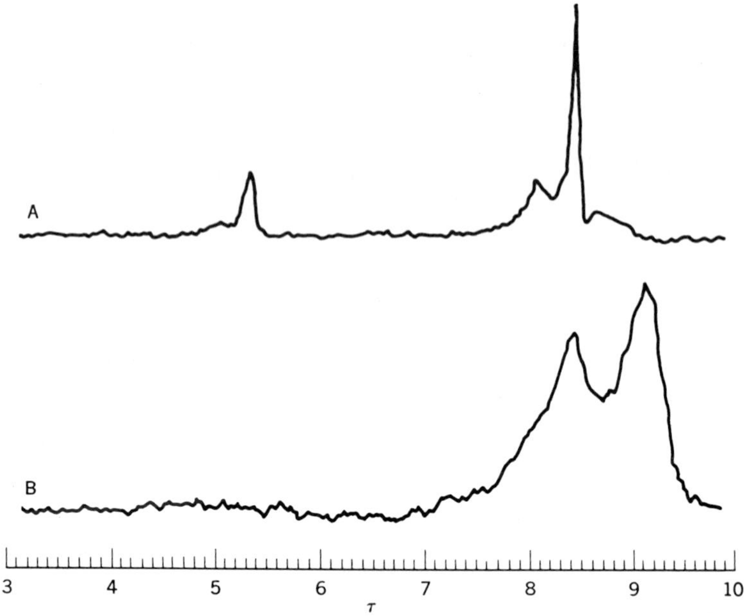

Fig. 6. NMR spectra of 3,4-polyisoprene before (A) and after (B) cyclization. (Taken from Ref. 53.)

polyisoprene. Owing to the presence of both 3,4 units

$$(\text{—CH}_2\text{—}\underset{\underset{\displaystyle\text{CH}_3}{|}}{\underset{|}{\overset{}{\text{CH}}}}\text{—})\quad \text{C=CH}_2 \text{ on CH}$$

(—CH_2—CH—)
        |
        C=CH_2
        |
        CH_3

and 1,4 units

        CH_3
        |
(—CH_2—C=CH—CH_2—)

in the initial polymer, the upper spectrum displays peaks at 8.7 τ

(—CH—CH_2—CH—), 8.4 (—C(—CH_3)=), 8.0 (—CH—C= or —CH_2—C=),

5.3 (>C=CH_2), and 4.9 τ (—CH=C—)

As a result of the cyclization, the olefinic proton peaks are greatly diminished (lower spectrum in Fig. 6) and the important peaks which appear are those at 9.1 ($CH_3{-}\overset{|}{\underset{|}{C}}{-}$) and at 8.4 τ superimposed on very broad resonance throughout the 7.5–9.5 τ region.

Angelo calculated from the NMR spectra that the cyclized 3,4 polyisoprene had, on the average, 3–7 fused rings in each polycyclic segment, but this estimate is unreliable, since he apparently based it on the relative area of the allylic methylene proton peak at 8.0 τ (which is very indistinct) and not on the much more distinct peak at 8.4 τ (due to methyls on unsaturated carbon atoms). However, there is no doubt the material is not monocyclic (**12**), since that would require, in addition to strong peaks at 8.4 and 9.1 τ (in the ratio of $\sim$1:2), another strong peak at 8.0

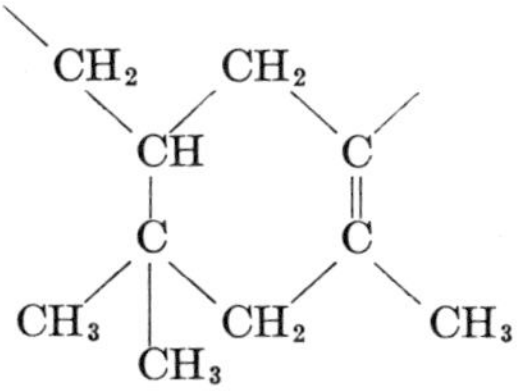

(12)

τ of comparable intensity, but this is clearly not the case. In view of the remarkable similarity of the NMR spectrum of cyclized 3,4 polyisoprene to that of cyclized rubber or even of tetracyclosqualene (Fig. 4), it seems reasonable to suggest that its cyclicity is likewise relatively low, perhaps of the order of 3 to 5, in line with the aromatization results. Indeed, by any plausible decomposition of the NMR spectrum of cyclized 3,4 polyisoprene, the maximum ratio of intensities for the methyl peaks at 9.0 and 8.4 τ ($CH_3{-}\overset{|}{\underset{|}{C}}{-}$ and $CH_3{-}\overset{|}{C}{=}$, respectively) would be around 4:1 or 5:1. These ratios correspond to tricyclic and tetracyclic structures, respectively, i.e., structure **10** with $n = 2$ to 3. Cyclized 3,4 polyisoprene is thus not a ladder polymer but a polymer containing a sequence of short ladderlike segments of varying size. In this connection, it should be noted that cyclized 3,4 polyisoprene and other cyclized diene polymers have been studied by Gaylord, Kössler et al. (32–35) from the standpoint of their similarity to ladderlike polymers formed in cyclopolymerization of various diene monomers.

Another cyclization reaction which 3,4 polyisoprene can undergo is that which occurs when this polymer is hydrochlorinated, and the overall reaction has been appropriately called cyclohydrochlorination (54). This reaction yields a product with a predominantly monocyclic structure containing very close to 1 chlorine atom for every 2 double bonds consumed. As such, it contrasts sharply with the hydrochlorination of the 1,4 polyisoprenes, which add 1 molecule of HCl for every double bond reacted and are slightly cyclized in the process (13). The reaction also contrasts with the cationic cyclization of 1,4 or 3,4 polyisoprene which, as we have seen, yields structures having a number of different polycyclic segments. The cyclohydrochlorination reaction 8 has been pictured as proceeding through a carbonium ion mechanism analogous to those

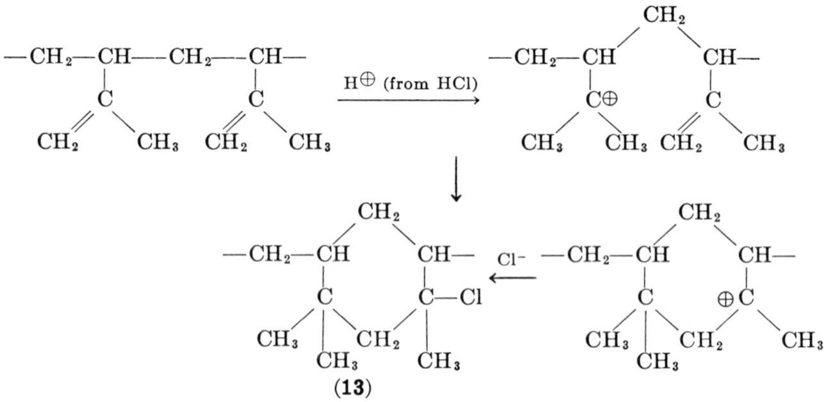

(8)

indicated above for the cyclization of the 1,4 or 3,4 polyisoprenes, except that no deprotonation takes place. In order to obtain an almost pure monocyclic structure, the tendency for attachment of Cl^- to the monocyclic ion in reaction 8 must dominate over such competing tendencies as (*1*) Cl^- attachment at the same time as the original protonation (to give straight hydrochlorination without cyclization); (*2*) deprotonation of the monocyclic ion; or (*3*) attack by the latter on an adjacent 3,4 unit to give monocyclic, bicyclic, or more highly fused segments.

The presence of some 1,4 and 1,2 polymerization units in the high 3,4 polyisoprene examined (54) gave rise to other hydrochlorinated groups: the 1,4 units added HCl in the manner of an all-1,4 polyisoprene to yield **14,** whereas the 1,2 units were attacked by adjacent 3,4 units to form other cyclohexyl groups according to reaction 9. The HCl-adduct

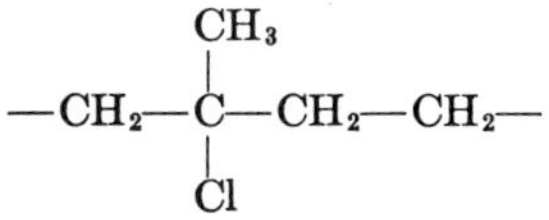

(**14**)

of the high 3,4 polyisoprene was thus seen to consist of a mixture of struc-

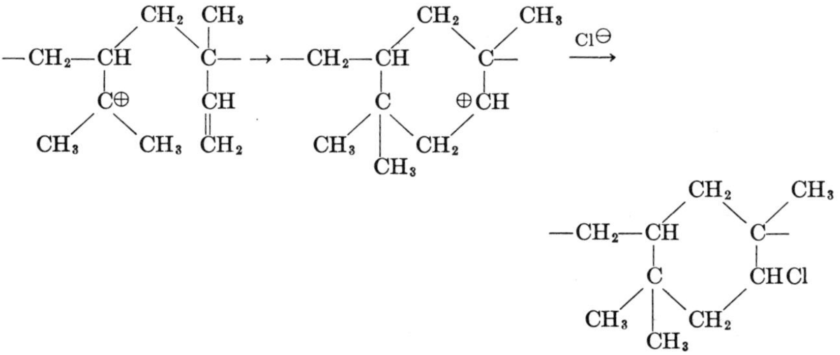

(9)

(**15**)

tures **13**, **14**, and **15**, along with a very minor amount of unreacted double bonds.

D. Cyclopolymerization of 1,3 Diene Monomers

Although cyclopolymerization of 1,3 diene monomers is not an example of elastomer preparation by postpolymerization techniques, and therefore does not fall strictly within the defined scope of this chapter, the topic is included because of the very close structural resemblance of the cyclopolymerized materials to cyclized rubber and cyclized 3,4 polyisoprene. However, we will not discuss cyclopolymerization of other monomers, even though this is an area of growing interest (55), but will mention only briefly, in Section II-E, one example of a ladder polymer (from vinyl isocyanate) which has been obtained thereby.

The cyclopolymerization of various conjugated diene monomers, along with the cyclization of the corresponding stereoregular diene polymers, has been the subject of an extensive series of papers by Gaylord, Kössler, and co-workers (32–35,51,56–60) starting in 1963. Their initial publications (32,33) on "Cyclo- and Cyclized Diene Polymers" reported the polymerization of butadiene, isoprene, and chloroprene with Ziegler-type catalysts (of low Mg/Ti or Al/Ti ratio) to insoluble, powdery polymers, the infrared spectra of which were similar to each other and to those of cyclized 1,4 or 3,4 polyisoprene but quite different from the spectra of the corresponding linear 1,4 polymers. The cyclic structure content in the cyclopolymers obtained from the diene monomers ranged from 60–90%, and was increased further by treating these polymers with dilute sulfuric acid in toluene. The reagents used in the preparation of the cyclopolymers were ineffective in cyclizing 1,4 or 3,4 polyisoprene under the same conditions.

It was suggested that these cyclopolymers were formed through a cationic polymerization of *trans* oriented monomer to isotactic or syndiotactic 3,4 units (in the case of isoprene or chloroprene) or isotactic or syndiotactic 1,2 units (in the case of butadiene), followed by cyclization

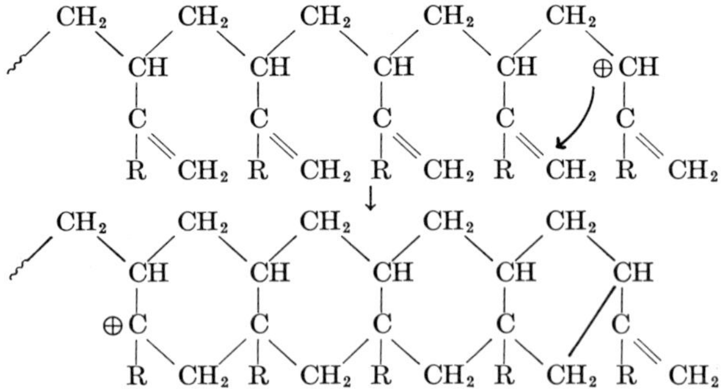

(10)

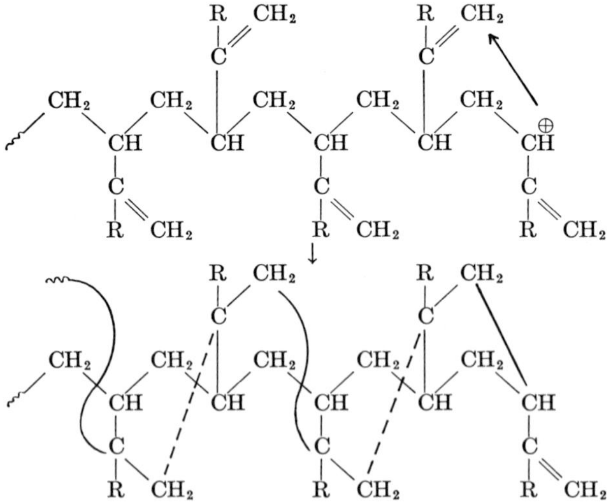

(11)

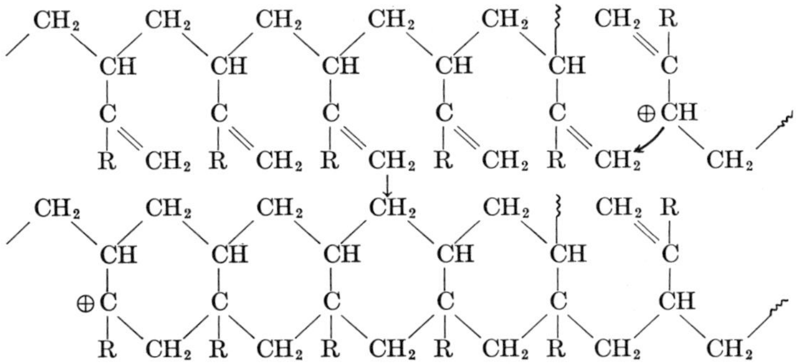

(12)

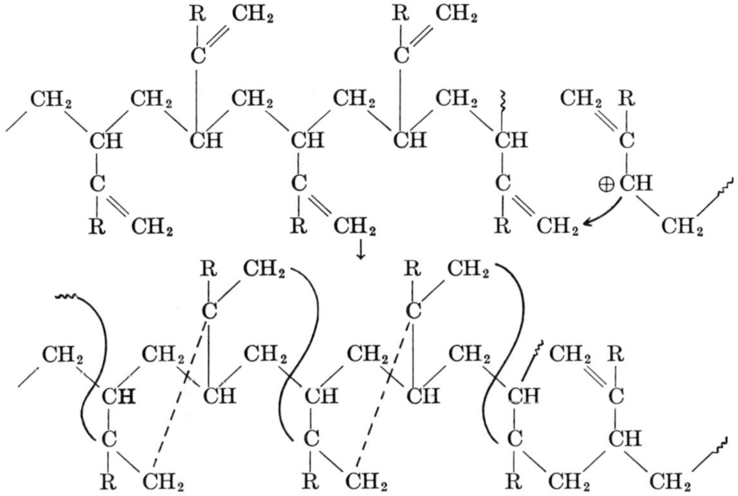

(13)

occurring in either of two ways. A reversal of the direction of polymerization involving an intramolecular cyclization would yield, after the formation of the initial five-membered ring, a sequence of fused six-membered saturated rings (reactions 10 and 11, where R = CH_3, Cl, or H). Alternatively, the cyclization could be initiated by the copolymerization of a monomer unit or a growing chain with the pendant 3,4 or 1,2 double bonds (reactions 12 and 13). In the isotactic case, the structure of the resulting cyclopolymer is that of a linear ladder polymer (reactions 10 and 12), whereas in the syndiotactic case the structure is that of a spiral ladder polymer in which one chain spirals around the backbone but is connected to it at every third carbon atom (reactions 11 and 13). The length of the fused segment would be limited by the number of isotactic or syndiotactic units in a given sequence, the sequences being interrupted by the presence of 1,4 units or pendant groups of the alternative type (1,2 or 3,4 units). The insolubility of the cyclopolymers was probably the result of crosslinking, which could arise through carbonium ion interaction between pendant 3,4 (or 1,2) double bonds on neighboring chains.

The cyclized 1,4 and 3,4 polyisoprenes used for infrared spectroscopic comparison with the cyclopolymers were obtained by treating the original linear polymers with 10% H_2SO_4 in toluene (34). As the infrared spectra of the cyclized polyisoprenes are similar to those presented earlier in this chapter, there is no need to consider them here; likewise, the spectra of the cyclopolymers, which have structures closely similar to those of the cyclized polymers, present few features of interest aside from the overall absence of bands associated with unsaturation. One detail, however, does stand out with regard to the spectra of cyclopolyisoprene and cyclized 3,4 polyisoprene: the latter polymer shows a definite doublet at 7.25 μ due to *gem*-dimethyls, while the former polymer does not. This signifies that the cyclized 3,4 polyisoprene is lightly fused, with about 2–5 rings per fused segment, whereas the cyclopolyisoprene is more highly fused (>5 rings per fused segment) and/or nowhere possesses *gem*-dimethyl groups (as indicated by reactions 10–13). It is unfortunate that the cyclopolymers are all insoluble and hence cannot be examined by NMR spectroscopy; otherwise it would be possible to throw light on the average length of the fused sequences in these polymers.

The most notable characteristic of the cyclopolymers is their thermal stability, indicative of a higher cyclicity than in the corresponding cyclized diene polymers. Cyclopolyisoprene, cyclopolybutadiene, and cyclopolychloroprene were found to have decomposition temperatures of 370, 405, and 422°C, respectively. When further cyclized with sulfuric acid, involving cyclization of residual 1,4 structures, the cyclopolymers showed an increase of about 10°C in decomposition temperature. The softening point in the region 95–103°C reported for cyclized rubber (15) attests to the likely difference in structure between the cyclopolymer obtained directly from monomer and the cyclized polymer obtained through cyclization of the linear polymer. Again, the softening point of 140–170°C noted for cyclized 3,4 polyisoprene stands in contrast to the decomposition temperature of 370°C observed for cyclopolyisoprene.

Kössler, Gaylord, and co-workers have very recently followed up their initial work on cyclo and cyclized diene polymers with an examination of the cyclization of *cis*- and *trans*-1,4 polybutadienes (51), the polymerization and cyclopolymerization of cyclopentadienes (57) and 2,3-dimethylbutadiene (58), the thermooxidation of diene cyclopolymers (59), and the formation of cyclopolyisoprenes by Ziegler-type catalysts generally (60).

E. Ladder Polymers

The earliest example of a ladder or double chain polymer is that obtained when polyacrylonitrile or polymethacrylonitrile is cyclized (reaction 14) either by heating or by treatment with base (61–63). Aromatization of the cyclized polyacrylonitrile by high temperature oxidation yields a polymeric material (**15a**) having semiconducting properties (64, 65). The thermal stability properties of this material are quite remarkable in that fabrics made from it are fireproof and have unusually high resistance to destruction upon short time heating (66).

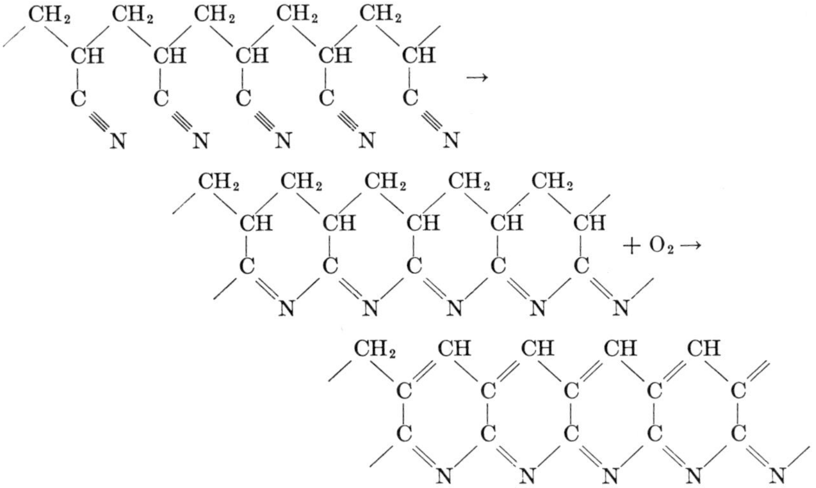

(14)

(15a)

Another example of a ladder polymer is the polyphenylsilsesquioxane prepared by Brown and co-workers (67,68) by base catalyzed equilibration of phenylsilicones to a *cis*-syndiotactic double chain structure (reaction 15). Under optimum polymerization conditions, the phenylsilsesqui-

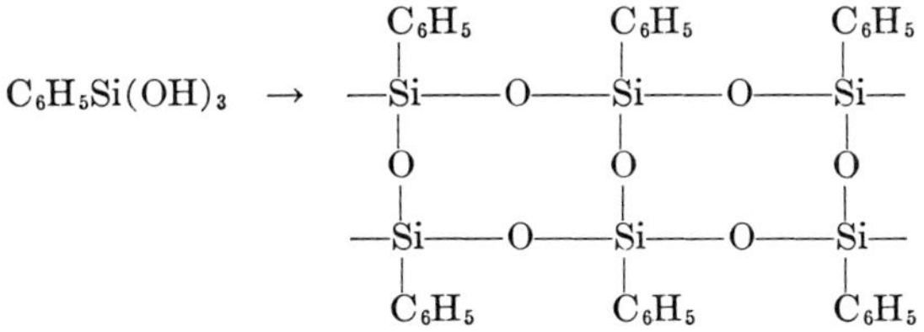

(15)

(16)

oxane monomer units join together in an ordered linear network in preference to a random crosslinked one. Unfractionated samples of this ladder polymer having intrinsic viscosities up to 6 dl/g and weight average molecular weights approaching ten million have been obtained. The high thermal stability expected for a double chain structure like **16** was borne out by the fact that when such a structure was heated in air in a thermobalance, weight loss did not start until 525°C.

There have been indications in recent years of interest in the possible cyclization of 1,2 polybutadiene or 1,2 polyisoprene (reaction 16, with R = H or CH_3) analogous to the cyclization of 3,4 polyisoprene, to produce a ladder polymer. Even if it were possible to induce this ring closure in an isotactic 1,2 polybutadiene, the reaction would probably be complicated by the occurrence of undesirable intermolecular reaction or cross-

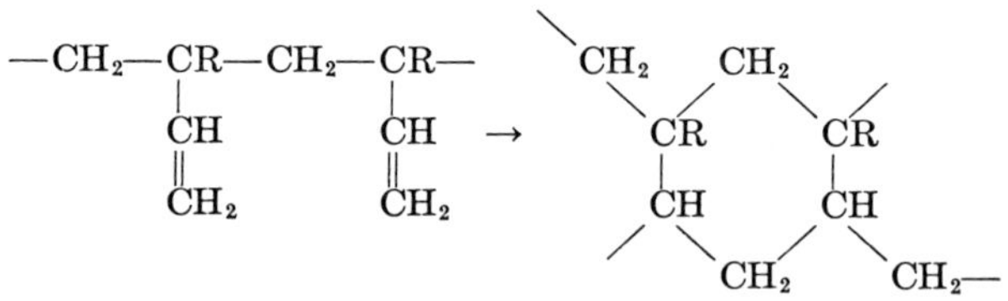

(16)

linking just as in the cyclopolymerization reactions discussed above.

A process such as reaction 16 is involved in one of the routes to a ladder polymer starting with vinyl isocyanate. Overberger, Ozaki, and Mukamal (69) polymerized this monomer through the vinyl group to yield polyvinyl isocyanate (**17**) and through the isocyanate group to yield *N*-vinyl-1-nylon (**18**), both polymers being further reacted to give the ladder polymer **19.** The cyclization of polyvinyl isocyanate was accom-

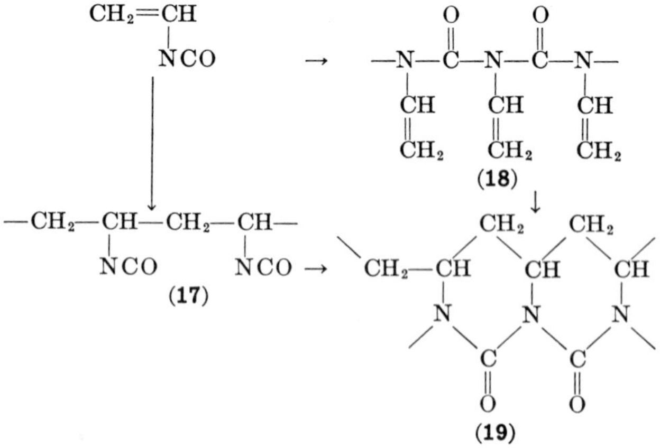

plished with γ-rays and that of the vinyl nylon by heating it with azobisisobutyronitrile or by irradiating it with ultraviolet light at room temperature in the presence of this free radical source. The product obtained from polyvinyl isocyanate had an 85% ladder structure and was insoluble, while the product from the vinyl nylon had a 90% ladder structure and was soluble in solvents of high dielectric constant. Attempts to make a complete ladder structure always resulted in insoluble polymer. The decomposition temperature of **19** was reported to be 380–390°C for the 90% ladder structure and about 300°C for the 85% ladder structure.

Very recently, Bell and Pezdirtz (70) and Dawans and Marvel (71) reported, independently and almost simultaneously, the preparation of a new class of ladder polymers, the poly(imidazopyrrolones), which exhibit high resistance to thermal, gamma, and ultraviolet radiation. These polymers were synthesized by polycondensation of aromatic dianhydrides with aromatic tetraamines, and had the typical structure **20**.

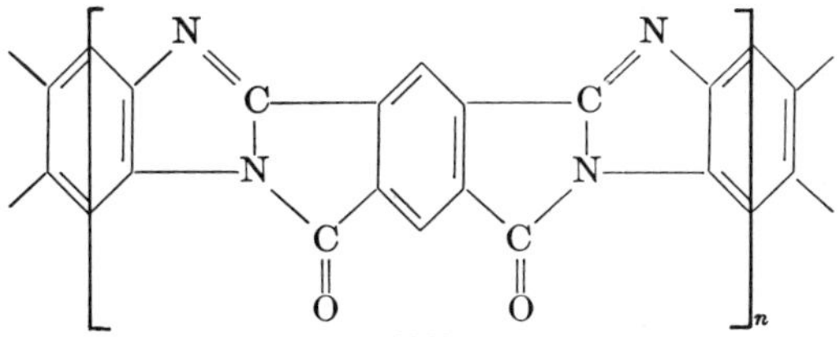

(20)

Attempts to prepare ladder polymers by random cyclization reactions of the polyacrylonitrile type will be frustrated by the statistical occurrence of isolated uncyclized units (20). Such units would constitute weak links in any ladder polymers formed in that way.

III. ISOMERIZED RUBBER

The recognition many years ago that the two different naturally occurring polyisoprenes, hevea (or natural rubber) and gutta-percha (or balata), are respectively *cis* and *trans* isomers of each other, prompted early attempts to effect the interconversion of these isomeric polymers. Meyer and Ferri (72) some thirty years ago irradiated a solution of hevea in cyclohexane with ultraviolet light in the hope of converting it into the more valuable gutta-percha, but were unsuccessful. Subsequently, Ferri (36) treated both hevea and gutta-percha with chlorostannic acid, titanium tetrachloride, or phosphorus oxychloride and obtained very similar resinous materials having properties apparently intermediate between those of the initial polyisoprenes, and which he attributed to isomerized rubber. However, in view of present knowledge on the cyclizing ability of the materials used, Ferri's results are explained in terms of the transformation of hevea and balata into essentially the same cyclized structure, rather than by *cis-trans* isomerization.

A. From 1,4 Polybutadiene

The first genuine *cis-trans* isomerization of carbon–carbon double bonds in an unsaturated high polymer, apart from the polyenes which are conjugated molecules of relatively low molecular weight, was observed by Golub (1,73). He found that a high *cis* polybutadiene could be isomerized to a high *trans* structure by means of ultraviolet irradiation in dilute benzene solution in the presence of a suitable sensitizer, such as an organic bromide, sulfide, disulfide, or mercaptan, or even elemental bromine. An equilibrium *cis/trans* ratio of about 20/80 is attained in this isomerization, starting with either a nearly all-*cis* or all-*trans* polymer (5). The equilibrium ratio given here constitutes a revision of the ratio originally published (~5/95 to 8/92), owing to a redetermination of the extinction coefficients of the *cis* and *trans* double bonds used in the infrared analysis of the isomerized polymers (74).

The photoisomerization reaction affords a convenient method for preparing a series of polymer samples of different *cis-trans* content but of practically the same molecular weight which could be used in studying structure–property relationships. In fact, Trick (75,76) has used this approach to investigate the effect of *cis/trans* ratio on the rate of crystallization of various polybutadienes. Berger and Buckley (77) also used the isomerization of *cis* and *trans* polybutadienes to study how segmental as well as compositional changes within the polymer affect the crystallinity, elongation, and tensile strength of the ultimate rubber. Moreover, the photoisomerization procedure has been used to obtain high *trans* forms of various deuterated polybutadienes for infrared studies from the corresponding stereoregular *cis* polymers (38,78).

Golub (79,80) later showed that polybutadiene could also be isomerized in benzene when irradiated with γ-rays in the presence of the same sensitizers as in the photosensitized isomerization. The mechanism with ultraviolet or ionizing radiation is that of a radical chain reaction involving the reversible formation of a freely rotating adduct from the double bond in polybutadiene, either *cis* or *trans*, and the bromine atom or thiyl radical formed in the photolysis or radiolysis of the organic bromine or sulfur compound employed as sensitizer (reaction 17). On release of the attached radical X·, representing either Br· or RS·, the double bonds are reestablished with the thermodynamically more stable configuration, *trans* being formed predominantly. Mechanism 17 is thus basically the

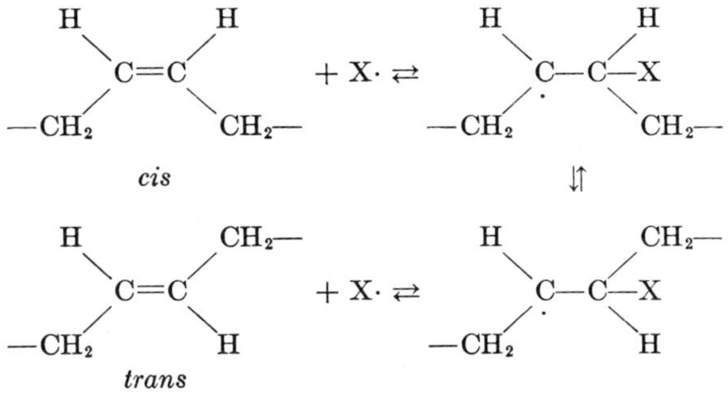

(17)

same as that described for *cis-trans* isomerization of simple olefins involving the same types of sensitizers (81,82). Although chlorine or iodine atoms are also generally effective as isomerization catalysts for low molecular weight olefinic compounds, quite surprisingly the bromides were the only halides which were found to promote the polybutadiene isomerization, either photochemically or radiation chemically.

Kinetic studies on the photosensitized (83) and radiation sensitized (79,80) isomerizations of polybutadiene have not only substantiated the above mechanism (reaction 17), but have also called attention to the long chain character of these reactions. It was calculated that the radiation produced $C_6H_5S\cdot$ radical can isomerize about 1000–1300 *cis* double bonds (84), and the corresponding photoinduced radical about 750 polymer double bonds (83,84), before these radicals are removed by some termination process.

The infrared spectrum of isomerized polybutadiene, obtained from *either cis* or *trans* polybutadiene by prolonged ultraviolet irradiation with diphenyl disulfide in benzene, is shown in Fig. 7, together with the spectra of the starting polymers. The *cis* polymer displays a pronounced diminution of the 13.6 μ band (*cis* —CH=CH— unit) and a corresponding increase of the 10.4 μ band (*trans* —CH=CH— unit), while the *trans* polymer shows a decrease in the latter band and a development of new absorption at 14.0 μ. It is a characteristic of the infrared absorption bands of the —CH=CH— double bonds that, whereas the *trans* band is invariably sharp with a nearly constant wavelength ($\sim$10.4 μ), the *cis* band is very broad and has a wavelength at maximum absorbance which shifts from 13.6 μ (at high *cis* content in polybutadiene) to around 14.0 μ as the *cis* content is progressively reduced. It is also noteworthy that

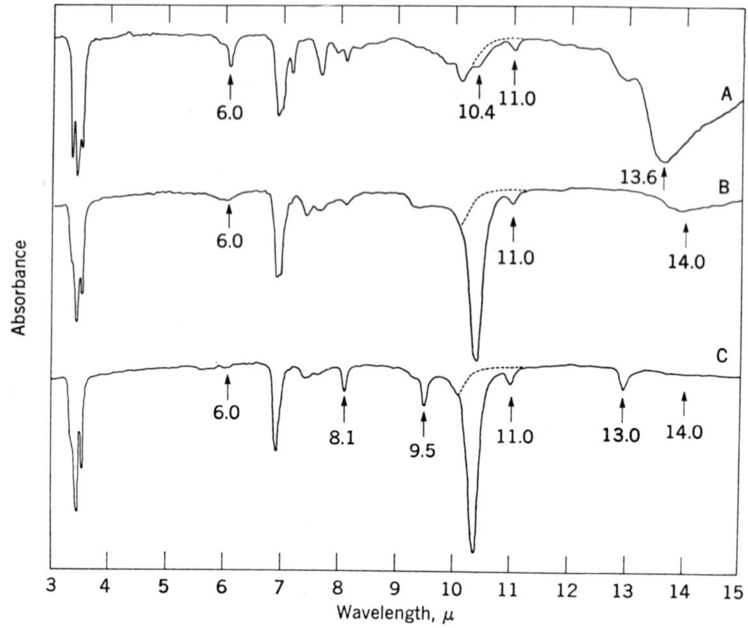

Fig. 7. Infrared spectra of *cis* and *trans* polybutadienes before (A,C) and after (B) isomerization.

as the *trans* polybutadiene isomerizes, its crystallinity bands at 8.1, 9.5, and 13.0 μ disappear. Minor absorption peaks appearing at 11 and 10.15 μ in both *cis* and *trans* polybutadienes are indicative of the presence of a small amount of vinyl unsaturation or 1,2-polymerization units

$$(\text{—}CH_2\text{—}\underset{\underset{\underset{CH_2}{\|}}{\underset{CH}{|}}}{CH}\text{—})$$

in these otherwise all-1,4 polybutadienes. The dotted lines shown in the 10–11 μ region outline the background correction used in the quantitative spectroscopic analysis. On the basis of a value of 3.65 for the ratio of *trans* to *cis* extinction coefficients, as well as the known extinction coefficients for the 1,2 absorption band (85), it was calculated that the structure of the initial *cis* polybutadiene (Fig. 7a) consists of approximately 96% *cis*-1,4, 2% *trans*-1,4, and 2% 1,2 units, while that of the initial *trans* polybutadiene (Fig. 7c) consists of approximately 93% *trans*-1,4, 5% *cis*-1,4, and 2% 1,2 units. At equilibrium, the *cis/trans* ratio is about 20/80 (Fig. 7b), but slightly different values for this ratio have been obtained by other workers, depending upon what extinction coefficients they used in the calculations. A final note with regard to the infrared spectra of the polybutadienes is that the C=C stretching vibration of the vinylene double bonds (at 6.0 μ) is moderately strong in the *cis* polymer and is extremely weak in the *trans* polymer. It should be added that unlike the situation with polyisoprene, which has distinguishable *cis* and *trans* CH_3—C= protons, it has not been possible to use NMR spectroscopy to reinforce the infrared determination of *cis-trans* content in polybutadiene, because the chemical shifts of the methylenic *or* olefinic protons in —CH_2—CH= units in *cis* and *trans* polymers are respectively too close together.

In addition to the radiation-sensitized *cis-trans* isomerization, polybutadiene has also been found to isomerize when γ-irradiated in benzene (or toluene) solution or in the solid state even in the absence of any deliberately added sensitizer (86–88). Starting with either *cis* or *trans* polybutadiene, the "unsensitized" isomerization approaches a radiostationary equilibrium in which the *cis/trans* ratio in the polymer is about 33/67. The fact that this value differs significantly from the thermodynamic equilibrium ratio of about 20/80 in the photo or radiation sensitized isomerization of polybutadiene indicates that a different mechanism must hold for the "unsensitized" reaction. It was shown that the isomerization, whether in solution or in the solid state, is a very efficient nonchain reaction when viewed from the standpoint of energy utilization, and, moreover, that the aromatic solvent, in the solution case, plays a profound role in bringing about energy transfer to the polymer double bonds. Thus, for example, the initial G value for the *cis-trans* isomerization, calculated as the number of double bonds converted per 100 eV deposited *directly* into the polymer, was 7.2 in the solid state case (86,88) and 66 in a 1% solution of *cis* polybutadiene in benzene (86,87). Since the latter value is some 9 times the value for the pure polymer itself, the obvious implication is that extensive energy transfer has taken place from the benzene molecules to the double bonds in polybutadiene in order to account for the very high isomerization yield in the solution case. The solution yield is, however, more conventionally expressed as the number of double bonds isomerized per 100 eV of energy absorbed by the *entire* solution, and this amounts to 0.66 for *cis-trans* isomerization in the 1% benzene solution. The corresponding G value for *trans-cis* isomerization in solution was seen to be 0.33, while that for the same isomerization in the solid state can be taken to be around 3.6 (87,88).

The mechanism for the radiation induced isomerization in the pure solid involves the direct as well as indirect excitation of the π electrons of the double bonds through interaction between the polymer molecules and the fast-moving electrons generated by the γ-ray photons. Energy deposited in the methylenic groups is, for the most part, transferred intramolecularly into the double bonds. In the solution case, such processes also take place but they are much less important than intermolecular energy transfer from excited solvent molecules to the polymer double bonds. Although ionized species are also formed in the γ-irradiation, these are almost completely neutralized to yield various highly excited states which, along with other highly excited states produced directly, are rapidly internally converted to the lowest excited states. The essential feature of the energy transfer mechanism, in contrast to the free radical–transitory adduct mechanism, is that the double bond is *excited* to a higher energy level in which the π electrons are no longer involved in bond formation; free rotation is then possible about the remaining single σ bond connecting the carbon atoms of the original double bond. When this so-called antibonding state returns to the ground state with release of its excess energy, the double bond is reestablished, but with the *trans* form predominating, although not to the same extent as in the free radical sensitized isomerization.

Whereas the radiation induced isomerization, sensitized by free radicals, is nearly free of side reactions, the corresponding "unsensitized" isomerization in pure benzene or in pure solid state is attended by several important side reactions. In benzene the polymer becomes phenylated through reaction with the solvent, while in the solid state it undergoes a pronounced loss of unsaturation (apparently due to radiation induced cyclization) as well as crosslinking and evolution of hydrogen, in addition to isomerization (88). It is also worth noting that work with *cis* polybutadiene-2,3-d_2 [$(\text{—}CH_2\text{—}CD\text{=}CD\text{—}CH_2\text{—})_n$] demonstrated unequivocally that the radiation induced formation of *trans* —CH=CH— in *cis* polybutadiene was due practically completely to *cis-trans* isomerization, with negligible contribution from a double bond shift such as reaction 18.

The fact that polybutadiene in the solid state and in the absence of a

$$\text{—}CH_2\text{—}CH\text{=}CH\text{—}CH_2\text{—} \rightsquigarrow \text{—}CH_2\text{—}CH\text{=}CH\text{—}\dot{C}H\text{—} \rightarrow \text{—}CH_2\text{—}\dot{C}H\text{—}CH\text{=}CH\text{—} \quad (18)$$

sensitizer could be isomerized by an energy transfer mechanism (the energy being provided through interaction with the ionizing radiation) suggested the possibility that this polymer could also undergo a direct (unsensitized) photoisomerization. In principle, such a reaction would occur if pure polybutadiene is exposed to suitable radiation in the vacuum ultraviolet range, i.e., below around 1800–1900 Å, where the unconjugated carbon–carbon double bonds begin to absorb. In this way, the π electrons of the —CH=CH— units could be excited by absorption of the appropriate optical photons, in analogy to excitation by energy absorption from γ-rays, thus leading eventually to the isomerization of the double bonds. This prediction has recently been borne out by the observation that irradiation of very thin polybutadiene films *in vacuo* with krypton 1236 Å radiation did indeed bring about *cis-trans* isomerization in these films (89). The isomerization, however, was accompanied by an even more prominent reaction, viz., loss of unsaturation, the quantum yields for these two reactions having been estimated as 0.25 and 1.53, respectively. The high quantum yield for the loss of double bonds is attributed to a chain cyclization similar to that postulated in the radiation chemistry of diene polymers (12,88).

In the course of this photochemical study, it was also discovered that *cis* or *trans* polybutadiene in the form of thin films can isomerize even when irradiated *in vacuo* with mercury 2537 Å radiation (89). In this case, the photoisomerization is assumed to be sensitized by the adventitious impurities present in the polymer which absorb in the ordinary ultraviolet (where the polymer per se is transparent) and which transfer some of their energy to the double bonds, causing the latter to be excited and eventually isomerize. The residual impurities, which could not be fully removed from the polymer through several reprecipitations, presumably comprise catalyst fragments and a very minor amount of carbonyl structure formed in the polymer backbone at the time of polymerization. Irradiation of polybutadiene films with mercury 2537 Å light resulted also in a moderate consumption of double bonds (though much less severe than in the krypton irradiation) as well as the formation of some vinyl groups. The latter were considered to arise through occasional chain scission (reaction 19). By way of contrast, little or no chain scission or formation of vinyl double bonds occurs in the krypton 1236 Å- or γ-irradiation of polybutadiene films.

Still another example of *cis-trans* isomerization of polybutadiene—one which has attracted much attention recently because of its implications in the vulcanization field—is brought about by heating the polymer with

$$
\begin{array}{l}
-CH_2-CH{=}CH-CH_2-CH_2-CH{=}CH-CH_2- \xrightarrow{h\nu} \\
\qquad\qquad -CH_2-CH{=}CH-CH_2\cdot + \cdot CH_2-CH{=}CH-CH_2- \\
-CH_2-CH{=}CH-CH_2\cdot \rightleftarrows -CH_2-\dot{C}H-CH{=}CH_2 \rightarrow -CH_2-CH_2-CH{=}CH_2 \\
\qquad\qquad\qquad\qquad\qquad\qquad\qquad\qquad \text{or crosslink} \\
\qquad\qquad\qquad\qquad\qquad\qquad\qquad\qquad \text{or endlink}
\end{array} \qquad (19)
$$

elemental sulfur at around 140–160°C (90–96). No thermal isomerization of polybutadiene takes place in the absence of sulfur. Since the physical properties of polybutadiene vulcanizates have been shown to be critically dependent upon stereoregularity near 100% *cis* or *trans* content (97), any isomerization accompanying the sulfur vulcanization is very undesirable. As a result, considerable effort has been devoted to improving cure recipes for the stereoregular polybutadienes in order to minimize or even eliminate the isomerization. The latter reaction is most pronounced with high sulfur levels and long cure times, but is still appreciable at ordinary sulfur levels and cure times. By way of illustration, after 80 min of conventional cure of gum stocks of high *cis* (>97%) polybutadiene, the *cis* content decreased by about 5% for a cure recipe having 4 phr (parts per hundred of rubber) sulfur, by about 2% for 1 phr sulfur, and by less than 1% for 0.5 phr sulfur (93). Corresponding to these changes in *cis* content, the tensile strength should drop, as estimated from the data of Kraus *et al.* (97), from around 1800 psi in the original (97% *cis*) polymer to 1500 psi at 96% *cis*, to 1200 psi at 95% *cis*, and to 500 psi in the 92% *cis* structure. Thereafter, the tensile strength drops further to around 250 psi and stays there over a wide range in *cis-trans* content. A similar sharp drop in tensile strength is noted in the case of the very high *trans* polybutadienes (>95% *trans*) which are isomerized to lower *trans* content. Other stress-strain properties show a comparably sharp drop from the optimum values with departure from nearly all-*cis* or all-*trans* structures (97).

Both the vulcanization induced and sulfur induced *cis-trans* isomerization of polybutadiene have been considered to proceed through a common polar mechanism (92,96) similar to that described recently for sulfur–olefin reactions generally (98–101). In this mechanism, a persulfenium ion, TS_a^+, where T is an alkyl or alkenyl group, adds to a double bond to form the transitory structure **21**. The TS_a^+ ion is derived from the heterolysis of the polysulfide, $TS_a \cdot S_bT$, formed in the initial sulfuration

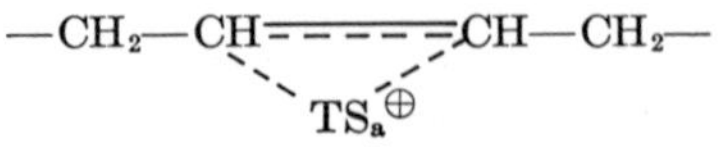

(21)

of the olefin. In the subsequent steps leading to cyclic sulfide formation, the persulfenium ion remains attached to the double bond of the polymer at all times. However, if this ion is easily detached, the double bond could then be reestablished with the more stable or *trans* form predominating. Thus, isomerization would compete with the formation of saturated ring structures in the overall vulcanization chemistry.

An alternative mechanism has been proposed (91) for the sulfur induced isomerization of polybutadiene. The mechanism involves the formation of a π-complex between sulfur (in the form of S_8 rings or polysulfides) and the polymer double bond and is analogous to the π complex formed between selenium and olefins (102,103). After homolytic cleavage of the polysulfide at the complexed sulfur atom, the resulting radical is free to rotate about the σ bond and, after splitting of a second sulfur-containing radical, yields eventually double bonds in either *cis* or *trans* configuration (reaction 20).

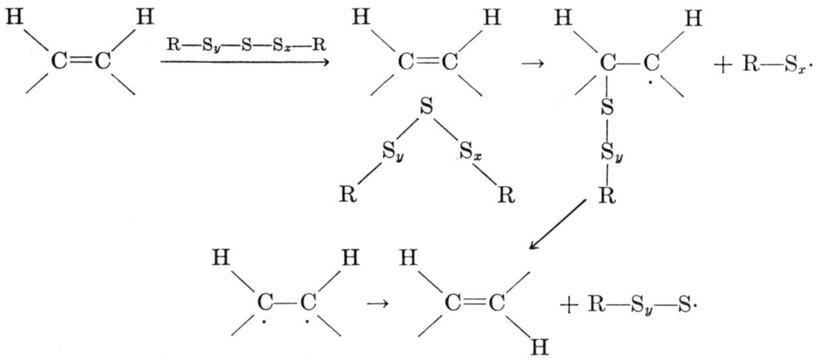

(20)

The minimum *cis* content which could be obtained in a high *cis* polybutadiene on reaction with sulfur under vulcanizing conditions was reported to be about 35–36% (91,92). On the other hand, a high *trans* polybutadiene treated with sulfur under the same conditions was isomerized to a *cis* content of about 22% (91). The latter value is close to the value indicated earlier (~20%) for the equilibrium *cis* content in the photo and radiation sensitized isomerizations. Activation energies of 30.1 and 34.5 kcal/mole have been obtained for the sulfur induced isomerization (91,96).

Once again, the use of polybutadiene-2,3-d_2 has made it possible to show that a double bond shift (of the form of reaction 18 or 21) makes little or no contribution to the observed formation of *trans* —CH=CH— units in polybutadiene isomerized (and vulcanized) with sulfur (92).

Thus, if the double bond shift (reaction 21) takes place in the deuterated polybutadiene when it is heated with sulfur, new *trans* —CD=CH—

$$\text{—CH}_2\text{—CD=CD—CH}_2\text{—} \rightarrow \text{—CH}_2\text{—CD=CD—CH—} \rightleftarrows$$
$$\text{—CH}_2\text{—CD—CD=CH—} \rightarrow \text{—CH}_2\text{—}\underset{|}{\text{CD}}\text{—CD=CH—} \qquad (21)$$

units would have to appear, but the evidence indicates that this either does not occur or at most occurs to only a very slight extent. In fact, reexamination of the infrared spectra of polybutadiene-2,3-d_2 isomerized with sulfur (92), with γ-rays in the absence of sensitizers (88), or with ultraviolet light in the presence of diphenyl disulfide (38), now suggests that the occurrence of weak absorption at 11.2 μ (*trans* —CD=CH— units) in all these spectra is strictly due to isomerization of *cis* —CD=CH— units present in the original *cis* polybutadiene-2,3-d_2 as an isotopic impurity.

It has been reported that polybutadiene also isomerizes when reacted with peroxides (91,104), when heated in benzene with nitrogen dioxide (105), when treated with various thiol acids or sulfur dioxide (42), or with rhodium salts (105a), or when treated in solution with elemental selenium at elevated temperatures (44). This last example of isomerization proceeds at around 180–200°C to an equilibrium *cis/trans* ratio in polybutadiene of about 26/74 (5) and is considered to involve a π complex mechanism essentially the same as that depicted by Fitzpatrick and Orchin for the selenium catalyzed isomerization of oleic acid (102) and stilbene (103).

B. From 1,4 Polyisoprene

Most of the procedures indicated above for achieving the *cis-trans* isomerization in polybutadiene have been applied successfully to the isomerization of polyisoprene; the governing mechanisms are essentially unchanged. However, because the infrared spectroscopic changes associated with the *cis-trans* isomerization of hevea or balata are rather subtle, this reaction remained unrecognized for nearly two years after the discovery of the polybutadiene isomerization (1), despite efforts to observe it. Later it was realized that the similar products obtained from hevea and balata, when treated with selenium under the very same conditions which brought about *cis-trans* isomerization in polybutadiene, were indeed isomerizates of the initial polyisoprenes; the infrared spectra of these products were not only nearly identical to each other but were, in all respects, intermediate between the spectra of the original *cis* and

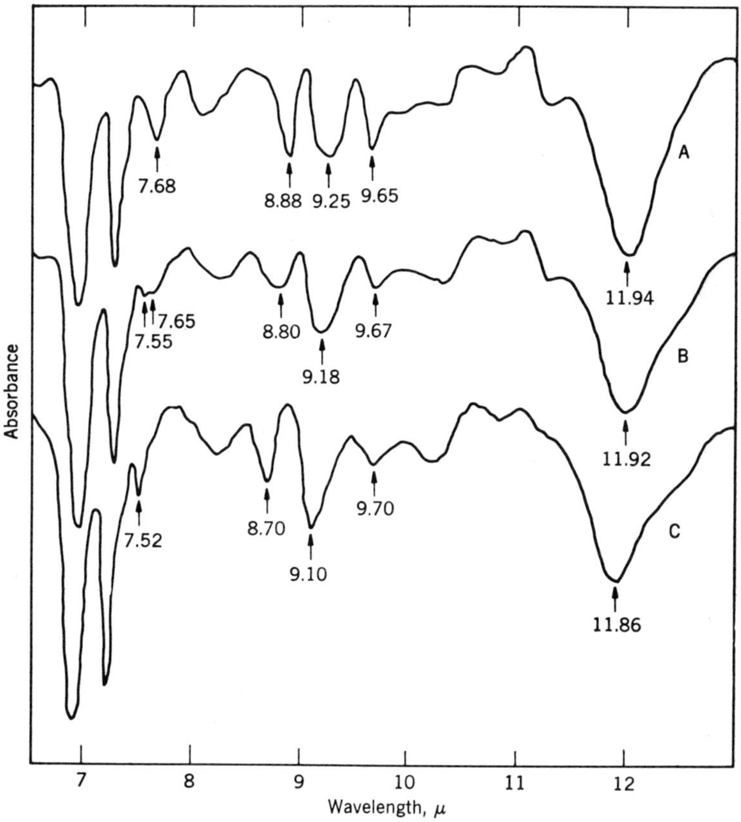

Fig. 8. Infrared spectra of hevea and amorphous balata before (A,C) and after (B) isomerization with selenium. (Taken from Ref. 44.)

trans polyisoprenes (44). This situation is shown in Fig. 8, where spectrum (b) represents the product obtained from *either* hevea or balata.

The spectrum of amorphous balata is shown rather than that of the crystalline polymer, since the transition from an all *cis* or all-*trans* polyisoprene to a common intermediate structure is not so readily apparent when the spectrum of the crystalline form is used instead of that of the amorphous. Moreover, as soon as normal balata is isomerized its crystallinity bands disappear, thus leading to greater spectroscopic changes than can be ascribed to the *trans-cis* conversion. As seen in Fig. 8, the bands in spectrum (b) at 8.80, 9.18, 9.67, and 11.92 μ all appear at wavelengths which are in between those of the corresponding bands in spectra (a) and (c) (respectively, 8.88 and 8.70 μ; 9.25 and 9.10 μ; 9.65 and 9.70 μ; 11.94 and 11.86 μ). Also, the strong band in (b) at about 12 μ which is due to absorption by both *cis*-1,4 and *trans*-1,4 units in polyisoprene, has a broadness and an intensity which are intermediate between those of the same bands in (a) and (c). The two peaks at 7.65 and 7.55 μ evidently arise from the 7.68 μ band in hevea and the 7.52 μ band in balata, respectively, and have been assigned to *cis* and *trans* units in the reaction product (106). By comparing spectrum (b) with the spectra of synthetic mixtures of the two naturally occurring polyisoprenes, and matching the two which looked most alike in the 7.5–7.7 and 8.80 μ regions, Golub (44) estimated the equilibrium *cis/trans* ratio in the isomerizate to be in the range 50/50 to 60/40. A more definite calculation using the method of Binder and Ransaw (107) was unwarranted at the time because of various anomalies in the spectral regions of interest; the more exact method of Cunneen and co-workers (42) had not yet been described. However, with subsequent development of high resolution NMR spectroscopy of polymers, it was possible to give a very reliable indication of the *cis/trans* ratio in the isomerizate, thereby sidestepping the somewhat thorny problem in infrared spectroscopy of changes in extinction coefficients of certain bands, with subsequent alteration in polymer structure.

Figure 9 shows a portion of the NMR spectra of hevea, balata, and isomerized polyisoprene (37) corresponding to the infrared spectra shown in Fig. 8. The peaks at 8.33 and 8.40 τ are associated with methyl protons

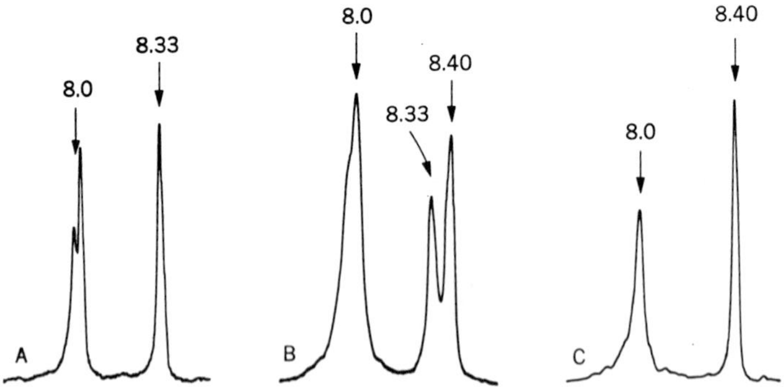

Fig. 9. NMR spectra of hevea (A), balata (C) and isomerized polyisoprene (B) at 100 Mc. (Taken from Ref. 37.)

on *cis* and *trans* double bonds [$—C(C\underline{H}_3){=}CH—$], respectively, while the 8.0 τ peak is due to methylene protons [$—C\underline{H}_2—C(CH_3){=}CH—C\underline{H}_2—$]. As unmistakable evidence for *cis-trans* isomerization, spectrum (b) displays *both* 8.33 and 8.40 τ peaks, while the original *cis* and *trans* polyisoprenes show only one or the other of these two peaks. From the relative areas under the two methyl proton peaks in spectrum (b), the *cis/trans* ratio was found to be 47/53, a more reliable value than that (given above) obtained by infrared analysis. Although the separation of the methyl peaks is adequate in these spectra, which were obtained with a 100 Mc NMR spectrometer using dilute polyisoprene solutions in CCl_4, better resolution could be obtained, even at 60 Mc, using benzene as solvent and employing the slow scan technique of Chen (108).

To complete the NMR picture for the polyisoprenes, Fig. 10 shows the olefinic proton region for hevea, balata, and a synthetic high-*cis* polyisoprene containing some 3,4 polymerization units. The broad peak at 4.92 τ corresponds to $—C(CH_3){=}C\underline{H}—$ protons, while the doublet at 5.35 τ corresponds to $\rangle C{=}C\underline{H}_2$ protons. The ratio of areas for these two kinds of protons in the synthetic *cis* polymer indicates the presence of 4.4% 3,4 units in this polymer, a value which agrees with that obtained (~4.7%) by infrared analysis (37). What is particularly significant, however, is that the NMR spectra of the natural polyisoprenes show no evidence of 3,4 units in these polymers. This was confirmed by detailed examination of the olefinic proton resonance obtained with a Computer of Average Transients (C.A.T.) which afforded spectra with very much higher signal-to-noise ratio than in the spectra shown in Fig. 10. From the analysis of the spectrum of a 9:1 balata-synthetic *cis* polyisoprene mixture, the minimum isopropenyl content which could be detected with the C.A.T. was thus found to be ~0.3% of the monomer units. The corresponding spectra of hevea and balata showed, in fact, that they contained even less than this amount of 3,4 units. This finding thus corroborated the conclusion reached by Fraga (109) from near infrared considerations that the microstructures of the naturally occurring polyisoprenes are essentially pure 1,4-type polymers. At the same time, the finding contradicts the contention by Binder (107,110) and others that hevea and balata contain as much as 2.2 and 1.3% of 3,4 units, respectively. This last contention was based on the unsupported assignment of weak 11.3 μ absorption in the infrared spectra of the natural polyisoprenes to such units.

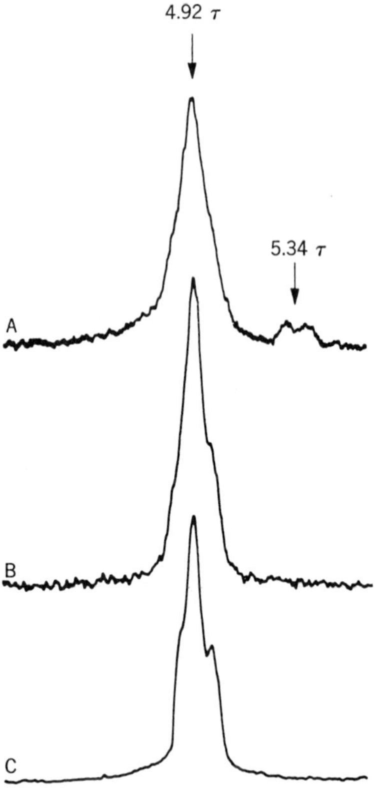

Fig. 10. NMR spectra of various polyisoprenes at 100 Mc. in the olefinic proton region: (A) synthetic *cis*; (B) hevea; and (C) balata. (Taken from Ref. 37.)

Careful examination also of the 100 Mc spectra of various synthetic mixtures of hevea and balata in the methyl proton region showed that the minimum detectable *cis* content in an otherwise all-*trans* polyisoprene, and *vice versa*, was ~1%. From this fact, it was established that the natural polyisoprenes contained less than this amount of the opposite isomeric form. High resolution NMR spectroscopy has thus demonstrated not only that hevea and balata are essentially 100% 1,4 structures but that their double bonds are at least 99% *cis* and 99% *trans*, respectively. This result could not have been obtained from infrared spectroscopy, since there is no way of knowing a priori what the spectrum of a truly 100% *cis* or 100% *trans* polyisoprene would look like.

At about the same time that Golub reported the selenium-catalyzed *cis-trans* isomerization of polyisoprene (44), Cunneen and co-workers (42,43,111–115) succeeded in isomerizing hevea and gutta-percha (balata) by treating them with thiol acids, sulfur dioxide, butadiene sulfone, and various other reagents. Their work developed during efforts to retard low temperature crystallization in natural rubber by the attachment of suitable side groups along the main polymer chain. The observation that certain thiol acids produced a much greater reduction in crystallization rate than could be accounted for by direct addition of these acids to the polyisoprene double bonds (111,112) led to the view that the reduced crystallization was the result of partial *cis-trans* isomerization. Cunneen and co-workers then showed that SO_2, which can add reversibly to olefinic double bonds above the "ceiling temperature" (116) for the given olefin complex, produced the same type of effect in natural rubber as did the thiol acids (113). Moreover, the effect of these reagents on gutta-percha, which is partly crystalline at temperatures up to about 65°C, was to yield a polymer which is rubbery at room temperature (114). Subsequently, the *cis-trans* isomerization picture was verified by the presentation of infrared spectral evidence (42), very similar to that shown in Fig. 8. The SO_2 catalyzed isomerization at 140°C was reported to give an equilibrium *cis/trans* ratio in polyisoprene of 43/57, a value close to that given above for the selenium catalyzed isomerization. However, the sulfur dioxide method for isomerizing polyisoprene is definitely superior to the selenium method, because the latter involves some chain scission while the former does not. A further advantage to the sulfur dioxide method is that it can be carried out easily in solid systems, for example, on polymer films or sheets, whereas the selenium method is carried out only in solution. From the standpoint of practical applications, butadiene sulfone is a very convenient reagent for the SO_2 type of isomerization, since it can be milled into rubber where it evolves SO_2 when the temperature is raised. This initiates the isomerization and produces eventually a polyisoprene with markedly lower rate of crystallization (115); thus, vulcanized rubber containing about 6% *trans* double bonds showed a 500- to 1000-fold reduction in the rate of crystallization at −26°C compared to that of an ordinary natural rubber vulcanizate. Sulfur dioxide has also been used to isomerize polybutadiene, squalene, and *cis* and *trans* 3-methyl-2-pentene (42).

The mechanism of the isomerization in the case of the thiol acid (or acyl disulfide) has been depicted by a scheme analogous to reaction 17, where X represents an RCOS· radical and one of the hydrogens on the double bond is replaced by a methyl group. The isomerization by SO_2 presumably occurs through a similar "on–off" reaction at the double bonds (reaction 22), but free radicals are not involved, since the rate of isomerization appears to be insensitive to free radical catalysts and inhibitors (43). Very recently, Cunneen and co-workers concluded, on the basis of a model compound approach, that the isomerization of polyisoprene according to reaction 22 is not accompanied by double bond

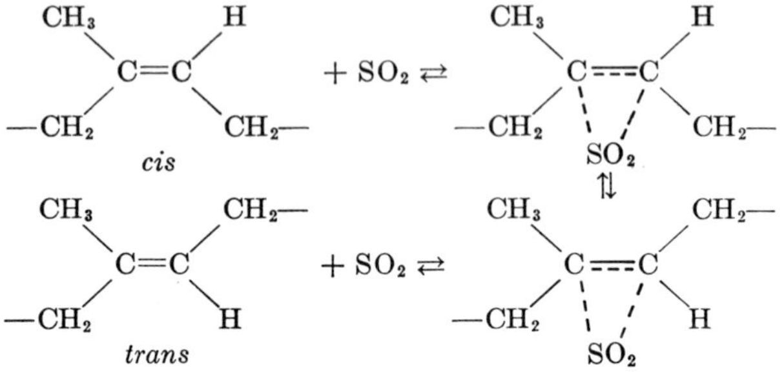

(22)

migration (117). This conclusion has been confirmed by Golub (118), who used polyisoprene-3-*d* and infrared and NMR spectroscopy to distinguish between geometrical and positional isomerization, i.e., reactions 22a and 22b.

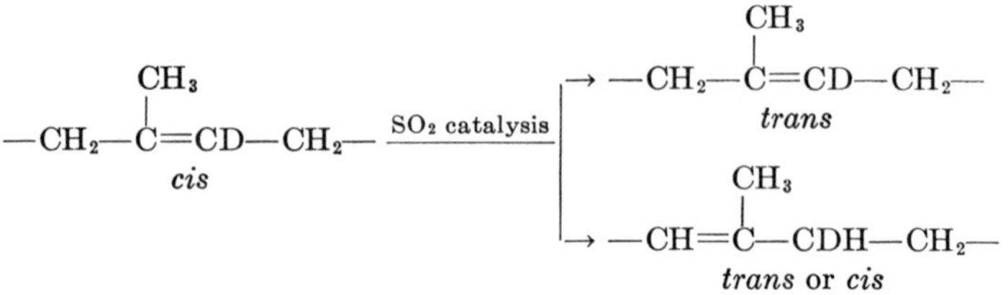

(22a)

(22b)

Cunneen and co-workers reported also the isomerization of milled natural rubber and balata by means of ultraviolet irradiation of benzene solutions of these polymers with dibenzoyl disulfide and thiolbenzoic acid as sensitizers (42). Diphenyl disulfide was also considered to photosensitize the isomerization of milled rubber, but the reaction product was crosslinked, preventing infrared analysis in this case. The previously reported failure by Golub (1) to obtain photoisomerization of polyisoprene with diphenyl disulfide (in contrast to the situation with polybutadiene) can be explained on the grounds that this reagent produces no detectable spectroscopic changes in hevea or balata when employed at a concentration low enough to avoid extensive gelation. Presumably, at the rather high concentrations of diphenyl disulfide (~25% by weight) employed by Cunneen and co-workers, a definite though small amount of isomerization did occur, as indicated by the greatly reduced crystallization rate of the treated rubber.

Despite the fact that elemental sulfur isomerizes polybutadiene under vulcanizing conditions, and vulcanization recipes containing sulfur have been reported to isomerize *cis* and *trans* 3-methyl-pentene-2 (119), the evidence seems to be that polyisoprene either does not undergo a sulfur catalyzed *cis-trans* isomerization or it does so only to a very limited extent. In fact, close inspection of the infrared spectra of *cis* polyisoprene before and after extensive reaction with sulfur at 140°C (Fig. 1; Ref. 92) fails to disclose any characteristic peaks at around 7.5 μ or in the 8.5–9.5 μ region which would indicate the formation of new *trans* $—C(CH_3){=}CH—$ units in this polymer. The observed changes around 9.0 μ appear to be associated instead with the disruption of the regular *cis*-1,4 structure, and with consumption of some of the original double bonds, brought about by the vulcanization process. A similar impression is obtained from a consideration of the spectra of the vulcanizates of polyisoprene-3-*d* and polyisoprene-d_8 (Figs. 3 and 2; Ref. 92). However, in view of the subtleness with which the infrared spectra reflect *cis-trans* isomerization in polyisoprene, as discussed earlier, it is probably fair to say that the evidence for or against such a reaction in the sulfur vulcanization of rubber remains unresolved at this time. Further work on this question is needed. On the other hand, there is no doubt that the appearance of the 10.4 μ band in the spectrum of vulcanized rubber, which had for a long time been assigned to $—CH{=}CH—$ units presumably formed in the double bond shift (reaction 23), is due not to this process but rather to the formation of saturated ring structures in the overall vulcanization (92). Moreover, infrared analysis of the sulfur vulcanizates of the deuterated polyisoprenes showed that double bond shift in the opposite

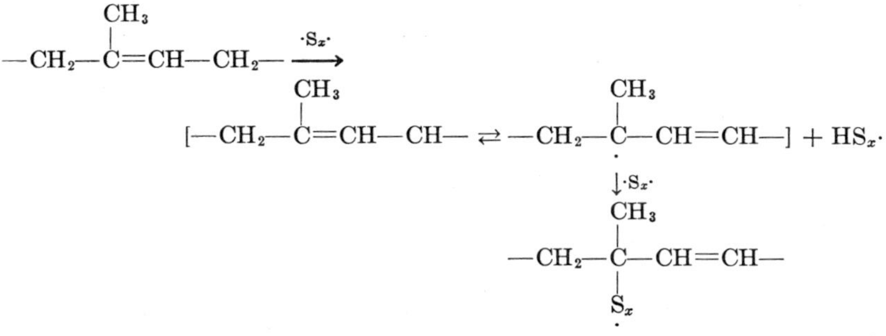

(23)

direction, to produce new $—CH{=}C(CH_3)—$ units, does not take place either.

Recently, polyisoprene, like polybutadiene, has been found to undergo radiation induced *cis-trans* isomerization both in the solid state and in benzene solution (12). Starting with various *cis* or *trans* polyisoprenes, the isomerization approaches an equilibrium in which the *cis/trans* ratio is around 50/50. The G values for either *cis-trans* or *trans-cis* isomerization, expressed as the number of *cis* (or *trans*) units isomerized initially per 100 eV absorbed by *both* polymer and solvent, in 1% solution, and by polymer alone, in the solid state were found to be about 1.0 and 10, respectively. These values are of the same order of magnitude as those given earlier for the radiation induced isomerization of *cis* polybutadiene (0.66 and 7.2, respectively), and, in fact, the energy transfer mechanism discussed for the latter reaction is assumed to hold for polyisoprene as well. Again, in common with polybutadiene, polyisoprene experiences a sharp decrease in unsaturation when irradiated with electrons or γ-rays in an inert atmosphere, and this has been attributed to a chain cyclization, probably of a carbonium ion type. From similar irradiations of polyisoprene-3-*d*, it was shown that various possible double bond shifts play an insignificant role in the radiation chemistry of polyisoprene. Squalene, a hexaisoprene which has often been used as a model compound in rubber chemistry studies, likewise undergoes radiation induced isomerization and loss of unsaturation in the pure liquid state and in benzene solution (120).

To round out the discussion on the radiation chemical isomerization of polyisoprene, mention should be made also of the work of Tsurugi et al. (121) who studied this reaction in hevea and gutta-percha (balata) sensitized by the same kinds of compounds used in the radiation induced isomerization of polybutadiene (79,80), viz., organic bromides and *n*-butyl mercaptan. These workers reported that the polyisoprene isomerization approached an equilibrium *cis/trans* ratio at room temperature of about 25/75. This value decreased with increase in the temperature at which the isomerization was carried out, an effect which was opposite to that encountered in the radiation sensitized isomerization of polybutadiene (80).

For a fuller account of some practical isomerization procedures, and a recent discussion of the properties of isomerized rubber, the reader is referred elsewhere (119).

By means of NMR spectroscopy, it has recently been confirmed (121a) that polyisoprene undergoes a diphenyl disulfide photosensitized *cis-trans* isomerization; this finding substantiates the earlier conclusions of Cunneen and co-workers (42) mentioned above. Also, Chen (121b) has extended the use of the Computer of Average Transients in the NMR spectroscopy of naturally occurring polyisoprenes (37) and again noted the microstructural regularity of these polymers. Thus, havea and balata were shown to contain *less* than 0.5% of the opposite geometric isomeric form and at the same time *less* than 0.1% of vinylidene double bonds.

References

1. M. A. Golub, *J. Polymer Sci.*, **25**, 373 (1957).
2. C. D. Harries, *Untersuchungen über die natürlichen und künstlichen Kautschukarten*, Springer, Berlin, 1919, p. 6.
3. For an extensive review of the history, technology, and properties of cyclized rubber, consult T. R. Dawson and P. Schidrowitz, in *Chemistry and Technology of Rubber*, C. C. Davis and J. T. Blake, Eds., Reinhold, New York, 1937, Chapt. XIX; J. D. D'Ianni, in *Synthetic Rubber*, G. S. Whitby, Ed., Wiley, New York, 1954, Chapt. XVIII; and G. F. Bloomfield, in *Applied Science of Rubber*, W. J. Naunton, Ed., Edward Arnold Publishers, London, 1961, Chapt. II, Part. 1.
4. H. Bartl, Ger. Pat. 1,124,683 (to Farbenfabriken Bayer A. G.); *Chem. Abstr.*, **57**, 6092h (1962).
5. M. A. Golub, in *Chemical Reactions of Polymers*, E. M. Fettes, Ed., Interscience, New York, 1964, Chapt. IIA.
6. N. Grassie, *Chemistry of High Polymer Degradation Processes*, Butterworths, London, and Interscience, New York, 1956, pp. 315–319.
7. G. F. Bloomfield, *J. Chem. Soc.*, **1943**, 289.
8. M. A. Golub and J. Heller, *Tetrahedron Letters*, **1963**, 2137.
9. M. A. Golub and J. Heller, *Can. J. Chem.*, **41**, 937 (1963).
10. H. Staudinger and W. Widmer, *Helv. Chim. Acta*, **9**, 529 (1926).
11. G. Fromandi, *Kautschuk*, **4**, 185 (1928).
12. M. A. Golub and J. Danon, *Can. J. Chem.*, **43**, 2772 (1965).
13. M. A. Golub and J. Heller, *J. Polymer Sci.*, **B2**, 723 (1964).
14. J. D. D'Ianni, F. J. Naples, J. W. Marsh, and J. L. Zarney, *Ind. Eng. Chem.*, **38**, 1171 (1946).
15. M. Gordon, *Ind. Eng. Chem.*, **43**, 386 (1951); *Rubber Chem. Technol.*, **24**, 940 (1951).
16. M. Gordon, *Proc. Roy. Soc. (London)*, **A204**, 569 (1951); *Rubber Chem. Technol.*, **24**, 924 (1951).
17. M. Gordon and J. S. Taylor, *J. Appl. Chem.*, **3**, 537 (1953); *Rubber Chem. Technol.*, **28**, 297 (1955).
18. N. V. C. Rao, *Makromol. Chem.*, **16**, 198 (1955).
19. C. S. Ramakrishnan, S. Dasgupta, and N. V. C. Rao, *Makromol. Chem.*, **20**, 46 (1956).
20. P. J. Flory, *J. Am. Chem. Soc.*, **61**, 1518 (1939).
21. H. L. Fisher and E. M. McColm, *Ind. Eng. Chem.*, **19**, 1325, 1328 (1927).
22. G. J. van Veersen, *Rec. Trav. Chim.*, **69**, 1365 (1950); *Rubber Chem. Technol.*, **24**, 957 (1951).
23. F. T. Wallenberger, *Monatsh. Chem.*, **93**, 74 (1962); *Rubber Chem. Technol.*, **36**, 558 (1963).
24. D. F. Lee, J. Scanlan, and W. F. Watson, *Proc. Roy. Soc. (London)*, **A273**, 345 (1963); *Rubber Chem. Technol.*, **36**, 1005 (1963); *Chem. Eng. News*, June 17, 1963, p. 44.
25. M. A. Golub and J. Heller, unpublished results.

26. I. A. Tutorskii, E. G. Boikacheva, and B. A. Dogadkin, Preprint P296, IUPAC, Prague Meeting, 1965.
27. I. A. Tutorskii, E. G. Boikacheva, G. S. Pol'sman, A. N. Shabodash, and B. A. Dogadkin, *Vysokomolekul. Soedin.*, **7**, 1394 (1965); *Chem. Abstr.*, **63**, 15069h (1965).
28. I. A. Tutorskii, V. V. Markov, L. P. Fomina, V. B. Belyanin, and B. A. Dogadkin, *Vysokomolekul. Soedin.*, **5**, 593 (1963); *Rubber Chem. Technol.*, **36**, 1019 (1963).
29. I. A. Tutorskii, I. Ya. Slonim, Ya. G. Urman, E. P. Kudryavtseva, and B. A. Dogadkin, *Dokl. Akad. Nauk SSSR*, **152**, 674 (1963).
30. D. Craig and N. M. Trivisonno, *J. Polymer Sci.*, **B1**, 253 (1963).
31. J. Scanlan, in *Chemical Reactions of Polymers*, E. M. Fettes, Ed., Interscience, New York, 1964, Chapt. IIB.
32. N. G. Gaylord, I. Kössler, M. Štolka, and J. Vodehnal, *J. Am. Chem. Soc.*, **85**, 641 (1963).
33. N. G. Gaylord, I. Kössler, M. Štolka, and J. Vodehnal, *J. Polymer Sci.*, **A2**, 3969 (1964).
34. M. Štolka, J. Vodehnal, and I. Kössler, *J. Polymer Sci.*, **A2**, 3987 (1964).
35. I. Kössler, J. Vodehnal, and M. Štolka, *J. Polymer Sci.*, **A3**, 2081 (1965).
36. C. Ferri, *Helv. Chim. Acta*, **20**, 1393 (1937); *Rubber Chem. Technol.*, **11**, 350 (1938).
37. M. A. Golub, S. A. Fuqua, and N. S. Bhacca, *J. Am. Chem. Soc.*, **84**, 4981 (1962).
38. M. A. Golub and J. J. Shipman, *Spectrochim. Acta*, **16**, 1165 (1960).
39. B. A. Dolgoplosk, E. N. Kropacheva, and K. V. Nelson, *Dokl. Akad. Nauk SSSR*, **123**, 685 (1958); *Rubber Chem. Technol.*, **32**, 1036 (1959).
40. I. I. Boldyreva, B. A. Dolgoplosk, E. N. Kropacheva, and K. V. Nelson, *Dokl. Akad. Nauk SSSR*, **131**, 830 (1960); *Rubber Chem. Technol.*, **33**, 985 (1960).
41. B. A. Dolgoplosk, G. P. Belonovskaja, I. I. Boldyreva, E. N. Kropacheva, K. V. Nelson, Ja. M. Rosinoer, and J. D. Chernova, *J. Polymer Sci.*, **53**, 209 (1961).
42. J. I. Cunneen, G. M. C. Higgins, and W. F. Watson, *J. Polymer Sci.*, **40**, 1 (1959).
43. J. I. Cunneen, *Rubber Chem. Technol.*, **33**, 445 (1960).
44. M. A. Golub, *J. Polymer Sci.*, **36**, 523 (1959).
45. E. N. Kropacheva, I. I. Ermakova, B. A. Dolgoplosk, A. I. Koltsov, and K. V. Nelson, Preprint P408, IUPAC, Prague Meeting, 1965.
46. M. B. Evans, G. M. C. Higgins, D. F. Lee, and W. F. Watson, *J. Appl. Polymer Sci.*, **4**, 367 (1960).
47. B. V. Buizov and A. B. Kusov, *J. Rubber Ind. (USSR)*, **12**, 46 (1935).
48. H. A. Endres, *Rubber Age (NY)*, **55**, 361 (1944); *Rubber Chem. Technol.*, **17**, 903 (1944).
49. H. Hani, T. Nishihara, and H. Hiraga, Japan. Pat. 5388(1960) (to Asahi Glass Co., Ltd.); *Chem. Abstr.*, **56**, 2592e (1962).
50. J. R. Shelton and L. H. Lee, *Rubber Chem. Technol.*, **31**, 415 (1958).
51. I. Kössler, J. Vodehnal, M. Štolka, J. Kálal, and E. Hartlová, *J. Polymer Sci.*, **C16** (3), 1311 (1967). IUPAC, Prague Meeting, 1965.
52. S. Tocker, *J. Am. Chem. Soc.*, **85**, 640 (1963).
53. R. J. Angelo, ACS Polymer Division, *Polymer Preprints*, **4**, 32 (1963); *Chem. Abstr.*, **62**, 645g (1965); *Chem. Eng. News*, Dec. 16, 1963, p. 43.
54. M. A. Golub and J. Heller, *J. Polymer Sci.*, **B2**, 523 (1964).
55. For a review of intraintermolecular cyclopolymerization, see C. S. Marvel, *J. Polymer Sci.*, **48**, 101 (1960), and G. B. Butler, *J. Polymer Sci.*, **48**, 279 (1960).

56. I. Kössler, M. Štolka, and K. Mach, *J. Polymer Sci.*, **C4**, 977 (1963).
57. V. Štepán, J. Vodehnal, I. Kössler, and N. G. Gaylord. Preprint P632, IUPAC, Prague Meeting, 1965.
58. N. G. Gaylord and I. Kössler. Preprint P633, IUPAC, Prague Meeting, 1965.
59. J. Dvořák, B. Matyska, J. Vodehnal, and I. Kössler, Preprint P62, IUPAC, Prague Meeting, 1965.
60. H. Krauserová, K. Mach, B. Matyska, and I. Kössler, *J. Polymer Sci.*, **C16** (1), 469 (1967).
61. W. J. Burlant and J. L. Parsons, *J. Polymer Sci.*, **22**, 249 (1956).
62. N. Grassie and I. C. McNeill, *J. Polymer Sci.*, **27**, 207 (1958).
63. N. Grassie and J. N. Hay, *J. Polymer Sci.*, **56**, 189 (1962).
64. A. V. Topchiev, M. A. Geĭderikh, B. E. Davydov, V. A. Kargin, B. A. Krentsel, I. M. Kustanovich, and L. S. Polak, *Dokl. Akad. Nauk SSSR*, **128**, 312 (1959); *Chem Ind. (London)*, **1960**, 184.
65. M. A. Geĭderikh, B. A. Davydov, B. A. Krentsel, I. M. Kustanovich, L. S. Polak, A. V. Topchiev, and R. M. Voĭtenko, *J. Polymer Sci.*, **54**, 621 (1961).
66. W. G. Vosburgh, *Textile Res. J.*, **30**, 882 (1960).
67. J. F. Brown, Jr., L. H. Vogt, Jr., A. Katchman, J. W. Eustance, K. M. Kiser, and K. W. Krantz, *J. Am. Chem. Soc.*, **82**, 6194 (1960).
68. J. F. Brown, Jr., *J. Polymer Sci.*, **C1**, 83 (1963).
69. C. G. Overberger, S. Ozaki, and H. Mukamal, *J. Polymer Sci.*, **B2**, 627 (1964); *Chem. Eng. News*, Dec. 30, 1963, p. 33.
70. V. L. Bell and G. F. Pezdirtz, ACS Polymer Division, *Polymer Preprints*, **6**, 747 (1965); *J. Polymer Sci.*, **B3**, 977 (1965); *Chem. Eng. News*, May 17, 1965, p. 38.
71. F. Dawans and C. S. Marvel, *J. Polymer Sci.*, **A3**, 3549 (1965).
72. K. H. Meyer and C. Ferri, *Helv. Chim. Acta*, **19**, 694 (1936); *Rubber Chem. Technol.*, **9**, 570 (1936).
73. M. A. Golub, U.S. Pat. 2,878,175–6 (March 17, 1959) (to B. F. Goodrich Co.); *Chem. Abstr.*, **53**, 15622e (1959).
74. M. A. Golub, *J. Phys. Chem.*, **66**, 1202 (1962).
75. G. S. Trick, *J. Polymer Sci.*, **31**, 529 (1958).
76. G. S. Trick, *J. Polymer Sci.*, **41**, 213 (1959).
77. M. Berger and D. J. Buckley, *J. Polymer Sci.*, **A1**, 2945 (1963).
78. M. A. Golub and J. J. Shipman, *Spectrochim. Acta*, **20**, 701 (1964).
79. M. A. Golub, *J. Am. Chem. Soc.*, **80**, 1794 (1958).
80. M. A. Golub, *J. Am. Chem. Soc.*, **81**, 54 (1959).
81. H. Steinmetz and R. M. Noyes, *J. Am. Chem. Soc.*, **74**, 4141 (1952).
82. C. Sivertz, *J. Phys. Chem.*, **63**, 34 (1959).
83. G. R. Seely, *J. Am. Chem. Soc.*, **84**, 4404 (1962).
84. M. A. Golub, *J. Phys. Chem.*, **68**, 2360 (1964).
85. R. Zbinden, *Infrared Spectroscopy of High Polymers*, Academic Press, New York, 1964, p. 25.
86. M. A. Golub, *J. Am. Chem. Soc.*, **82**, 5093 (1960).
87. M. A. Golub, *Discussions Faraday Soc.*, **36**, 264 (1963).
88. M. A. Golub, *J. Phys. Chem.*, **69**, 2639 (1965).
89. M. A. Golub and C. L. Stephens, *J. Polymer Sci.*, **C16** (2), 765 (1967).
90. G. Kraus, paper presented before the German Chemical Society, Plastics and Rubber Division, Bad Nauheim, May 1960.

91. W. A. Bishop, *J. Polymer Sci.*, **55,** 827 (1961).
92. J. J. Shipman and M. A. Golub, *J. Polymer Sci.*, **58,** 1063 (1962).
93. E. W. Madge, *Chem. Ind.* (*London*), **1962,** 1806.
94. C. A. Ceselli, T. Garlanda, M. Camia, and G. Manza, *Chim. Ind.* (*Milan*), **44,** 1203 (1962); ibid, **45,** 347 (1963); *Chem. Abstr.*, **58,** 9307e (1963).
95. H. Blümel, *Kautschuk Gummi*, **16,** 571 (1963); *Rubber Chem. Technol.*, **37,** 408 (1964).
96. D. Reichenbach, *Kautschuk Gummi*, **18,** 213 (1965); *Chem. Abstr.*, **63,** 3145d (1965).
97. G. Kraus, J. N. Short, and V. Thornton, *Rubber Plastics Age*, **38,** 880 (1957); *Rubber Chem. Technol.*, **30,** 1118 (1957).
98. L. Bateman, R. W. Glazebrook, and C. G. Moore, *J. Chem. Soc.*, **1958,** 2846.
99. L. Bateman, R. W. Glazebrook, and C. G. Moore, *J. Appl. Polymer Sci.*, **1,** 257 (1959).
100. L. Bateman and C. G. Moore, in *Organic Sulfur Compounds*, N. Kharasch, Ed., Vol. 1, Pergamon Press, New York, 1961.
101. L. Bateman, C. G. Moore, M. Porter, and B. Saville, in *The Chemistry and Physics of Rubber-like Substances*, L. Bateman, Ed., Wiley, New York, 1963.
102. J. D. Fitzpatrick and M. Orchin, *J. Am. Chem. Soc.*, **79,** 4765 (1957).
103. J. D. Fitzpatrick and M. Orchin, *J. Org. Chem.*, **22,** 1177 (1957).
104. D. Reichenbach, *Kautschuk Gummi*, **18,** 9 (1965); *Chem. Abstr.*, **62,** 13354d (1965).
105. I. I. Ermakova, B. A. Dolgoplosk, and E. N. Kropacheva, *Dokl. Akad. Nauk SSSR*, **141,** 1363 (1961); *Rubber Chem. Technol.*, **35,** 618 (1962).
105a. R. E. Rinehart, H. P. Smith, H. S. Witt, and H. Romeyn, Jr., *J. Am. Chem. Soc.*, **84,** 4145 (1962).
106. J. L. Binder, *J. Polymer Sci.*, **A1,** 37 (1963).
107. J. L. Binder and H. C. Ransaw, *Anal. Chem.*, **29,** 503 (1957).
108. H. Y. Chen, *Anal. Chem.*, **34,** 1793 (1962).
109. D. W. Fraga, *J. Polymer Sci.*, **41,** 522 (1959).
110. J. L. Binder, *Rubber Chem. Technol.*, **35,** 57 (1962).
111. J. I. Cunneen and F. W. Shipley, *J. Polymer Sci.*, **36,** 77 (1959).
112. J. I. Cunneen, W. P. Fletcher, F. W. Shipley, and R. I. Wood, *Trans. Inst. Rubber Ind.*, **34,** 260 (1958); *Chem. Abstr.*, **53,** 9711d (1959).
113. J. I. Cunneen and W. F. Watson, *J. Polymer Sci.*, **38,** 521 (1959).
114. J. I. Cunneen and W. F. Watson, *J. Polymer Sci.*, **38,** 533 (1959).
115. J. I. Cunneen, P. McL. Swift, and W. F. Watson, *Trans. Inst. Rubber Ind.*, **36,** 17 (1960); *Chem. Abstr.*, **54,** 12631e (1960).
116. R. E. Cook, F. S. Dainton, and K. J. Ivin, *J. Polymer Sci.*, **26,** 351 (1957).
117. J. I. Cunneen, G. M. C. Higgins, and R. A. Wilkes, *J. Polymer Sci.*, **A3,** 3503 (1965).
118. M. A. Golub, *J. Polymer Sci.*, **B4,** 227 (1966).
119. J. I. Cunneen and G. M. C. Higgins, in *The Chemistry and Physics of Rubber-like Substances*, L. Bateman, Ed., Wiley, New York, 1963, Chapt. 2.
120. J. Danon and M. A. Golub, *Can. J. Chem.*, **42,** 1577 (1964).
121. J. Tsurugi, T. Fukumoto, M. Yamagami, and H. Itatani, *J. Polymer Sci.*, **A-1,4,** 563 (1966).
121a. M. A. Golub, unpublished results.
121b. H. Y. Chen, *J. Polymer Sci.*, **B4,** 891 (1966).

AUTHOR INDEX

Numbers in parentheses are reference numbers and indicate that an author's work is referred to although his name is not mentioned in text. Numbers in *italics* indicate the pages on which the full references appear.

A

Abkin, A., 561, 563 (403, 462), 572(403), *595*, *596*
Abrams, J. T., 816(21), *840*
Achterhoff, M., 743, *764*
Adamek, S., 835, 836, 838(60), 839(60), *841*
Adams, D. G., 498(63), *584*
Adams, G. M., 498(46), *584*
Adams, H. E., 506, 514(154, 155), 515(155), 524(239), 525, *587*, *590*, 634(121), 638, 639, *676*
Agens, M. C., 768(4), 769, 774(4), *802*
Alcock, T. C., 915(45), *935*
Alderson, T., 874(17, 17a), 876(17a), 886(17a), *890*
Aldoshin, V. G., 554(374), *594*
Alexander, P., 923(93), *936*
Aleyev, K. M., 544(361), 547(358, 361), 549(358, 361), 551(361), 552(361), *593*
Alferov, A. V., 617(93), *675*
Alfrey, T., Jr., 542(340), 543, 544(341), *593*
Allegra, G., 645(142), 646(145), 651(142, 145), 657(170), *676*, *677*, 709(17), 712(17, 33), *724*, *725*
Allen, K. R., 740(15–17), 746(15, 17), 747–749(17), 750(15), 753(15), 756(15), 757(15), *763*
Alliger, G., 504(149), 516(180, 181), 518(180, 181), 520, 529, 530(180, 181), 540(149), 557(180), 558, *587*, *588*, 798(67), *804*, 846(7), *864*
Amato, F., 522(216), *589*
Amberg, L. O., 929(108), 930(114), *936*
American Petroleum Institute, 535(309), 536(309), *592*
Anantakrishnan, S. V., 497(42), *584*
Anderson, R. C., 776, *803*
Andrews, K. J. A., 816(22), *840*
Andrianov, K. A., 768, 769(7), 773, 786, *802*, *803*
Angelo, R. J., 957, 959(33), 960(33), *988*
Apukhtina, N. P., 831, *841*, 863(57), *865*
Araldi, M., 606(48–50), 615(48–50, 87), 616(48–50, 87) 653(87), *673*, *674*
Archer, W., 740(15), 743(48, 51), 744(53), 746(15), 750(15), 753(15), 756(15), 757(15), *763*, *764*
Arcozzi, A., 651(151), *677*
Arcus, C. L., 602(21), *672*
Arest-Yakubovich, A. A., 502(138), 503(138), 506(138), 507(138), 512(138), 521(210), 562,563(410), 565, 566, 567(407, 410), 568(407, 410, 411), 572,(407), *587*, *595*
Arnett, R. L., 719(52), 720(52), *725*
Arnold, R. G., 728(6), 741(42), *762*, *764*
Arundale, E., 856(35), *865*
Asahi Glass Co., Ltd., 955(49), *988*
Asahina, M., 933(145), *937*
Athey, R. J., 740(23), 759, *763*, *765*
Atkins, D. C., 789(51), *803*
Aufdermarsh, C. A., Jr., 712(38), 714(38), *725*
Axelrood, S. L., 740(25), 741, *763*

B

Baba, H., 544(342), *593*
Babitskii, B. D., 658(172), *677*, 874(27, 29), 888, *890*

Backus, J. K., 729, *763*
Badische Anilin- & Soda-Fabrik, A.-G., *674*, 861(40), *865*
Baer, J. E., 820(41), *841*
Bafus, D. A., 498(52, 56, 66), 499(52), *584*, *585*
Bagdanovic, B., 654(163), 657(163), *677*
Bagdasar'yan, A. K., 502(140), *587*
Bahary, W. S., 525, *590*
Bailey, D. L., 798(68), *804*
Bailey, G. C., 723(68), *726*
Bailey, W. J., 573, *595*
Baird, C. C., 558(391), *594*
Balas, J. G., 610(65), 611(69, 71), 617(69, 71), 622, 658(65), *674*, 880(55), *891*
Baldwin, F. P., 922–925, 928(90, 95), 929, *936*
Ballard, S. A., 816(20), *840*
Bamford, C. H., 872, 873(13), *889*, *890*
Bandermann, F., 509(162), 512, *587*
Banks, R. L., 723(68), *726*
Barbagallo, A., 688(19), 689(19), *702*
Barker, M. G., 525(250), *590*
Barney, A. L., 900–903(6), *903*
Baroni, A., 607(53, 55), 611(53, 55), 617(53, 55), *673*
Barry, A. J., 772(17), 773, *802*, *803*
Bartl, H., 940(4), *987*
Bartley, W. J., 719(50), 720(50), *725*
Basova, R. V., 521(210), 562, 567(407), 568(407), 572, 573, *589*, *595*
Bassi, A. C., 604(37), 651(153), *673*, *677*, 705(9), 707(9), 711(9, 22–25), 717(9), *724*
Bateman, L., 976(98–101), *990*
Baum, B., 916, 933(55), *935*
Bawn, C. E. H., 503(144), 531, 562(144), 575(433), *587*, *591*, *595*, 607(60), 617 (60), 621(60), 622(60), 657(60), 659 (175) *673*, *677*
Baxter, J. P., 907(6), *933*
Bayer, O., 728, 740(3), 741, 743(56), 755 (2), 756(2), *762*, *764*
Baysal, A., 818(28), *841*
Beal, R. E., 743(55), *764*
Beattie, W. H., 524, *590*
Bebb, R. L., 506(155), 514(155), 515 (155), 560(400), *587*, *594*
Beears, W. L., 611(80), *674*
Beerman, C., 603(31), 654(31), *673*
Behnken, D. W., 542, *593*
Beinert, G., 567(464), *596*
Belt, R. F., 609(63), 622(63, 180), 658 (63), *674*, *678*
Bell, V. L., 969, *989*
Belonovskaja, G. P., 950(41), *988*
Belyanin, V. B., 945(28), 952(28), *945*
Bennett, G. M., 816(17, 18), 833(17), *840*
Benning, C. F., 719(47), *725*
Berding, C., 871(11), *889*
Berenbaum, M. B., 807, 809–811(2), 823, 826, *840*, *841*
Berestneva, Z. Ya., 575(434), *595*
Berger, M., 970, *989*
Berger, R. S., 870, *889*
Berger, S. E., 741, *763*
Berkowitz, J., 498(66), *585*
Berridge, C. A., 800, *804*
Bertozzi, E. R., 810, *840*, 864(59), *866*
Bertrand, G., 558(394), *594*
Bestian, H., 603(31), 654(31), *673*
Beu, K. E., 598(11), *672*
Bezhan, I. P., 874(29), *890*
Bhacca, N. S., 519(193), *588*, 947(37), 980–982(37), 986(37), *988*
Bhattacharyya, D. N., 564, *595*
Bier, G., 682(1), 683(1, 7), 684(7), 687(1), 688(1, 7, 18), 691(7), *701*, *702*
Billmeyer, F. W., Jr., 906(1), 919(69), *933*, *935*
Binder, J. L., 493, 496(11), 518, 521(182), 523(182), 559(395), 566(11, 395), 567–569(11), 571, 573(395), 578(11, 445), *583*, *588*, *594*, *596*, 598(10), 634(121), 638(121), 639(121, 128), *672*, *676*, 980, 981, *990*
Bingham, W. R., 689(20), 692(20), *702*, 930(113), *936*
Bishop, W. A., 522(230), 523(230), *590*, 976–978(91), *990*
Bisio, A. L., 523, *590*
Black, R. M., 923(93), *936*

Blackie, M. S., 872(13), 873(13), *889*
Blaich, C. F., Jr., 740(20, 24), *763*
Blaise, J., 846(5), *864*
Bloomfield, G. F., 907(7, 9), 909–911, *934*, 939(3), 942, *987*
Blümel H., 522(221), 530(221), *589*, 906(5), *933*, 976(95), *990*
Bobear, W. J., 787, 792, 798(77), 802, *803*, *804*
Bock, W., 869(5), *889*
Böck, F., 604, *673*
Boikacheva, E. G., 945(26, 27), *988*
Boileau, S., 834, 835(54, 56), 839(72), *841*, *842*
Boldyreva, I. I., 950(40, 41), *988*
Bolland, J. L., 561, 563(404), 568(404), 572(404), *595*
Bolton, F. H., 578(447), *596*, 599(16), *672*
Bond, G. C., 875(44), 876(44), *890*
Bond, W. C., 743(55), *764*
Boor, J., Jr., 719(48), *725*
Booth, C., 524(248), *590*
Boozer, C. E., 920(77), *935*
Borsini, C., 930(130), *937*
Bortolini, W., 621(97), *675*
Bostick, E. E., 498(72), 499(72, 90), 502 (139), 503(72, 148), 504(139), 506(72, 148), 507(72), 508(72), 509(72, 148), 510(72, 148), 512(72), 528(72), *585*, *587*, 782(35), 785(79), *803*, *804*
Boyer, R. F., 529, *591*
Boyer, T. W., 846(1), *864*
Bozzacco, F. A., 499(115, 117), 522(117), *586*
Bradford, E. B., 878(51), *891*
Bradshaw, C. P. C., 723(69), *726*
Bradshaw, J. S., 537(314), *592*
Braude, E. A., 497(49), *584*
Braun, R. M., 719(52), 720(52), *725*
Breil, H., 642(138), *676*, 707(13), *724*
Brennan, J. J., 526(258), *590*
Bresler, L. S., 541(329), 542(329), 547 (356), 549(329), *593*, 653(161), 655, 667(184), 670, *677*, *678*
Bresler, S. E., 525, *590*, *593*
Bresler, S. Y., 555, 556, *594*
Briggs, E. R., 870(10), *889*
Brini, M., 538(322, 323), 552(365), 553 (322), 570, *592*, *594*, *595*
Britain, J. W., 743(48), 760, *764*, *765*
Brockway, C. E., *674*
Brody, H., 495(23), 504(23), 561(23), 571(23), *583*, 848(17), *864*
Brooks, R. E., 916(53), 917(61), 931 (53), *935*
Brossas, J., 912(35), *934*
Brown, H. C., 917(59), *935*
Brown, H. P., 848(10), 849(10), *864*
Brown, H. W., 533(300), *592*
Brown, J. F., Jr., 712(36), *725*, 780, *803*, 967, *989*
Brown, P. L., 863(55), *865*
Brown, T. L., 497(71), 498, 499, 501, 502, 510, 512(71), 531, 533, *584*, *585*, *587*
Bruce, J. M., Jr., 900–903(6), *903*
Bruckner, G., 874(34), 880(34), *890*
Bruner, L. B., 863(53), *865*
Bruzzone, M., 522(216), *589*, 666(181), *678*, 930(111, 128, 130, 132), 931, 932 (136, 141), 933(128), *936*, *937*
Bua, E., 699, *702*
Bucci, M., 698(37), 699, *702*
Buck, O. G., 534(306), 535(306), *592*, 846, 847(8), 851(8), 853(8), 854(8), *864*
Buckley, D. J., 522(231), 523(231), *590*, 923–925(95), 928(95), 929(95), *936*, 970, *989*
Bueche, A. M., 795(62), 796, 801, *804*
Bueche, F., 528(276), *591*
Bürger, G., 880(56), *891*
Buist, J. M., 741(41), *764*
Buizov, B. V., 955, *988*
Bull, W. C., 743(55), *764*
Bunn, C. W., 651(155), *677*, 915(45), *935*
Burgin, J., 907(16), *934*
Burlant, W. J., 967(61), *989*
Bushick, R. D., 687(17), *702*
Busse, W. F., 918(67), 919(67, 69), *935*
Butler, G. B., 963(55), *988*
Butta, E., 522(219), *589*
Bykhovskii, V. K., 580, *596*
Bylsma, H. R., 740(26), *763*

Bywater, S., 497(127), 498, 499(103), 502 (127), 503, 505(146), 507(103), 508 (103, 146), 510, 511(103), 512(103, 127), 519, 534, 541(127, 146), 549(146), 562(59), 569(103), *584*, *586*, *587*

C

Cain, W. P., 932, *937*
Calderon, N., 499(75), 509(75), 510(75), 520(75), *585*, 711(30), 720(55), 723(65, 66, 71), *725*, *726*
Cameli, N., 693(27), *702*, 930(127), *937*
Camia, M., 522(226), *589*, 976(94), *990*
Campbell, T. W., 932(138), *937*
Canale, A. J., 611(71), 617(71), *674*, 874 (21, 33), 878(21),879(21, 33, 53), 880 (21), *890*
Canter, N., 830(46), *841*
Canterino, P. J., 912, 915(49), 916(49), 920, 931(79), *934*, *935*
Carbonaro, A., 607–609(59), 610(66), 622 (66), 623(100), 625(100), 626(100), 629(108), 641(100), 642(108), 643(108), 645(100, 143), 646(144, 145), 647(143), 651(145), 653(108, 143), 655(166), 656(167), 658(66), 662(108), 666(182, 183), 667(182), 668(182), 669(183), 670 (183), *674–678*
Carella, G., 705(9), 707(9), 711(9), 716 (43), 717(9), *724*, *725*
Carlson, E. J., 603(23), 611(23), 623(23), 625(23), 633(23), 641(23), *673*
Carmack, M., 820(41), *841*
Carmichael, J. B., 779, *803*
Carney, P. A., 506(157), *587*
Carr, E. L., 559(395), 566(395), *594*
Carrick, W. L., 684(9), *701*
Carrow, D. J., 534(304), *592*
Carter, J. H., 874(39), 881(39), 882(39), *890*
Carter, W. C., 524(246), *590*
Cartledge, F. K., 506, *587*
Case, L. C., 528(280), *591*
Casling, R. A. H., 500, *587*
Castelli, R., 607(51, 54), 611(54), 617 (51, 54), 621(51, 96), 622(96),630(111), *673*, *675*
Cazes, J., 525(253), *590*
Cesare, F. C., 877(50), 879(50), *891*
Cesca, S., 684(10), 687(10), *701*
Ceselli, C. A., 522(226), *589*, 976(94), *990*
Chalfant, D. L., 634–636(122), 637(124), 638(124), 639(126), 640(122), *676*
Chalk, A. J., 875(42, 43), 876(42), *890*
Chambers, D. H., 907(19), *934*
Champetier, G., 554, *594*, 834(56), 835 (56), *841*
Chang, R., 564(419), *595*
Chao, T. H., 917(59), *935*
Charlesby, A., 773, *802*, 923, *936*
Cheema, Z. K., 499(79), *585*
Chemical and Engineering News, 493 (8, 9), 494(9), *583*, 729(8), *763*
Chemische Werke Hüls A.-G., 607(57), *673*, *674*, 854(26), 861(39), *865*
Chen, H. Y., 519(192, 196), 548(192), *588*, 723(65), *726*, 981, 986, *990*
Chernova, J. D., 950(41), *988*
Chesnokova, N. N., 499(95), 501(95), 505–507(95), 531(95), 533 95), 544–546(345), *585*, *593*, 874(27, 29), *890*
Childers, C. W., 655, 657(164), *677*
Ciampelli, E., 874(34), 880(34), *890*
Ciampelli, F., 518(187, 189), *588*, 611 (83), 613(83), 644(141), 645(142), 651 (141, 142, 145), 666(183), 667(186), 669 (183), 670(183, 186), 671(186), *674*, *676*, *678*, 698, *702*, 706(10), 707(10), 709(17), 712(17, 37), *724*, *725*
Ciferri, A., 704(2), *724*
Clark, W. B., 917(62), *935*
Clarke, J. T., 818(29), *841*
Clarke, R. G., 502(139), 504(139), *587*
Clayton, J. O., 920, *935*
Cleary, J. W., 854(27), *865*
Cleland, R. R. 572(467), 579, 580(451), *596*
Cleveland, T. H., 740(16), *763*
Cluff, E. F., 578(447), *596*, 599(16), *672*
Coates, G. E., 497(40), 498(40), 514(40), *584*
Cobine, J. D., 776(27), *803*
Coffey, S., 926(100, 101), *936*
Coffman, D. D., 856(36), *865*

Coker, J. N., 900–903(6), *903*
Cole, O. D., 529(288), *591*, 862(45), *865*
Coleman, B. D., 515(176), *588*
Collette, J. W., 693(25), 695(25),696(25), *702*, 930(123), *937*
Collins, F. W., 578(447), *596*, 599(16), *672*
Colodny, P. C., 829, *841*
Colombo, A., 657(170), *677*
Conti, F., 663(179), *677*
Cook, N. C., 776(27), *803*
Cook, R. E., 983(116), *990*
Coombes, J. D., 495(23), 504(23), 561 (23), 571(23), *583*
Cooper, G. D., 782, *803*
Cooper, L. V., 921(85), *936*
Cooper, M. L., 603(25), 604(25), *673*
Cooper, W., 516(177), 518(177), 530 (177), 575(177), *588*, 627(105), 641 (136), 650(157), 652(157), 653(136, 165), 655, 660(105), *675–677*, 706(11), 712(11), *724*, 848, *864*
Coops, J., 719(51), 720(51), *725*
Corradini, G., 522(216), *589*
Corradini, P., 604(37), 610(67, 68), 611 (67), 624(103), 641(103), 644(103, 141), 651(68, 103, 141, 147, 148, 150, 152–154), *673–678*, 705(5, 6), 707(5, 12), 711, 712(5, 6, 37), *724*, *725*
Corrin, M., 781(34), *803*
Corrish, P. J., 518(191), *588*
Côté, R. J., 740(15), 743(48), 746(15), 750(15), 753(15), 756(15), 757(15), *763*, *764*
Cotten, E. W., 846(6), *864*
Counsell, R. C., 537(314), *592*
Cowan, D. O., 537(314), *592*
Cowan, J. C., 743(55), *764*
Cox, J. D., 719(54), 720(54), *725*, 933(147), *937*
Crafts, J. M., 768, *802*
Craig, D., 536, *592*, 945(30), *988*
Crain, D. L., 723(70), *726*
Cram, D. J., 501(133), *587*
Cramer, R., 874(19), 876(19), 886, 889(19), *890*
Crammond, D. N., 499, 503(106), 505–509(106), 511, *586*
Crane, E. J., 770(13), *802*
Crawford, J. W. C., 623(76), 641(76), *674*
Crawford, R. A., 921, *936*
Cremonesi, P., 712(32), *725*
Crespi, G., 651(151), 652(159), *677*, 693(24, 26, 27), 695(26), 696(26), 700(40), *702*, 929(110), 930(110, 111, 125, 127, 128, 132), 931, 932(136, 141), 933(128), *936*, *937*
Cripps, H. N., 887(66), *891*
Croce, G. F., 607(51, 54), 611(54), 617(51, 54), 621(51), *673*
Crouch, W. W., 575(438), *596*, 846 (2, 60), 849(2, 18, 19, 67), 850, *864*, *866*
Crowley, G. P., 741(41), *764*
Csaszar, F. C., 916(56), *935*
Cubbon, R. C. P., 497(128), 503(128), 505(128), 507(128), 521(128), 541(128), *586*
Cucinella, S., 605(39, 40), 629(109), 640(39, 40, 129), *673*, *675*, *676*
Cummings, W., 870(10), *889*
Cunneen, J. I., 522(233, 235), *590*, 950(42, 43), 978(42), 980, 983, 984, 985(119), 986, *988*, *990*
Cunningham, R. E., 695(31), 696(31), *702*

D

Dainton, F. S., 522(223), *589*, 720(56), *725*, 817, *840*, 983(116), *990*
Dall'Asta, G., 705(7–9), 707(7–9), 711(8, 9), 712(8), 713(7, 39, 40), 715 (7, 8, 39–41), 716(8, 43, 44), 717(9), 722(40, 64), 723(8), *724–726*, 874 (36, 37), 882(37), 883(58, 59), *890*, *891*
Dalton, C., 537(314), *592*
Damman, J. A., 869(3), *889*
Danon, J., 944(12), 975(12), 986(12, 120), *987*, *990*
Dantzig, L. L., 544(361), 547(361), 549(361), 551(361), 552(361), *593*
Danusso, F., 621–623(118), *675*, 690 (22), *702*, 712(31), *725*

Darcy, J., 606(43), *673*
Darr, W. C., 740(17), 746–749(17)
Das, B., 874(26), 877(26), 878(26), 880(26), *890*
Dasgupta, S., 944(19), 987
Dauby, R., 874(24, 25, 30), 878(24), 886(25), 888(24, 25), *890*
Davies, J. A., 817, *840*
Davies, N. R., 875(45, 46), *891*
Davis, D. D., 519(199), *589*
Davis, F. O., 817, 818(24), 833, *840*, *841*
Davison, J. A., 567(430), 574, *595*, 598 (1), *672*, 850(20), *864*
Davydov, B. E., 967(64, 65), *989*
Dawans, F., 874(30), *890*, 969, *989*
Dawson, I. M., 820(36, 37), *841*
Dawson, T. R., 939(3), *987*
Deanin, R., 869(2, 4), *889*
Dearborn, R. J., 869(3), *889*
De Bataafsche Petr. Maat., 607(56), 611(69, 71), 617(69, 71), 631(114), *673–675*
Degler, G., 627(105), 655(105), 660(105), *675*
Deisz, M. M., 782(35), *803*
De La Mare, H. E., 610(65), 622(65), 658(65), *674*, 880(55), *891*
Della Fortuna, G., 684(10), 687(10), *701*
Deluzarche, A., 538(321–323), 552(365), 553(321, 322), *592*, *594*
De Maldè, M., 605(39, 40), 606(48–50), 615(48–50, 87), 616(48–50, 87), 629(109), 640(39, 40, 129), 653(87), *673–676*
Dermer, O. C., 839, *842*
Dersch, F., 492(4), 496(4), *582*
Desreux, V., 602(22), *672*
Dessy, R., 497(129), *586*
Desyatova, N. V., 521(210), 562(407), 567(407), 568(407), 572(407), *589*, *595*
Deutschman, A. J., 869(3), *889*
DeVault, A. N., 920, *935*
Devlin, T. R. E., 720(56), *725*
Dewhurst, H. A., 795(62), *804*
Diaconescu, A. I., 617(94), 621(94), 622(94), *675*
D'Ianni, J. D., 493(6), 537(316), 579, 581, 582(448), *583*, *592*, *596*, 599(17), 639(127), 650(127), 652(127), *672*, *676*, 906(4), 907(10), 910(10), 912(10), 913(10), *933*, *934*, 939(3), 944, *987*
Dickerhoof, D. W., 498(56), *584*
Diem, H. E., 494(19), 495(19), 496(35), 499(19), 500(19), 504(19), 520(19), 521(19), *583*
Dietrich, H., 498(68), *585*
Dinbergs, K., 743(45), 757(45), *764*
Dinsmore, R. P., 582(461), *596*, 728(5), *762*
Dixon, J. A., 499(76), *585*
Dobson, G. R., 528(279), *591*
Dogadkin, B. A., 522(236), *590*, 945 (26–29), 952(28), *988*
Dole-Robbe, J. P., 519(194), 538(194), *588*
Dolgoplosk, B. A., 499(87), 502(140), 509(87), 512(87), 521(96, 209, 211), 522 (228), 547(356), *585*, *587*, *589*, *593*, 617(89, 90, 93), 619(90), 621(95), 658 (172), 667(184), 670(184), *675*, *677*, *678*, 950, 951, 978(105), *988*, *990*
Dolgov, B. N., 768
Dollinger, R. E., 555(376, 379), *594*
Donati, M., 663(179), *677*
Donohue, J., 820(38), *841*
Doran, M. A., 498(57, 60, 61, 64), 499 (61, 130), 500, 502, 506, 512(60, 130), 533(299), *584*, *586*, *592*
Doszlop, S., 874(28), *890*
Dow Chemical Co., 839(69), *842*
Dow Corning Corp., 783(40), *803*
Down, J. L., 851(24), *865*
Druesdow, D., 916, 931, *935*
Duck, E. W., 499(125), *586*
Dunbrook, R. F., 559(395), 560(397, 401), 566(395), 573(395), *594*, *595*
Dunham, M. L., 798, *804*
Dunlap Tire & Rubber Co., 815(12), *840*
Du Pont de Nemours, E. I., & Co., 514(170), 515(172), *588*, 617(73), *674*, 717(45), *725*, 739(13), 760(75), *763*, *765*, 839(70), 840(70), *842*, 848(14, 64), *864*, *866*, 874(17), 890, 917(58), 918(68), 930(112, 122, 131), 932(140), *935–937*

Durgaryan, A. A., 542, *593*
Durham, L. J., 920(76), *935*
Dvořák, J., 963(59), 967(59), *989*
Dynamit Nobel A. G., 728(1), *762*

E

Eaborn, C., 769(9), 773, 768(9), *802*
Eagle-Picher, 743(50), *764*
Earle, F. R., 743(55), *764*
East, G. C., 499(89), *585*
Eastham, J. F., 498(69), 499(69, 79, 80, 84, 85), 501, 533(85), *585*
Eastmond, G. C., 872(14, 15), *889*, *890*
Eaves, D. E., 627(105), 641(136), 653 (136), 655(105, 165), 660(105), *675–677*
Eberly, K. C., 506, 514(154, 155), 515 (155), 571, *587*, *595*
Edmonds, J. T., Jr., 920, 931(79), *935*
Edwards, C. D., 921(84), *936*
Egloff, G., 788(48), *803*
Ehrenburg, E. G., 527, 572, 575(272), 575(435), *591*, *595*, 832(50), *841*
Ehrig, R. J., 499(110), *586*
Ehrlich, A., 743(54), *764*
Eimers, E., 850(22), *864*
Eirich, F., 494(27), 496(27), *583*
Eisch, J., 497(43), *584*
Ekar, A. F., *674*
Ellegast, K., 740(15), 746, 750(15), 753(15), 756(15), 757(15), *763*, *764*
Elliot, D. J., 522(227), *589*
Elliot, J. R., 782, *803*
Ells, F. R., 545, 567–569(424), 571, 573(424), 574(424), *593*, *595*
Emerson, G. F., 884(60), 886(60), *891*
Endres, H. A., 911, *934*, 955, *988*
Engel, E. F., 861, *865*
Englin, M. A., 920, *935*
Engs, W., 907(16), *934*
Epstein, L. M., 800, *804*
Ermakova, I. I., 522(228), *589*, 951(45), 978(105), *988*, *990*
Erussalimskii, B. L., 617(89), *675*
Eschard, F., 924(98), *936*
Eskin, V. E., 835(57), *841*
Esso Research & Engineering Co., 499 (108, 113), 575(436, 437), *586*, *596*, 930(116), 933(146), *936*, *937*
Eustance, J. W., 967(67), *989*
Evans, A. G., 500, *587*
Evans, D. M., 522(223), *589*
Evans, M. B., 951(46), *988*
Evenhuis, K., 693(28), 702
Ewart, R. H., 641(133), *676*

F

Faberov, M. I., 603(35), *673*
Fagherazzi, G., 711(24, 25), *724*
Fahey, R. C., 908, *934*
Faina, S., 695(30), 696(30), *702*
Farbenfabriken Bayer A.-G., 492(3), 496(31), 526(259, 263), *582*, *583*, *590*, 606(44), *673*, 741(32, 34), 743(32, 57), 753(65), 755(65), *763*, *764*, 940(4), *987*
I. G. Farbenindustrie A.-G., 815(11), *840*
Farbwerke Hoechst, 916(57), *935*
Farhat, K., 524(239), 525, *590*
Farina, M., 602(19), *672*
Farr, J. A., 862(48), *865*
Farrar, R. C., 606(46), 616(88), 623 (88), 625(88), 641(88), *673*, *674*
Farson, F. S., 741(37), *763*
Fauser, E. E., 741(37), *763*
Fawcett, M. S., 930(124), *937*
Felterman, M. Q., 743(50), *764*
Ferguson, H. R., 813, *840*
Feringer, D. P., 522(214), *589*
Ferraris, M., 621(96), 622(96), *675*
Ferri, C., 947, 969, *988*, *989*
Fetters, L. J., 498(73), 499(75, 90), 503 (148), 506(148), 509(75, 148, 160), 510, 511(160), 512, 513(160), 520 (75, 160), 534, 554, 569(160), *585*, *587*, *594*
Fettes, E. M., 807(3), 815(10), 817, 818(24), 819, 820, 831–833, *840*, *841*, 863(58), 864(58, 59), *865*, *866*
Field, J. E., 579(448), 581(448), 582 (448), *596*, 599(17), *672*
Figgis, B. N., 880(54), *891*

Fikhtengol'ts, V. S., 775(78), *804*
Finaz, G., 855(66), *866*
Finch, C. A., 872(12, 13), 873(13), *889*
Finelli, A. F., 741(37), *763*
Fineman, M., 542, *593*
Finnegan, R. A., 577(441), *596*
Fiore, L., 604(38), 611(72), 617(72), 625(38), 627(107), 629(107), 641(38), *673–675*
Firestone Tire & Rubber Co., 494(15), 496(30–32, 34), 499(114–117, 121, 126), 526(255), 548(353), *583*, *586*, *590*, *593*, 598(4), *672*
Fischer, B. S., 930(123), *937*
Fischer, D. J., 795(63), *804*
Fischer, E. O., 609, 658, *674*, 880(56), *891*
Fisher, B. S., 693(25), 695(25), 696(25), *702*
Fisher, H. L., 944, *987*
Fitzpatrick, J. D., 977(102, 103), 978, *990*
Fiumani, D., 682(2), 687–689(2), 692 (2), *701*
Fletcher, W. P., 983(112), *990*
Fletcher, W. R., 522(235), *590*
Flisi, U., 651(151), *677*
Flory, P. J., 513, 523(167), 526, *587*, 704(2), 709(20), *724*, 771(14), 780, 801, *802–804*, 944, 969(20), *987*
Flurry, R. L., Jr., 920(77), *935*
Folt, V. L., 634(119), *675*
Fomina, L. P., 945(28), 952(28), *988*
Fono, A., 614(85), *674*
Fonrobert, E., 912, *934*
Ford, E. W., 921(85), *936*
Fordham, S., 769(11), 773(11), 786(11), *802*
Forman, L. E., 494(15), 496(30, 33), 499(33, 114–117), 500(33), 504(33, 149), 506(156), 518, 520, 521(33), 522(117), 523(237), 529(149), 530, 540(149), 555(385), 565(422), 567 (422), 568(422, 443), 569(33, 422, 443), 571(422), 578(443), *583*, *586*, *587*, *589*, *590*, *594–596*
Foss, O., 820(39), *841*
Foster, F. C., 493, 496(11), 566–569(11), 571, 578(11), *583*
Foster, R. J., 743(55), *764*
Fox, H. W., 772, *802*
Fox, T. G., 528(281), *591*
Fraenkel, G., 498(63), *584*
Fraga, D. W., 981, *990*
France, H., 741(41), *764*
François, B., 494(17), 496(17), 499(17, 132), 500(132), 501(132), 502, 503 (132), 505(17, 132), 506, 507, 508 (132), 509(132), 511(132), 521(17), 527(17), 542(132), *583*, *587*
Fredrick, M. R., 611(80), *674*, 923(96), *936*
Frenkel, S. Ya., 554(374), 555(386), 556(386), *594*
Friedel, C., 768, *802*
Friedländer, H. N., 603(29), *673*
Friedman, G., 538(322, 323), 552(365), 553(322), 570, *592*, *594*, *595*
Frisch, K. C., 729, 738(9b, 9d), 740(25), 741(29, 30), 743(9e, 9i), 746(9c), 750(9c), 760, 762(9i), 773, *763*, *802*
Frolov, V. M., 502(140), *587*
Fromandi, G., 944(11), *987*
Frosini, V., 522(219), *589*
Frost, R. E., 609(63), 622(63), 658(63), *674*
Frulla, F. F., 788(49), *803*
Frye, B. F., 740(15–17), 743(48), 746 (15, 17), 747–749(17), 750(15), 753 (15), 756(15), 757(15), *763*, *764*
Fryling, C. F., 598(11), *672*, 869(1), *889*
Fueno, T., 542, *593*, 640(130), *676*
Fujita, Y., 835, *841*
Fukumoto, T., 986(121), *990*
Fuqua, S. A., 519(193), *588*, 947(37), 980–982(37), 986(37), *988*
Furukawa, J., 542, 546(355), 549, *593*, 640(130), *676*, 835, 836, *841*, *842*, 856, 857(37), 858(37, 38), 859(38), 860(38), *865*, 869(8), *889*, 900(7), *903*
Fusco, J. V., 930(116), *937*

G

Gable, C. L., 743(51), 744(53), *764*
Gallazzi, M. C., 537(319), *592*, 598(7),

623(102), 627(102),628(102), 645(7), 656(102), 657(170), 658(102), 662 (177), *672*, *675*, *677*, 715(42), *725*, 874(35), 880(35), *890*

Gallo, S. G., 922(91), 925, 926(91), *936*

Gallot, B., 556, *594*

Gallot, Y., 855(66), *866*

Gamble, L. W., 525(252), *590*

Gannon, J. A., 815(10), *840*

Gantmakher, A. R., 498, 499(88, 91, 92), 500(88), 502(91, 138), 503(138), 505 (88), 506(138), 507(91, 138), 508(88, 91), 509(92), 510(91), 512(91, 138, 161), 521(210), 546(88, 360), 547(88), 549(88, 359, 360), 562(359, 406, 407–409), 567(407), 568(407), 571(359, 408), 572, 573, *584*, *585*, *587*, *589*, *593*, *595*, 641(135), *676*

Garlanda, T., 522(226), *589*, 976(94), *990*

Garner, H. K., 641(133), *676*, 689(20), 692(20), *702*, 930(113), *936*

Gaylord, N. G., 611(81), 613, *674*, 946, 959(33), 961, 963, 966, 967(58), *988*, *989*

Geĭderikh, M. A., 967(64, 65), *989*

Geiseler, G., 518(188), *588*

Geller, N. M., 499(87), 509(87), 512(87), 521(211), *585*

Gellert, H. G., 498(45), *584*

Genkin, A. N., 831, *841*

Gerber, A., 499(97), 500(97), 520(97), 521, 531, *585*

German, R., 683(4), 695(4), *701*

Gerteis, R. L., 498(52), 499(52), *584*

Geyer, A. M., 846(5), *864*

Ghymes, G., 603(33), *673*

Giachetti, E., 621(97), 642(139), 653(139, 162), *675*, *676*

Giannini, U., 874(34), 880(34), *890*

Gianotti, G., 621–623(118), *675*

Gibbs, C. F., 494(19), 495(19), 499(19), 500(19), 504(19), 520(19), 521(19), *583*, 634(119), 637(131), 650(131), 652 (131), *675*, *676*, 916, 931, *935*

Gibbs, F., 603(23), 611(23), 623(23), 625 (23), 633(23), 641(23), *673*

Gibbs, W. E., 603(24), 614(24), 634(24), 639(24), 640(24), 653(24), *673*

Gibson, G. W., 499(79, 80), *585*

Gilkey, R., 598(8), *672*

Gillard, R. D., 880(54), *891*

Gilman, H., 497(38, 43, 47, 48), 506, 514 (38), 560(38), 562(38), *584*, *587*, 926 (104), *936*

Gippin, M., 607(52), 617(52, 92), 618, 621 (52), *673*, *675*

Gladding, E. K., 693(25), 695(25), 696 (25), *702*, 930(123), *937*

Gladstone, J. H., 910(27), *934*

Glaze, W. H., 498(46), *584*

Glazebrook, R. W., 976(98, 99), *990*

Gleason, A. H., 575(436), *596*

Gleitsmann, G. B., 534(305), *592*

Gobran, R. H., 823, 838(67), *841*, *842*

Göbel, G., 863(69), *866*

Gössl, T., 699, *702*

Goldberg, E. J., 514(170), *588*, 854(28), *865*, 930(112, 124), *936*, *937*

Golub, M. A., 519, 522(225, 229, 232), 523(225, 229, 232), *588–590*, 913, 915 (40), *934*, 939(1), 940(5), 942(8), 943(9), 944(12, 13), 945(8, 9, 25), 946(9), 947 (9, 37), 948(9), 949(9, 38), 950(9, 44), 952(8), 954(8, 9), 962(13, 54), 970, 971 (79, 80, 84), 973(86–88), 974(87, 88), 975(88, 89), 976(92), 977(92), 978(1, 5, 38, 44, 88, 92), 979(44), 980, 981(37), 982, 983(44), 984, 985(92), 986(12, 37, 79, 80, 120, 121a), *987–990*

Goodrich, B. F., Co., 499(107), 514(169), 515(169), *586*, *588*, 921, 923(96), *936*, 970(73), *989*

Goodrich-Gulf Chemicals, Inc., 603(23), 607(58), 611(23, 70, 80), 617(70), 623 (23), 625(23), 633(23), 641(23), 657 (58), *673*, *674*

Gordon, M., 528(279), *591*, 944, 955, 966(15), *987*

Gornick, F., 515(176), *588*

Gould, E. S., 912(38), *934*

Grace, N. S., 516(177), 518(177), 530 (177), 575(177), *588*

Graessley, W. W., 528(278), *591*

Graf, R., 920, *935*

Graham, J. W., 848(13), *864*

Graham, W. A. G., 769(12), 773(12), 786 (12), *802*
Grassie, N., 942(6), 967(62, 63), *987*, *989*
Gratch, S., 528(281), *591*
Gray, P., 922, *936*
Grechanovskii, V. A., 524(247), *590*
Greco, A., 655(166), *677*
Green, M. L. H., 875(49), 887(65), *891*
Greenberg, H., 576, 579, 580(452), 581, 582(440), *596*
Greenley, R. Z., 696(32), *702*
Gresham, W. F., 930(122), *937*
Grimaud, E., 846(5), *864*
Groene, H., 496(31), 521(212), *583*, *589*, 606(44), *673*
Groll, H. P. A., 907(16, 17), *934*
Grosse, A. V., 497(36), *583*
Grubb, W. T., 781, 783(38), *803*
Gruver, J. T., 524(244, 245), 528, *590*, 852(25), *865*
Gueniffey, H., 911, 912(30, 35, 36), *934*
Gumboldt, A., 683(7), 684(7), 688(7, 18), 689(7), 691(7), *701*, *702*
Gurgiolo, A. E., 839, *842*
Gur'yanova, E. N., 498(70), 499(70), *585*
Guyot, A., 617(91), *675*
Guzetta, G., 652(159), *677*
Gwinner, P. A., 499(76), *585*

H

Haag, E. C., 743(51), *764*
Habgood, B. J., 741(39), *764*
Hafner, W., 875(41), *890*
Haggerty, M., 498(69), 499(69), *585*
Halpern, J., 888(68), *891*
Halverson, G., 519, *589*
Ham, G. E., 541(327, 328), *592*, 681
Ham, J. S., 528(277), *591*
Hamann, K., 720(58), *725*
Hamermesh, C. L., 720(60), *725*
Hamilton, C. W., 741(29), *763*
Hammer, C. F., 917–919(63), *935*
Hammond, C. H., 499(114), 518(213), *586*, *589*
Hammond, G. S., 536, *592*
Hampton, R. R., 567(430), 574, *595*, 598(1), *672*, 850(20), *864*
Hani, H., 955(49), *988*
Hank, R., 627(105), 655(105), 660(105), *675*, 683(4), 695(4), 700, 701(41, 42), *701*, *702*, 930(126), *937*
Hanlon, T. L., 637(124), 638(124), *676*
Hanmer, R. S., 558(392), *594*
Hanry, E. V., 720(60), *725*
Hans-Helmut, F., 916(57), *935*
Hansley, V. L., 576, 579, 580(452), 581, 582(440), *596*
Hanson, E. E., 519, *589*
Hardman, K. V., 862(46, 47), *865*
Hardt, P., 654(163), 657(163), *677*
Hardy, E. E., 740(17), 746–749(17), *763*
Hargreaves, C. A., 708(16), *724*
Harker, D., 772(15), *802*
Harper, D. A., 728(4), 741(38, 39), *762–764*
Harries, C., 912, *934*
Harries, C. D., 939(2), 940(2), 944(2), *987*
Harries, C. H., 492, 560, *582*
Harrington, R., 759, *764*
Harris, J. F., 898, *903*
Harrod, J. F., 875(42, 43), 876(42), *890*
Hartlová, E., 956(51), 963(51), 966(51), *988*
Harwood, H. J., 542(339), 543, 550–552, *593*
Hatano, M., 561(405), 572(405), *595*
Haubein, A. H., 506, *587*
Havens, N. L., 743(50), *764*
Haws, J. R., 522, 558(391, 393), *589*, *594*
Haxo, H. E., 689(20), 692(20), *702*, 930 (113), *936*
Hay, J. N., 967(63), *989*
Hayashi, K., 514(171), 534, *588*, *592*, 743(60), *764*, 855, *865*
Hayes, R. A., 529(287), *591*
Hearne, G., 907(16, 17), *934*
Hechelhammer, W., 850(22), *864*
Heck, R. F., 887(67), *891*
Heillier, M., 875(44), 876(44), *890*
Heinbach, P., 642(138), 654(163), 657 (163), *676*, *677*
Heiss, H. L., 741(27), 743(27), 761(27), 762(27), *763*
Heller, J., 913, 914(40), *934*, 942(8), 943 (9), 944(13), 945(8, 9, 25), 946–950(9),

952(8), 954(8, 9), 962(13, 54), *987*, *988*
Helm, D. F., 788(48), *803*
Helmer, J. D., 529(286), *591*
Henderson, J. F., 524(240), 525(240, 249), 527(240), 528, *590*, 614(86), 617 (86), 653(86), *674*
Hendry, D. G., 932(144), *937*
Herbrandson, H. F., 918(66), *935*
Heusel, H. R., *674*
Hewett, W. A., 874(21, 33), 878(21), 879 (21, 33), 880(21), *890*
Heying, T. L., 788(49), *803*
Hibbert, W., 910(27), *934*
Higashimura, T., 532, *591*
Higasi, K., 544(342), *593*
Higgins, G. M. C., 522(233), *590*, 950 (42), 951(46), 978(42), 980(42), 983 (42), 984(42, 117), 985(119), 986(42, 119), *988*, *990*
Hildebrand, J. H., 792, *804*
Hill, E. A., 884(62), *891*
Hill, F. B., 728(6), 741(42), *762*, *764*
Hinschberger, A., 494(12, 13), 494(13), 495(12a), 496(12b), *583*
Hiraga, H., 955(49), *988*
Hoare, F. E., 522(223), *589*
Hochwalt, C. A., 611(74), *674*
Hock, A. L., 816(18), *840*
Hodgkins, J. E., 932(140), *937*
Hoehn, H. H., 887(66), *891*
Hoewe, C. A., 704(2), *724*
Hoff, B. M. E. van der, 524(240), 525 (240), 527(240), 528, *590*
Hoffman, R., 532(298), *592*
Hofmann, W., 500(131), 501(131), 503 (131), 504(131), 508(131), *586*
Holden, G., 555(377), *594*
Holtschmidt, H., 743(57), 759(71), *764*, *765*
Holzkamp, E., 707(13), *724*
Hooton, J. R., 606(45), 614(45), *673*
Horn, C. L., 917(58), *935*
Horne, S. E., Jr., 603(23), 611(23), 623 (23), 625(23), 633(23), 634(119), 637 (131), 641(23), 650(131), 652(131), *673*, *675*, *676*
Howard, E. G., 893(1), 894(1), 899(1), *903*
Howard, R. O., 818(29), *841*
Howk, B. W., 887(66), *891*
Howman, E. J., 723(69), *726*
Hsieh, H. L., 494(29), 496, 499(93, 104, 105, 109), 500, 501(109), 503(104, 143), 504, 505(150), 506, 507, 508(104, 143), 509(104, 143), 514(169), 515(173), 520, 521, 532, 534(306), 535(306, 307), *583*, *586–588*, *592*, 846, 847(8), 851(8), 853 (8), 854(8), *864*
Huggins, M. L., 602(22), *672*
Hughes, E. D., 908(21), *934*
Hulme, J. M., 525(249), *590*
Hunt, M., 930(122), *937*
Hunter, M. J., 772(17), *802*, 862(50), *865*
Hurd, D. T., 497(39), *584*, 775, 781(34), *803*
Hurley, D. J., 915(48), *935*
Hurst, H. G., 603(34), *673*
Huxtable, R. L., 555(376), *594*
Hyde, J. F., 768, 769, 774(4), *802*, 863 (55), *865*

I

Ichikawa, M., 684, 688, 689(8), 692, *701*
Igarashi, S., 542, *593*
Imoto, M., 873, *890*
Imperial Chemical Industries, 623(76), 641(76), *674*, 741(39), *764*
Ingold, C. K., 908(21), *934*
Inskeep, G. E., 573, *595*, 869(3), *889*
Irako, K., 546(355), 549, *593*
Isaac, R., 518, *588*
Isbell, A. F., 920(74), *935*
Ishii, Y., 835, *841*
Itatani, H., 986(121), *990*
Ito, A., 932(144), *937*
Ivey, D. G., 529(282), *591*
Ivin, K. J., 983(116), *990*
Iwayanagi, S., 711(29), *725*

J

Jackson, H. L., 776(27), *803*
Jackson, J. E., 743(55), *764*

Jacobson, H., 780, *803*
Jacobson, H. W., 893(2), 894(2), 896(2), 898(2), 899(2), 900–903(6), *903*
Jaffeux, P., 833, *841*
Jakob, L., 492(4), 496(4), *583*, 850(21), *864*
Janzen, E. G., 580, *596*
Jeffrey, G. A., 651(160), *677*
Jenner, E. L., 856(36), *865*, 874(17a), 876 (17a), 886(17a), *890*
Jenner, G., 507(158), 538(324, 325), 539, 552(325), 553(324), *587*, *592*
Jensen, W. L., 920, *935*
Jira, R., 875(41), *890*
Johannsen, O. K., 785(44), *803*
Johnson, A. F., 498(59), 545, 546(349), 562(59), *584*, *593*
Johnson, B. L., 504(149), 506(155), 514 (155), 515(155), 520, 523(239), 525, 526(255), 527, 529(149), 540(149), 559 (395), 566(395), 571, *587*, *590*, *594*, 846 (7), *864*
Johnson, C. S., Jr., 531(311), 536(311), 564(419), *592*, *595*
Johnson, D. R., 722(63), *725*, 880(57), 881(57), *891*
Johnson, P. R., 918(65), 919, 930(131), *935*, *937*
Johnson, R. R., 918, *935*
Johnson, W. D., 525(250), *590*
Johnston, H. W., 869(3), *889*
Jones, E. B., 862(49), *865*
Jones, M. H., 603(32), *673*
Jones, R. C., 533(300), *592*
Jones, R. G., 497(47), *584*
Jorczak, J. S., 819, 820, 863(58), 864(58), *841*, *865*
Journal of Polymer Science, 703(1), 705(1), *724*
Judy, W. A., 720(55), 723(66, 71), *725*, *726*
Junghanns, E., 683(7), 684, 688(7), 689(7), 691, *701*

K

Kaarsemaker, S., 719(51), 720(51), *725*
Kahle, G. R., 499(122), *586*, 915(49), 916(49), *935*
Kálal, J., 874(28), *890*, 956(51), 963(51), 966(51), *988*
Kallert, W., 759(71), *765*
Kambara, S., 561(405), 572(405), *595*, 638–640(125), 667(185), 670(185), *676*, *678*, 685(12), 688(12), *701*
Kantor, S. W., 783, 795, 796, *803*, *804*
Karapinka, G. L., 684(11), *701*
Kargin, V. A., 516(178), 518(178), 530 (178), 557, 559, 575(434), *588*, *595*, 967 (64), *989*
Karol, F. J., 684(9), *701*
Kastning, E.-G., 871, *889*
Katchman, A., 967(67), *989*
Kawakami, M., 631(115), *675*
Kawasaki, A., 640(130), *676*, 869(8), *889*
Kay, E. L., 506(155), 514(155), 515(155), *587*
Keaveney, W. P., 874(38), 880–882(38), *890*
Keckler, N. F., 526(255), *590*
Kelley, D. J., 494(29), 496, 545, 549(343), 573, *583*, *593*, 657(168), *677*
Kelly, R. J., 689(20), 692, *702*, 930(113), *936*
Kelly, W. S., 918(66), *935*
Kemp, A. R., 911, 912(33), *934*
Kendrick, T. C., 783, *803*
Kennedy, J. P., 531, 532, 562(295), *591*, 696(33a), *702*
Kent, E. G., 522(220), *589*
Kern, R. J., 603(34), *673*
Kharasch, M. S., 917(59), *935*
Khodzhemirov, V. A., 641(135), *676*
Kibler, R. W., 499(115, 117), 522(117), *586*
Kiehl, J. P., 634(119), *675*
Kiepert, K. M., 861(41, 42), *865*
Kilb, R. W., 527, *591*
Killof, D. A. Mc., 700(42), 701(42), *702*
King, K. F., 918(65, 68), 919, *935*
Kinoshita, Y., 873(16), *890*
Kinsinger, J. B., 771(14), *802*
Kipping, F. S., 768, *802*
Kiser, K. M., 967(67), *989*
Kitching, W., 497(129), *586*
Klapproth, W. J., 926(102), *936*
Klauzen, N. A., 522(236), *590*

Klebanskii, A. L., 775(78), *804*
Klein, W., 654(163), 657(163), *677*
Klenin, S. I., 555(386), 556(386), *594*
Knipp, E. A., 525(252), *590*
Knowlton, J. W., 719(49), 720(49), *725*
Kobayashi, R., 835(62), *842*
Koch, H. P., 820(40), *841*
Kocheskov, K. A., 498(70), 499(70, 78), *585*
Kössler, I., 518(186), *588*, 643(140), *676*, 946, 956, 959(33), 961, 963, 966, 967 (58–60), *988*, *989*
Kohl, C. F., Jr., 791(56), *803*
Kolechkova, M. F., 547(356), *593*, 667 (184,) 670(184), *678*
Kolesnikov, G. S., 554, *594*
Kolthoff, I. M., 869, *889*, 911, 912, 927, *934*
Koltsov, A. I., 951(45), *988*
Koningsberger, C., 907(11), 909(11), 914, *934*, *935*
Kormer, V. A., 658(172), *677*, 874(27, 29), *890*
Korotkov, A. A., 493(18), 496(18), 499 (95, 100), 501(95), 505(95), 506(95), 507, 521, 522(214), 525(243), 531, 533, 544(344, 345, 361), 545, 546(18, 344–346, 367), 547(344, 358, 361), 548–554, 562(18), 565, 573, 581, *583*, *585*, *586*, *589*, *590*, *593–595*
Kovacic, P., 928, *936*
Kraus, G., 522(215, 217), 524(244, 245), 526(258), 528, *589*, *590*, 906(2), 907 (12), 909(12), 910(12), *933*, *934*, 976, *989*, *990*
Krause, E., 497(36), *583*
Krauserová, H., 963(60), 967(60), *989*
Kreider, L. C., 611(80), *674*
Krentsel, B. A., 967(64, 65), *989*
Kröner, M., 642(138), 654(163), 657 (163), *676*, *677*
Kropachev, V. A., 499(87, 96), 509(87), 512(87), 521(96, 211), *585*, *589*, 617 (90), 619(90), 621(95), *675*
Kropacheva, E. N., 522(228), 523(228), 547(356), *589*, *593*, 617(89), 667(184), 670(184), *675*, *678*, 950(39–41), 951 (45), 978(105), *988*, *990*
Krupyshev, M. A., 567(460), 582(460), *596*
Kubu, E. T., 915(47), 916(47), *935*
Kucera, M., 782, *803*
Kudryavtseva, E. P., 944(29), *988*
Kuhn, B. M., 869(2), *889*
Kume, S., 561, 572(405), *595*
Kuncl, K. L., 534(304), *592*
Kuntz, I., 499(97, 101), 500(97, 101), 520 (97), 521, 531–533, 545, 546(362), 549 (362), 555(382), *585*, *586*, *593*, *594*, 922, 923–925(90, 95), 928(90, 95), *936*
Kuriacose, J. C., 924(98), *936*
Kusov, A. B., 955, *988*
Kustanovich, I. M., 967(64, 65), *989*
Kusumato, H., 772(18), *802*
Kutch, E. L., 835(64), *842*
Kutin, A. M., 603(35), *673*
Kuz'minskii, A. S., 789, 790, *803*
Kwei, T. K., 611(81), 613(81), *674*

L

Lachi, M. P., 696(33, 34), *702*
Ladacki, M., 495(23), 504(23), 561(23), 571(23), *583*, 848(17), 855(17), *864*
Ladd, J. A., 498(52, 53), 499(52, 53), *584*
Laius, L. A., 555(386), 556(386), *594*
Lal, J., 529(285), *591*, 603(24), 614(24), 634(24), 639(24), 640(24), 653(24), *673*
Lamola, A. A., 537(314), *592*
Landes, G. B., 869(2), *889*
Landler, Y., 545, *593*
Lang, J., 862(46, 47), *865*
Lange, G., 499(77), *585*
Langer, A. W., Jr., 499(86), 531, 532, 562 (295), *585*, *591*
Lansbury, P. T., 526, *591*
Larcher, T. B., 788(49), *803*
Lasky, J. S., 641(132–134), *676*, 875(47), *891*
Latham, J. L., 507(159), *587*
Lawry, P. S., 499, 503(106), 505–509 (106), 511, *586*
LeClair, H. G., 772(16), *802*
Ledwith, A., 503(144), 531, 562(144), *587*
Lee, C. L., 564, *595*
Lee, D. F. 944, 951(46), *987*

Lee, L. H., 955, *988*
Lee, T. S., 869(7), *889*, 911, 912, 927, *934*
Leghissa, S., 652(159), *677*
Lehr, M. H., 611(82), 613, 614(82), 616 (82,) *674*
Leng, M., 554, *594*
Leonard, E. C., Jr., 931(133), *937*
Leonard, F., 817(25), *840*
Leser, W. H., 795(64), *804*
Letsinger, R. L., 497(51), 579, 580(451), *584*, *596*
Leventer, S. E., 869(4), *889*
Levy, M., 553, 572(368), 574, 580(429), *594*, *595*, 848(16), 855(16), *864*
Lewis, F. M., 542, *593*, 769(8), 773(8), 774, 779(41), 785(43), 786(8), 800(69), 801(41), *802–804*
Lewis, R. N., 497(39), *584*
Lewis, Y., 851(24), *865*
Lightbown, I. E., 921(86), *936*
Limido, G. E., 924(98), *936*
Lindner, H. H., 609(64), 658(64), *674*
Lindsay, R. D., 869(4), *889*
Lindsey, R. V., Jr., 874(17a), 876(17a), 886(17a), *890*
Lini, D. C., 499(76), *585*
Link, T. H., 605(42), 606(42), 614–616 (42), *673*
Litt, M., 515(174, 175), *588*
Livigni, R., 498(72), 499(72), 503(72, 148), 506(72, 148), 507(72), 508(72), 509(72, 148), 510(72, 148), 512(72), 528(72), *585*, *587*
Livingston, J. W., 849(34), *865*
Livshits, I. A., 539(326), *592*
Lobak, M. I., 658(172), *677*
Loeb, W. E., 931(133), *937*
Longi, P., 603(28), *673*
Longiave, C., 607(51, 53–55), 611(53–55), 617(51, 53–55), 621(51, 96), 622(96), 630(111), *673*, *675*
Lorenz, J. C., 739(13), *763*
Loshaek, S., 528(281), *591*
Lossing, F. P., 719(50), 720(50), *725*
Lucken, E. A., 498(44), *584*
Lugli, G., 666(181, 182), 667(182), 668 (182), *678*
Lukach, C. A., 683(5), 687(5), *701*
Lundborg, C., 499(102), 500(102), 501 (102, 134), 503(134, 148), 505(102, 134), 506(102), 507(102), 508(102, 134, 147), 509(102), 510(134), 511(102), 520(102), 531(102), 533(102), *586*, *587*
Lydon, J. E., 657(169), *677*, 884(63), 886 (63), *891*
Lyman, D. J., 932(138), *937*
Lynch, C. S., 849(18), *864*
Lynch, P. F., 499(89), *585*
Lynn, M., 521, 533, *589*

M

McAlevy, A., 916(53), 917(61), 931(53), *935*
McClellan, W. R., 887(66), *891*
McColm, E. M., 944, *987*
McElroy, W. R., 738(12), *763*
Macey, J. H., 637(131), 650(131), 652 (131), *676*
McGregor, R. R., 769(11), 773(11), 786 (11), *802*
Mach, K., 963(56, 60), 967(60), *989*
Machon, J.-P., 835, *842*
McIntosh, C. R., 862(48), *865*
Mack, E., 788(48), *803*
McKinney, O. F., 504(150), 505(150), *587*
MacKnight, W. J., 807(5), 828(5), 830, 831(45), 832(45, 46), *840*, *841*
McLeod, L. A., 614(84), *674*
McMurry, H. L., 598(11), *672*
McNeill, I. C., 924, *936*, 967(62), *989*
McNulty, B. J., 908(21), *934*
McWhorter, J. F., 743(50), *764*
Madge, E. W., 976(93), *990*
Maffezzoni, U., 607(53, 55), 611(53, 55), 617(53, 55), *673*
Magat, E. E., 579, 580(451), *596*
Magat, M., 524(246), 560(398), 561(398), 571(398), 574(398), *590*, *594*
Magnus, G., 740(22), *763*
Magnusson, A. B., 741(28), *763*
Maillard, A., 538(321–323), 552(365), 553 (321, 322), *592*, *594*
Mairs, M. A., 869(7), *889*, 911, 912, 927, *934*

Makowski, H. S., 521, 533, *589*, 696(33a), *702*, 704(4), 707(4), *724*, 930(116), 932, 933(146), *937*
Maltman, W. R., 872(15), *890*
Mamontova, O., 563(462), *596*
Manaresi, P., 699, *702*
Mandelkern, L., 712(34), *725*, 771(14), *802*
Manetti, R., 716(44), *725*
Manning, P. O., 817, *840*
Manoviciu, I., 518(187), *588*
Manza, G., 522(226), *589*, 976(94), *990*
Marandzheva, E. W., 499(100), 521(100), *586*
Marans, H. S., 800(70), *804*
Marchal, J., 494(12, 13), 495(12a, 13), 496(12b), 499(98), 501(98), *583*
Marconi, W., 605(39, 40), 606(48–50), 615(48–50, 87), 616(48–50, 87), 629 (109), 640(39, 40, 129), 653(87), 666 (181), *673–678*, 684(10), 687(10), *701*
Mare, P. B. D. de la, 908(22), *934*
Margerison, D., 497(128), 498(54), 499 (89), 503(128), 505(128), 507(128), 521 (128), 541(128), *584*, *586*
Marion, L., 572(426), *595*
Mark, H. F., 494(27), 496(27), *583*, 602 (22), 611(81), 613(81), *672*, *674*, 773 (23), 802, 831, 832, *841*
Markov, V. V., 945(28), 952(28), *988*
Marra, J. V., 930(114), *936*
Marsden, J., 768(4), 769, 774(4), 797, *802*
Marsh, J. W., 907(10), 910(10), 912(10), 913(10), *934*, 944(14), *987*
Marshall, T. B., 760(76), 761(76), *765*
Martel, R. F., 740(18), *763*
Martellock, A. C., 791, *803*
Martin, H., 603(30), *673*, 707(13), *724*
Martin, I., 773(23), *802*
Martins, U., 603(32), *673*
Marullo, G., 607(53,55), 611(53,55), 617 (53, 55), *673*
Marvel, C. S., 514(171), 534, 537, 573, *588*, *592*, *595*, 598(8), *672*, 696(32), *702*, 743(60), *764*, 819, 834, *841*, 855, 862 (49), *865*, 869(2, 3), *889*, 963(55), 969, *988*, *989*
Mason, J. H., 931(133), *937*
Masterman, S., 908(21), *934*
Mastin, T. G., 741(35, 37), *763*
Mathieson, A. M., 820(36), *841*
Matthews, F. E., 492, 560, *582*
Matyska, B., 963(59, 60), 967(59, 60), *989*
Mayer, P. H., 603(26), 605(26), 606(26), *673*
Mayer, R., 556, *594*
Mayer, R. H., 906(3), *933*
Mayes, W. G., 546(357), 548(357), *593*
Mayeur, G., 924(98), *936*
Maynard, I., 709(18), 712(18), *724*
Maynard, J. T., 599(13, 14), *672*, 918, *935*
Mayo, F. R., 542, *593*, 785(43), *803*, 870 (10), *889*, 920(75, 76), *935*
Mayor, R. H., 493(7), 522(218), 523 (218), *583*, *589*, 633(120), 634(120, 122), 635(122), 636(122), 639(126), 640 (122), 650(157), 652(158), *675–677*
Mazzanti, G., 603(28), 605(39, 40), 623 (98), 640(98), 644(98), *673*, *675*, 682 (2), 683(3), 684(3), 687(2, 13–16), 688 (2, 19), 689(2, 19), 690(21), 691(23), 692(2), 693(26, 29), 695(26), 696(26), 697(3), 698(3), *701*, *702*, 705(7, 8), 707 (7, 8, 12), 711(8), 712(8), 713(7, 39), 715(7, 8, 39), 716(8), 723(8, 67), *724–726*, 883(58, 59), *891*
Mazzei, A., 603(27), 604(27), 606(48–50), 611(27), 613(27), 614(27), 615(48–50, 87), 616(48–50, 87), 623(27), 624 (104), 625(27), 629(109), 640(39, 40, 129), 653(87), 666(181), *673*, *675–678*
Mead, D. J., 771(14), *802*
Meals, R. N., 769(8), 773(8), 774, 786(8), *802*
Medvedev, S. S., 498, 499(88, 91, 92), 500 (88), 502(91, 138), 503(138), 505(88), 506(138), 507(91, 138), 508(88, 91), 509(92), 510(91), 512(91, 138, 161), 521(210), 531, 546(88, 360), 547(88), 549(88, 359, 360), 561, 562, 563(294, 403, 410, 462, 565, 566, 567(407, 410), 568(407, 410, 411), 571(359, 408), 572 (403, 407–409), 573, *584*, *585*, *587*, *589*, *591*, *593*, *595*, *596*, 617(94), 621(94), 622(94), 641(135), *675*, *676*

Meerwein, H., 720(57, 58), *725*
Mehltretter, C. L., 743(55), *764*
Meier, J. F., 499(75), 509(75), 510(75), *585*
Meise, W., 893(3), 894(3), *903*
Melia, T. P., 522(223), *589*
Meltzer, T. H., 818(27), *840*
Merker, R. L., 783, 785, *803*
Meyer, A. W., 567(430), 574, *595*, 598(1), *672*, 850(20), *864*
Meyer, F. J., 499(77), *585*
Meyer, K. H., 969, *989*
Michelotti, F. W., 874(38, 39), 880(38), 881(38, 39), 882, (38, 39), *890*
Middleton, W. J., 893(1, 2), 894(1, 2), 896(2), 898(2), 899(1, 2, 5), *903*
Mikeska, L. A., 856(35), *865*
Milkovich, R., 495(23), 504(23), 553, 555 (377), 561(23), 571(23), 572(368), 574, *583*, *594*, 848(16, 17), 855(16, 17), *864*
Miller, H. C., 856(33), *865*
Milligan, B., 816, *840*
Mineo, I. C., 506(157), *587*
Minoux, J., 494(17, 21, 22), 495(22, 24), 496(17), 499(17, 22, 98), 501(98), 505 (17), 506(22), 507, 508(21, 22), 521(17), 526(17), 554, 560(24), 563(463), 569 (463), *583*, *585*, *594*, *596*
Minsker, K. S., 580, *596*
Misono, A., 631(113), *675*
Mitzengelder, S. P., 544(361), 547(358, 361), 549, 551(361), 552(361), *593*
Mixer, R. Y., 798(68), *804*
Miyake, A., 513, *588*
Mnookin, N. M., 806(1), 807(1), *840*
Mobay Chemical Co., 756(67), 743(49), *764*
Mochel, W. E., 599(13, 14), *672*, 709(18), 712(18), *724*
Modern Plastics, 557(390), *594*
Moncrieff, R. A., 862(44), *865*
Monsanto Chemical Co., 611(74), *674*
Montague, B. A., 880(57), 881(57), *891*
Montague, B. H., 722(63), *725*
Montecatini, 607(53–55), 610(66, 67), 611 (53–55, 67, 72), 617(53–55, 72), 621(97), 622(66), 623(98, 99), 627(106), 631 (116), 640(98), 641 (99, 106), 644(98), 646(144), 658(66), *673–675*, 683(6), *701*, 930(121, 129, 130), 932(139), *937*
Montecatini Edison, 716(43), *725*
Moore, B., 851(24), *865*
Moore, C. G., 976(98–101), *990*
Moore, G. R., 743(47), 757(47), *764*
Moore, J. E., 525(251), *590*
Moore, J. G., 907(6), *934*
Moraglio, G., 621–623(118), 651(149), 670(188), *675*, *676*, *678*, 712(31), *725*
Morero, D., 518(189), *588*, 603(27), 604 (27), 611(27, 83), 613(27, 83), 614(27), 623(27), 624(103,)625(27), 641(103), 644(103), 651(103, 152), *673–675*, *677*, *678*, 705(6), 711(28), 712(8), *724*, *725*
Morgan, C. R., 598(8), *672*
Morgan, P., 931(134), *937*
Morita, E., 598(6), *672*
Morita, H., 499(94), *585*
Moriwaki, Y., 835(62), *842*
Morris, M. C., 711(30), *725*
Morris, R. C., 816(20), *840*
Morrissey, R. T., 921, 923(96), 925(87), 926, 927, 928(87, 89), 929(87), *936*
Morrow, R. C., 567–569(424), 571, 573 (424), 574(424), *595*
Mortimer, G. A., 542, *593*
Morton, A. A., 575–581, *596*, 599(15, 16), *672*
Morton, J. W., 497(48), *583*
Morton, M., 498, 499(72, 74, 75, 90), 502, 503(72, 145, 148), 504, 505(145), 506 (72, 145, 148), 507(72), 508(72, 145), 509–512, 513(160), 520, 521(145), 528 (72), 531, 533, 534, 541(145, 330), 540 (330), 545, 546(330), 549(145), 569, *585*, *587*, *593*, 782, 785(79), *803*, *804*, 874(26), 877(26), 878(26), 880(26), *890*
Moser, L., 604, *673*
Mosevitskii, M. I., 525(243), *590*
Motovilova, N. N., 534, *592*
Motroni, G., 713(39, 40), 715(39, 40), 722(40, 64), *725*, *726*, 874(36), 883(59), *890*, *891*
Moyer, P. H., 611(82), 613, 614(82), 616 (82), *674*

Müller, E., 728(2, 3), 729, 740(3, 10, 14, 15), 741(2, 32, 34), 743, 746(15), 750 (15), 753(15), 755(2), 756(2, 15), 757 (15), 759, *762–764*
Mueller, G. S., 911, *934*
Müller, H., 642(138), *676*
Muetterties, E. L., 887(66), *891*
Mukamal, H., 968, *989*
Mulvaney, J. E., 561(402), 571(402), *595*, 657(168), *677*
Murphy, C. M., 789(51), *803*

N

Naarmann, H., 871(11), *889*
Nagao, R., 709(19), *724*
Nagy, P. L. I., 875(49), 887(65), *891*
Nakane, H., 711(29), *725*
Nakata, T., 873(16), *890*
Naples, F. J., 579(448), 581(448), 582 (448), *596*, 599(17), *672*, 907(10), 910(10), 912(10), 913(10), *934*, 944 (14), *987*
Nasonova, T. P., 831, 832(50), *841*
National Distillers Corp., 514(170), *588*
Natta, G., 537(319), *592*, 598(7), 602(19, 22), 603(27, 28), 604(27, 37, 38), 608 (61, 62), 610(66–68), 611(27, 67, 72), 613(27), 614(27), 617(61, 72), 618(62), 620(61), 622(66), 623(27, 61, 98–100, 102), 624(103, 104), 625(27, 38, 100), 626(100), 627(61, 102, 106, 107), 628 (61, 102), 629(61, 107, 108), 631(116, 117), 632(117), 640(98), 641(38, 99, 100, 103, 106), 642(61, 108, 139), 643 (108), 644(98, 103, 141), 645(7, 61, 100, 142, 143), 646(61, 62, 144, 145), 647 (143), 648(62, 146), 650(61), 651(68, 103, 141–143, 145–150, 152–154), 653 (61, 108, 139, 143, 162), 654(61), 655, 656(102, 167), 658(66, 102), 660(62), 662(62, 108), 663(61), 664(61), 666–668(182), 669(188), *672–678*, 682(2), 683(3), 684(3), 687(2, 15, 16), 688(2, 19), 689, 692(2), 693(24, 26, 27), 695 (26), 696(26), 697(3), 698(3), 700(40), *701*, *702*, 704(3), 705, 706, 707(5, 7–10, 12), 709(17), 711(8, 9, 28), 712(5, 6, 8, 17, 32, 33, 37), 713(7, 39, 40), 715(7, 8, 39–42), 716(8), 717(9), 722(40), 723(8), *724*, *725*, 874(35–37), 880(35), 882(37), 883(58, 59), *890*, *891*, 929(109, 110), 930(110, 125, 127, 130, 132), 931(132), *936*, *937*
Naylor, F. E., 522(217), *589*, 606(45, 46), 614(45), *673*
Neale, A. E. T., 815(12), *840*
Nelidow, I., 578(444), 579(444), *596*
Nelson, J. A., 728(6), *762*
Nelson, J. F., 921(83), 922(91), 925, 926 (91), *936*
Nelson, J. Q., 741(42), *764*
Nelson, K. V., 567(460), 582(460), *596*, 950(39–41), 951(45), *988*
Nersasian, A., 918(65), 919, *935*
Nesterov, A. E., 835(57), *841*
Neumann, W., 759, *765*
Nevin, R. S., 839(71), *842*
Newing, M. J., 772, *802*
Newman, G. N., 498(53), 499(53), *584*
Newport, J. P., 498(54), *584*
Newton, E. B., 634(119), *675*
Nicholson, J. K., 657(169), *677*, 875(48), 884(63), 886(63), *891*
Nielsen, J. M., 790(52, 53), *803*
Nikitina, V. D., 520(202), 568(465), *589*, *596*
Nikolayev, N. I., 499(87, 96), 509(87), 512(87), 521(96, 211), *585*, *589*, 617 (90), 619(90), 621(95), *675*
Nishihara, T., 955(49), *988*
Nishikawa, G., 561(405), 572(405), *595*
Nitzsche, S., 800, *804*, 862(51), *865*
Nolen, C. D., 740(16), *763*
Noll, W. S., 769(10), 771, 773(10), 774, 786(10), *802*
Norlander, J. E., 531(310), *591*
North, A. M., 659(175), *677*
Noth, J. F., 598(8), *672*
Novoselov, F. B., 863(57), *865*
Noyes, R. M., 971(81), *989*
Nummy, W. R., 819, *841*
Nyburg, S. C., 651(156), *677*
Nyholm, R. S., 880(54), *891*

O

Oakes, W. G., 914(43), 915(43), *935*
Obara, M., 835, *841*
Oberkirch, W., 654(163), 657(163), *677*
O'Driscoll, K. F., 520(206), 532, 545, *589*, *591*
Ofstead, E. A., 720(55), 723(66, 71), *725*, *726*
Ogden, W. G., 741(44), 742(44), *764*
Ohno, T., 631(113), *675*
Oita, K., 603(29), *673*
Okita, J., 816, *840*
Oliver, C. S., 768(4), 769, 774(4), 796, *802*
Oliver, J. P., 526, *591*
Olofson, R. A., 532(298), *592*
Olson, L. E., 819, *841*
Omietanski, G. M., *803*
Onishi, A., 640(130), *676*
Onozuka, M., 933(145), *937*
Onsager, O. T., 499(102), 500(102), 501 (102, 135), 502(135), 505–509(102), 511(102), 520(102), 531(102), 533(102), *586*, *587*
Oppegard, L. A., 869(3), *889*
Orchin, M., 977(102, 103), 978, *990*
O'Reilly, D. E., 609(63), 622(63), 622, 658(63), *674*, *678*
Orr, R. J., 565(421), *595*
Ortlieb, C., 494(12), 495, 496(12b), 538 (321), 553(321), *583*, *592*, *594*
Osborn, S. W., 835(63, 64), 838(67), *842*
Osthoff, R. C., 781, 783(38), *803*
Oswald, H. J., 915(47), 916(47), *935*
Otsu, T., 873(16), *890*
Otsuka, S., 631(115), *675*
Otto, W. M., 846(7), *864*
Overberger, C. G., 494(16), 560(402), 571(402), *583*, *595*, 657(168), *677*, 968, *989*
Owen, G. D. T., 641(136), 653(136), *676*
Ozaki, S., 968, *989*

P

Pajaro, G., 642(139), 653(139), *676*, 683(3), 684(3), 687(13, 14), 690(21, 22), 691(23), 697(3), *701*, *702*
Palvarini, A., 631(116, 117), 632(117), *675*
Pampus, G., 496(31), 521(212), *583*, *589*, 606(44), *673*
Pande, H., *866*
Pande, J. B., 907(13, 14), 909(13), 910 (13, 14), 913(39), *934*
Panek, J. R., 807(4), 814, 819, 820, *840*, *841*
Pappas, L. G., 743(46), *764*
Pariser, R., 712(38), 714(38), *725*
Park, J. C., 743(46), *764*, 854(29), *865*
Parrish, C. I., 788(48), *803*
Parrod, J., 495(24), 499–501(132), 502, 503(132), 505(132), 506(132), 507, 508(132), 509(132), 511(132), 542 (132), 560(24), 567(464), *583*, *587*, *596*, 855(66), *866*
Parsons, J. L., 967(61), *989*
Paschke, R. F., 743(55), *764*
Pasquon, I., 642(139), 653(139, 162), 667(186), 670, 671(186), *676*, *678*, 706(10), 707(10), *724*
Patat, F., 501(136), 509(136), 510, *587*, *590*
Patnode, W., 768
Patrick, J. C., 806, 807(1), 812, 813, 815(13), 817(23), 819(13, 30), *840*
Patton, T. C., 743(54), *764*
Pauling, L., 494(14), 497, 498(41), *583*, *584*
Pavan, A., 712(32), *725*
Pavlikova, A. V., 575(431), *595*
Pearce, E. M., 839(71), *842*
Pegoraro, M., 712(32), *725*
Peraldo, M., 602(19), *672*
Peter, J., 759(71), *765*
Peters, H., 912(33), *934*
Petersen, S., 728(2, 3), 740(3), 741(2), 755(2), 756(2), *762*
Petree, M. C., 522(224), *589*
Petrochemicals, Ltd., *935*
Petrov, E. S., 564(418), *595*
Pett, R. A., 498(74), 499(74), 502, *585*
Pettit, R., 884(60), 886(60), *891*
Pezdirtz, G. F., 969, *989*
Phillips Petroleum Co., 499(111, 119, 120, 122, 123), 514(169–171), 515

(169, 173), 526(259), 548(354), *586*, *588*, *590*, *593*, 605(41), 606(45–47), 610(47), 611(41), 614(41, 45, 47), 616 (41, 88), 623(47, 88), 625(41, 88), 641(88), *673*, *674*, 707(14), 717(46), 723(70), *724–726*, 846(4, 65), 851(63, 68), *864*, *866*, 916(52), 920(70, 79), 931(79), *935*
Piepenbrink, H. F., 728(2, 3), 740(3), 741(2, 32, 34), 743(32), 755(2), 756(2), 759(32), *762*
Pierson, R. M., 493(7), 522(218), 523 (218), *583*, *589*, 633(120), 634(120), 650(158), 652(158), *675*, *677*, 906(3), *933*
Pieski, E. T., 917–919(63), *935*
Pigott, K. A., 740(15–17), 743(48, 49, 51), 744(53), 746, 747–749(17), 750 (15), 753(15), 756, 757(15), *763*, *764*
Piirma, I., 874(26), 877(26), 878(26), 880(26), *890*
Pike, M., 846(3), *864*
Pimentel, G. C., 719(52), 720(52), *725*
Pinazzi, C., 911, 912(30, 35, 36), *934*
Pino, P., 602(20), 603(28), *672*, *673*
Pinten, H., 728, *762*
Piotrovskii, K. B., 522(214), *589*
Piskarewa, E. P., 832(50), *841*
Pitzer, K. S., 719(52), 720(52), *725*
Podalinskii, A. V., 524(247), *590*
Poddubnyi, I. Ya., 524(247), 525(243), 527, 567(460), 572, 575(272, 435), 582 (460), *590*, *591*, *595*, *596*, 653(161), 655(161), *677*, 831, *841*, 874(27, 29), *890*
Podolsky, A. F., 565, *595*
Polak, L. S., 967(64, 65), *989*
Polizzotti, G., 712(31), *725*
Polmanteer, K. E., 529(286), *591*
Pol'sman, G. S., 945(27), *988*
Polykov, D. K., 498(58), 499(88, 92), 500(88), 502(138), 503(138), 505(88), 506(138), 507(138), 508(88), 502(92), 510(91), 512, 546(88, 360), 547(88), 549(88, 359, 360), *584*, *585*, *587*, *593*
Polymer Corp. Ltd., 606(43), 614(84), *673*, *674*
Poole, C. P., 622(180), *678*
Porri, L., 518(189), 537, *588*, *592*, 598 (7), 603(27), 604(27), 607(59), 608 (59, 61), 609(59, 62), 610(66, 67), 611(27, 67, 72, 83), 613(27, 83), 614 (27), 617(61, 72), 618(62), 620(61), 622(66), 623(27, 61, 98–100, 102), 624 (103, 104), 625(27, 38, 100), 626(100), 627(61, 102, 106, 107), 628(61, 102), 629(61, 107, 108), 631(116, 117), 632 (117), 640(98), 641(38, 99, 100, 103, 106), 642(61, 108), 643(108), 644 (98, 103, 141), 645(7, 61, 100, 142, 143), 646(61, 62, 144, 145), 647(143), 648 (62, 146), 650(61), 651(103, 141–143, 145, 146, 148), 653(61, 108, 143), 654 (61), 655(166), 656(102, 167), 657 (170), 658(66, 102), 660(62), 662(62, 108, 177), 663(61), 664(61), 666(182, 183), 667(182, 186), 668(182), 669 (183), 670(183, 186), 671(186), *672–678*, 705(6, 7), 707(7), 709(17), 711 (28), 712(6, 17, 37), 713(7), 715(7, 41, 42), *724*, *725*, 874(35, 37), 880 (35), 882(37), 883(58), *890*, *891*
Porter, L. M., 499(112), 555(378), *586*, *594*, 611(69), 617(69), 631(114), *674*, *675*
Porter, M., 976(101), *990*
Post, H. W., 769(6), 773(6), 786(6), *802*
Poutsma, M. L., 908, *934*
Powell, J., 657(171), *677*
Price, C. C., 542(340), 543, *593*
Prickett, C. S., 907(19), *934*
Putnam, R. E., 893(2), 894(2), 896(2), 898(2), 899(2), *903*
Pye, D. G., 893(2), 894(2), 896(2), 898 (2), 899(2), *903*
Pyke, J. B., 639(126), *676*
Pyrkov, L. M., 554(374), 555(386), 556 (386), *594*

R

Raghunath, D., 907(13, 14), 909(13), 910(13, 14), 912(39), *934*
Railsback, H. E., 522, 558(391, 392), *589*, *594*
Rainard, L. W., 869, *889*

Rakova, G. V., 544(344), 545, 546(344, 346), 546(367), 547(344), 548–551, 552(367), 553, *593*, *594*
Ramakrishnan, C. S., 907(13, 14), 909 (13), 910, 912(39), *934*, 944(19), *987*
Rands, R. D., Jr., 598(8), *672*
Ransaw, H. C., 518(184), *588*, 980, *990*
Rao, N. V. C., 944(18, 19), *987*
Rausch, K. W., Jr., 740(18, 19), *763*
Ray, G. C., 723(70), *726*
Reed, C. F., 917(58), *935*
Rees, N. H., 500, *587*
Reeve, W., 907(19), *934*
Rehner, J., Jr., 922, 927, 930(115, 117–120), *936*, *937*
Reich, L., 550, *593*
Reichel, B., 696(32), *702*
Reichenbach, D., 522(234), *590*, 976(96), 977(96), 978(104), *990*
Reid, R. J., 862(45), *865*
Reid, W. G., *803*
Reikh, V. N., 575(431), *595*
Reinhart, M. A., 634(119), *675*
Reis, H., 871(11), *889*
Rembaum, A., 495(23), 504(23), 544 (342), 561(23), 567–559(424), 571, 573, 574(424), *583*, *593*, *595*, 785(79), *804*
Rempp, P., 855(66), *866*
Renfrew, A., 931(134), *937*
Renolds, R. J., 611(69), 617(69), *674*
Revue Generale du Caoutchouc, 557(389), *594*
Reynolds, R. J. W., 741(39), *764*
Reynolds, S. I., 794, *804*
Reynolds, W. B., 514(169), 515(169), *588*, 598(11), *672*, 846(6), *864*, 907 (12), 909(12), 910(12), *934*
Reztsova, Y. V., 575(434), *595*
Rhone-Poulenc, S. A., 800(73), *804*
Richards, J. H., 884(62), *891*
Richards, R. B., 914(43), 915(43, 51), *935*
Richardson, W. S., 518(184), *588*, 598 (9), 599(12), *672*
Ries, E. L., 846(1), *864*
Riley, M. W., 753(64), 754(64), *764*
Rinehart, R. E., 874(20, 22, 31, 40), 875(22, 47), 876(22), 877(22, 31), 878 (20, 22, 52), 881(40), 886(22, 52), 887(52), 888(52), *890*, *891*, 978(105a), *990*
Rinke, H., 760, *765*
Ritchey, W. M., 542(339), 543, 550 (339), 551, 552, *593*
Roberts, J. D., 531, *592*
Robertson, J. M., 820(36, 37), *841*
Robertson, R. E., 572(426), *595*
Robinson, A. E., 929(108), 930(114), *936*
Robinson, I. M., 722(63), *725*, 880(57), 881(57), *891*
Robinson, S. D., 658(173), *677*, 884 (61), *891*
Robinson, V. J., 872(14), *889*
Robison, S. B., 923–925(95), 928(95), 929(95), *936*
Roche, I. D., 917(62), *935*
Rochina, M., 617(91), *675*
Rochow, E. G., 497(39), *584*, 768, 769, 772(16), 773–775, 786(5), *802*
Rodionov, A. N., 498(70), 499(70, 78), *585*
Roeser, G. P., 817(25), *840*
Rogers, C. E., 499(99, 118), 521(99, 208), 566, 569(423), *586*, *589*, *595*, *678*
Rogers, M. T., 498(55), *584*
Roha, M., 494(20), 495(20), 504(20), 531, 532, 562(20, 293), 578, *583*, *591*, 659(176), *677*
Roha, M. E., 611(80), *674*
Romeyn, H., Jr., 874(20, 22), 875–877 (22), 878(20, 22), 886(22), *890*, 978 (105a), *990*
Rose, J. B., 603(25), 604(25), *673*
Rosenthal, N. A., 826, *841*
Rosenthal, R. W., 915(48), *935*
Rosinoer, Ya. M., 950(41), *988*
Ross, S. D., 542, *593*
Rosser, R. J., 816(22), *840*
Rossini, F. D., 719(49, 52), 720(49, 52), *725*
Roth, W. L., 772, *802*
Rubber Plastics Age, 557(389), *594*

Rugg, J. S., 728(7), 741(43), *762*, *764*
Runge, F., 497(37), 514(37), 560(37), *584*
Russell, G., 580, *596*
Russell, G. A., 789, *803*, 931(135, 137), 932, *937*
Rust, F. F., 907(17), *934*
Ryan, P. W., 534(304), *592*

S

Sabbioni, F., 652(159), *652*
Sabel, A., 875(41), *890*
Sacher, A., 518(184), *588*, 599(12), *672*
Sadron, C., 494(17), 496(17), 499(17), 505(17), 507, 521(17), 527(17), 556, 575(432), *583*, *594*, *595*
Saegusa, T., 546(355), 549, *593*, 640 (130), *576*, 835(58), *841*, 869(8), *889*
St. Pierre, L. E., 795, *804*
Saito, T., 631(113), *675*
Sakurai, I., 711(29), *725*
Salomon, G., 907(11), 909(11), 914, *934*, *935*
Saltiel, J., 537(314), *592*
Saltman, W. M., 493(7), 522(218), 523 (218), *583*, *589*, 603(24), 605, 606(42), 614(24, 42), 615(42), 616(42), 633 (120), 634(24, 120, 123), 635(122), 636(122), 639, 640, 650(158), 653(24), *673*, *675–677*, 906(3), *933*
Samoletova, V. V., 534, *592*
Sampson, A. J., 740(20, 24), *763*
Sander, M., 833, *841*
Santambrogio, A., 518(189), *588*, 611 (83), 613(83), *674*, 698(37), *702*
Sartori, G., 682(2), 687(2, 15, 16), 688 (2, 19), 689(2, 19), 690(21), 691(23), 692(2), 693(24, 27, 29), 695(26, 30), 696(26, 30, 33, 34), *701*, *702*, 704(3), *724*, 930(127), *937*
Sasaki, K., 667(185), 670(185), *678*
Satas, D., 758(68), *764*
Sato, T., 856(37), 857(37), 858(37, 38), 859(38), 860(38), *865*
Sauer, R. O., 771(14), *802*
Saunders, C. E., 789(51), *803*
Saunders, J. H., 729, 738(9b, 9d), 740 (15–17), 743(9e, 9i, 48, 49), 746(9c, 15, 17, 63), 747–749(17), 750(9c, 15, 63), 751(63), 752(63), 753(15), 756 (15), 757(15), 760, 762(9i), *763*, *764*, 869(3), *889*
Saville, B., 816(14, 15), *840*, 976(101), *990*
Sayigh, A. A. R., 740(18, 19), *763*
Saylor, J. C., 785(44), *803*
Scala, L. C., 789, *803*
Scanlan, J., 944, 945, *987*
Schaefer, J., 861(41, 42), *865*
Schaffling, D. G., 788(49), *803*
Schidrowitz, P., 939(3), *987*
Schildknecht, C. E., 598(2), *672*
Schilit, J. R., 760(75), *765*
Schiller, A. M., 560(402), 571(402), *595*, 657(168), *677*
Schissler, D. D., 610(65), 622(65), 658 (65), *674*, 880(55), *891*
Schleitzer, G., 688(18), *702*
Schlick, S., 574, 580(429), *595*
Schlosser, M., 562(412), *595*
Schmalz, E. O., 518(188), *588*
Schmidt, F. W., 728(3), 741(32, 34), 743(32), 759(32), *762*, *763*
Schoenberg, E., 534, 578(444), 579 (444), *592*, *596*, 634–636(122), 637, 638, 639(126), 640(122), *676*, 850(23), 851, 852(23), *864*
Scholfield, C. R., 743(55), *764*
Schollenberger, C. S., 743, 757, *764*
Schomaker, V., 820(38), *841*
Schonfeld, E., 743(58, 59), *764*
Schroeder, H., 788(49), *803*
Schroeder, J. P., 920, *935*
Schubert, C., 908(25), *934*
Schué, F., 494(13), 495(13), 519, 538 (194, 197, 320–323), 553, 570, *583*, *588*, *589*, *592*, *594*
Schultz, W. B., 771(14), *802*
Schulze, W. A., 846(60), 849(18, 67), *864*, *866*
Schwab, A. W., 743(55), *764*
Scott, G. W., 728(7), 741(43), *762*, *764*
Scott, H., 607(58), 609(63), 622, 657 (58), 658(63), *674*, *677*, *678*, 743(47), 757(47), *764*

Scott, K. W., 522(218), 523(218), 529 (285), *589*, *591*, 650(158), 652(158), *677*, 723(65, 66, 71), *726*, 906(3), *933*
Scott, M. J., 785(42), *803*
Scott, R. L., 524(246), *590*, 792(59), *804*
Screttas, C. G., 499(84, 85), 501, 533 (85), *585*
Sedlmeier, J., 875(41), *890*
Seeger, N. V., 741(35–37), *763*
Seelbach, C. W., 933(146), *937*
Seely, G. R., 971(83), *989*
Seiner, J. A., 546, *593*
Seitz, L. M., 498(62), 499(82), 502, *584*, *585*
Semlyer, J. A., 780(31), *803*
Serniuk, G. E., 930(119, 120), *937*
Settle, R. A., 498(69), 499(69), *585*
Sevskaia, G. S., 603(35), *673*
Seyferth, D., 531, 536(311), *591*
Shabodash, A. N., 945(27), *988*
Shannon, J. A., 916(56), *935*
Sharkey, W. H., 893(1, 2), 894(1, 2), 896(2), 898(2), 899(1, 2), 900–903(6), *903*
Shatenstein, A. I., 564(418), *595*
Shaw, B. L., 657(169, 171), 658(173), *677*, 875(48), 884(61, 63), 886(63), *891*
Sheehan, C. J., 523, *590*
Shell International Research Co., 499 (110), *586*
Shell Internationale Research Maatschappij N. V., 855(31, 32), 856(32), *865*
Shell Oil Co., 499(112), *586*
Shelton, J. R., 955, *988*
Shepherd, D. A., 869(3), *889*
Shibayev, L. A., 554(374), *594*
Shigorin, D. N., 498(70), 499(70, 78), *585*
Shima, M., 520(207), 574, *589*
Shipley, F. W., 522(235), *590*, 983 (111, 112), *990*
Shipman, J. J., 522(225), 523(225), *589*, 634(119), *675*, 949(38), 970(38, 78), 976(92), 977(38, 92), 985(92), *988–990*
Shlyakhter, R. A., 831, 832, *841*, 863 (57), *865*
Short, J. N., 514(169, 171), 515(169), 522, *588*, *589*, 906(2), *933*, 976(97), *990*
Shotton, J. A., 846(2), 849(2), 850, *864*
Shryne, T. M., 874(21, 32), 878(21, 32), 879(21), 880(21), 888(32), *890*
Shuikin, N. I., 536(313), *592*
Sianesi, D., 690(22), *702*
Sieber, R., 875(41), *890*
Sigwalt, P., 834, 835, 839(72), *841*, *842*
Silas, R. S., 518(185), *588*
Sim, S. Y., 506(153), *587*
Simon, A., 603(33), *673*
Simonazzi, M., 698(37), 699, *702*
Simril, V. L., *935*
Sinclair, E. A., 741(37), *763*
Sinclair Petrochemicals, Inc., 743(61), 762(61), *764*
Sinn, H., 499(102), 500, 501(102, 131, 134–136), 502(135), 503(131, 134, 147), 504(131), 505(102, 134), 506 (102), 507(102), 508(102, 131, 134, 147), 509(102, 136, 162), 510, 511 (102), 512, 520(102), 531, 533, *586*, *587*
Sinn, V., 494(21), 499–501(132), 502, 503(132), 505(132), 506, 507, 508 (21, 132), 509(132), 511(132), 542 (132), *583*, *587*
Sivertz, C., 971(82), *989*
Sjothun, I. J., 798(67), *804*
Skeist, I., 542(333), *593*
Skell, P. S., 743(55), *764*
Skinner, H. A., 720(53), *725*
Sleddon, G. J., 776, *803*
Slichter, W. P., 519(198, 199), *589*
Slocombe, R. J., 611(74), *674*
Slonim, I. Ya., 519(200), *589*, 945(29), *988*
Slotterbeck, O. C., 921(82), *936*
Slusarzuk, G. M. J., 780(31), *803*
Small, P. A., 720(59), *725*
Small, R. M. B., 524(240), 525(240, 249), 527(240), 528, *590*, 720(56), *725*
Smid, J., 520(207), 545(347), 562, 564, 565(413), 574, *589*, *593*, *595*
Smidt, J., 875(41), *890*
Smirnova, V. K., 538(318), *592*

Smith, C. H., 740(21), *763*
Smith, D. R., 605(41), 606(47), 610(47), 611(41), 614(41, 47), 616(41), 623(47), 625(41), *673*
Smith, F. A., 862(52), *865*
Smith, F. M., 755, *764*
Smith, H. P., 871(11a), 874(20, 22, 31, 40), 875(22), 876(22), 877(22, 31), 878(20, 22), 881(40), 886(22), *889*, *890*, 978(105a), *990*
Smith, J. J., 684(11), *701*
Smith, L. C., 741(30), *763*
Smith, M. K., 743(54), *764*
Smith, T. L., 741(28), *763*
Smith, W. A., 529, *591*, 634(121), 638 (121), 639(121), *676*
Smith, W. F., 728(4), *762*
Smook, M. A., 917(62, 63), 918(63, 67), 919(63, 67), 930(131), *935*, *937*
Soborovsky, L. Z., 920, *935*
Sokolov, V. N., 653(161), 655(161), *677*, 874(27, 29), *890*
Solovykh, D. A., 521(210), 562(407), 567(407), 568(407), 572(407), *589*, *595*
Sopchak, W. P., 920, *935*
Soura Eleuteris, H., 717(45), *725*
Sovarzi, G., 648(146), 651(146), *676*
Spänig, H., *674*
Sparks, W. J., 921(81, 82), *936*
Speight, C., 862(43), *865*
Spirin, Yu. L., 498, 499(88, 91, 92), 500(88), 502(91, 138), 503(138), 505 (88), 506(138), 507(91, 138), 508 (88, 91), 509(92), 510, 512(91, 138, 161), 546(88, 360), 547(88), 549(88, 359, 360), 562(359), 571(359), 573 (359), *585*, *587*, *593*
Spott, G., *590*
Spurlin, H. M., 683(5), 687(5), *701*
Stacey, F. W., 898, *903*
Standard Oil Co. of Indiana, 707(15), *724*
Standard Oil Development Co., 921, *936*
Staudinger, H., 907(8), 910, 912(8), 913(8), *934*, 942(10), *987*
Standinger, H., 907(8), 910, 912(8), 913(8), *934*
Stavely, F. W., 493, 494(10), 496(10), 519(10), 525(10), 559(10), *583*, 598 (5), *672*
Staverman, A. J., 516(179), 518(179), 530(179), *588*
Stearns, R. S., 496(33), 499(33, 117, 126), 500(33), 504(33), 518, 520(33), 521(33), 522(117), 530, 538(317), 553(317), 569(33), *583*, *586*, *592*, 614 (85), 634(121), 638(121), 639(121), *674*, *676*
Stedefeder, J., 603(30), *673*
Steingiser, S., 740(17), 743(51), 744 (53), 746–749(17), *763*, *764*
Steinmetz, H., 971(81), *989*
Steinrücke, E., 654(163), 657(163), *677*
Stenstrom, J. A., 931(133), *937*
Štěpán, V., 963(57), 966(57), *989*
Stepanova, V. I., 539(326), *592*
Stepanova, Z. D., 567(460), 582(460), *596*
Stephens, C. L., 975(89), *989*
Stephens, W. D., 862(48), *865*
Stevens, J. R., 529(282), *591*
Stevenson, P. E., 498–500(60), 512(60), *584*
Stewart, R. A., 579, 581, 582, *596*, 599 (18), 614(84), *672*, *674*
Stivala, S., 550, *593*
Stockmayer, W. H., 579, 580(451), *596*, 513, *588*, 780, *803*, 818(29), *841*
Štolka, M., 643, *676*, 946(32–35), 956 (51), 959(33), 961(32–35), 963(32–35, 51, 56) 966(34, 51), *988*, *989*
Stone, F. G. A., 769(12), 773(12), 786 (12), *802*
Stoppa, G., 645(142, 143), 646(144), 647(143), 651(142), 143), 653(143), *676*, 709(17), 712(17), *724*
Storey, E. B., 921(84), *936*
Strain, D. E., 916(53), 917(61), 931 (53), *935*
Strange, E. H., 492, 560, *582*
Strobel, C. W., 515(173), *588*
Strom, E. T., 580, *596*
Stucker, R. O., 846(1), *864*
Suminoe, T., 638–640(125), 667(185), 670, *676*, *678*, 685(12), 688(12), *701*

K. K. Sumitomo Densen Seizosho, 816(16), *840*
Sundermeyer, W., 776, *803*, 893(3), 894(3), *903*
Susa, E., 607(53, 55), 611(53, 55), 617 (53, 55), 630, *673*, *675*
Švec, F., 874(28), *890*
Swan, J. M., 816(14, 15), *840*
Sweet, E., 863(56), *865*
Swift, P. McL., 983(115), *990*
Swinney, F. B., 522(220), *589*
Szukiewicz, W., 741, *763*
Szwarc, M., 495, 504(23), 512, 513, 515, 516(166), 520(207), 527, 532, 534, 536(297), 545, 553, 554, 561, 562, 564, 565, 570, 571(23), 572(368), 573, 577, *583*, *587–589*, *591–595*, 848(15–17), 855, *864*

T

Tada, K., 542, *593*
Taft, R. W., Jr., 907(18), 908, *934*
Taft, W. K., 537(315), 539(315), 560 (399), 572, 574(399), 575(399), 582 (399), *592*, *594*
Takahashi, A., 561(405), 572(405), *595*
Takahashi, M., 830, 831(45), 832(45), *841*
Talalaeva, T. V., 498(70), 499(70, 78), *585*
Talalay, A., 560(398), 561(398), 571 (398), 574(398), *594*
Talcott, T. B., 520(205), *589*
Tanaka, K., 654(163), 657(163), *677*
Tate, D. P., 531, *591*
Taylor, J. S., 944(17), *987*
Taylor, L. D., 581(469), *596*
Taylor, P. W., 772(20), *802*
Taylor, S. M., 888(68), *891*
Teeter, H. M., 743(55), *764*
Temin, S. C., 720(61), *725*
Tepenitsyna, Y. P., 603(35), *673*
Tertian, R., 820(34, 35), *841*
Testroet, F. B., 759(72), *765*
Teyssié, P., 874(23–25, 30), 878(23, 24), 886(25), 887, 888(24, 25), *890*
Thiokol Chemical Corp., 835(59, 63), 838(59), *841*, 847(9, 61), *864*, *866*
Thomas, R. M., 921, *936*
Thompson, G., 932(140), *937*
Thompson, H. W., 915(46), *935*
Thornber, M. N., 499(125), *586*
Thorne, J. A., 529(286), *591*
Thorne, M. P., 603(32), *673*
Thornton, V., 518(185), 522(215), *588*, *589*, 906(2), *933*, 976(97), *990*
Thorpe, M. A., 926(105), *936*
Tidwell, P. W., 542, *593*
Tiger, G. J., 537(315), 539(315), 560 (399), 572, 574(399), 575(399), 582 (399), *592*, *594*
Tikhomirov, B. I., 575(431), *595*
Tinyakova, E. I., 502(140), 521(209), *587*, 617(89, 93), 658(172), *675*, *677*
Tobolsky, A. V., 494(28, 29), 496, 499 (93, 94, 118), 521(208), 545, 549(343), 566, 567(424), 568(424), 569(423, 424), 571, 573, 574(424), *583*, *585*, *586*, *589*, *593*, *595*, 598(6), 657(168), *672*, *677*, *678*, 807(5), 817, 818(27, 28), 828–830, 831(45), 832, *840*, *841*
Tocker, S., 956, *988*
Topchiev, A. V., 967(64, 65), *989*
Torkington, P., 915(46), *935*
Trambouze, P., 775(78), *804*
Trambuze, Y., 617(91), *675*
Trappe, G., 741(41), *764*
Treloar, L. R. G., 801(75), *804*
Trepka, W. J., 499(124), *586*, 717(46), *725*
Trick, G. S., 522(218), 523(218), *589*, 650 (158), 652(158), *677*, 906(3), *933*, 970, *989*
Trillat, J. J., 820(34), *841*
Trivisonno, N. M., 945(30), *988*
Troussier, M., 907(15), 909, *934*
Truckmanova, L. B., 499(95), 501(95), 505–507(95), 531(95), 533(95), *585*
Truett, W. L., 722(63), *726*, 880(57), 881 (57), *891*
Truter, M. R., 884(63), 886(63), *891*
Tschunkur, E., 869(5), *889*
Tsurugi, J., 986, *990*
Tsuruta, T., 640(130), *676*, 900(7), *903*

Tszuan-Chan Li, 546(367), 552(367), 553, *594*
Tucker, H., 494(19), 495(19), 499(19), 500(19), 503(19), 520(19), 521(19), *583*, 611(70), 617(70), 637(131), 650(131), 652(131), *674*, *676*
Tulupov, V. A., 536(313), *592*
Tunnicliffe, M. E., 700, 701, *702*
Turba, V., 693(27), 696(33, 34), *702*, 930 (127), *937*
Turner, L., 723(69), *726*
Turner-Jones, A., 711(26), *724*
Turro, N. J., 537(314), *592*
Tutorskii, I. A., 945(26–29), 952(28), *988*
Twiss, D. F., 815(12), *840*

U

Uchida, Y., 631(113), *675*
Uelzmann, H., 531, 562(292), 577, 580, *591*
U. S. Rubber Co., 641(132, 134), *676*
Uraneck, C. A., 499(122), 514(169), 515 (169), 525(250), 534(306), 535(306), *586*, *588*, *590*, *592*, 717(46), *725*, 846, 847(8), 851, 853(8), 854(8), *864*
Urman, Ya. G., 945(29), *988*
Urwin, J. R., 499, 503, 505–509(106), 511, *586*

V

Valvassori, A., 682(2), 683(3), 684(3), 687 (2, 13–16), 688(2, 19), 689(2, 19), 690 (21), 691(23), 692(2), 693(24, 26, 27, 29), 695(26, 30), 696(26, 30, 33, 34), 697(3), 698(3), *701*, *702*, 704(3), *724*, 930(127), *937*
Van Amerongen, G. L., 907(11), 909(11), *934*
Van der Castle, J. F., 499(113), *586*
Vanderhoff, J. W., 878(51), *891*
Van Schooten, J. J., 693(28), *702*
Van Winkle, J. L., 816(20), *840*
Vanzo, E., 556, *594*
Vasil'eva, V. N., 498(70), 499(70), *585*
Vaughan, G., 627(105), 641(136), 653 (136), 655(105, 165), 660(105), *675–677*, 683(4), 695(4), *701*
Vaughan, W. E., 907(17), *934*
Vaughan, L. G., 531(311), 536(311), *592*
Veersen, G. J. van, 944, *987*
Verbanc, J. J., 874(18), *890*, 930(124), *937*
Verdol, J. A., 534, *592*
Versnel, J., 918(66), *935*
Vickroy, V. V., Jr., 743(46), *764*
Vincent, H. L., 499(110), *586*
Vincent, M. F., 623(76), 641(76), *674*
Vodehnal, J., 518(186), *588*, 643(140), *676*, 946(32–35), 956(51), 959(33), 961(32–35), 963(32–35, 51, 57, 59), 966(34, 51, 57), 967(59), *988*, *989*
Vogel, E., 722(62), *726*
Vogel, G., 498(67), *585*
Vogt, L. H., Jr., 967(67), *989*
Vogt, V., 536(314), *592*
Voĭtenko, R. M., 967(65), *989*
Voorhoeve, R. J. H., 775(78), *804*
Vosburgh, W. G., 967(66), *989*
Vydrina, T. K., 617(93), *675*

W

Waack, R., 495(23), 498(57, 60, 61), 499 (60, 61, 83, 130), 500, 502, 503(23), 506, 512(60, 130), 553(299), 561(23), 571 (23), *583*, *584*, *586*, *592*
Wadsworth, F. T., 920(74), *935*
Wakefield, L. B., 560(400), *594*
Walker, J. S., 659(175), *677*
Wallenberger, F. T., 944(23), 958, *987*
Walling, C., 870(10), *889*, 923(94), *936*
Walter, D., 654(163), 657(163), *677*
Walter, H. C., 893(2), 894(2), 896(2), 898(2), 899(2), *903*
Wanless, G. G., 930(115), *936*
Ward, F. K., 578, *596*
Ward, J. P., 723(66, 71), *726*
Warfield, R. W., 522(224), *589*
Wargin, R. V., 528(280), *591*
Warner, R. R., 917(60), *935*
Warrick, E. L., 768(4), 769, 772, 774(4), 795(63), *802*, *804*
Wartman, L. H., 916, 933(55), *935*
Watson, W. F., 945, 950(42), 951(46), 978(42), 980(42), 983(42, 113–115), 984(42), 986(42), *987*, *988*, *990*

Watts, J. T., 741(40), *764*
Waugaman, C. A., 744(52), *764*
Waugh, J. S., 531(311), 536(311), *592*
Weber, C. O., 910(28), 912, *934*
Wei, P. E., 698, *702*, 930(115, 117–120), 932, *936*, *937*
Weil, E. D., 834, *841*
Weinbrenner, E., 728(3), 740(3), 741 (32–34), 743(32, 33), 759(32), *762*
Weiner, M. A., 498(65, 67), 531(311), 536 (311), *584*, *585*, *592*
Weir, C. E., 795, *804*
Weiss, E., 498(44), *584*
Weiss, G., 515(176), *588*
Weissert, F. C., 516(180, 181), 518(180, 181), 529, 530(180, 181), 557(180), 558, *588*
Welch, L. M., 921(83), *936*
Wells, T. F., III, 835(64), 838(67), *842*
Wenz, A., 492(4), 496(4), *583*, 850(21), *864*
Werber, F. X., 719(47), *725*
West, P., 499(83, 130), 500(130), 502, 512 (130), *585*, *586*
West, R., 498(65, 67), 506(157), *584*, *585*, *587*
Westerman, L., 525(252), *590*
Westheimer, F. H., 926(102), *936*
Weyenberg, D. R., 863(54), *865*
Wheat, R. C., 558(391), *594*
Wheeler, D. H., 743(55), *764*
Whitby, G. S., 560(396), *594*, 598(3), *672*
White, D. M., 712(36), *725*
White, H. G., 728(4), *762*
Whitmore, F. C., 926(105), *936*
Wiberg, K. B., 719(50), 720(50), *725*
Wick, M., 800, *804*, 862(51), *865*
Widmer, W., 943(10), *987*
Wiese, H. K., 922(91), 925, 926(91, 99), *936*
Wilcock, D. F., 772, *802*
Wilcoxen, C. H., Jr., 611(71), 617(71), *674*
Wilder, C. R., 522, *589*
Wilke, G., 641, 642(138), 654(163), 657 (163), *676*, *677*, 885(64), *891*
Wilkes, R. A., 522(233), *590*, 984(117), *990*
Wilkinson, G., 851(24), *865*, 880(54), *891*
Williams, H. L., 525(249), 579, 581, 582, *590*, *596*, 599(18), *672*
Williams, J., 493(63), *584*
Williams, K. C., 499(81), 501, *585*
Williams, P. G., 534(303), *592*
Williamson, R. C., 915(48), *935*
Willis, J. M., 529, 559(395), 566(395), *591*, *594*, 846(7), *864*
Willson, E. A., 634(119), *675*
Wilms, H., 850(22), *864*
Wilson, H. L., 921(83), *936*
Windemuth, E., 728(2), 741(2), 755(2), 756(2), *762*
Winger, R., 779(30), *803*
Winkler, H., 503(142), *587*
Winkler, H. J. S., 503(142), *587*
Witt, H. S., 874(20, 22), 875–877(22), 878 (20, 22), 886(22), *890*, 978(105a), *990*
Witte, J., 606(44), *673*
Wittenberg, D. W., 631(112), *675*
Wittig, G., 497(50), 499, 503(141), *584*, *585*, *587*
Wofford, C. F., 528, *591*
Wolfangel, R. E., 527, *591*
Wolfe, J. K., 776(27), *803*
Wolff, I. A., 743(55), *764*
Wolff, T., 494(12), 495(12a), 496(12b), *583*
Wollthan, H., 492(4), 496(4), *582*, *583*, 850(21), *864*
Wood, B. B. J., 835, 836, 838(60), 839 (60), *841*
Wood, L. A., 572(466), *596*, 795(64), *804*
Wood, R. I., 522(235), *590*, 983(112), *990*
Woodhams, R. T., 835, 836, 838(60), 839 (60), *841*
Woodward, F. N., 816, *840*
Worsfold, D. J., 498, 499(103), 503, 505 (146), 507(103), 508(103, 146), 510, 510 (103), 512(103), 541(146), 545, 546 (349), 549(146), 562(59), 569(103), *584*, *586*, *587*, *593*
Wright, G., 768(4), 769, 774(4), 796, *802*
Wright, G. F., 926(103), *936*
Wszolek, W. R., 719(47), *725*

Y

Yakovlev, V. A., 658(172), *677*
Yakubchik, A. I., 520(202), 538(318), 568(465), 575(431), *589*, *592*, *595*, *596*
Yamagami, M., 986(121), *990*
Yamamoto, N., 494(16), *583*
Yamashita, I., 869, *889*
Yamashita, S., 856(37), 857(37), 858(37, 38), 859(38), 860(38), *865*
Yamazaki, N., 638–640, 667(185), 667 (185), *676*, *678*, 685(12), 688(12), *701*
Yaralov, L. K., 554, *594*
Yates, J., 518(185), *588*
Yen, T. F., 712(35, 36), *725*
Yonezawa, T., 532, *591*
Young, C. A., 728(6), 741(42), *762*, *764*
Young, C. H., 598(8), *672*
Young, L. J., 543, 544(341), *593*
Youngman, E. A., 607(56), *673*, 719(48), *725*, 870, 874(21), 878–880(21), *889*, *890*
Youngquist, O. G., 917(62), *935*
Yu, A. J., 838(67), *842*

Z

Zabolotskaya, Y. V., 641(135), *676*
Zack, J. F., 795(63), *804*
Zahir, S. A., 817, *840*
Zahn, H., 534(305), *592*
Zambelli, A., 667(186), 670(186), 671 (186), *678*, 706(10), 707(10), *724*
Zanini, G., 627(107), 629(107), 631(117), 632(117), 644(141), 651(141), *675*, *676*, 712(37), *725*
Zarney, J. L., 907(10), 910(10), 912(10), 913(10), *934*, 944(14), *987*
Zavalei, V. M., 538(318), *592*
Zbinden, R., 972(85), *989*
Zelinski, R. P., 514(169, 171), 515(169, 173), 522(217), 528, 555(383), *588*, *589*, *591*, *594*, 605(41), 606(47), 610(47), 611(41), 614(41, 47), 616(41), 623(47), 625(41), *673*
Zgonnik, V. N., 499(87), 509(87), 512 (87), 521(211), *585*, *589*, 617(90), 619, 621(95), *675*
Zharikova, Z. F., 575(434), *595*
Ziegler, K., 492, 493, 494(5, 25), 496, 498, (45), 521(26), 560, 574(5, 25), *582–584* 707(13), *582–584*, 850, 851, *864*
Zimm, B. H., 527, *591*
Zimmermann, H., 654(163), 657(163), *677*
Zinovyev, Y. M., 920, *935*
Zisman, W. A., 772(20), *802*

SUBJECT INDEX, PARTS 1 and 2

A

Acetaldehyde, block copolymers of, 449
  peroxides of, 421
  preparation of, 188
  solubility of, 430
Acetaldehyde polymerization, initiators for, 433–434
  mechanism of, 435–437
  propagation in, 437
  using radiation, 434–435
  in solution, 429–433
    initiators for, 431–432
    solvents for, 431
  using x-rays, 434
  using γ rays, 434
Acetal endgroup, 338
Acrylate copolymers, 266
Acrylate esters, from acetylene, 254
  from ethylene oxide, 254
  polymerization of, 255–258
  from β-propiolactone, 254
  from propylene, 255
Acrylate monomers, hydrolysis of, 257
  reactivity ratios of, 259–260
Acrylate polymers, isotactic, 258
  syndiotactic, 258
Acrylic acid, 261
Acrylic elastomers, 110, 253–270
  See also individual compounds.
  aging of, 268–270
    effect of carbon black on, 269
  commercially available, 269
  copolymerization of, 259–260
  glass transition temperatures of, 263–268
  monomer synthesis for, 254–255
Acrylic elastomers, oil resistance of, 263–268
  polymerization of, 255–258
    in bulk, 255
    in emulsion, 256–257
    initiators for, 255–258
    stereoregular, 257–258
    in suspension, 255–256
  reactivity ratios for, 259–260
  vulcanization of, 260–263
    cure systems for, 261
Acrylonitrile, 266, 903
  See also Butadiene-acrylonitrile copolymerization, 192–206.
  analysis of, 191
  catalysts for preparation of, 189–190
  as comonomer with butadiene, 73
  copolymer with butadiene, 192–206
  effect on nitrile rubber vulcanizates, 202
  preparation of, 187–191
  properties of, 191
Acrylonitrile modified natural rubber, 221–222
  swell resistance of, 222
Acylium ion salts, 392
Acyl peroxides, 157
Adipamide, as stabilizer, 444
Adiprene, 275
Aging, 117–118
Aldehydes, copolymers of, 448–450
  reactivity ratios of, 450
Aldol-α-napthyl amine, 217
Alfin catalysts, components, 575
  derivation of name, 87
  discovery of, 87
  mechanism of polymerization, 580
  potassium analog, 578

Part 1: pages 1–490; Part 2: pages 491–1044.

Alfin catalysts, reaction rates, 579
  role of salt component, 578
Alfin copolymers, butadiene and α-methylstyrene, 581
  butadiene and styrene, 581
  divinylbenzene and vinyl crotonate, 582
Alfin polymers, 103
Aliphatic aldehydes, elastomeric polymers of, 420
Alkali metals, alkyl derivatives of, 497
  as polymerization initiators, 82
1-Alkenyl alkyl ethers, 342
Alkoxides, effect on initiation by organolithium compounds, 503
Alkyl chloroformate, 902
Alkyllithium catalysts, impurities in, 505
Alkyllithium compounds, complexes with Lewis bases, 498
  solubility, 498
Allophonate, 732
Allyl acetate, 901
Allyl chloride, 901, 903
Allyl chloroform, 901
Allyl chloroformate, 901
π-Allyl complex, 875
tert-Allylic chloride, 242
Allyltrichlorosilane, 901
Allyl vinyl ether, 901
Alternating copolymers, 540
Alumina, calcination temperature of, 423–424
  as initiator, 423–424
  treatment with acids, 425
Aluminum alkyl derivatives, as catalysts, 301–307, 409–413
Aluminum hydrides, catalysts from, for the polymerization of diolefins, 605
  reaction with $TiCl_4$, 605
Aluminum oxides as initiators, 423
Aluminum sulfate–sulfuric acid, as initiator, 429
Amines, in vulcanization of chlorosulfonated polyethylene, 919
Ammonium benzoate, 261
Anionic copolymerization, in hydrocarbon solvents, 545
  of butadiene–isoprene, 545
  of butadiene–styrene, 545
Anionic initiation, by dimethylformamide, 894, 896–898
  by tetraisopropyl titanate, 894, 895, 897
Anionic polmerization, in polar solvents, 545
Antioxidants, 117–118, 133
  early use of, 59
Antiozonanats, 117–118
Aryl diazonium salts, 393–394
Association phenomena, influence on kinetic data, 508
Atactic, origin of term, 87
4,4′-Azobis (4-cyanopentanoic acid), 845, 848
2,2′-Azoisobutyronitrile, 257

B

Balata, NMR spectrum of, 980, 982
  ozonization of, 862
Bayer process, 187
Benzothiazyl, 216
Benzoyl peroxide, 256, 260
3,3-Bis(chloromethyl)oxacyclobutane, 382, 384
Bisiospropyl xanthogen disulfide, 169
Biuret, 732
Blends, of elastomers, 114
  of nitrile rubber, 218–219
Block copolymers, 156, 540
  physical properties of, 555
  preparation of, 553
  review of, 554
Bondi's van der Waals volumes, 13
Boron trifluoride, 425
  as initiator, 422, 448

Branching, determination of, 527
effect of high temperature on, 527
in polybutadienes, 526
in polyisoprenes, 527
Brominated butyl rubber, vulcanization of, 928
Bromination, of butyl rubber, 921
of *cis*-1,4 polybutadiene, 912
of natural rubber, 911
of polyisoprenes, 910
Brønsted acid-type initiators, 422
Buna, anionic polymerization of, 849
derivation of name, 72
Buna N, 73
production in Germany of, 73–74
Buna S, 73
production in Germany of, 73–74
Buna 32, 72
Buna 85, 72
Buna 115, 72
Burchfield test, 213–214
Butadiene, 128–131, 261
as comonomer with acrylonitrile, 73
as comonomer with styrene, 73
effect of metal salts on free radical polymerization of, 869
polymerization, 871
activators in Co catalysts for, 618
with alkali metal alkyls, 64
by π-allyl–Ni–I, 627
by $AlEt_3$–$V(acac)_3$ systems, 627
by AlR_3–$TiCl_4$ systems, 625
by catalysts from aluminum alkyls and vanadium chlorides, 624
by catalysts from $Al(C_2H_5)_3$ and Cr compounds, 632
by catalysts from $Ti[N(C_2H_5)_2]_4$ and $AlH_2N(CH_3)_2$, 629
by catalysts from violet $TiCl_3$, 625
by cobalt catalysts, 617, 879
in emulsion, 71
first, 46, 57
by homogeneous systems, 625
by iridium catalysts, 879
Butadiene, polymerization, by the $LiAlH_4$–$TiCl_4$ system, 625
by nickel catalysts, 879
by palladium catalysts, 879
by potassium, 72
by rhodium catalysts, 877
by ruthenium catalysts, 879
by sodium, 46, 71–72, 74
by $TiCl_4$-based catalysts, 611
by titanium catalysts containing iodine, 614
preparation of, 128–131
catalysts for, 129–130
by dehydrogenation of butanes, 129–130
by dehydrogenation of butenes, 129–130
by halogen-free process, 131
by halogen process, 131
Lebedev process, 129
Ostromislensky process, 129
by oxidative dehydrogenation, 130–131
processes based on acetylene, 128–129
processes based on ethanol, 128–129
Reppe process, 129
by thermal cracking of hydrocarbons, 129
purification of, 131
Butadiene-acrylonitrile copolymerization, 192–206
See also Butadiene-acrylonitrile copolymers, 192–206.
additives for, 202–206
effect of mercaptans on, 204
emulsifiers for, 203
initiators for, 203
modifiers for, 204
monomer proportions in, 201–202
polymerization charges in, 200–201
reactivity ratios for, 193
Butadiene polymers, 610, 623, 627
See also Styrene-butadiene copolymer, 145.

Butadiene polymers, amount of *cis*-1,4 microstructure, 871
by coordination catalysts, 599
copolymers, 540
with acrylonitrile, 192–206
composition of, 195–200
effect of mercaptans on, 204
tensile strength of, 204
plasticity of, 204
with isoprene, 670
with α-methylstyrene, 160
with pentadiene, 668
with 2-phenyl butadiene, 667
with styrene, 847
homopolymers, 492, 598
1,2-isotactic polybutadiene, 631
by radical intitiators, 598
Butadiene-styrene rubbers. *See* SBR.
Butane, butadiene from, 129–131
oxidative dehydrogenation of, 130–131
Butanone, 437
Butarez, 850
2-Butene, 901
Butenes, butadiene from, 129–131
dehydrogenation of, 129–130
oxidative dehydrogenation of, 130–131
3-Butenyl acetate, 901
tert-Butyl-*p*-cresol, 206
tert-Butylethylene, 901
p-*t*-Butylisopropylbenzene, 154
Butyllithium, 258
polymerization intiation by, 499
n-Butyllithium, distillation of, 498
sec-Butyllithium, decomposition of, 498
Butyl methacrylates, 142, 147
Butyl rubber, 76–78, 106–108, 315–327, 921
Burchfield test for, 214
characteristics of, 319–322
consistency of, 319
copolymerization of isobutene and diene, 322–325
degradation time of, 215
glass transition temperature of, 106
Butyl rudder, manufacture of, 317–319
molecular weight of, 325–326
properties of, 316–317, 321
structure of, 319–322
n-Butyraldehyde polymerization, 437

C

CHC, 387
CHR, 387
Calcination temperature of alumina, 423–424
of metal sulfates, 428
Caoutchène, from natural rubber, 32
Caoutchine, 35, 36
from natural rubber, 32, 33
Caotchouc, origin of word, 23
Capping reaction, 442
Carbodiimides, 732
Carbon black, 135
Carbonium ion salts, 391, 392–393
m-Carborane, heat stability of, 789
Castor oil, 729
Catalysts, chromium containing, 715
organoaluminum compounds, 721
organometallic, development of, 78–88
Cationic mechanisms, 291–451
Cationic polymerization, 291–327
of butyl rubber, 315–327
cocatalysis in, 296–308
of cyclic ethers, 388
of isobutene, 296–308
Poisson coefficients for, 312–315
of polyacetaldehyde, 422
termination of, 308–310
transfer coefficients for, 312–315
of vinyl alkyl ethers, 340–342
Ceiling temperature, 396, 398
definition of, 398
of polyacetaldehyde, 441–442
Cesium, organo compounds of, 559
Chain extenders, 845
Chain transfer, 255
in *t*-butanol, 256

Chain transfer, of methyl acrylate, 256
in solvents, 256
Chelates, 871
Chemical reactions, functional groups and, 534
Chlorinated butyl rubber, vulcanization of, 928
Chlorinated ethylene-propylene copolymers, effect of solvent on vulcanization of, 932
Chlorinated polyethylenes, 111, 914
properties, 916
effect of chlorine content on, 914
Chlorinated polyisoprenes, 910
preparation of, 907
stability of, 907, 909
structure in, 909
Chlorination, of aliphatic compounds, 931
of butadiene-acrylonitrile copolymers, 911
of butadiene polymers, 912
of butadiene-styrene copolymers, 911
of butyl rubber, 923
of ethylene-propylene copolymers, 931
of isotactic polypropylene, 932
of linear olefins, 908
of polyethylene, 915
of polyisoprenes, 910
Chlorine-containing elastomers, 111–112
Chlorobutadiene rubber, Burchfield test for, 214
2-Chloro-1,3-butadiene, 227
See also Chloroprene, 227–242.
Chlorodifluoroacetyl fluoride, 899
2-Chloroethyl vinyl ether, 261
Chlorofluorothioacetyl fluoride, 898
Chlorohydrin elastomers, 111–112
Chloroisopropylbenzene, 154
Chlorophosphonation, 920, 930
of polyethylene, 920
Chloroprene, 227–242, 901
addition reactions of, 229
Chloroprene, copolymerization of, 238–239
reactivity ratios for, 238
using sulfur, 244
with vinyl alkyl ethers, 356
Diels-Alder reactions of, 229
dimerization of, 229
free radical polymerization of, 232–240, 599
emulsifying agents for, 232
heat of, 232
initiators for, 232–233
molecular weight control of, 233–235
stabilizing agents for, 232–233
Grignard reagent from, 229
hazards of, 228
ionic polymerization of, 240–242
in anionic systems, 241
cationic initiators for, 241
Ziegler-type catalysts for, 241
peroxides of, 229
polymerization of, first, 75
preparation of, 230–232
by acetylene process, 230–231
by alternate processes, 231–232
by butadiene process, 231
properties of, 228–230
solubility of, 228
thermal polymerization of, 242
toxicity of, 228
Chloroprene-nitrile test, 214
Chloroprene rubbers, vulcanization of, 245
Chlorosilanes, hydrolysis of, 778
Chlorosulfonated polyethylene, 111
Burchfield test for, 214
vulcanization of, 917
Chlorosulfonation, 930
of polyethylene, 917
of poly-α-olefins, 930
Chlorotrifluoroethylene, 279, 280, 903
copolymer with vinylidene fluoride, 284
β-Chlorovinyl alkyl ethers, 342

Cinene, 36
cis-trans isomerism in polydienes, first discussion of, 82
cis-trans isomerization, of balata, 970
of hevea, 970
cis-polymers. *See individual polymers.*
Cocatalysis, in cationic polymerizations, 296–308
Cocatalysts, efficiency of 303, 305–307
in polymerization of vinyl alkyl ethers, 339, 340, 344–345
Cohesive energy density, 14
Cold rubber, recipe for, 133
Competitive olefin reactions, 875
Compounding, 115–119
aging, 117–118
extenders, 116
fillers, 115–116
processing, 118–119
rheology, 118–119
vulcanization, 117–118
Conjugated dienes, polymerization of, by alkali metals, 56, 78
by sodium, 46
Coordination catalysis, 873
Coordination catalysts, for conjugated diolefins, 602
Copolymerization, 157–160
of butadiene, 73, 145
of chloroprene, 238–239
first use of, 73
H-S-E theory for, 144–148
of isobutene with a diene, 77
rate of, 144–148
by rhodium chloride, 870
of styrene, 145
theory, 541
Copolymers, irregular, 540
of butadiene, 540
of isoprene, 540
of piperylene, 540
with styrene, 543
regular, 540
styrene, 540
Corresponding states. *See* Principle of corresponding states.
Crosslinking, 76–77, 117, 360
in fluoroelastomers, 282
in neoprene, 242
in nitrile rubbers, 205
in poly(vinyl ethers), 360
in SBR, 173
Crystalline poly-alpha-olefins, discovery of, 87
preparation with Ziegler-Natta catalysts, 87
Crystalline polypropylene, discovery of, 87
preparation of, 87
Crystallinity, 16
effect of melting point on, 16
Crystallization polymerization, 422
Cumene, 154
Cured elastomers, permeability of, 814
resistance to organic solvents, 814
resistance to water, 814
2-Cyanoethyl, 266
Cyclic disulfides, free radical polymerization with, 818
Cyclic ethers, 377–413
cationic polymerization of, 388
copolymerization of, 405–406
elastomeric materials from, 383–388
homogeneous anionic polymerization of, 406–408
initiator systems for, 388–395
initiation via Friedel-Crafts halides of, 394–395
mechanism for polymerization of, 388
polymerizability of, 380–383, 384
ring-opening polymerization of, 380
solid state polymerization of, 395
Cyclic hydroperoxides, 157
Cyclic olefins, elastomers from, 703
Cyclic siloxanes, polymerization of, 780
Cyclization, *cis*-polyisoprene, 945
of dihydromyrcene, 942
of ethylene-isoprene copolymer, 957

Cyclization, *trans*-polyisoprene, 945
Cyclized rubber, structure of, 944
Cyclobutene, polymerization, 882
  catalyst systems for, 715
Cyclodimethyltetrasiloxane, kinetics of polymerization of, 781
Cyclohexene, 706, 901
Cyclohydrochlorination, of 3,4-polyisoprene, 961
1,5-Cyclooctadiene, as termonomer in ethylene-propylene terpolymers, 695
Cycloolefins, alkylsubstituted, 720
  polymerization, by coordinated anionic mechanism, 719
    thermodynamics of, 719
  ring strain in, 720
  stereospecific polymerization of, 713
Cyclopentadiene, copolymerization of, 355
  polymerizability of, 44
  of dialdehydes, 448
  of diene monomers, 963
Cymel 300, 262

D

Degradation of polyacetaldehyde, 440–441
  rate constants for, 444
Degradation times, of rubbers, 215
Dehydrochlorination, of chlorinated polyethylene, 920
Depolymerized rubber, 862
Desulfurization, by aqueous hydroxides, 812
Diak No. 1, 283
Dialkyl (alkylperoxy) borane, 900
Dialkyl xanthogen disulfide modifier, 848
Diamines, 260
Diazo compounds, 156, 157
Diazothioethers, 156
  as initiators, 846
  as modifiers, 846
2,3-Dichloro-1,3-butadiene, 903
Dichloroethyl-formal, 864
Dicumyl peroxide, 359, 360
Dielectric constant, effect on polymerization of, 350
Diene-isobutene copolymers, 322–325
Dienes, copolymerization with vinyl alkyl ethers, 355–356
  emulsion polymerization of, 140
Diethylaluminum chloride, as initiator, 448
Diethyl ether, 431
Difluorothioacetyl fluoride, 898
1,1-Dihydroperfluorobutyl acrylate, 266
Dihydrotoluene, polymerizability of, 44
p-Diisopropylbenzene, 154
Diisopropylbenzene hydroperoxide, 141, 156
Diisopropyl xanthogen disulfide, 204
Dilithiopolyisoprene, 851
Dimercaptans, monomeric, oxidation of by air, 818
  oxidation of by bromine, 819
  oxidation of by nitric acid, 819
N,*N*-Dimethyl acrylamide, 266
2,3-Dimethyl-1,3-butadiene, 141, 850
  preparation from acetone, 58–59
  polymerization of, first, 43
  polymerization by sodium of, 46
  useful rubber from, first, 57
2,4-Dimethyl-2-butene, 901
1,5-Dimethyl cyclooctadiene, 39
Dimethylsilicone polymers, effect of molecular weight on viscosity of, 770
Diolefin elastomers, halogenation of, 906
Diolefin polymers, isomerism in, 599
  properties of, 649
1,4-Dioxane, 383, 399
1,3-Dioxolane, 328–384, 399
Dipentene, 35
  from natural rubber, 34
  polymerization by hydrochloric acid of, 54

Diphenylamine, 445
Diphenylmethane diisocyanate, preparation of, 730
  vapor hazard of prepolymers from, 740
Disulfide crosslinks, 360
Disulfide thiokol, 863
1,2-Dithiacyclohexane, reaction with alkali-terminated polymers, 854
Dithioalkyl dicarboxylic acid, 847
Dodecylisopropylbenzene, 154
Dodecyl mercaptan, 845
t-Dodecyl mercaptan, 133, 203
Duprene, 75
Duradene, 105, 558
Dye partition test, 157
Dynagen, 385
Dynamic moduli, 362, 363
  effect of temperature on, 367–370
Dynamic resilience, 362, 363, 367–370
  definition of, 362
  effect of temperature on, 367–370

E

e value, 238
Elastic equation of state, 3
Elastic fiber, 728
Elastomers. *See also* Technology of elastomers and individual elastomers.
  acrylic, 253–270
  blends of, 114
  chlorine-containing, 111–112
  by condensation polymerization, 767
  glass transition of, 529
  oxygen-containing, 109–111
  preparation using Ziegler catalysts, 87
  properties of, 516
  structure of, 96–98
  structure–property relationships in, 97–98
  technology of, 95–122
  uses for, 98–99
Emulsifiers, first synthetic, 72–73
Emulsion copolymerization, to form nitrile rubber, 191
  absolute rate constant for, 148–149
  of butadiene, 71, 846
  Harkins-Smith-Ewart theory of, 135–138
  initiation systems for, 151–157
  kinetic expressions for, 138–151
  of liquid rubbers, 845
  locus of initiation for, 135
  locus of propagation for, 135
  number of radicals per particle in, 149–151
  particle formation in, 137, 139–143
  propagation rate of, 139
  proposal of, first, 64
  of SBR, 132–157
  solution state in, 138
  steady-state stage of, 137–138, 143–151
Emulsion recipes, metal compounds in, 868
Endgroups, in polytetrahydrofuran, 396
Epichlorohydrin, 384
  copolymer with ethylene oxide, 386
  elastomers from, 386
Episulfides, copolymers with epoxides, 839
  copolymers with vinyl monomers, 839
Epoxides, as catalysts, 409–413
  heterogeneous polymerization of, 408–409
  iron catalysts for, 409
Erythro diisotactic polymers, 342
Estane, 743
Ethyl acetate, 437
Ethyl acrylate, 901, 903
Ethylaluminum chlorides, 85
Ethylbenzene, catalytic dehydrogenation to styrene, 131–132
  oxidation to styrene, 132
Ethylene, copolymerization with thiocarbonyl fluoride, 901
Ethylene, polymerization of, by aluminum, $AlCl_3$, and $TiCl_4$, 85

Ethylene, polymerization of, by beryllium alkyls, 83
to high molecular weight polymers, 82–83
by lithium alkyls, 81
by lithium powder, 82–83
by nickel powder, 82–83
by trialkylaluminum, discovery of, 84
by Ziegler catalysts, 84–85
as solvent for polymerization, 431
Ethylenediamine tetraacetic acid salt, 133
Ethylene–ethyl acrylate, 109–110
Ethylene oxide, 381, 384, 399
copolymer with epichlorohydrin, 386
Ethylene–propylene copolymerization, reactivity ratios in, 679
Ethylene–propylene copolymers, composition of, 679
copolymerization procedure, 683
determination of composition, 697
effect of nature of catalyst on composition, 684
effect of reaction conditions on composition, 684
effect of reaction conditions on viscosity of, 688
intrinsic viscosity of, 687
necessity of halogen in the catalyst for, 682
polymerization rate for different catalysts, 691
reactivity ratios in, 686
synthesis of, 679, 682
viscosity of, 679
Ethylene–propylene rubbers, 106–108, 679
Ethylene–propylene terpolymers, 693
composition of, 679
determination of composition, 700
termonomers in, 694
Ethylene-vinyl acetate, 109–110
Ethyllithium, distillation of, 498
polymerization initiation by, 499
Ethyl vinyl ether, 901
Eupione, from natural rubber, 34
Expansivity, 11, 12
Extenders, 115–116

F

Faradyine, from natural rubber, 32, 33
Ferrous sulfate, 133
Fillers, 115–116
Flash polymerization of vinly alkyl ethers, 334
Flexibilities of elastomers, 385
Fluorel, 280
Fluorinated butadienes, 277
elastomers from, 278
Fluorinated nitrosoalkanes, 287
polymerization of, 287
Fluorinated nitrosoelastomers, 286–288
Fluorination, of butyl rubber, 928
Fluorine. *See* Fluorelastomers.
Fluoroacrylates, 277
polymers of, 277
Fluoroelastomers, 273–288
See also Heterofluoroelastomers, 286–288.
comparison with other elastomers, 275
crosslinking in, 282
from olefins, 276–286
properties of, 275
vulcanization of, 282–286
Fluorothioacyl chlorides, 899, 902
Fluorothioacyl fluorides, 898, 899
Fractional free volume, 13
Fractionation, 171
Free radical polymerization, 900
of chloroprene, 232–240
effects of metal compounds, 868
Free radicals, as polymerization initiators, first disclosure of, 73
Friedel-Crafts halides, 391, 394–395
as catalysts, 333–340
Functionality, for crosslinking, 76–77
Furnace blacks, 128

G

GR-S rubber. *See* SBR.
Gehman's procedure, 446
Glass transition temperature, 10–15, 98
 of acrylic elastomers, 263–268
 of acrylic homopolymers, 264
 cohesive energy density, 14
 definition of, 96
 effect on dynamic resilience on, 369–370
 Gordon-Taylor equation for, 264–265
 internal pressure effect on, 14
 of polybutadiene, 104
 poly(butyl ether disulfide), 823
 poly(butyl formal disulfide), 823
 poly(ethylene disulfide), 823
 of poly(ethyl ether disulfide), 823
 poly(ethyl ether tetrasulfide), 823
 poly(ethyl formal disulfide), 823
 poly(ethylene tetrasulfide), 823
 poly(hexamethylene disulfide), 823
 poly(pentamethylene disulfide), 823
 of poly(vinyl ethers), 353–354, 364–370
Glutaraldehyde, polymerization of, 448
Glycidyl methacrylate, cure of, 262
Gordon-Taylor equation, 264–265
Grignard reagent, as catalyst, 343
 from chloroprene, 229
Growth reaction, origin of name, 83
Gutta-percha, 40
Gutta-percha, ozonization of, 862

H

H-S-E. *See* Harkins-Smith-Ewart theory.
Halocarbons, as cocatalysts, 872
Halogenation, 905, 931
 of butadiene rubbers, 911
 of butyl rubber, 921
 of ethylene-α-olefin copolymers, 929
 of poly-α-olefins, 929
Harkins-Smith-Ewart theory, 134–138
Heterofluoroelastomers, 286–288
Heterogeneity index, 171
Heterogeneous polymerization of epoxides, 408–409
 of vinyl alkyl ethers, 336, 340, 343, 346
Hevea. *See* Natural rubber, 947
Hévéène, from natural rubber, 32
Hexafluoropropylene, 279, 280, 287, 900
 copolymer with vinylidene fluoride, 284
Hexafluorothioacetone, 899
Hexa[1-(2-methyl)-aziridinyl] triphosphantriazine, 853
Hexamethylene diisocyanate, as chain extender, 858
Hexamethylene oxide, 383
High impact resins, 114–115
Homogeneous polymerization, of vinyl alkyl ethers, 336–337, 340, 343
Homopolymerization, 139
Hot rubber, recipe for, 133
Hycar 4021, 254, 261
 cure of, 261
Hydrocarbon block copolymers, 516
Hydrohalogenation, of butadiene styrene rubber, 914
 of gutta-percha, 912
 of 1,2-polybutadiene, 914
 of polydimethylbutadiene, 912
 of 3,4-polyisoprene, 913
 of synthetic polyisoprene, 912
Hydroperoxide, 154
β-Hydroxyethyl methacrylate, 261
Hydroxyl polybutadiene, 845
N-Hydroxymethyl acrylamide, 262
Hypalon, 274–275

I

Infrared analysis, microstructure determination by, 518
Initiation, first use of term, 81
 of acetaldehyde polymerization, 431, 432

Initiation, of acrylate ester polymerization, 255–258
of butadiene-acrylonitrile copolymerization, 203
of emulsion polymerization, 151–157
loci of, 134
by metal acetylacetonates, 871
of polyacetone polymerization, 450
of solid state polymerization, 395
Initiator reactions, 395–396
Initiator residues, 442
Initiator systems, 388–395
acylium ion salts, 392
aluminum organic compounds, 433–444
aryl diazonium salts, 393–394
carboxonium ion salts, 391
diethylaluminum chloride/$TiCl_4$, 448
Friedel-Crafts halides, 391, 394–395
Lewis acids, 448
oxonium salts, 389–390
protonic acids, 390–391
stable carbonium ion salts, 392–393
Inorganic polymers, 113
Internal pressure, 14
Intrinsic viscosity, 175
Inverse Langevin chains, 3–4
Iodination, of butyl rubber, 925
Iodine halides, reaction with butyl rubber, 926
reaction with emulsion polyisoprenes, 911
reaction with gutta-percha, 911
reaction with natural rubber, 911
reaction with sodium polyisoprenes, 911
Ionic polymerization, of chloroprene, 240–242
Iron catalysts, for epoxide polymerization, 409
Isobutene, 901
copolymer with diene, 322–325
history of, 291–293
polymerization of, 296–308
Isobutene–$AlCl_3$ system, 298–301
Isobutyraldehyde polymerization, 437
Isocyanates, 733
catalysis of reactions of, 733
rates of reactions of, 733
reactions of, 731
Isomerization, of polybutadiene, 974
Isomerized rubber, 969
Isoprene, 141
conversion into rubber, 42
copolymers, 540
determination of structure of, 35
early synthesis of, 45
hydrochlorides of, 34
from natural rubber, 32, 33
polymerization, 33, 76
by AlR_3–$TiCl_4$ systems, 639
by catalysts from Al alkyls and VCl_3, 641
by catalysts from $Al(C_2H_5)_3$ and a titanium tetraalcoholate, 642
in emulsion of, 71
by heat, 46
by hydrochloric acid, 34, 54
with lithium alkyls, 53
by sodium, 46, 48
spontaneous, 35
relation to natural rubber, 37
relation to terpenes, 37
telomerization of, 858
from terpenes, 45
from turpentine, 35
Isoprene polymers, *cis*-1,4 polyisoprene, 633
by coordination catalysts, 599
copolymers with butadiene, 670
homopolymers, 492, 598
by radical initiators, 599
Isotactic, origin of term, 87
definition of, 334
Isotactic structure of poly(vinyl ethers), 334, 336

K

Kel-F, 280
  copolymer with vinylidene fluoride, 284
Knapsack process, 188

L

Ladder polymer, 961
Lassaigne nitrogen test, 213
Lebedev process, 129
Lewis acids as initiators, 422, 448
Light scattering, 171
Liquid carboxylic copolymers, table of, 849
Liquid polybutadiene, by anionic polymerization, 849
  by butyllithium, 854
Liquid polymers, by solution polymerization, 845
  ease of oxidation of, 814
  molecular weight of, 813
  with azodicarboxylic acids, 845
Liquid polysulfide polymers, 863
Liquid rubbers, 848, 854
  by addition methods, 862
  alkali-terminated, 854
  by anionic polymerization, 848
  by cationic polymerization, 856
  by condensation methods, 862
  by coordination methods, 861
  definition, 843
  from nickel catalysts, 861
  by radical polymerization, 845
Liquid thiokols, 863
Lithium alkyls, as polymerization initiators, 81–82
Lithium compounds, reaction with butadiene, 492
  reaction with 2,3-dimethylbutadiene, 492
  reaction with isoprene, 492
  reaction with piperylene, 492
Lithium metal, adduct with 2,3-dimethylbutadiene-1,3, 496
  crystal structure of, 493
  energy of activation with, 494
  initiation with, 494
  microstructure of polymers obtained from, 495
  polymerization of butadiene, 494
  polymerization of isoprene, 494
  temperature effect on rate with, 494
Lithium-terminated polymers, 855
Living polymerizations, of liquid polymers, 848
Low functionality, 320

M

M/P particles, 137
  diameters of, 150
Magnesium sulfate–sulfuric acid complex, in polyaldehyde polymerization, 447
Mark-Houwink equation, 175
Masterbatches, 135
Mechanism of polymerization, with lithium compounds, 530
  role of coordination complex in, 531
  role of electron transfer in, 533
Melting temperature, isotactic 1,4 polypentadiene, 712
  1,4 polybutadiene, 712
  1,4-poly-α-chloro-butadiene, 712
  1,4-poly-2,3-dimethylbutadiene, 712
  1,4 polyisoprene, 712
  poly-2-chlorobutadiene, 708
  polypentenamer, 712
p-Menthane hydroperoxide, 133
Mercaptans, effect on butadiene-acrylonitrile copolymers, 204
Mercaptan-terminated polymers, block copolymers from, 815
  curing in, 814
  physical and cured properties of, 814
2-Mercapto benzimidazole, 217

2-Mercaptoimidazoline, 261
10-Mercaptostearohydrazide, 847
Metal alkoxide–sulfuric acid catalyst, 351–352
Metal compounds, effect on polymerization rate, 873
  effect on polymer structure, 873
Metal oxides, in vulcanization of chlorosulfonated polyethylene, 917
Metal sulfate–sulfuric acid complex as catalyst, 345–352
Methacrylic acid, 848
Methaldehyde, 430
p-Methane, 154
Methanol-C^{14}, reaction with poly-(thiocarbonyl fluoride), 896
1-Methoxy-1,3-butadiene, copolymerization of, 355
N-Methoxymethyl methacrylamide, cure of, 262
Methyl acrylate, 903
2-Methyl butene, from natural rubber, 32
3-Methyl cyclobutene, 720
1-Methyl-1,5-cyclooctadiene, as termonomer in ethylene-propylene terpolymers, 695
2-Methylene-5-norbornene, as termonomer in ethylene-propylene terpolymers, 695
Methyllithium, polymerization initiation by, 499
  solubility of, 498
Methyl methylacrylate, 142, 147
2-Methyl-1,3-pentadiene, copolymerization of, 355
Methylphenyl silicones, carbonyl groups from oxidation of, 790
  oxidation of, 789
Methyl rubber, derivation of name, 59
  production of, figures for, 68–69
    first, 62–66
    in Germany, 66–69
Methyl rubber BK, preparation of, 68
Methyl rubber H, preparation of, 67
Methyl rubber W, preparation of, 67
Methyl silicone gum, molecular weight distribution in, 779
Methyl silicone polymers, base-catalyzed polymerization of, 779
  mechanism of curing, 796
  swelling in hydrocarbon solvents, 793
Methyl silicone rubbers, resistance to corona, 794
Micelles, 134
  critical concentration of, 135
Microgel, 171, 172
Microstructure, with alkali metal catalysts, 566
  application of NMR, 519
  factors affecting, 520
Modification function, 161
Modified Friedel-Crafts catalysts, 341
Modifier depletion, 160–161
Modifiers, bis-type, 173
  incremental addition of, 166–170
Molecular weight, effect of temperature on, 302
  kinetic, 504, 523
  of natural rubber, 41
  number average, 504, 523
  of polyacetaldehyde, 437–439
  of poly(vinyl ethers), 349–350
  viscosity average, 523
  weight average, 523
Molecular weight distribution, control by incremental addition of, 166–170
  effect on properties of polymer, 97–98
  by fractional precipitation, 525
  by gel permeation chromatography, 525
  with organolithium compounds, 505
  by ultracentrifuge, 525
Molecular weight jump reaction, 102
Molecular weight regulators, in polymerization of butadiene by cocatalysts, 621

Molybdenum catalysts, 715
Monomeric amides, as stabilizers, 444
Monosulfide elastomers, preparation from olefin sulfides, 807
Mooney equation, 3–4
Mooney viscosity, 164
  of nitrile rubbers, 205
Mooney viscosity average molecular weight, 175

N

1,5-Naphthalene diisocyanate, 728, 740
β-Naphthylamine, as stabilizer, 445
Natural rubber, 128, 275
  analysis by destructive distillation of, 32
  biochemical synthesis of, 37
  bromination of, 36
  Burchfield test for, 214
  composition of, early work, 30–40
  consumption statistics of, 27–30
  cyclization of, 945, 951
  degradation time of, 215
  discovery of, 22–23
  halogenation of, 907
  hydrogenation of, 70
  linear structure concept of, 70
  molecular weight of, 41
  NMR spectrum of, 980, 982
  ozonization of, 862
  ozonolysis of, 38
  price statistics for, 28–31
  production statistics for, 28
  relation to isoprene and terpenes, 37
  structure of, early concepts, 30–40
Nekal, 72
Neoprene, 75, 111, 247, 274–275, 387
  adhesive grades of, 247
  crosslinking site in, 242
  manufacture of, 239–240
  types of, 245–248
  uses of, 245–248
Neoprene, vulcanization of, 242–245
    acid acceptors, 243
    with bisphenols, 243
    crosslinking site, 242
    with diamines, 243
    with substituted thioureas, 244
    with ZnO, 243
Neoprene FC, 848
Neoprene GN, manufacture of, 239–240
  molecular weight distribution of, 235
Neutral phosphates, as initiators, 433
Nickel catalysts, 715
Nickel effect, discovery of, 84
Nickel peroxide, 873
Nitrile rubber, 73, 185–222, 387
  applications of, 221
  blends of, 218–219
  Burchfield test for, 214
  compounding, 215–218
  crosslinking in, 205
  degradation time of, 215
  fillers for, 217
  history of, 186–187
  identification of, 213–215
  manufacture of, 206–212
  Mooney viscosity of, 205
  plasticizers for, 217–218
  preparation of, 191–212
  processing of, 219
  properties of vulcanizates of, 215–218, 219–221
  stabilizers for, 217
  structure of, 212–213
  vulcanization systems for, 215–217
Nitrile rubber manufacture, 206–219
  apparatus for, 206–207
  coagulation in, 209–212
  drying in, 209–212
  latex concentration in, 209–212
  polymerization process, 207–209
Nitrile rubber vulcanizates, abrasion resistance of, 221
  elastic properties of, 220
  gas permeability of, 221

Nitrile rubber vulcanizates, high temperature behavior of, 220
 low temperature behavior of, 220
 properties of, 215–221
 stress–strain behavior in, 220
 swell resistance of, 220
Nitrogen-containing rubbers, 185–224
Nitrosite C, 38
Nitroso rubbers, 112
Nonconjugated diolefins, as termonomers in ethylenepropylene terpolymers, 695
Norbornene, 722
Norbornene, polymerization by metal catalysts, 880
Nordel hydrocarbon, 275

O

Octamethylcyclotetrasiloxane, reaction with benzoyl peroxide, 797
Oil resistance, of acrylic elastomers, 263–268
Olefin isomerization, by salts of noble metals, 875
Oppanol, 295, 856
Organolithium compounds, active species in initiation by, 502
 effect of concentration on rate of polymerization by, 500
 effect of polar substances on initiation by, 502
 molecular weight of polymer obtained from, 503
 order of initiation reaction with, 500
 polymerization by, 497
 polymerization reaction with, 503
 solvent effect on initiation by, 501
Organometallic catalysts, development of, 78–88
Osmometry, 171
Oxacyclobutane, 382, 384
1-Oxa-4,5-dithiacycloheptane, 817
Oxepane, 383, 384
Oxetane, 382, 384
Oxirane, 381
Oxonium salts, 389–390
Oxygen, as an impurity, 421
Oxygen-containing elastomers, 109–111
Ozonization, of balata, 862
 of gutta-percha, 862
 of natural rubber, 862
 of *cis*-1,4 polybutadiene, 862

P

PA-21, 254
PBD, 100
Paraldehyde, 430
Parker's swelling analysis, 216
1,3-Pentadiene, polymerization, by $Al(C_2H_5)_3$–VCL_3 systems, 644
 by catalysts from Al alkyls and Ti alkoxides, 647
 by Co catalysts, 646
 See also Piperylene.
1,3-Pentadiene polymers, by coordination catalysts, 599
 isotactic *cis*-1,4 polypentadiene, 645
 syndiotactic *cis*-1,4 polypentadiene, 646
 1,2 syndiotactic polypentadiene, 648
Penton, 382
Perbunan, 73
Perfluoro thiopropionyl fluoride, 899
Peroxides, as polymerization initiators, 63, 73
Persulfate initiation, 151–153
Phenol-formaldehyde resins, blends with nitrile rubber, 219
Phenylbutadiene polymerizability of, 44
2-Phenylbutadiene, copolymers with butadiene, 667
Phenylcyclohexane, 154
Phenylethanol, dehydration to styrene, 132
2-Phenyl isopropylpotassium, addition to unsaturated hydrocarbons, 80

Phenyl magnesium bromide, 258
Physical properties, of elastomers, 529
Physical testing, 119–122
Piperidine, as antioxidant, 59
Piperylene, 43
  See also 1,3-Pentadiene.
  isomerism in, 536
  polymerization, 537
  polymerization of, first, 42
Piperylene polymers, 644
  copolymers, 540, 552
    with butadiene, 668
    with styrene, 543
  emulsion polymers, 539
  homopolymers, 535, 598
Plantation rubber, production statistics for, 29
Plasticizers, 135
Poisson coefficient, 312–315
  of conjugated dienes, 315
Polyacetaldehyde, 421–446
  ceiling temperature of, 441–442
  degradation of, 440–441
    by acid, 440
    by base, 440–441
    by radicals, 441
  dielectric studies on, 446
  molecular weight of, 437–439
  properties of, 446
  solution viscosities of, 439
  stabilization of, 441–445
  structure of, 439–440
  tacticity of, 420
  tensile strength of, 446
  thermal stability of, 445
  torsional modulus of, 446
  transition temperature of, 446
Polyacetaldehyde polymerization, activated with BF_3, 426
  by alumina, 423–424
  beneficial impurities for, 421
  with cationic initiators, 422, 426
  by cationic mechanism, 422
  free radical mechanism for, 421
Polyacetaldehyde polymerization, importance of reaction vessel in, 423
  initiation with UV light, 421
  initiators for, 422, 425, 426
  with inorganic salts, 427
  with metal sulfate–sulfuric acid complexes, 428–429
  with polyoxymethylene, 426
  role of surface in, 422
  with silica gel, 426
  with solid initiators, 422–429
  with sulfates as initiators, 427, 429
Polyacetals, 419–451
  See also individual compounds.
  elastic properties of, 420
  as rubber candidates, 420
Polyacetone, 450
  initiators for, 450
  polymerization of, 450
Polyacrylonitrile, cyclized, 966
Polyaldehydes, in amorphous form, 420
  in crystalline form, 420
  polymerization of, 421
  preparation of, 447
  stereoregularity of, 420
Polyalkenamers, 703
  branching in, 709
  polyhexenamer, 706
  stereoregular, 705
cis-Polyalkenamers, 712
trans-Polyalkenamers, crystal structure of, 709
Poly-alpha-olefins, discovery of, 87
Polyamides, as stabilizers, 443, 445
Polyamine activator, 140
Polybutadiene, 101–103, 128
  by alkyllithium catalysts, 849
  cis-trans isomerization, 939
  copolymers based on, 104–106
  cyclization, 939, 955
  cyclized, structure of, 955
  α, ω derivatives of, 855
  gel content, 871

Polybutadiene, glass transition
temperatures of, 104
infrared spectra of, 972
isomerization of, photosensitized, 970
radiation sensitized, 970
with selenium, 978
liquid, 845
by lithium catalysts, 849
photoisomerization of, 975
sulfur-induced isomerization, 977
1,2 syndiotactic, by Co catalysts, 630
1,2 Polybutadiene, cyclization of, 968
cis-1,4 Polybutadiene, cyclization of, 966
isomerization of, 970
melting temperature, 705
ozonization of, 862
trans-1,4 Polybutadiene, 956
cyclization of, 966
melting temperature of, 705
Polybutadienyllithium, association of,
498
Polybutenamer, 707
Polycarbonates, 110–111
Polychloroprene, 75, 227, 242
See also Chloroprene, 227–242
blends with nitrile rubber, 218
crystallization of, 237
degradation time of, 215
elastomeric properties of, 236
geometrical isomers of, 235
liquid polymer of, 848
molecular weight control of, 233–235
polymerization of, 232–240
positional isomers of, 235
sequence isomers of, 235
structure of, 235–238
temperature effect on, 237
Polycyclobutene, 714
Polydienes, *cis-trans* isomerism in, 82
Polydodecenamer, 707
Polyepichlorohydrin, 386
Polyesteramides, 728
Polyesters, preparation of, 730
in urethane elastomers, 746
Polyethers, 729
conformational parameters for, 379
melting points of, 378
preparation of, 731
Polyethylene, elastomeric properties of,
704
from transition metal acetylacetonates,
871
Poly(ethylene adipate), 728
Polyfluoroprene, 274, 277
Poly(fluorothiacyl halides), 893, 898
Polyformaldehyde, 420
Polyfunctional alcohols, in vulcanization
of chlorosulfonated polyethylenes,
918
Polyheptenamer, 707
Polyhexafluorothioacetone, 893, 899
Polyhexenamer, 707
Poly(imidazopyrrolones), 969
Polyisobutene, 291–315
continuous polymerization of, 295
effect of HCl on synthesis of, 300
manufacture of, 295–296
molecular weight of, 294–295, 302
polymerization of, with $AlEt_2Cl$,
303, 306
cocatalysis in, 296–308
at low temperature, 308–315
structure of, 293–294
synthesis of, 294–296
Polyisobutylene. *See* Polyisobutene.
Polyisoprene, 99–101
cyclization, 940
α, ω derivatives of, 855
glycols from, 855, 860
halogenation of, 907
α-irradiation of, 944
isomerized, NMR spectrum of, 980
NMR spectrum of, 982
synthetic, physical properties, 517
1,2 Polyisoprene, cyclization of, 968
1,4 Polyisoprene, cyclopolymers, 966
isomerization of, 978

3,4 Polyisoprene, 641
  cyclization of, 956
  cyclized, infrared spectroscopy, 958
    NMR spectra of, 959
    NMR spectroscopy, 958
    structure of, 957
  cyclopolymers, 966
  NMR spectra of, 959
Polyisoprene-3-D, cyclization of, 948
cis-1,4 Polyisoprene, 940
  infrared spectrum of, 946, 950
  effect of catalyst concentration on molecular weight, 637
    effect of polymerization temperature on, 637
  NMR spectrum of, 945
  preparation of, first, 86
    with lithium catalysis, 86
    with Ziegler catalysts, 87–88
trans-1,4 Polyisoprene, 640, 940
  infrared spectrum of, 946
Polyisoprenyllithium, association of, 498
Polyketone, 421
Polymerization catalysts, from aluminum alkyl halides, 606
  from aluminum trihalides, 609
  from cobalt compounds, 606, 609
  from $TiCl_4$, 603
  from TiI_4, 605
Polymerization–depolymerization equilibrium, 720
Polymerization in ethers, kinetics of, 512
Polymerization kinetics, of butadiene by sodium, 561
Polymerization rates, role of ionic species, 563
Polymerization stopper, 133
Polymer structure, Staudinger's first publication on, 70
Polymerizability, of cyclic ethers, 380–383
  of cyclopentadiene, 44
  of dihydrotoluene, 44
  of phenyl butadiene, 44
Poly(*N*-methoxymethyl) caprolactam as stabilizer, 445
Polymethyl methacrylate, 172
Poly(α-methylvinyl methyl ether), syndiotactic, 337
Polyoctenamer, 707
Poly(1,4-oxybutylene) glycol, 728
Polyoxymethylene, 426
trans-1,4 Polypentadienes, 644
  See also 1,4 Polypiperylene.
Polypentenamer, 707
cis-Polypentenamers, elastomeric properties of, 710
trans-Polypentenamers, elastomeric properties of, 710
Polyphase polymerization, of vinyl alkyl ethers, 334, 348
Polyphosphoric acid as initiator, 432
1,4 Polypiperylene, ozone resistance, 539
Polypropenamer, 707
Polypropylene, 426
Polypropylene oxide, 110
Polypropylene oxide rubbers, 385
Polypropylene sulfide elastomers, preparation by polycondensation, 833
  preparation from ring opening, 833
Polystyrene, α, ω derivatives of, 855
  by lithium or organo lithium catalysis, 855
Polystyrene diacetates, 857
Polystyrene glycols, properties of, 857
Polysulfide crosslinks, 360
Polysulfide elastomers, 75, 113
  acidity required to initiate hydrolysis, 827
  as binders, 807
  chain extention in, 809
  characterization by solution techniques, 819
  configuration of sulfide linkages, 820
  crosslinks in, 808
  decomposition of, 826
  definition, 806

Polysulfide elastomers, effect of crosslink density on physical properties of, 822
effect of crosslinking agent on physical properties of, 822
effect of dihalide structure on cyclization of, 809
effect of filler on physical properties of, 822
effect of molecular weight on physical properties, 820
effect of molecular weight on the physical properties of, 821
elimination of water in curing, 826
from bis-2-hydroxyethyl disulfide, 816
from "Bunte Salts," 815
from polycondensation of polythiodiglycals, 816
from ring opening of cyclic disulfides, 817
general properties of, 820
high temperature properties, 826
low temperature properties, 823
molecular weight distribution of, 831
partial crystallization in, 823
permeability of, 807
physical properties of, 807, 819
preparation by condensation reactions, 807
reduction to low molecular weight mercapton-terminated polymers, 813
ring formation in, preparation of, 809
role of inorganic polysulfide in preparation of, 810
stoichiometry in, preparation of, 808
"sulfur rank" in, 810
surface active agent, role in preparation of, 807
thermal instability from salt bonds in, 827
viscoelastic properties of, 829
Polysulfide polymers, conversion to low molecular weight liquids, 806
Polysulfide polymers, copolymers, kinetics of crystallization, 825
preparation of, 807
homopolymers, kinetics of crystallization, 824
as sealants, 807
solvent resistancy, 807
terpolymers, preparation of, 807
Polytetrahydrofuran endgroups in, 396
Poly(thiocarbonyl fluoride), 288, 893, 896–898
chemical resistance of, 895
heat stability of, 895
molecular weight, 895
molecular weight control of, 899
physical properties of, 895
reaction with antimony pentafluoride, 897
Polyurethanes, 108–109
Burchfield test for, 214
Polyurethane vulcanizates, physical properties of, 860
Poly(vinyl chloride), 426
bends with nitrile rubber, 218–219
Burchfield test for, 214
Poly(vinyl ethers), 331–372
crosslinking during vulcanization, 360
degree of isotacticity of, 339
dynamic mechanical properties of, 361–370
dynamic resilience of, 362, 363, 369–370
effect of polymer structure on dynamic mechanical properties, 363–365
effect of temperature, on dynamic mechanical properties, 365
on the dynamic modulus, 367–370
on the dynamic resilience of, 367–370
endgroup structure, 338–339
glass transformation temperatures of, 353–354, 364–370
history of, 333

Poly(vinyl ethers), isotactic structure of, 334, 336–337
metal sulfate–sulfuric acid complex as catalyst for, 345–352
molecular weights of, 349–350
optical activity of, 352–353
radiation curing, 357–358
Russian investigation of, 343
scission during vulcanization, 360
stereoisomerism of, 333–335
stereoregular polymerization of, 337, 350–351
syndiotactic structure of, 334
volatile products during vulcanization, 360
vulcanizable copolymers of, 346
vulcanization of, 354–361
with dicumyl peroxide, 361
homopolymers, 357–361
with peroxides, 358–361
Polyvinylisocyanate, cyclization of, 968
Potassium, organo compounds of, 559
Potassium oleate, 257
Potassium persulfate, 257
Prepolymers, preparation of, 738
vapor hazard in, 740
vapor hazard in curing of, 739
Principle of corresponding states, 9–11
Principle of low functionality. *See* Low functionality.
Product performance, 119–122
Proliferous polymerization, of vinyl alkyl ethers, 334, 335
Propagation, first use of term, 81
Propylene, copolymerization with thiocarbonyl fluoride, 901
Propylene oxide, 384
Protonic acids, 390–391
Pyrane units, 448

Q

Q value, 238

R

Radiation curing, 357–358
effect of sulfur on, 357
Radical mechanisms, 128–288
Radical ply tire, 121
Rate of polymerization, effect of monomer concentration on, 507
effect of pressure on, 507
effect of solvent on, 507
Rate of propagation, effect of temperature on, 506
Reactivity ratios, 238, 357
of acrylates, 259–260
of acrylonitrile, 193
of aldehyde comonomers, 450
of butadiene, 193
of cyclic ethers, 406
Redox catalysts, 203
Redox initiating systems, oxidants for, 153–155
Redox mechanisms, 128–288
Regulating index, 161–166
Reinforcement of elastomers, 115
Reppe process, 129
Rheology, 118–119
of polybutadienes, 528
Rhodium catalysts, 715
Rhodium-catalyzed polymerization, mechanism of, 883
Rhodium chloride, as initiator of polymerization, 870
Ring opening of cyclic disulfides, by anionic route, 817
by cationic route, 817
heat of polymerization in, 817
Ring-opening polymerization, 380, 703
of cyclic ethers, 720
of cycloolefins, 722
mechanism of, 717
Rotation barrier, 4–5
Rotational potential, 4–7, 8, 16
Rubber, butadiene-styrene, 955
carboxyl-terminated, 852

Rubber, cyclized, 939
NMR spectrum of, 952, 954
physical properties of, 954
structure of, 953
Rubber, definition of, 96
isomerized, 939
natural, isomerization of, 951
origin of word, 24
Rubber cement, preparation of, first, 24
use of, 24
Rubber Commission, in Germany, 66
Rubber consumption, 316
Rubber goods, manufacture of, first, 24–25
Rubber plantations, establishment of, 26–27
Rubidium, organocompounds of, 559
Ruthenium catalysts, 715

S

SBR, 127–178
See also Styrene-butadiene copolymer, 145.
blends with nitrile rubber, 218
Burchfield test for, 214
cold, 128
cyclized, 955
degradation time of, 215
emulsion polymerization of, 132–157
molecular weight of, 160–172
molecular weight distribution of, 160–172
polymerization of, 132–135
inhibitors for, 134
temperature of, 133
polymerization procedures for, 177–178
stereochemistry of, 176–177
structure of, 172–177
Side chain effect, 335–336, 348–349
Silica gel, as a solid initiator, 426
Silicone, origin of name, 768
Silicone copolymers, block, 785
block types from living systems, 785
preparation, 784
with inorganics, 785
Silicone curing agents, table of, 799
Silicone elastomers, curing, 795
structure of linear, 770
swelling in different solvents, 793
ultimate thermal stability, 788
Silicone intermediates, review of, 768
Silicone monomers, polymerization of, 778
Silicone polymerization, silanolate ion as active species in, 781
Silicone polymers, antioxidants in, 790
by direct coupling, 768
by products from oxidation of, 789
composition and rate of polymerization, 779
control of molecular weight, 778
crosslinks by radiation, 794
definition, 768
determination of cyclic structures in, 780
direct process for preparation, 774
distribution of cyclic structures in, 779
fluidity, 771
fractionation of, 779
from hydrolysis reactions, 778
hydrolytic depolymerization of, 791
insulating properties, 787
low-temperature elastomers, 795
macro- and microstructure, 773
methods for preparation, 774
molecular weight distributions, 773
oxidation of aromatic hydrogens in, 789
oxidative stability, 789
ozone resistance, 794
radiation resistance, 794
rearrangement in presence of acid or base catalysts, 790
review of synthetic methods, 773
stability, 786
structure, 770
termination in, 778
thermal stability, 786
thermodynamic measurements on, 772

Silicone rubber, 112
attack by water, 791
Burchfield test for, 214
strength and reinforcement of, 801
Silicone technology, review of, 768
Siliketones, double bonds in, 768
Siloxane, bond rearrangement, 790
Siloxane depolymerization, activation energy for, 791
kinetics of, 791
Siloxane fluids, helical structures in, 772
Siloxane polymers, "solubility parameter" and, 792
solvent resistance of, 792
swelling of, 792
Siloxane rearrangement, rate of, 790
Siloxane stability, effect of filler on, 792
Siloxanes, bond distances in, 772
cyclic components in, 772
effect of various bases on, 780
Simha-Boyer relation, 12
SK rubber, 74
Sodium, organo compounds of, 559
Sodium addition, to unsaturated hydrocarbons, 79
Sodium formaldehyde sulfoxylate, 133, 155–157
Sodium *meta*-silicate, 260
Sodium polymerization, discovery of, 46, 48
Solid initiators, for polyacetaldehyde, 422–429
Solid state polymerization, 395
Solprene, 558
Solution properties of, polybutadienes, 523
polyisoprenes, 523
Sovpol, 74
Spandex, 728
Spandex elastic fibers, 759
preparation of, 760
properties of, 760
Specialty rubbers, 253
Hycar 4021, 254
PA-21, 254
Squalene, cyclization of, 945
Stabilization of polyacetaldehyde, 441–445
stabilizers, 443
Staudinger, on structure of polymers, 70
Staudinger equation for molecular weight determination, 437
Stearylamine, 445
Stereoregular polydiene, 87–88, 128
Stereospecific polymerization of diolefins, mechanism of, 652
Stevenson plan, 30
Strain. *See* Stress–strain behavior.
Stress–strain behavior, 3–8
barrier to rotation, 4–5
curve for, 3, 7–8
displacement distribution for, 7
elastic equations of state, 8
energy effects on, 7
Gaussian treatment of, 2–3, 7
interactions with neighboring groups, 7
inverse Langevin chains, 3–4
Mooney equation for, 3–4
rotational potentials, 4–7, 8
semiempirical equation of state for, 3
Strontium tetraethylzincate, 257
Structure–property relationships, 1–18
polyalkenamers, 704
Styrene, 131–132, 903
See also Styrene-butadiene copolymer, 145.
as comonomer with butadiene, 73
copolymers, 540
initiation systems for, 151
polymerization of, 80, 140
preparation of, by catalytic dehydrogenation of ethylbenzene, 131–132
by oxidation of ethylbenzene, 132
by phenylethanol dehydration, 132

Styrene-butadiene copolymerization, effect of silver nitrate on rate of, 869
Styrene-butadiene copolymers, 145
copolymerization function for, 145
monomer distribution in, 132
monomer ratio in, 132
reactivity ratios for, 157–158
solution copolymerization of, 157
Succinaldehyde, 448
Sulfates of organic amines, as initiators, 429
Sulfur-chloroprene copolymers, vulcanization of, 244
Sulfur cure, 261
Sulfur modified neoprenes, 234
Sulfur rank, in polysulfide rubber, effect of excess alkali sulfide on, 811
Swelling analysis, 216
Syndiotactic, origin of term, 87
Syndiotactic structure of poly(vinyl ethers), 334
Synthetic elastomers, history of, 21–88
Synthetic rubber, 41–69, 55, 65
controversy regarding priorities, 49–58
developments in U.S.A., butyl rubber, 76–78
neoprene, 75
thiokols, 74–75
English developments, 47–49
German developments, 41–47, 70–74
preparation of, first, 88
Russian developments, first, 74

T

Technology of elastomers, 95–122
Teflon, 274
Telechelic polymers, 173
alkali metal type, 852
metal carboxylate type, 852
Temperature, effect on polymerization, 350
Temperature–time dependence. *See* Time–temperature superposition principle.
Temperature–viscosity dependence, 9
Termination, by acidic hydrocarbons, 514
by complexation, 514
by molecular oxygen, 515
by protonic agents, 514
by sulfur, 515
Terpenes, relation to isoprene and natural rubber, 37
Terpilene, 35
Tetracyclosqualene, 953
NMR spectrum of, 954
Tetraethylene pentamine, 141
2,2,4,4-Tetrafluoro-1,3-dithietane, 894
Tetrafluorethylene, 274, 276, 280, 286, 287
Tetrahydrofuran, 382, 384, 388
Tetrahydropyran, 383
Tetrahydropyran endgroup, in poly(vinyl ethers), 338
2,2,4,4-Tetrakis(trifluoro methyl)-1,3-dithietane, 899
Tetrasulfide thiokol, 863
Texin, 743
Thermal polymerization, of chloroprene, 242
Thermolastic, 105
Thermoplastics, 557
THF, bulk polymerizations of, 398
Thiocarbanilide, as vulcanization accelerator, 62
Thiocarbonyl chlorofluoride, 903
Thiocarbonyl fluoride, 895, 898–900, 902
copolymer with propylene, 901
polymerization of, 894
Thiokol, 74–75
degradation time of, 215
Thionation, 811
Threo diisotactic polymers, 342
Threshhold temperature, for vinyl alkyl ethers, 336

Time-temperature superposition principle, 9
Tire, 98–99
Titanium catalysts, 715
Titanium tetrachloride, 258
Titanium trichloride, α and β modifications, 604
Toluene diisocyanate, as chain extender, 858
Tolylene diisocyanate, 729
  elastomers from, 729
  preparation of, 729
  vapor hazard of, 740
Transfer agents, 160–161
Transfer coefficients, 312–315
Transfer coefficients, of conjugated dienes, 315
Transfer constant, 161
Transition metals, polymerization by, 874
Transition metal salts, reaction with olefins, 870
Transition temperature, using Gehman's procedure, 446
  of polyacetaldehyde, 446
Trialkylborane oxygen couple, 900
Trialkylphosphines, as initiators, 432
Tributylamine, 445
Trichloropropane, 864
Triethylaluminum, as initiator, discovery of, 84
Triethylenetetramine, 141
Trifluoroacetic acid, 425
Trifluoronitrosomethane, 286–287
Trifluorothioacetyl fluoride, 899
1,1,4-Trihydroperfluorobutyl acrylate, 266
Trioxane, 384
Tris-2,4,5,-(1-aziridinyl)-1,3,5,triazine, 853
Tris[1-(2-methyl) aziridinyl], phosphine oxide, 853
Tungsten catalysts, 715

U

Ultracentrifuge, 171
Unstable fraction, 444
Ureas, 732
Urethane elastomers, abrasion resistance of, 753
  allophonate branch points in, 736
  andioxidants in, 759
  antimicrobial agents in, 759
  applications of, 728
  biuret branch points in, 736
  block copolymers, 735
  carbodiimides in, 759
  carbon black in, 758, 759
  casting process, 728, 736, 738
  castor oil in, 743
  catalysts for, 736, 741, 759
  chain extenders in, 735, 747
  Clash-Berg torsional modulus of, 747
  coatings from, 737
  cost of consumption of, 729
  crosslinks in, 735, 746
  crosslinking in thermoplastic types, 743
  crosslinking of, 732
  crystallization in, 751, 753
  degree of crosslinking, 747
  diamines in, 735
  dimerized fatty acid polyesters in, 743
  environmental resistance of, 755
  fillers in, 751
  glycols in, 735
  hydrogen bonding in, 735, 749
  hydrolysis of, 759
  hydroxy-terminated butadiene polymers in, 743
  isocyanate cure, 737
  low modulus types, 760
  low modulus types, properties of, 761
  low-temperature flexibility of, 756
  microbial attack on, 759
  millable gums, 728, 736, 741
  miscellaneous types, 743

Urethane elastomers, one-shot process for, 736, 740
oxidation of, 758
peroxide cure, 737
physical properties of, 747
plasticizers in, 756
polyacetals in, 743
polyesters in, 729, 730, 762
polyethers in, 731, 762
polythioethers in, 743
preparation of, 737
prepolymer process for, 735, 738
properties, 728, 749, 753, 754, 762
raw materials for, 729
relation between structure and property, 745
segments in, 735, 760
Spandex fibers from, 760
sulfur cure, 737
tear strength of, 753
temperature resistance on, 755
thermoplastic types, 737, 742
molding of, 743
extrusion of, 743
thiopolyacetals in, 743
urea groups in, 736
urethane groups in, 736
UV absorbers in, 759
van der Waals attraction in, 735
water in, 735
weathering of, 756
Young's modulus of, 753
Urethanes, 732

V

Vanadium catalysts, 715
Van der Waals volume, 13, 14
Vandenberg's modified catalyst, 342–343
Vinyl acetate, 142, 901, 903
Vinylacetate, copolymers of, 901
Vinyl alkyl ethers, 331–372
See individual compounds.
catalysts for polymerization of, 333–340
Vinyl alkyl ethers, cationic coordination polymerization of, 340–343, 345, 346
cocatalyst for, 339, 340, 344–345
copolymerization, with chloroprene, 356
with cyclopentadiene, 355
with dienes, 355–356
with 1-methoxy-1,3-butadiene, 355
with 2-methyl-1,3-pentadiene, 355
with vinyl allyl ether, 356–357
with 1-vinyloxy-2-allyloxyethane, 356
with β-vinyloxyethyl methacrylate, 356
flash polymerization of, 334
heterogeneous polymerization of, 336, 340, 343, 346
homogeneous polymerization of, 336–337, 340, 343
metal alkoxide–sulfuric acid catalyst for, 351–352
modified Friedel-Crafts catalyst for, 341
multicentered coordinated polymerization of, 340, 345
polymerization of, activator for, 335, 344
with Grignard reagent, 343
kinetics of, 337–340, 346, 348
mechanism of, 346–348, 352
with Ziegler-Natta catalysts, 340–343
polyphase polymerization of, 334, 348
proliferous polymerization of, 334, 335
rate constants for, 349
reactivity ratios of, 357
resonance effect, 332
side chain effect on, 335–336, 348–349
stereoregular polymerization of, 345
stereospecific polymerization of, 340–342, 345–346
effect of dielectric constant on, 350
temperature effect on, 341, 342, 350

Vinyl alkyl ethers, threshold polymerization temperature of, 336
Vandenberg's modified Ziegler-type catalysts for, 342–343
copolymer with vinyl alkyl ethers, 356–357
Vinyl aromatic compounds, 158
Vinyl aryl ethers, 332
resonance effect, 332
Vinyl caproate, 148
Vinyl chloride, 901
Vinyl chloroacetate, cure of, 261
Vinyl fluoride, 901
Vinylidene, copolymers of, 280
NMR spectra of, 280
Vinylidene fluoride, 277, 279, 280, 287
copolymer with chlorotrifluoroethylene (Kel-F), 284
copolymer with hexafluoropropylene (Viton A), 284
elastomers of, 280
polymerization of, 281
N-Vinyl-1-nylon, cyclization of, 968
1-Vinyloxy-2-allyloxyethane, copolymers with vinyl alkyl ethers, 356
β-Vinyloxyethyl methacrylate, 341
copolymers with vinyl alkyl ethers, 356
Vinylpyridine rubber, 222–224
quaternization of, 223
Vinyltrichlorosilane, 901
Viscoelastic behavior, 9–15
Viscometry, 171
Viscosity–temperature dependence. *See* Temperature–viscosity dependence.
Vistanex, 295, 856
Viton, 112, 274–275
Viton A, 280, 283
copolymer with vinylidene fluoride, 284
Viton B, 280
Vulcanizates, of nitrile rubber, 215–218, 219–221
Vulcanization, 117–118
of acrylic elastomers, 260–263
by cadmium oxide, 819
of chloroprene rubbers, 245
crosslinking in, 360
with dicumyl peroxide, 361
by diisocyanates, 819
discovery of, 25–26
effect of sulfur on, 359
of fluoroelastomers, 282–286
of homopolymers, 357–361
by lead oxide, 819
of neoprene, 242–245
with peroxides, 358–361
of polybutadiene, 975
of poly(vinyl ethers), 354–361
scission during, 360
of sulfur-chloroprene copolymers, 244
by zinc oxide, 810
Vulcanization accelerators, controversy regarding priorities, 60
discovery of, 58–62
Vulkollan, 741

W

WLF equation, 10
Water's gel permeation apparatus, 170

Z

Zerovalent metals, carbonyl derivatives from, 872
Ziegler-Natta catalysts, discovery of, 84–85
for polymerization of vinyl alkyl ethers, 340–343
Zinc oxide, 902
Zirconium catalysts, 716